THE
GOLF
GUIDE

PGA

WHERE TO PLAY
WHERE TO STAY

1991

Endorsed by
The Professional Golfers' Association

FHG Publications
Paisley

Acknowledgements

The Publishers wish to acknowledge the assistance of the Professional Golfers' Association and their staff at the Belfry in the preparation of this edition of *THE GOLF GUIDE*. Thanks are particularly due to Laraine Beeching and Sally Lane for editorial contributions.

We thank our lead-writer Keith Brain, who has a long association both with *THE GOLF GUIDE* and with the PGA. Also Barry Took for permission to reprint his article 'A Short Walk to the First Tee'.

Our front cover features Kosaido Old Thorns Golf Course, Hotel and Restaurants where a combination of the old and new has created the appeal of a country estate with modern leisure and sports facilities. Further details of Old Thorns can be seen in the full colour advertisement on page 27.

Also on the front cover, with acknowledgements to Yours in Sport, the Lawerence Levy Golf Picture Collection, are Tony Jacklin and Bernard Gallacher – outgoing and incoming Captains respectively of the Great Britain and Europe Ryder Cup Team.

Title page picture: Shrigley Hall, Near Macclesfield.

ISBN 1 85055 136 7 © FHG Publications 1990-91

Published by FHG Publications, a member of the U.N. Group, Abbey Mill Business Centre, Seedhill, Paisley PA1 1JN (041-887 0428)

Distribution. **Book Trade:** Moorland Publishing, Moor Farm Road, Ashbourne, Derbyshire DE6 1HD (Tel: 0335 44486. Fax: 0335 46397.)
News Trade: UMD, 1 Benwell Road, Holloway, London N7 7AX (Tel: 071 700 4600. Fax: 071 607 3352.)

US ISBN 1-55650-242-7
Distributed in the United States by
Hunter Publishing Inc., 300 Raritan Center Parkway, CN94, Edison, N.J., 08818, USA

Typeset by R.D. Composition Ltd., Glasgow
Printed and bound by Benham's Ltd., Colchester

PRINTED AND PUBLISHED IN BRITAIN

Foreword

1991 is the ninetieth year since the initiation of The Professional Golfers' Association, and what a ninety years it has been!

PGA Members are based at golf courses and driving ranges across Great Britain and Ireland, and *The Golf Guide* provides you with all the information you need on where you can play and how to make sure you can do so.

It may interest you to know that every PGA Member is always happy to help and advise you in any aspect of your game – from expert tuition to providing you with the latest in golf equipment. And as we have done for ninety years, we will continue to assist you towards a better game in the future.

The Golf Guide will help you both to improve your golf, by trying the many new and traditional golf courses, and to enjoy the game more by sampling the neighbouring hotels and inns which offer hospitality to golfers.

Richard Bradbeer
PGA Captain

COUNTRY CLUB HOTELS.
MASTERS
OF GOLF.

If you take your golf seriously then Country Club Hotels can offer you the perfect solution to improving your game. As market leaders in golf and leisure based hotels we provide an unrivalled range of locations and golf programmes. Whether it's St Pierre and Dalmahoy, our tournament venues, or one of the new and exciting developments such as the Forest of Arden, you'll discover our uncompromising standards extend from the courses to the hotels themselves. You can even brush up on your game with a special golf tuition holiday, join one of our golf schools or we can help to organise a thoroughly entertaining company golf day. Whatever your choice, as an individual, a couple or as part of a larger group we can provide the perfect golfing package.

COUNTRY CLUB HOTELS

320 Redwood House, Beggar Bush Lane, Failand, Bristol BS8 3TG
Tel: Bristol (0272) 394000 Telex: 449344 Fax: (0272) 394289.

4

How to Use The Golf Guide

THE GOLF GUIDE Where to Play ● *Where to Stay*, contains up-to-date basic information on every course (as far as we know) in Britain. Details are provided by the clubs themselves. You will also find a new section 'Golf in Portugal'. The guide also carries entries from hotels, guest-houses and other accommodation convenient to specific courses or areas. These are generally 'paid' entries and usually follow a recommendation from a club. *THE GOLF GUIDE* itself is endorsed by the Professional Golfers' Association and is usually available for sale in golf clubs through the Professional and/or the Secretary – as well as bookshops etc.

Golf Course Information

For virtually every course you will find the following details, updated annually:

1. Name, address and telephone number.
2. Location.   3. Brief description.
4. Number of holes, length and Standard Scratch Score.   5. Green fees.
6. Details of facilities for visitors – individuals, groups and societies.
7. Name and telephone number of the Professional and the Secretary.

The accuracy of details published depends on the response of the clubs and to our best knowledge is correct at the time of going to press (October 1990). However, we cannot accept responsibility for errors or omissions and we recommend that you check important details with clubs before making any arrangements.

Choosing a Course

The golf clubs and courses are listed alphabetically by nearest town or village within the appropriate county section for England, Scotland, Wales, Ireland, the Isle of Man and the Channel Islands. There is a new section for Portugal. We have chosen to classify by place-name rather than club or course name since this seems more straightforward and recognisable to the majority.

If you want to find a club or course by its name, you should simply refer to the Index where you will see the page number of the listing. In each entry the name of the club or course is always shown in bold type after the place-name heading.

Accommodation

Accommodation entries are placed as near a particular club or course as possible and there are also hotel displays in the front colour section. Most of the accommodation advertised has been recommended by the local golf club. A full index is provided.

Maps

At the back of *THE GOLF GUIDE* you will find a set of maps showing cities, towns and villages in Britain with counties, motorways and main roads. Although many of the place-names under which the courses are classified are on the maps, please note that the maps are not golf course or club location maps.

The location details supplied with each entry should get you there and if you are in any doubt at all you should ask directions from the club itself.

Please mention *THE GOLF GUIDE Where to Play* ● *Where to Stay* when you make a hotel booking or play at courses after using our guide.

"Ca' canny." Some invaluable advice when golfing at Turnberry.

In the Scottish golfing idiom, "ca' canny" means "take care". Good advice when tackling either of the Turnberry Hotel's two championship courses, Ailsa and Arran.

Of course, taking care with your every shot is often easier said than done, as even champions have discovered since 1906.

Not for nothing is the Ailsa rated amongst the top twenty golf courses in the world. Nor is it surprising that the self same course, venue for the 1977 and 1986 Open Championships, will be so again in 1994.

Thankfully, after your round, there is the less taxing prospect of staying at the Turnberry Hotel. Its fine accommodation, country-house atmosphere, superb Scottish cuisine and thoughtful service has won it an enviable reputation. (And most recently, the coveted title 'RAC Hotel of the Year 1990'.)

So, whatever our golf courses have taken out of you, our hotel will surely put back.

Turnberry Hotel and Golf Courses, Turnberry,
Ayrshire, KA26 9LT, Scotland.
For private or business reservations.
Tel. 0655 31000 Telex 777779 Fax 0655 31706

A MEMBER OF *The Leading Hotels of the World*

ORIENT-EXPRESS HOTELS

Golf in the Nineties

A review by KEITH BRAIN

There are over 2,000 golf courses listed in this edition of *The Golf Guide* and these are used regularly by some 2 million players and less regularly by several million others. Golf has been long established as a popular outdoor activity and the vast majority of British courses have in fact been in existence for over 50 years.

It is reckoned that about 700 courses have been built since 1930 but such is the growth in demand that the same number of courses will have to be built in the 1990's to significantly reduce the pressure on facilities and players.

As well as the development of the traditional club, many new golfing opportunities exist or are planned in the context of other leisure facilities and an associated hotel development and also as a 'Pay As You Play' type of operation. Following on the success of established 'golfing hotels', many of which naturally appear in *The Golf Guide*, it seems natural therefore, to include a brief review of some notable golf developments in different parts of the country.

THE SOUTH AND WEST OF ENGLAND

It is in the South that the growth of demand for golf is strongest and probably

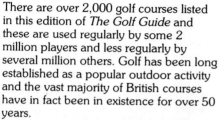

Wentworth Club, set in

glorious countryside, offers one 9-hole and

three 18-hole golf courses, tennis, and heated

outdoor swimming pool. Complementing

its prestigious sporting reputation with

comfortable and friendly ambience the Club

is charmingly informal. Residential golfing

breaks are available.

For information please contact: Sports and House Manager,
Wentworth Club, Virginia Water, Surrey GU25 4LS.
Or telephone: 0344 842201.

most pressing. Fortunately there are a number of new developments currently being undertaken. In two or three years' time the travelling golfer should have a much improved choice of where to stay and play.

One destination some will head for is Hanbury Manor in Hertfordshire, on the A10 just 22 miles from London. Once the sporting estate of the Hanbury family, and their country seat, the Manor itself has been transformed into a luxurious and well-equipped country house hotel. Faithfully restored at enormous cost, the manor stands in 200 acres which includes 40 acres of woodland and famed gardens which were laid out at the end of the nineteenth century. Lakes and ponds are scattered throughout the extensive grounds together with a number of individual gardens each with its own distinctive character. They include the Sundial Garden, the Garden of Remembrance, the beautiful Secret Garden and the Victorian Walled Garden with two huge greenhouses containing a large collection of exotic plants.

Guests staying at the 98-bedroom hotel have a choice of three restaurants. Other facilities in the complex include all-weather tennis courts and squash courts. Sauna and steam baths, clay pigeon shooting, archery, horse riding, fly fishing and even hot air ballooning are also available nearby.

More to the point, however, hotel guests can also play the 160-acre golf course at nominal fees. The original nine holes, designed by Harry Vardon, a member of the Great Triumvirate of James Braid, James Taylor and Vardon himself, have been sensitively renovated by course architect Jack Nicklaus Jnr and re-opened this year. Next year sees the completion of Nicklaus's 'new' nine holes taking the course to a full eighteen holes.

Course designer Nicklaus Jnr said: "Hanbury Manor is blessed with a variety of land features which include significant elevation changes, an impressive stock of hardwoods as well as lakes and streams. I have designed a course which will accommodate a wide range of golfers. It will possess the ability to tax the most skilled golfers yet will be enjoyable to all who play it."

It is anticipated that once the course has matured it will host some of the smaller championships. Golfers in the South who want the challenge of a Nicklaus course and the seclusion of a country hideway will find both their requirements at Hanbury Manor.

THE WEST COUNTRY

From a touring golfer's point of view things are really happening in the West Country and South Wales with a number of new choices available in 1990 and 1991. The new courses include developments at Bodmin, Bowood Park, Camelford, Woodbury near Exeter, Lulsgate, Bristol, Bulbury Woods near

There's More than Golf at Gloucester

Excellent golfing facilities are just one reason why the Gloucester Hotel and Country Club is well worth a visit – but there are many more attractions for the whole family.

Set in over 200 acres of beautiful Cotswold countryside, this modern hotel has 117 luxury bedrooms. An investment of over £3.5 million has ensured it offers a unique combination of sporting and leisure facilities including ski-ing, snooker, swimming, squash and tennis. With so much on offer, your golfing break could well turn into a family holiday.

For the keen golfer the 6,127 yard par 70, 18 hole course features a strategically laid out bunker formation. The natural hazards – trees, copses, small lakes and a variety of hillside undulations test all golfing skills.

The 9 hole par 3 course appeals to those who don't have time for a full round of golf, and the 12 bay floodlit driving range is always available for practising your swing.

Catering for all levels of golfing skills, tailored courses and special breaks are available, with tuition from the Club's 3 resident professionals.

For those learning the game, the residential beginners golf instruction week covers basic techniques, discussion of rules and etiquette by the experts, and, for fun, concludes with a competition on the 9 hole course.

Away from the fairways, members of the whole family may wish to try out the

premier dry ski slopes in England – and the excellent "apres-ski" facilities at the new Ski Lodge. Perhaps a game of tennis or squash for the more energetic, or chalk your cues for a game of snooker or pool.

Warm and welcoming water attractions include an exciting leisure pool, complete with rapids, spa pool, steam room, sauna and jacuzzi to provide that period of relaxation.

Not only catering for leisure breaks, the Hotel has extensive conference facilities ranging from rooms for select confidential business meetings to a full scale delegation of 150 people. The Redwell Restaurant, a popular venue for business lunches offers haute cuisine standards and an extensive wine cellar.

Should you wish to make the most of your stay in this most attractive area, Gloucester boasts an excellent shopping centre, many surrounding sites of historic interest and scenic walking routes in the Cotswolds. Reception staff are fully informed on all seasonal activites in the area.

The complex enjoys easy access from the M5 motorway, and is just 1½ miles from the City Centre.

The Gloucester Hotel and Country Club is a member of the Embassy Hotels Group – part of Allied Lyons plc.

A golfing break for people who hate golf.

Firstly, the bad news. At the Gloucester Hotel & Country Club, set among 240 acres of the Cotswolds you'll find a superb, if testing, 18-hole par 70 golf course, plus a pleasing 9-hole course, floodlit driving range and a well stocked shop.

But, the good news is that this luxurious hotel also boasts a magnificent new leisure complex, complete with superb pool, whirlpools, steam room, sauna and solarium.

Not to mention squash, twin tennis courts and a fully-equipped, supervised gym.

Of course, all 117 bedrooms are appointed to the highest standards and our 'Redwell' á la carte restaurant can more than cater for the gourmet in you.

So whether golf is the love or bane of your life, call us on (0452) 25653 for more details about our great value short stay breaks.

GLOUCESTER HOTEL AND COUNTRY CLUB

Robinswood Hill, Gloucester GL4 9EA. Telex: 43571. Embassy Hotels

11

Bournemouth, Libbaton, North Devon, St Mary's, Bridgend, Cape Cornwall, and a new "Pay As You Play" course which particularly welcomes visitors at Peterstone, near Newport.

The development which is perhaps awaited most eagerly of all is at Orchardleigh Park, at Lullington between Frome and Bath. Former Ryder Cup Captain Brian Huggett has designed two courses and described the site as quite magnificent and the best he has seen in over ten years of looking at sites in the UK.

The Lakes course, being built to Championship standard, retains almost all the fine mature trees on the site and will feature dry-stone walling around greens, tees and lakes to complement the existing walls on the estate. The entire course is dominated by a twenty-three acre lake which, naturally, means that water comes into play on a number of holes. There's none more spectacular than the short 160-yard eleventh, right across the corner of Orchardleigh Lake with the tee, at the

water's edge, only a few feet above the water level.

The second course, called the Park course, is no pushover. Again the layout is spread through a superb parkland setting with play through mature oaks and pines and like the Lakes course, water will again feature on a number of holes.

The Orchardleigh estate has over 400 acres of parkland with over 8,000 specimen trees, some of which are over 800 years old. Orchardleigh House offers splendid views over the Wiltshire Downs and the historic house will be restored under the overall development scheme. Part of it will then become a 34-bedroom luxury hotel with the existing walled garden and original greenhouses and conservatory reinstated to their period character.

A new 123-bedroom hotel is being built with all the modern facilities of swimming pool, sauna, solarium, squash courts, gymnasium and fitness rooms together with conference rooms and the

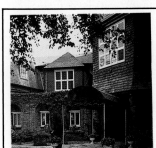

facilities required for modern businessmen.

The development, thought by many to be much needed in that part of the world, is scheduled for opening in the autumn of 1991.

THE NORTH OF ENGLAND

For someone like myself, born and raised in agricultural Cheshire, it is sad to see the decline in the once prosperous farming community. The great agricultural belt that comprises the Cheshire Plain is changing shape. A drive through any rural area will no longer reveal mile after mile of the familiar black and white Freisian cows grazing in pastureland. The EEC rules and regulations and cuts in milk quotas and subsidies have sent farmers scurrying away to find an alternative use for their land in a bid to stay solvent and in

business. Many of them are turning to golf.

Cheshire as a golfing centre? It would have sounded preposterous a few years ago but if all the current plans reach fruition it will become a reality. Cheshire already has its share of fine courses. Who will ever forget Roberto de Vicenzo's historic Open Championship win at Royal Liverpool? Nearby are the links courses of Caldy and Heswall, further inland Wilmslow, host to the Greater Manchester Open for many years and also to the old Martini International tournament won by Nick Faldo, and nearby the superb courses of Mere, Sandiway, Delamere and Prestbury to name but a few.

But they all have 'full house' notices for membership applications and long waiting lists. That, together with the new rules of the farming game, has encouraged a number of Cheshire

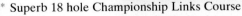

The North Course at Portal Estate, Tarporley, near Manchester.

farmers to investigate the golfing market. Now, with the creation of several new courses, it should be possible for golfers to stay in the historic city of Chester for a golfing week, playing a different course every day of the week and never driving for more than half-an-hour to find their pleasure.

The first new complex they would be likely to visit is on the Portal Estate at Tarporley, near to the city boundaries and three-quarters of an hour's drive from Manchester's international airport. At Portal, Donald Steel has designed two 18-hole Championship standard courses, the first of which was completed early in 1990 and will be open to the public in the autumn of 1991, once it has matured. The complex, reputed to be costing around £30 million, is already being heralded as the new jewel in Cheshire's crown. When completed, apart from the two courses, the development will include a 120-bedroom, five-star hotel, a leisure centre, driving range and golfing academy, all set in the heart of Cheshire with spectacular views across the plain to the Welsh hills beyond.

The site, which already possesses oustanding gardens with a spectacular rhododendron collection and a fine country house, is already classified as one of architectural interest and in an area of outstanding beauty. Course architect Donald Steel says of it: "It is one of the best pieces of land I have ever seen. It has the potential of becoming as fine an inland course as we currently have in Britain." The first course, less than 7,000 yards long, winds its way through long-established and mature trees. Where water has been added as a hazard it has been carefully landscaped with waterfall effects built in. What is different about the Portal concept compared with the others in the area is that the course will not have any members but will be available on a 'Pay-and-Play' basis.

Nearby is the newly completed Oaklands Golf and Country Club, and amongst other notable developments in Cheshire are the Donald Steel designed course at Shrigley Hall near Macclesfield and, just down the road, the Tytherington Club where the course was designed by Dave Thomas and the site is home to the women professional golfers of Europe. Another Dave Thomas course which should open in 1991 is at Mottram Hall, near Prestbury, owned by the De Vere hotel group who so successfully operate The Belfry, scene of the Ryder Cup.

There are other new developments in the North Region including notable ones in Blackpool and Chorley and, up in Northumberland, the spectacular Slaney Hall with its fine course, hotel and leisure complex. That development has an added attraction in that their tournament professional is Christy O'Connor whose remarkable two-iron shot to the eighteenth green at The Belfry ensured that the Ryder Cup stayed on this side of the Atlantic for a further term.

The Belfry

This beautiful country manor, set in the heart of the Warwickshire Countryside and surrounded by two top class golf courses is now world renowned, largely due to the success of the European Team during the Ryder Cup matches, played on the famous Brabazon Course.

The Belfry is a 220 bedroomed, four star hotel with restaurants, bars, magnificent leisure club with indoor swimming pool, squash courts, saunas etc. It has a range of Conference facilities ranging in size to cater for numbers from 4 to 350, in luxurious surroundings. For those who want to dance the night away, there is the fabulous Bel-Air Nitespot, Winner of the Disco Mirror New Venue of the Year Award.

Without doubt the ever expanding attractions of the Belfry complex now offer the most comprehensive opportunities for anyone interested in playing golf or looking to hold a Conference with a difference. The Belfry can cater for the individual with his family or for the Company and the organised day or weekend golfing and business affairs.

A further luxury development has transformed an already impressive scene into a continental plaza type village with high class shops, executive suites and extra facilities.

 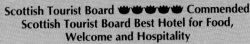

SCOTLAND

Scotland isn't just the home of golf, it is a Mecca for millions of golfers from all parts of the world and particularly from enthusiasts living within these shores. Few golfers in their lifetime fail to make the trek north to sample some of the finest courses in the world, in many cases treading the same hallowed ground of their current golfing heroes or legendary names from the past. Whatever a golfer wants in terms of golf courses can be found north of the border whether it be one of the great Championship links or some remarkable relatively 'unknown' course which is a pleasure to discover. Such a course may be an added pleasure to play because the green fees and the food are extremely cheap compared with the prices charged throughout the golfing hot-spots of Europe.

Despite the high density of courses which proliferate throughout Scotland, new ones appear each year as the golfing boom continues. It takes something really special to make the natives sit up and take notice and at the moment they are more than excited about two projects.

The first is at the famous Gleneagles Hotel, already renowned throughout the golfing world for its all-round excellence. The two major championship Kings and Queens courses, to say nothing of the hotel itself with its leisure centre and off-course attractions, have earned accolades from all parts of the world. Set in idyllic surroundings in the magnificent Perthshire countryside, now virtually the permanent home of the European Tour Scottish Open Championship, Gleneagles already holds a special niche in golf. Now the great Jack Nicklaus is designing a third new course, to be named the Monarch's course. It will be the first Nicklaus-designed course in Scotland and the second in Britain.

The other exciting development in Scotland is in Dunbartonshire where the much discussed Loch Lomond club is

EVERYTHING JUST COMES TOGETHER.

Admittedly conditions were perfect (and the King's Course one of the world's finest) but the 13th, Braid's Brawest, is as hard a hole as they come.

I was playing it like a dream.

After a few days of complete relaxation in one of the world's greatest hotels something strange seems to happen to my game.

Distinctions between ball, club and action seem to blur. The swing is sweeter, the drives truer, the putting more assured.

There is a perfect balance between the demands of the fairways, the subtleties of the greens, the richness of the scenery and a wonderful stillness.

This is golf at its best. The least my game can do is rise to the occasion.

THE GLENEAGLES HOTEL

BELL'S
Scottish Open
GLENEAGLES

For full details of the Gleneagles Golfing Experience please write to the Sports Manager,
THE GLENEAGLES HOTEL, AUCHTERARDER, PERTHSHIRE, SCOTLAND PH3 1NF OR TELEPHONE 0764 62231.

one of The Leading Hotels of the World

taking shape. Situated in 1,200 acres, the site is destined to become one of the world's outstanding golfing and leisure sites. Two championship courses are being constructed by Tom Weiskopf and Jay Morrish. Rossdhu House, formerly the home of the Clan Colquhoun, is being restored to its former glory and will become a focal point clubhouse incorporating suites, restaurants, bars and indoor leisure facilities including a swimming pool, sauna and solarium. Weiskopf, one of the best players in the world in the late sixties, is one of the few Americans invited to design a course in Scotland. Jay Morrish himself has designed over 100 courses. The heavily wooded site, on the banks of world-famous Loch Lomond, is ideal golfing country with enormous potential. It is envisaged that the High Road course will open in July 1991 and the Low Road course a year later, followed by the completion of the hotel and other off-course facilities.

These two unique developments alone are destined to keep Scotland generally in the forefront of the golfing world but

A bird's eye view of Loch Lomond Golf Club, showing what will be holes 9, 10, 11, 16, 17 and 18 of the 'High Road' course. Rossdhu Bay in the centre, borders the 18th hole and Ben Lomond disappears in the clouds in the background. Also seen are a few of the many small islands on Loch Lomond.

they are by no means the end of the
development of new courses and
complexes in Scotland. Many new
venues which will be of interest to the
travelling golfer will be started during
1991 and available for general play a
year or so later. Four new eighteen-hole
courses and four nine-hole courses are
currently under construction with another
nine or ten in the planning stage.

IRELAND

The discerning golfer who wants
uncrowded but challenging courses and
hospitality that is unmatched anywhere in
Europe, heads for Ireland and with just
cause.

Ireland already possesses some
formidable courses but the next two years
may well see the creation of three or four
new complexes which will make the rest
of Europe sit up and take notice. The

country, and some of the major concerns who are ploughing in the cash to support the proposals, see a market not only from Britain and Europe but also from Japan, Australia and America. All projects are aimed at the top of the market and, when completed from late 1991 onwards, will all create the highest possible standards both on and off the course.

The Kildare Country Club project for the huge Jefferson Smurfit group will be a 36-hole complex with the major course designed by the legendary Arnold Palmer. Also planned is a 200-bedroom, five-star hotel and all the facilities off course associated with that kind of development.

Adare Manor is a new development just 45 minutes from Shannon's international airport set in rolling acres of golfing country in an area already famous as fishing and riding country. Centrepiece will be the old Aldare Manor where Robert Trent Jones, the famous American architect, is the designer for two courses which thread through the estate and involve many riverside holes. Mount Juliet at Kilkenny is another exciting project which again envisages a luxury hotel and a 36-hole complex designed by Jack Nicklaus. At Portmarnock near Dublin is a proposed development from the I.M.G. Group headed by Mark McCormack close to the existing Portmarnock Golf Club.

United Kingdom based golfers visiting Ireland may have to wait for some time before they can actually play any or all the proposed courses but they are well worth waiting for.

IVYSIDE
HOTEL

AA ★★ RAC
ETB 🌷🌷🌷🌷

Sea Road, Westgate on Sea, Kent   Tel: (0843) 31082

Facing the golden sands of St. Mildred's Bay. The ideal centre for 7 different golf courses, including 2 championship, all within easy reach. 25 minutes by car. Recommended Hotel for the 1993 Sandwich Open Championship.

Royal St. Georges	SSS 72 – 12 ml	Westgate	SSS 65 – 1 ml
Prince's	SSS 72 – 12 ml	North Foreland	SSS 70 – 5 ml
Royal Cinque Ports	SSS 72 – 17 ml	St. Augustine's	SSS 70 – 6 ml
		Canterbury	SSS 70 – 13 ml

Badminton/tennis courts open all year – 1 ml.
4 Hardcourt tennis courts – ¼ ml.
Riding Stables 4 ml. Gliding and Flying 5 ml.

Hotel facilities:
* Large heated indoor pool 84° (air conditioned)
* Heated outdoor pool and children's pool
* Steam room, sauna, spa, solarium, masseuse
* 2 Squash courts (balconied for spectators)
* En-suite rooms (intercommunicating family rooms), colour TV, satellite station, teamakers, telephones – from £26 pp D,B&B
* Conference and seminar suites

Excellent cuisine with extensive wine list – from excellent house wines to chateau bottles. Vegetarian/individual diets catered for.

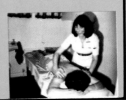

Featured on "WISH YOU WERE HERE".

24

A Short Walk to the First Tee

BARRY TOOK reviews some favourite golf hotels and courses

There is no such thing as a bad golf course – only one less good than another. However nothing is likely to please a golfer more than when a good course is combined with an excellent hotel. My memories of both are mixed but one experience when I was playing the Ferndown course just outside Bournemouth stands out.

Firstly, I was privileged to be part of the pro-am team in 1988, which won, thanks largely to our professional, Ronan Rafferty, who was at the beginning of a year in which he became European golf's highest money earner.

My other memory – a painful one, is of the same event a year earlier, when a bee found its way up my trouser leg and stung me on what, for want of a better description, I shall call my inner thigh. This caused great agony to me but great mirth to my playing companions, Tim Brooke-Taylor and Henry Kelly. My wife, who was caddying for me, was most resourceful and ordered me to drop my trousers, inspected the red and swelling site of the sting and, in the best traditions of Girl Guide and St John Ambulance training, sucked out the poison. She was as astonished as I was to find we'd attracted a number of spectators who gave her a round of applause as she completed her mission of mercy. But I wonder to this day what the episode must have looked like from a distance where the cause of my wife's first aid would not have been apparent.

My favourite hotel/golf course combination is the **Welcombe Hotel** in

the heart of Shakespeare country, Stratford-upon-Avon. The hotel was once the stately home of a Victorian millionaire, built in the mid-19th century in a Jacobean style but recently modernised so effectively and so discreetly that you feel as if you're present at a country house party rather than staying at a hotel.

Built on a hilltop it commands views of Warwickshire, and beyond the formal gardens that surround the house lies a challenging 18-hole golf course. It's not an easy course; hilly and tiring, but golf buggies are available and whether walking or riding, Welcombe is a golf course that is constantly stimulating and the pro shop is small but good.

The hotel deserves great praise. The public rooms are large and comfortable, the restaurant is excellent, and the

The Welcombe Hotel: an impressive and stately home.

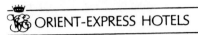

bedrooms have every facility. The staff are friendly and helpful and the whole enterprise is so beautifully managed that you feel at home from the time you arrive to the moment you – reluctantly – depart.

There's quite a different atmosphere at the **Seaford Golf Club** in East Blatchington, Sussex. There the residential accommodation is confined to 18 guests in the **Dormy House** and catering is comparatively simple, although the dining room is well patronised by the local members.

The golf is "seaside golf" with views of the English Channel from most of the downland – perhaps better described as "upland" – course. When the wind blows off the sea the going can be tough but on a balmy day playing golf at Seaford is a joy.

Not far along the south coast lie the three courses of Eastbourne: **Eastbourne Downs, Willingdon,** and **Royal Eastbourne.** None of these has hotels attached but Eastbourne itself has

a number of hotels ranging in price and quality, with the **Grand Hotel** at the peak, and the three star **Lansdowne Hotel** offering special "golfing breaks" of remarkable value.

One of the finest hotels on the south coast, the **Dormy House,** is just yards from Ferndown Golf Course, the one on which I had the nasty experience with the bee. The hotel has expanded in recent years and accommodation is modern and luxurious. If I put a faint question mark by the cuisine it is because I've only eaten there on the eve of pro-ams (the annual Alliss-Manitou, a joint promotion of Peter Alliss and the Manitou machinery conglomerate) as one of the vast crowd assembled for the event, and mass catering is not the same as a discreet *diner à deux.*

Another Peter Alliss charity event (for cancer research) takes place at the **Old Thorns Golf Club** near Liphook in Hampshire. Now owned by a Japanese consortium it is nonetheless open to all,

Old Thorns Golf Course, Hotel and Restaurants complex is a unique combination of old and new creating a country estate appeal with the traditional beauty of the old tile hung farmhouse providing blazing log fires in winter and terraces which overlook the magnificent 200 acres of Hampshire downs. The regal oaks, beeches and Scotch pines have been painstakingly conserved and the superb course is enhanced by the creation of water features fed from natural water springs.

Our testing 18-hole championship course provides a fine challenge for the enthusiastic golfer. The fairways wind their way through parkland, over lakes and streams and some holes cut through the pines or over the heathered slopes. A fleet of 30 golf cars has a track carefully incorporated within the contours of the fairways. Mid-week enjoyment for societies and golfing weekends is ensured by a driving range and practice green on hand for the individual golfer and adds up to perfect golf for everyone.

Our resident teaching professional will assess, encourage and monitor golfing skills. Everything needed to play is available on hire from the Pro's shop which carries a very comprehensive selection of golfing accessories. A wide range of brand name items are stocked as well as a variety of prizes for societies.

The tranquillity and peace of Old Thorns is complemented by the elegant new Japanese Centre carefully developed to blend naturally into the background of the undulating countryside thus cleverly uniting Eastern and Western culture.

Within one hour's drive of London, Heathrow and Gatwick airports, Old Thorns can provide the perfect venue for any business or social function.

MORETONHAMPSTEAD:
A SECRET NO LONGER

"The ubiquitous motorways are not everyone's choice of road, but they have proved of benefit to holidaymakers and visitors seeking easier access to the more remote corners of the country, not least the West Country.

The M5 to Exeter has been a boon to that part of England, a green and tranquil corner where countryside on the edge of Dartmoor has remained unchanged for centuries, compelling in its beauty and serenity. Here are to be found dozens of lovely villages, all thatched roofs and flowerpots, and miles of golden beaches.

Golf here is a particular delight and nowhere is it better or more appealing than at Moretonhampstead, where the gracious old Manor House Hotel sits in regal splendour overlooking a golf course that is a sight for sore eyes at any time of year.

Only 17 miles from the ancient cathedral city of Exeter, near the village of North Bovey, the Manor House and its golf course was once the best-kept secret in British golf, the haunt for those to whom it represented all that was best in life.

Set on the edge of the Dartmoor National Park, the course provides a stunning combination of natural beauty and ideal golf terrain perhaps without peer. It is a rare mix of moor and parkland folded into the floor of a valley that winds around the 270 acre estate hidden from the eyes of the unknowing who pass the gatehouse lodge and the entrance to the mile-long driveway which splits the course and leads to the elegant hotel.

Formerly a country retreat for the rich and titled and built when the Great Western Railway opened up the region early this century, the former mansion stands on high ground overlooking the valley where a host of splendid surprises await the golfer playing there for the first time.

Stand on the hotel's terrace and immediately below is the first tee. Down to the right, tucked into a bend in the River Bovey, lies the first green.

The river is a ubiquitous feature of the first eight holes as it threads its way through the valley imposing its presence on virtually every shot played.

Springtime and its flowers are a delight to the eye; June, the time of rhododendrons and azaleas, is unforgettable; autumn brings a panoply of gold that is little short of breathtaking. Indian summers, a common bonus must be experienced.

Another bonus, and part of the formerly well-kept secret, is the elegant former country home that is now the Manor House, a hotel in the grand tradition with oak panelled lounges, lots of open fireplaces, wide sweeping staircases, superb cuisine and impeccable service.

The hotel also offers squash racquets, tennis, fishing and a challenging par three course.

Add walks through countryside of matchless beauty, where hidden villages offer a treasure trove of lovely restaurants and shops in a setting of total tranquillity, and the prospect is one of idyllic holidays you will want to re-live again and again".

Richard Wade writing in 'Golf Holiday Digest'.

COME AND EXPERIENCE THE SECRET.

♛ The Manor House Hotel

Formerly a private residence and now a luxurious country house hotel, the Manor House is a sportsman's paradise and a golfer's haven.

The River Bovey meanders through our picturesque grounds and adds to the exciting challenge of playing one of the country's finest inland golf courses. Our championship par 69 course and Hotel is only minutes away from the M5 motorway. Squash, snooker, tennis and excellent fishing are also available.

Oak panelled halls, open log fires, cream teas and unparalleled scenery – the essence of Devon and a taste of the Manor House.

Company Days and Golf Societies welcome!

The Manor House Hotel, Moretonhampstead, Devon TQ13 8RE

Telephone: (0647) 40355   Telex: 42794   Fax: (0647) 40961

CROWN ♛ HOTELS

and both English and Japanese cuisine are excellent. There are 32 modern bedrooms, all excellently equipped, a comprehensively stocked pro shop, and buggies by the dozen.

Old Thorns has been designed to keep the player on his toes. It snakes its way up hill and down, through wooded country with breathtaking views from its high points. It is advisable to take a buggy as you need to be in good shape to walk it.

For views, two courses stand out in my mind: one in Dorset, the other in Scotland.

The Dorset course is the **Isle of Purbeck.** Today it is owned and run by the Robinson family, but a previous owner was authoress Enid Blyton. The course is situated on the site of an extinct volcano (extinct millions of years ago, I should add) and is reached either by road from Wareham or by ferry from Sandbanks near Poole.

The views of Wessex, Poole Harbour and the Isle of Wight are unrivalled. There is no hotel attached to the course, although the clubhouse has an excellent dining room, but just up the road is **Knoll House,** a 1990 winner of a family hotel award. It is a family affair and caters briskly for the holidaymaker. I have stayed there on several occasions and have never been disappointed. The recent addition of a health centre (sauna, jacuzzi, etc.) has brought it right up-to-date but fundamentally, though large, Knoll House is homely.

So to the hotel that has everything – **Gleneagles.** Facilities include two golf courses, riding stables, clay pigeon shooting, tennis, a modernistic health and leisure centre and swimming pool, first class public rooms, excellent service, luxurious bedrooms, and a well deserved international reputation. It's probably the most expensive of all the places I've mentioned but you are paying for the best.

I hardly need to mention **The Belfry** in Warwickshire, so famous has it become since the Ryder Cup successes of recent years, but both hotel and the two courses are as good as one could wish.

Turnberry too, thanks to extensive TV coverage, needs little comment from me. The hotel can hardly be faulted, the golf courses are delightful but the weather in that part of the world can be, to say the least, "changeable".

I can't conclude this piece without mentioning the **St. Pierre Golf and Country Club,** Chepstow, which caters brilliantly for conferences and individuals alike, and Moretonhampstead in Devon where the **Manor House Hotel** sits proudly on a hilltop surrounded by a beautiful, if exacting course. It's a hotel in the grand manner (no pun intended) offering oak panelled halls, log fires, and cream teas.

The future? Well, I can report on two great new courses which when completed will be Country Clubs to rival anything in the golfing world. One now playing is the **East Sussex National Golf Club** at Little Horsted, Nr. Uckfield, East Sussex – two 18-hole championship courses, magnificent practice facilities, and under construction a luxury club house and hotel. You can always stay at Horsted House (a Prestige Hotel) until it opens. The other, in many ways the equal of the East Sussex course, is **Collingtree Park** in Northamptonshire.

When these two are up and running, more than one famous old established golf course will have to look to its laurels (and its facilities) to compete with these multi-million pound newcomers.

The 18th hole at Collingtree Park, Northants.

Kiawah Island, USA
Preview of the Ryder Cup 1991

Imagine the tenor, Luciano Pavarotti, discovering a new aria by Puccini to sing and you get some idea of the excitement that Pete Dye felt when he was shown a thin strip of coastal land on an island just off the South Carolina coast.

America's premier golf architect knew that outline planning permission for a course had been granted and he stood rapt as he took in all of its high notes. "I told the owners that I would kill to build this course. It was God's country out there. No one in America has ever had a site to compare with this one."

And so it came to pass that the PGA of America's controversial decision to take the Ryder Cup to a course not even built, metamorphosed into a debate as to whether we are in at the birth of one of the world's great courses.

Kiawah Island is but 10,000 acres and much of it untouched by human hand. Already in play, the course at Turtle Point has welcomed the best of Europe and the USA's club professionals as the September 1990 venue of the 'mini-Ryder' PGA Cup.

This new course will complement Turtle Point and two others already built in a grand and tasteful development but while these are typical examples of American golf on reclaimed marshland, this ocean site recalls some of the great links courses. "It reminds me of Portmarnock and Portrush in places," Dye said, while the US Ryder Cup captain, Dave Stockton, saw similarities with some of the great American names like Shinnecock Hills and Cypress Point.

It is a breathtaking piece of land. Photographs from the air give the full picture of how close to the ocean every

Kiawah Island, USA: the 15th hole on the Turtle Point course, venue of the 1990 PGA Cup.

hole is. Indeed the furthest from the water, the opening hole, is no more than 300 yards away. The closing five holes on both the outward and inward halves will forever walk arm in arm with a currently deserted beach. "No other course in the

Kiawah Island, USA: looking east towards the new 1991 Ryder Cup course.

Northern Hemisphere has ten ocean holes," Dye said proudly.

When a fellow architect, Rees Jones, saw the site he said: "A course designer would give his right arm to be let loose round here."

Dye was undoubtedly the right man for the job. He may be controversial himself in some quarters, but no other architect gives each course the personal touches like he does. While most work on, say, 20 to 30 courses round the world with a full-time army of back-up personnel, Dye builds them one at a time, refusing to start another assignment until the one that commands his attention has been completed. And despite the obvious point that he has given his name to far fewer courses than his peers, he still has more in the top 50 rated venues than any other architect.

Nevertheless, the feeling is that it is this site in Kiawah Island that future generations will probably regard as his 'signature' course, the one to fully remember him by.

During the course construction Dye was asked whether he would be happy if the course was rated in the top 50 in, say, ten years' time. "Ten years' time?" Dye replied. "From the year dot this course will be born great. It will look 50 years old from day one."

Time will tell! What is certain is that Kiawah Island will host a great competition when Bernard Gallacher, the new captain of the Britain and Europe team, leads out his troops to defend the Ryder Cup against the United States. But that's another story . . . and for next year's *Golf Guide!*

Contents

ENGLAND and WALES

— Counties —

Isle of Man

1 London	12 Devon	23 Lancashire	34 Salop	45 Yorkshire, South
2 Avon	13 Dorset	24 Leicestershire	35 Somerset	46 Yorkshire, West
3 Bedfordshire	14 Durham	25 Lincolnshire	36 Staffordshire	
4 Berkshire	15 Essex	26 Manchester, Greater	37 Suffolk	A Clwyd
5 Buckinghamshire	16 Gloucestershire	27 Merseyside	38 Surrey	B Dyfed
6 Cambridgeshire	17 Hampshire	28 Midlands, West	39 Sussex, East	C Glamorgan, Mid
7 Cheshire	18 Hereford & Worcester	29 Norfolk	40 Sussex, West	D Glamorgan, South
8 Cleveland	19 Hertfordshire	30 Northamptonshire	41 Tyne & Wear	E Glamorgan, West
9 Cornwall	20 Humberside	31 Northumberland	42 Warwickshire	F Gwent
10 Cumbria	21 Isle of Wight	32 Nottinghamshire	43 Wiltshire	G Gwynedd
11 Derbyshire	22 Kent	33 Oxfordshire	44 Yorkshire, North	H Powys

SCOTLAND

—

Counties

—

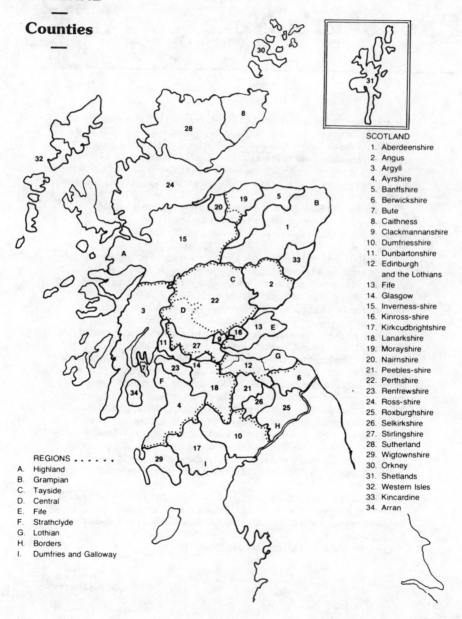

SCOTLAND

1. Aberdeenshire
2. Angus
3. Argyll
4. Ayrshire
5. Banffshire
6. Berwickshire
7. Bute
8. Caithness
9. Clackmannanshire
10. Dumfriesshire
11. Dunbartonshire
12. Edinburgh
    and the Lothians
13. Fife
14. Glasgow
15. Inverness-shire
16. Kinross-shire
17. Kirkcudbrightshire
18. Lanarkshire
19. Morayshire
20. Nairnshire
21. Peebles-shire
22. Perthshire
23. Renfrewshire
24. Ross-shire
25. Roxburghshire
26. Selkirkshire
27. Stirlingshire
28. Sutherland
29. Wigtownshire
30. Orkney
31. Shetlands
32. Western Isles
33. Kincardine
34. Arran

REGIONS . . . . . .

A. Highland
B. Grampian
C. Tayside
D. Central
E. Fife
F. Strathclyde
G. Lothian
H. Borders
I. Dumfries and Galloway

Publisher's Note

We acknowledge the assistance of Club Secretaries, Club Professionals and the PGA in compiling this new, revised and updated edition of *THE GOLF GUIDE: Where to Play ● Where to Stay*. We hope that you will enjoy our editorial features and our new sections on 'Golf in Portugal' and 'Golf in Majorca'. Course entries are hopefully self-explanatory (also see page 5) and the following notes may be helpful when you are arranging accommodation with any of our advertisers.

Enquiries and Bookings. It is quite normal to confirm a booking in writing and also to receive written confirmation – and a receipt for any advance payment. You should check prices and also any special requirements.

Cancellations. Any booking is a form of contract for both parties. If you have to cancel, try to give maximum notice. With reasonable notice the hotel should normally refund any advance payment but on short notice a full refund is not necessarily a legal entitlement.

Complaints. Most owners/managers are anxious to sort out problems on the spot so that you are a satisfied customer. If a problem persists you can get advice from a Citizens' Advice Bureau, Consumers' Association, Trading Standards Office, Tourist Board or indeed your own solicitor.

Serious complaints are unlikely to arise with the kind of accommodation you'll find on our pages. FHG Publications Ltd. do not inspect accommodation and an entry does not imply a firm recommendation. However, most of the advertisers have been recommended or proposed by local golf clubs and have standards which satisfy and in many cases far exceed those expected by inspecting authorities. In addition we will be pleased to hear from you if you have a serious complaint and although we cannot act as intermediaries or accept responsibility for our advertisers, we will record the complaint and follow it up with the advertiser in question.

Please mention *THE GOLF GUIDE* when you make a booking or contact a club.

As Golf continues to flourish and grow, we hope that *THE GOLF GUIDE* grows with the game. We are always pleased to hear from readers who have suggestions or comments, critical or otherwise, which we can consider for future editions.

Enjoy your golf — this could be your year!

Peter Clark
Publishing Director

The PGA Year

The Professional Golfers' Association organises around 500 golf events throughout its network of regions for PGA professionals every year. There are some ten national events held annually in Great Britain and with the Winter Pro Ams held in Southern Europe and the USA, every month of the year is a busy one for tournament personnel.

THE TRUSTHOUSE FORTE PGA SENIORS' CHAMPIONSHIP

Brian Waites began his professional career at Brough Golf Club, Humberside, venue for the 10th PGA Seniors' sponsored by Trusthouse Forte and local knowledge no doubt paid off during the 72-hole tournament.

It was a consummate performance by the professional who celebrated his 50th birthday at the start of the season, to qualify for the £45,000 event. Waites began as one of the clear favourites along with defending champion Neil Coles, five times Open winner Peter Thomson and Ireland's Christy O'Connor Snr.

And in the end it was the big names who were challenging for the title and £10,000 first prize with a display of golf which left the record crowds delighting in the visit of some of golf's greats to the North-east.

Seven players found themselves tied for the lead at the end of the first day with one over par rounds of 69 over the testing course which had been brought to impressive condition despite the recent dry spell. The leaderboard read like the 'Who's Who' of seniors' golf with Waites, Coles, Thomson and O'Connor Snr up

Brian Waites, PGA Seniors Champion 1990-91.

there with Fred Boobyer, the retired club professional from West Berkshire, Hugh Boyle from Royal Wimbledon and Ian Hayes, professional at Basingstoke.

The championship was blessed with fine weather for the duration and that coupled with the names at the top of the leaderboard brought out the crowds with a vengeance and the 'golden oldies' really rose to the occasion on the second day.

It was 75-year-old Robert Halsall, the retired professional from Royal Birkdale, who stole the early headlines. Halsall,

"It was a solid round of golf."
Brian Waites, PGA Senior Champion.

private tutor to Prince Rainier of Monaco, earned himself £1,000 by becoming the first professional to beat his age when he shot a five over par 73.

But Irish wizard Christy O'Connor is not a man to be upstaged and it was not long before his marvellous talents were delighting the crowds once again as he played his way to a brilliant four under par 64, one shot off the course record. Sponsors, THF, could not help but recognise his achievement by awarding another £1,000 to the 65-year-old for beating his age. More importantly, it earned him a two shot lead over his nearest rivals Coles and that man again Waites with a three under par second day aggregate of 133.

The final three ball on the third day — Waites, O'Connor and Coles — would have graced any tournament and the following crowd looked set to witness a great match as O'Connor Snr leapt further into the lead with an eagle at the

Alastair Webster (Edzell), receives the Wilson Club Professional Championship.

third to move to five under.

But the wizard failed to magic himself out of trouble two holes later when he knocked his second shot into the water and then finally three-putted to run up a triple bogey seven and lose control of the lead. All three jostled for position during the remaining holes but it was Waites who had nosed in front at the turn on three under, with Coles on two under and O'Connor back on one under.

Coles and Waites vied for the lead over the back nine but eventually both finished with rounds of 68 for a one under par aggregate of 203 with O'Connor on 204. Royal Wimbledon professional Hugh Boyle, a leader after the first day, had played himself back into contention with a third round 67 for a 206 aggregate.

Large crowds again turned out to witness the final round as the 'young pretender' Waites attempted to steal the crown from Neil Coles, the defending champion and bidding for his sixth title. Waites got off to a cracking pace with two birdies in the first three holes but it was the long fifth hole where fortunes really turned.

Coles played his way to a disastrous seven which all but cost him the championship and by the turn Waites was a convincing five shots ahead. As any class golfer he did what was necessary and played solid golf for the remainder of his round, never really threatened as Coles, Boyle and O'Connor slipped out of contention.

Not even a dropped shot on the last marred his performance as a clearly delighted Waites shot a last round 66 for a three under par aggregate of 269, the title and £10,000 winner's cheque by four shots.

"I have never hit my irons as well as I did during that last round. It was a solid round of golf and easily the best I played all week. I had a nightmare in my first seniors event in the States some weeks ago which left me at one of the lowest ebbs in my career.

"This must be one of the highest points and I hope I am around and in contention for a good many years yet."

THE WILSON CLUB PROFESSIONAL CHAMPIONSHIP

Elspeth Burnside reports

Edzell's Alastair Webster was only called into the event as a last-minute replacement, but he displayed no such reserve on the course when he swept to a two shot victory over fellow countryman Kevin Stables (Montrose) and Russell Weir (Cowal) in the Wilson Club Professional Championship at Carnoustie.

It was an astounding performance from the 31-year-old Scot who won playing in the Championship for a first time, and had never won a major 72-hole Professional event.

Webster learned of his late call-up at 2 pm on the eve of the tournament — Ballater's Fraser Mann had to pull out due to a side muscle injury — and, following a first round 74, he grabbed the lead with a superb second day four under par 68.

With persistent rain and wind making Carnoustie a far from welcoming host, Webster's score of four under was the only sub-par return of the opening two rounds. He produced six birdies in the opening fifteen holes, but equally important was his taming of the Open Championship links' tiger finish. He chipped and putted to save par at the final three holes which, compared to the majority of the field, represented the equivalent of two or three under par.

Webster's level 144 half-way total earned a one stroke advantage over Paul Carman from Huddersfield, and it was at that point that the Scot declared: "I think this could be my lucky week. It was the same first week in July that I won, back-to-back Scottish Boys' Strokeplay titles in 1975 and '76. I think it's an omen."

They were prophetic words from the popular redhead. On another day of atrocious weather conditions, he stretched his lead to four, over Carman with a third round 74 and, in the final 18 holes, his lead was never seriously threatened.

Webster went to the turn in 37 in far friendlier conditions while Carman still struggled out in 41. At that stage it was Weir, a two time former winner and three strokes behind, who was the nearest challenger.

But the new champion was in easy street, and after producing a string of pars that were only interrupted by a birdie four at the long fifteenth, he could well afford to drop shots at the final two holes for a closing 74, and a two shot triumph.

Webster's winning loot comprised the £4,750 first place cheque, a year's free use of a £14,000 Rover car, an invitation to the PGA of America Club Professional Championship at PGA West in California in October and, perhaps most importantly, a place in the European team to take on the Americans in the PGA Cup Match at Turtle Point, Kiawah Island, South Carolina from 21-23 September 1990.

With Webster, who made it five in a row for Scotland in the Club Professional Championship, who always looked a cast iron winner, the final day excitement turned to the battle for the PGA Cup places. The top seven eligible professionals in the Wilson event were guaranteed a place on the plane to America in September, and the cream of Britain's club professionals responded to the challenge by producing a barrage of birdies over Carnoustie's fearsome finish.

David Screeton (Chorlton-cum-Hardy) started the exhibition golf with a string of six birdies in a row from the 9th, while Carman, after his disappointing opening nine, proceeded to produce two eagles and two birdies in five holes from the eleventh. Weir and Stables also contributed their fair share of red figures

to the scoreboard, both returning 71's to share second spot.

Not to be outdone, Bruce Fleisher, the PGA of America Club Professional Champion who was competing in the event as an invited guest, went to the turn in three under par 33 and finished the day by equalling Webster's tournament best 68 and securing a share of fifth place.

When the dust had settled, Webster, Stables, Weir, Carman and Screeton could rest easy in the knowledge that their cup places were safe, whilst Brian Waites (Notts), David Scott (Latham Grange) and Tim Rastall (Prestbury) faced the prospect, having tied on 298, of a play-off to decide the final two spots.

However, PGA Captain Richard Bradbeer made the popular decision of granting one of his 'wild card' places to include all of the trio. That meant that eight places were decided, and the only remaining question to be answered was — who would be Bradbeer's second 'wild card' choice? Brian Barnes has been allocated the spot. Barnes, who was unable to defend the title this year, justifiably takes his spot by winning the . Championship last year.

The tenth place in the side goes to the winner of the European Club Pro's Championship in Holland, with, if the victor is in the team already or ineligible, Captain Bradbeer making another 'wild card' selection.

Barnes' inclusion raised Scotland's representation to five for the bi-annual encounter. And, while Barnes may be a newcomer to the event, his six Ryder Cup appearances, which included a now legendary two victories in the same day over Jack Nicklaus, will provide a welcome bank of experience.

Waites is another ex-Ryder Cup man and, after a break of eleven years, he returns to make his seventh PGA Cup appearance. Weir, who has played in the last two matches, is the only other member of the side to have played in previous matches.

However, Bradbeer has a ready-made foursomes partnership in Webster and Stables. The Scottish pair have finished joint fourth in the last two Golf Plus PGA National Fourball Championships, while they have also reached the semi-finals of the Sunningdale Foursomes this season.

Good Luck to them all!!!

LORD DERBY'S KNOWSLEY SAFARI PARK TOURNAMENT

Ernie Wilson, an affable Scot with a philosophical attitude to the vagaries of golf, won Lord Derby's Knowsley Safari Park Tournament at Bury after leading in all three rounds. Wilson, who described golf as a "nice walk", didn't exactly stroll to victory but was only briefly challenged throughout the three rounds.

The 28-year-old assistant professional at Aycliffe, County Durham, won by two strokes and was convinced his relaxed

approach was the reason for his success over the past 12 months during which he also won two other titles. Wilson said: "The more uptight you become, the worse you are likely to play. I'm convinced golf is all in the mind and once you put yourself under pressure you're bound to make mistakes."

He made few of those as he laid the foundation for his triumph, equalling the course record with a five-under-par 64 in the first round. He collected an eagle and five birdies, using his power off the tee to drive two of the par-four holes.

His eagle came at the second where he rifled his tee-shot to just three feet short, before dropping a stroke at the next then retrieving the situation with a birdie two at the short, 202-yard seventh. That particular hole was the only one to give him problems for the remainder of the tournament – with two double bogeys.

Leading by three strokes over Andrew Stokes of Birchwood after the first round, Wilson slipped to a 71 in the second

Ernie Wilson (Aycliffe), Knowsley Safari Park tournament winner, with Lord Derby (on his left).

round, when his putting lost some of its magic. Wilson, however, appeared quite unconcerned about the chasing pack which included the unattached Romford-based assistant with the ominous-sounding name of Dominic Eagle! He had coupled his opening round of 70 with a sparkling 66 to find himself only one stroke off the overnight pace.

Eagle's dream of his first major title turned into something of a nightmare the next day when Wilson started with four birdies in the first five holes. And even after Wilson had run up another double bogey at the seventh, he still reached the turn six ahead of Eagle who was to fall right out of contention over the inward half and finish joint sixth with a closing 75.

Wilson dropped a shot at the 14th, where he had to stand in a bunker to play his first putt, and at this point he became aware of the challenge from John Murray, of Cherry Lodge, Kent, who after being three behind overnight, was back in the clubhouse with his second 68 of the tournament.

His only hope was for Wilson to slip up over the remaining four holes. He three-putted the 17th for another bogey but took no more risks and a par at the last for a 69 was sufficient to give Wilson the title and £1,650 – the biggest pay cheque of his career.

Otley's Stephen Field, who earlier in the week had won the Sunderland Masters, made a belated charge with a 67 – the best of the day – to finish third one stroke behind Murray and three shots adrift of the leader.

Wilson, who received his award from the Rt Hon The Earl of Derby, the PGA President, toasted his success with a double magnum of Moet and Chandon. Winner of the MacGregor Tournament in April and the Mizuno Assistants' Championship last summer, he was the fifth North Region player to capture the Lord Derby title since its inception in 1985.

PEUGEOT CUP FOR THE PGA ASSISTANTS' CHAMPIONSHIP

Will the sixtieth PGA Assistants' Championship for the Peugeot Cup be remembered for the golf, its diamond anniversary or the tormenting weather responsible for its abandonment on the final day?

One man, Tony Ashton, will proudly look at his trophy and see his name inscribed alongside such greats as Peter Alliss, Tony Jacklin, Dai Rees and Bernard Hunt. He will think of his performance over three rounds of variable conditions at Hillside, Southport as probably the best of his career to date. Some, such as the Scots, headed by Drew Elliott of Ralston poised to attack on the final day will not forget "what might have been, if only . . ." Others, past victors of the PGA Assistants including Gwyn James (1932), George White (1939), George Low (1957), Derek Nash (1960), Ross Whitehead (1962), Malcolm Gregson (1964), Craig Defoy (1968) and John Oates (1988) will recall their trip down memory lane at the Diamond Anniversary Dinner.

Everyone will look back and say: "Do you remember the night we were spellbound by Peter Alliss and his great golfing tales? That was the Diamond Anniversary Dinner of the PGA Assistants' Championship at Hillside. What a night!"

Hillside Golf Club will have been quiet after the buzz of the 132 young professionals who descended upon its magnificent course on Monday, August 13th, 1990 for the 72-hole stroke-play final. The championship opened in fine style, with the Southern match-play champion, Tony Ashton of Huntercombe, equalling the course record with a six-under-par 66 first round. Hot on his heels, rookie Drew Elliott led a strong Scottish challenge on the second day to catch Ashton and share the lead, one stroke ahead of his compatriot, Colin Gillies of Glenbervie, with a third Scot

Tony Ashton (Huntercombe), with the Peugeot PGA Assistants' Cup.

Andrew Crerar from Blairgowrie two shots further back.

On the third day, Mike Ure, the former Durham Amateur Champion "prayed for wind and rain," he said. He got it and returned the best round of the day, a three-under-par 69. The leaders bore the brunt of the weather as the wind rose later in the day. "The last few holes were almost impossible," they chorused.

The leader for the third day running was Tony Ashton, this time on his own as he had broken free of Drew Elliott. After 54 holes Ashton was three-under-par 213. One stroke behind, Drew Elliott led a solid bunch of Scots with Gillies on 216 and Gary Collinson of Windyhill on 217. Ashton admitted afterwards: "I'm surprised the others fell away and I'm still up there." He added: "I'm okay downwind as I hit a high ball but not so good against it."

The Northerners and the Scots waited in anticipation for the final round, poised to attack in what they considered to be ideal conditions for them – windy. The fated final round started but never finished. It didn't simply blow a gale – the wind howled up to 40 mph! The tendency of the balls to be blown all over the greens, particularly on the back nine, proved to be the deciding factor. The 13th was the major stumbling block, in spite of a changed pin position to a less exposed point on the green. Craig Corrigan, one of the few to reach it, saw his ball double the distance from the hole, from 10 ft to 20 ft, before he had the good fortune to mark it. His playing partner David Geall had thoughts of using a £1 coin as a marker, so strong were the gusts.

All but three pairs had still to tee off when play was suspended at 1.00 pm. A two-hour wait followed in which the restaurant thrived while the players waited in tense anticipation of how "their" championship would end.

The final act was cut short. Ashton was announced as winner over 54 holes and sighs of relief mingled with disappointment clouded the atmosphere. "It's been a sad way to win," the new champion said. "But I'm not complaining." Neither were the disappointed Scots. Elliott conceded: "It would have been a bit of a lottery out there anyway."

At the end of the day Ashton had proved himself to be a worthy champion, leading from the start and equalling the course record, even though it won't appear in the record books. The championship tees were not used, leaving the course short of the layout for the PGA Championships of 1982, when two rounds of 66 were recorded. All qualifiers were duly rewarded from the £30,000 Peugeot prize fund, with the winner collecting £3,750 for his efforts.

However, it wasn't the end of the event – the final round had yet to come: the Diamond Anniversary Dinner, the PGA Assistants' Championship sixtieth birthday party at the splendid Prince of Wales Hotel in Southport. The players had one more round in which to celebrate or commiserate.

We don't remember much commiserating! How could anyone be down with the likes of Peter Alliss, the 1952 Assistants' Champion and guest of honour, regaling us with incidents from his golfing memos far into the night? A splendid end to a splendid championship.

THE WILSON PGA JUNIOR CHAMPIONSHIP

Bedecked with titles and oozing confidence, Michael Welch (Hill Valley) and Janice Moodie (West of Scotland Girls' Golfing Association) came, saw and conquered at the Wilson PGA Junior Championship at Selsdon Park Hotel in Surrey.

Welch, the defending champion, arrived in London having won the Carris Trophy, the British Boys' Championship and the Doug Sanders World Boys' title

within the previous few weeks. He continued his phenomenal run by equalling his own year-old Selsdon Park course record of 68 in the second round to retain the coveted Wilson title by a three-stroke margin from Jon Brien (Broome Manor).

Janice had enjoyed an equally productive summer with victories in the Scottish Under-21 and British Under-18 strokeplay championships among the highlights. She added the Wilson Junior title to her collection with a six-shot triumph over Wakefield's Nicola Buxton.

In the opening round, a couple of wayward iron shots reflected Welch's self-confessed state of exhaustion. But his determination to hang on to the title shone through, and a birdie 3 from five feet at the last saw him round in a level par 73.

"I'm very, very tired," confessed Welch, a protégé of Sandy Lyle's father, Alex. "But I certainly won't be giving the title away without a fight."

At the halfway stage, he stood three strokes adrift of surprise first-round leader, Jon Brien. The slightly-built 17-year-old, a full-time amateur who hoped to spend the winter working with a professional in Austria, carded five birdies in a round of three-under-par 70, his best ever score away from his home course.

Accurate iron play was the key to Brien's success, with his handful of gains all coming from inside 10 feet. His only mistake came at the short 6th – and it cost him dear. A pulled three-iron tee shot at the 193-yard hole, followed by a poor pitch and three putts added up to a double-bogey 5.

Robert Holland from Bognor Regis, on 72, was Brien's nearest challenger after day one, with Welch and Sundridge Park's Paul Easto sharing third spot on 73.

The second round turned into a two horse race between Brien and Welch, and it was the defending champion who made the early move with an eagle 3 – a

Michael Welch (Hill Valley) and Janet Moodie (West of Scotland GGA), Wilson PGA Junior Champions.

drive, 2-iron and 18 foot putt – at the 501 yard first. "That really got me going," he later confessed.

Welch, out in two-under-par 34, had drawn level by the turn, and he edged into the lead for the first time with a birdie 4 at the 510-yard tenth, a distance he covered with a drive and 7-iron. Still one ahead, the more experienced boy virtually clinched victory when he birdied the long 15th and Brien, having tangled with the trees, ran up a bogey 6.

"It was so close all the way, that I was just trying to concentrate on playing my own game," said Welch. "I wasn't really aware of the situation until I was coming down the last." Having realised he was set to retain the title, he duly celebrated by slotting home a six-foot putt for a closing birdie 3 to equal his second round course record of 1989.

Brien had the consolation of taking the runner-up spot, while Ian Pyman (Scarborough North Cliff) sneaked into third place on 146 thanks to a fine second round of 71.

In the girls' event, Janice's victory was the perfect final preparation before making her first Scottish senior debut, the following week, in the women's Home Internationals at Hunstanton in Norfolk.

The talented 17-year-old had won the Scottish strokeplay title over Troon Portland in August by a runaway 13 strokes, and her victory margin at Selsdon could have been equally awesome had the Scottish girl not suffered from a dose of three-putting on the opening day. She used her putter 39 times in a round of one-over-par 74 and had to settle for a two-shot advantage over her closest challengers, Nicola Buxton and Joanne Berry (Coxmoor).

"I couldn't get the hang of the greens at all," bemoaned the youngster. "But it will be different tomorrow. I'm going to shoot the lights out. I can feel a nice wee 68 coming on."

Her predicted score may have been a little wide of the mark but, with a two-hour session on the Selsdon Park putting green having helped restore her confidence, her victory was never in doubt. In fact, the contest was all but over at the opening hole when the champion-elect made a pitch and putt birdie 4, while both Nicola and Joanne ran up double-bogey 7's.

"That start took the pressure off, and I never thought I would lose," said the confident teenager, who was the first Scottish winner of the title since Tracey Craik in 1984.

THE PGA CUP

Europe's club professionals slip to PGA Cup defeat against strong USA opponents.

Europe's hopes of emulating their 1987 Ryder Cup colleagues with a first-ever victory on American soil came to an end when they lost 19-7 in the 15th PGA Cup match at the Turtle Point course, Kiawah Island, in South Carolina, USA. An experienced American line-up containing several regular members of the Hogan Tour allied to the alien tropical climate of 90° plus temperatures, and extreme humidity, proved to be too big a hurdle for the side – competing under a European banner as opposed to Great Britain and Ireland, for the first time.

The home side led by five points after the opening day's foursomes and fourballs, and a similar result in the repeat format on the second day ensured they could not be beaten, even if Europe won all ten singles matches on the final day. In the event, the American side ensured victory by taking six of the singles matches. The win raised the tally of American victories to nine in the series, inaugurated in 1973, two of the matches having finished all square.

Europe did have a star man in Cowal's Russell Weir. The 39-year-old Scot, appearing in his third successive PGA Cup encounter, won a foursome and fourball in partnership with former Ryder Cup man, Brian Waites, and went on to collect a third full point when he won the final two holes to defeat Bob Boyd by one hole in the singles.

In the first day's fourballs, Weir and Waites, a partnership that could call on the experience of a combined total of eight PGA Cup encounters, defeated Boyd and Bob Ford by 3&2 in the fourballs and, on the second day, collected the scalps of Ray Freeman and Stu Ingraham by 2&1 in the foursomes. Europe's half point from the opening day came in more dramatic fashion. Alastair Webster and Kevin Stables, 3 up with 4 holes to play in the very first match of the series, had to settle for a half against Boyd and Ford when the latter holed from 35 feet for a birdie 3 at the final hole. On the second day, Tim Rastall and David Scott added another half point to Europe's total when Dale Fuller and Jeff Thomsen sportingly conceded the Prestbury professional's 12-foot putt for a half at the 18th.

Europe set out on the final day facing the task of having to win all ten singles for a draw, and it was the reigning US club professional champion, Bruce Fleisher, who ensured an American victory, and retained his 100% record with a 4&3 win over Waites.

The visitors salvaged a little pride by claiming four of the ten singles points on the final day, blessed with cooler conditions. Webster, the Wilson club professional champion, played his lead role to perfection with a 4&3 win over Freeman, while Paul Carman dented the unbeaten record of Phil Hancock with a 3&2 victory. With Weir's point having been added to the haul, John Woof, the Hague-based professional who won the European Championship for Teaching Professionals at Broekpolder in August, celebrated the new European status of the team with a two-hole triumph over Kim Thompson.

Richard Bradbeer, the European team captain, admitted his side had got off to an unfortunate start, but stated: "It was a

The 1990 PGA Cup Team (left to right): Paul Carmen, Brian Waites, Russell Weir, Alastair Webster, Richard Bradbeer, David Screeton, Tim Rastall, David Scott, Kevin Stables.

great experience, especially for the younger players. They were facing different pressures from normal, and coped better as the week went on. It will have done them all a power of good for the future."

The American team's greater knowledge of the Bermuda-type grass, their acclimatisation to the weather conditions, and more regular and concentrated competition were all pertinent factors in their victory.

Your Club Pro: the Man with all the Answers

Unlike that of a successful tour professional, the life of a PGA club professional is far from glamorous. The hours are long and the work hard, but on the whole, someone with the right skills and temperament can be greatly rewarded. Contrary to the views of many golfers and club members, who are often not aware of the difference between the golf professional at their club and the professional golfers they see on television, the club pro doesn't spend

most of his time playing golf. So they ask: "What exactly do the club pro's do?"

Every club member has an opinion on that question — on what he or she feels the pro should be doing. To satisfy these disparate demands, the golf professional must wear many hats — teacher, player, equipment and clothing merchant, administrator and public relations person. The club pro also has to be a golf 'generalist' who is an expert in everything from the Rules of Golf to repairing clubs,

The Club Pro: Bobby Mitchell in his shop at Knebworth Golf Club.

have achieved examination success the newly elected PGA member will be eligible for a position as a qualified assistant professional and another 'training' period ensues during which he or she is expected to take their first steps to secure a long-term position as a head professional of a golf club.

So, how is the 'pro' likely to operate? According to recent reports, the average pro spends twice as much time selling than on the more traditional duties of teaching and playing. The recent emphasis on his retail operation has not been entirely voluntary as in many cases the pro has been forced into spending more time in the shop by financial necessity. The pro-as-businessman has emerged in part as a response to heightened competition. Golfers are confused with the myriad of new clubs, balls and equipment that glossy advertising states will help them improve their game and with the recent explosion of new technology, the pro's skills as a club fitter will be in greater demand than ever. The club professional can take some comfort in the fact that you can't go to the supermarket and expect somebody to know the difference between a boron graphite shaft and titanium.

As club professionals are under no illusion that members are in any way obliged to purchase from their pro shop, the club professional has to be an expert in handling people. The public relations aspect of the job takes on many forms, from conducting clinics for juniors to greeting guests and being the front man for a whole host of enquiries and complaints. If someone isn't satisfied with the condition of the course or the food in the dining room, the pro is more likely to hear about it than the club steward who is responsible for that part of the operation. In representing this and all the other sides of a golf club, the professional lays himself on the line. If he has all the answers he'll be well rewarded!

from conducting tournaments to maintaining a fleet of golf trolleys!

Naturally, jobs differ depending on whether the pro is working at a private club, municipal course or country club, but the bottom line is to make sure the customer's day at the course is as pleasant as possible. If it isn't the pro is usually the first one to hear about it.

When you need advice on legal matters or completing your tax return, you will most likely seek the services of a 'professional'. Lawyers and accountants spend a large part of their training 'on-the-job', culminating in theory and practical examinations. To qualify as a PGA professional golfer the training programme takes a similar approach over a three- or four-year period — covering the skills of teaching, club repairs, business studies and, of course, developing their own game. Once they

Golf in England
WHERE TO PLAY • WHERE TO STAY

Elsewhere in *THE GOLF GUIDE* Barry Took features some of England's better-known golfing hotels and for the travelling golfer there is an excellent range of accommodation readily available from the Wash to the Lizard and from Northumberland to the Needles.

One usually associates hotels with holiday golf and there is, not surprisingly, the widest selection in the south-west. For those who prefer country air and a rural atmosphere, a possible choice would be Collacott Farm, Umberleigh or Batch Farm Country Hotel near Weston-super-Mare. For more of a golfing environment and perhaps the livelier amenities of a resort, choose between Burnham-on-Sea in Somerset, Bude or Falmouth in Cornwall, or Ilfracombe or Seaton in Devon. One would also think quite naturally of Moretonhampstead before moving east to Avon and Bristol and, of course, Gloucester.

The south, through Dorset and Hampshire, whose Old Thorns illustrates our front cover this year, offers both inland and seaside golfing interest with well-established golfing hotels in Sussex and Kent and such metropolitan favourites as Sheldon Park in Surrey.

Further north, the Birmingham area has always catered for golfers and as one travels through Shropshire, with Patshull Park, and Cheshire where there are many new developments in hand, one is caught by the approaching aura of the Lancashire golfing centres around Southport and Lytham. Off-shore the Isle of Man supplies not only the golfer but his family and friends with a warm welcome and leisure attractions. Equally

the Isle of Wight and the Channel Islands offer more than just golf with their relaxed and almost 'overseas' flavour.

Staying away to play golf, whether on business or on holiday, is no problem. There are friendly, comfortable and experienced hosts who make accommodation easy to obtain and enjoy. Harder, however, is raising the level of one's game to the same high plane – and *THE GOLF GUIDE: WHERE TO PLAY AND WHERE TO STAY* cannot guarantee any assistance in that endeavour!

One of the attractive greens at Old Thorns, Hampshire.

49

London

ASHFORD. **Ashford Manor Golf Club,** Fordbridge Road, Ashford, Middlesex (Ashford (0784) 252049). 18 holes, 6343 yards. S.S.S. 70. *Green Fees:* information not provided. *Visitors:* welcome with introduction. Professional: M. Finney (0784 255940). Secretary: B.J. Duffy.

BARNET. **North Middlesex Golf Club,** Whetstone, The Manor House, Friern Barnet Lane, Barnet N20 0NL (081-445 1604). *Location:* five miles north of Finchley, A1000. 18 holes, 5611 yards. S.S.S. 67. *Green Fees:* weekday round/day £20.00; weekends and Bank Holidays £27.00. *Visitors:* welcome (with Official Handicap), weekends playing with a member and in possession of Official Handicap. *Society Meetings:* catered for. Professional: A. S. R. Roberts. General Manager/Secretary: M.C.N. Reding (081-445 1604).

BARNET. **Old Fold Manor Golf Club,** Hadley Green, Barnet, Herts EN5 4QN (081-440 9185). *Location:* Junction 23 M25. A1000 one mile north of Barnet. Heathland course. 18 holes, 6449 yards. S.S.S. 71. Large practice ground, putting green. *Green Fees:* £20.00 per round, £25.00 per day (except Mondays and Wednesdays £5.50). *Eating facilities:* restaurant and bar except Mondays and Wednesdays. *Visitors:* welcome weekdays. *Society Meetings:* catered for Thursdays and Fridays. Professional: Peter Jones (081-440 7488). Manager: D.V. Dalingwater (081-440 9185).

BEXLEY HEATH. **Barnehurst Golf Club,** Mayplace Road East, Barnehurst, Bexley Heath (Crayford (0322) 523746). 9 holes, 5320 yards. S.S.S. 66. *Green Fees:* Information not provided. *Visitors:* welcome Monday, Wednesday and Friday without reservation. *Society Meetings:* not catered for. Professional: Tom Cullen. Secretary: Mr H. Esler.

BROMLEY. **Bromley Golf Club,** Magpie Hall Lane, Bromley. *Location:* off A21 Bromley to Farnborough road. Short, flat, open course with a few trees. 9 holes, 2745 yards. S.S.S. 35. Putting green and teaching facilities. *Green Fees:* information not available. *Eating facilities:* snacks available. *Visitors:* no booking required as this is public course. *Society Meetings:* by arrangement with Bromley District Council. Professional: Alan Hodgeson (081-462 7014).

CHINGFORD. **Chingford Golf Club,** 158 Station Road, Chingford (081-529 2107). 18 holes. S.S.S. 67. *Visitors:* welcome, an article of red must be worn.

CHINGFORD. **Royal Epping Forest Golf Club,** Forest Approach, Chingford, London (081-529 6407). *Location:* 250 yards east of Chingford (BR) Station. 18 holes, 6620 yards. S.S.S. 70. *Green Fees:* weekdays £4.50, weekends £6.00. *Visitors:* welcome all week. Red coats or trousers compulsory. *Eating facilities:* bars

only. Professional: R. Gowers (081-529 5708). Secretary: J.H. Shaw (081-529 2195).

CHINGFORD. **West Essex Golf Club,** Bury Road, Sewardstonebury, Chingford, London E4 7QL (081-529 0928). *Location:* two miles north of Chingford BR Station. M25 (Junction 26) and Waltham Abbey follow directions to Chingford (Daws Lane on left). Parkland, wooded, hilly. 18 holes, 6289 yards. S.S.S. 70. *Green Fees:* weekdays £20.00 per round, £25.00 per day; weekends with member only. *Eating facilities:* restaurant and bar facilities. *Visitors:* welcome weekdays except Tuesday mornings and Thursday afternoons; after 3pm competition days. Phone first. *Society Meetings:* catered for by arrangement Mondays, Wednesdays and Fridays. Professional: C. Cox (081-529 6347). Secretary: P.H. Galley MBE (081-529 7558).

DULWICH. **Dulwich and Sydenham Hill Golf Club,** Grange Lane, College Road, London SE21 (081-693 3961). *Location:* off South Circular, Dulwich Common. 18 holes, 6051 yards. S.S.S. 69. *Green Fees:* information not available. *Eating facilities:* lunch every day. *Visitors:* welcome, with reservation on weekdays. *Society Meetings:* catered for, maximum 30. Professional: David Baillie. Secretary: Brian Harmer.

EDMONTON. **Leaside Golf Club,** Pickett's Lock Sports Centre, Edmonton N9 0AS (081-803 4756). *Location:* near North Circular Road. Flat parkland. 9 holes, 2496 yards. S.S.S. 32. Driving range, putting green. *Green fees:* information not available. Reductions weekdays for Senior Citizens and Juniors. *Eating facilities:* cafe and bar. *Visitors:* booking required at weekends. *Society Meetings:* by arrangement with Sports Centre. Professional: R. Gerken.

EDMONTON. **Picketts Lock Golf Course,** Picketts Lock Centre, Edmonton, London N9 0AS (081 803 3611). *Location:* north east London, near North Circular Road and A10. River Lea borders course. 9 holes, 2600 yards. S.S.S. 32. Floodlit driving range. *Green Fees:* weekdays £3.30, weekends £4.00. Weekday discounts for Senior Citizens £1.40. 18 holes (weekdays only) £5.60. *Eating facilities:* available. *Visitors:* open to public every day, weekend booking advisable (contact Professional). *Society Meetings:* small societies welcome weekdays. Professional: Richard Gerken. Manager: S. Welch.

ELTHAM. **Eltham Warren Golf Club,** Bexley Road, Eltham SE9 2PE (081-850 1166). *Location:* five minutes' walk from Eltham Station. Parkland. 9 holes, 5840 yards, 5339 metres. S.S.S. 68. *Green Fees:* weekdays £14.00, weekends with member only. *Eating facilities:* meals and snacks by arrangement, lounge bar and stud bar. *Visitors:* welcome, but must be members of a Golf Club. *Society Meetings:* by arrangement. Professional: Ian Coleman (081-859 7909). Secretary: D.J. Claze (081 850 4477).

ELTHAM. **Royal Blackheath Golf Club,** The Clubhouse, Court Road, Eltham SE9 5AF (081-850 1795). *Location:* off Court Road, Eltham. 18 holes, 6209 yards. S.S.S. 70. Practice area. *Green fees:* £30.00 per day (£8.00 with member); weekends £8.00 (only with member). *Eating facilities:* excellent diningroom and two bars. *Visitors:* welcome weekdays, weekends if introduced by and playing with member. Museum. *Society Meetings:* catered for midweek, prior booking essential. Professional: Ian McGregor. Secretary: R. Barriball.

ENFIELD. **Crews Hill Golf Club,** Cattlegate Road, Crews Hill, Enfield EN2 8AZ (081-363 0787). *Location:* off Junction 24 M25, follow directions to Enfield. Parkland. 18 holes, 6230 yards. S.S.S. 70. Practice area, Professional instruction. *Green Fees:* on application. *Eating facilities:* restaurant by arrangement. *Visitors:* welcome by arrangement. Handicap Certificate required. *Society Meetings:* by arrangement. Professional: J.R. Reynolds (081-366 7422). General Manager: E.J. Hunt (081-363 6674).

ENFIELD. **Enfield Golf Club,** Old Park Road South, Off Windmill Hill, Enfield, Middlesex EN2 7DA (081-363 0083). *Location:* one mile north of Enfield Chase Station. Bus route 107. Parkland. 18 holes, 6137 yards. S.S.S. 70. *Green Fees:* weekdays £20.00 per round, £25.00 per day; £8.00 with member. *Eating facilities:* restaurant/bar. *Visitors:* welcome weekdays only, with current Handicap Certificate. *Society Meetings:* catered for Mondays, Wednesdays and Fridays by prior arrangement. Professional: Lee Fickling (081-366 4492). Secretary: c/o Mrs S. Rowe (081-363 3970).

ENFIELD. **Whitewebbs Golf Club,** Beggars Hollow, Clay Hill, Enfield (081-363 2951). *Location:* due north of Enfield, turn one mile past Civic Centre, left turn off Baker Street. Wooded course with a stream crossing 1st, 8th and 9th holes. 18 holes, 5755 yards. S.S.S. 68. Small practice area. *Green Fees:* £3.80 weekdays, £5.20 weekends. Reduction on season ticket for Senior Citizens. *Eating facilities:* cafe on site, bar open to members only. *Visitors:* welcome without reservation weekdays, bookings weekends (Municipal Golf Course). *Society Meetings:* can be booked via club. Professional: D. Lewis (081 363 4454). Secretary: I Van Graan.

FINCHLEY. **Finchley Golf Club,** Nether Court, Frith Lane, Finchley, London NW7 1PU (081-346 0883). *Location:* close A1/M1 Mill Hill East tube station. Wooded course. 18 holes, 6411 yards. S.S.S. 71. *Green Fees:* weekdays £21.00, weekends £30.00. *Eating facilities:* bar; diningroom open daily except Mondays. *Visitors:* welcome weekdays except Thursdays, weekends after mid-day. *Society Meetings:* catered for Wednesdays and Fridays. Professional: David Brown (081-346 5086). Secretary: John Pearce (081-346 2436).

GREENFORD. **Ealing Golf Club,** Perivale Lane, Greenford, Middlesex UB6 8SS (081-997 2595). *Location:* on Western Avenue A40 half a miles from Hanger Lane Gyratory System. Flat parkland. 18 holes, 6216 yards. S.S.S. 70. *Green Fees:* £20.00. *Eating facilities:* men's bar, mixed lounge, restaurant – lunches and snacks. *Visitors:* welcome with reservation on Mondays, Wednesdays and Thurdays. *Society Meetings:* catered for Society and Company days. Professional: A. Stickley (081-997 3959). Secretary: C.F.S. Ryder (081-997 0937).

GREENFORD. **Horsenden Hill Golf Club,** Whitton Avenue, Woodland Rise, Greenford UB6 0RD (081-902 4555). *Location:* off Whitton Avenue, running alongside Sudbury Golf Club. Parkland course. 9 holes, 3200 yards. S.S.S. 56. Practice area, nets and putting green. *Green Fees:* weekdays £2.50 for 9 holes; weekends £3.75 for 9 holes. *Eating facilities:* restaurant and bar. *Visitors:* welcome at all times, unrestricted. Professional: Tony Martin. Secretary: V. Le Picq.

HAMPTON HILL. **Fulwell Golf Club,** Wellington Road, Hampton Hill, Middlesex TW12 1JY (081-977 3188). *Location:* opposite Fulwell Railway Station and bus garage. Flat parkland course. 18 holes, 6490 yards. S.S.S. 71. Practice ground. *Green Fees:* weekdays £22.00, weekends £27.00. £10.00 with member. *Eating facilities:* lunches, teas except Mondays. *Visitors:* welcome weekdays. *Society Meetings:* welcome weekdays. Professional: D. Haslam (081-977 3844). Secretary: D.C. Evans (081-977 2733).

HAMPTON WICK. **Home Park Golf Club,** Hampton Wick, Kingston-upon-Thames (081-977 2658). *Location:* between Hampton Court and Kingston Bridge, one mile west of Kingston. 18 holes, 6519 yards. S.S.S. 71. *Green Fees:* weekdays £10.50 (£16.50 all day), weekends and Bank Holidays £18.00 (£28.00 all day). *Eating facilities:* full catering all week except Mondays. *Visitors:* welcome, no advance booking. *Society Meetings:* catered for by arrangement. Professional: Mr L. Roberts. Secretary: Mr A.R.W. White (081-977 2658).

HEATHROW. **Holiday Inns Golf Club,** Heathrow, London. 9 holes, S.S.S. 62. Par 60. *Green Fees:* £3.50 weekdays, £4.00 weekends. Secretary: P. Davies.

HENDON. **Hendon Golf Club,** off Sanders Lane, Devonshire Road, Mill Hill, London NW7 1DG (081-346 8083). *Location:* leave M1 southbound at junction 2. Turn off A1 into Holders Hill Road. 10 miles north of London. Parkland, wooded, well bunkered. 18 holes, 6241 yards. S.S.S. 70. *Green Fees:* weekdays £20.00 per round, £27.00 per day; weekends £33.00. *Eating facilities:* full bar and catering facilities (snacks only on Mondays). *Visitors:* welcome weekdays (limited at weekends and Bank Holidays), book through Pro Shop. *Society Meetings:* catered for by arrangement Tuesdays to Fridays, book through Secretary's office. Professional: Stuart Murray (081-346 8990). Secretary: David Cooper (081-346 6023).

HIGHGATE. **Hampstead Golf Club,** Winnington Road, Highgate, London N2 0TU (081-455 7421). *Location:* by road from Highgate Village or one mile down Hampstead Lane adjacent to Spaniards Inn. Undulating parkland with trees. 9 holes, 5812 yards. S.S.S. 68. *Green Fees:* £15.00 (£20.00 a day) weekdays; weekends £20.00. *Eating facilities:* bar; snacks and afternoon teas; lunches bookable. *Visitors:* welcome weekdays (not Tuesdays) if members of a golf club or have Handicap Certificate. Limited at weekends. *Society Meetings:* small societies catered for weekdays by prior arrangement. Professional: Peter

Brown (081-455 7089). Secretary: K.F. Young (081-455 0203).

HIGHGATE. **Highgate Golf Club,** Denewood Road, Highgate N6 4AH (081-340 1906). *Location:* near A1, turn down Sheldon Avenue, opposite Kenwood House and first left. 18 holes, 5982 yards. S.S.S. 69. *Green Fees:* weekdays £23.00, weekends only with member. *Eating facilities:* available. *Visitors:* welcome weekdays except Wednesdays. *Society Meetings:* catered for weekdays except Wednesdays. Professional: Robin Turner (081-340 5467). Secretary: S. Zuill (081-340 3745).

HILLINGDON. **Hillingdon Golf Club,** 18 Dorset Way, Hillingdon, Middlesex UB10 0JR (Uxbridge (0895) 39810). *Location:* near A40, adjacent to RAF Uxbridge. Very undulating – well wooded course, sloping down to river. 9 holes, 5459 yards, 4480 metres. S.S.S. 67. *Green Fees:* weekdays 18 holes £15.00. *Eating facilities:* sandwiches only in bar lunchtimes, no evening facilities except club functions and by special arrangement. *Visitors:* welcome Mondays, Tuesdays and Fridays; Thursdays – Ladies Day, weekends with members only. *Society Meetings:* catered for by special arrangement only with committee through club Secretary. Professional: D.J. McFadden (0895 51980). Secretary: L.A.N. Holland (0895 33956).

HOUNSLOW. **Airlinks Golf Club,** Southall Lane, Hounslow TW5 9PE (081-561 1418). *Location:* Junction 3 on M4, A312 to Hayes. Same entrance as D. Lloyd Tennis Centre. Flat course with water holes and doglegs. 18 holes, 5332 yards. S.S.S. 68. *Green Fees:* weekdays £6.50 per round, weekends £8.50 per round. *Eating facilities:* bar snacks, salads. *Visitors:* welcome anytime except Saturday and Sunday mornings. *Society Meetings:* catered for. Professional: S. Smith (081-561 1418).

HOUNSLOW. **Hounslow Heath Municipal Golf Course,** Staines Road, Hounslow TW4 5DS (081-570 5271). *Location:* Staines Road A315 between Hounslow and Bedfont. Undulating course with water hazards. 18 holes, 5820 yards. S.S.S. 68. *Green Fees:* weekdays £4.00 per round, £6.50 per day; weekends £5.00 per round, £7.50 per day. Reduced rates for Juniors and Senior Citizens weekdays except Bank Holidays. *Eating facilities:* snacks; tea, coffee, soft drinks. *Visitors:* welcome at all times, bookings required at weekends and Bank Holidays. *Society Meetings:* by arrangement with Professional. Professional: P. Cheyney (081-570 5271). Secretary: E. Rogan.

ISLEWORTH. **Wyke Green Golf Club,** Syon Lane, Osterley, Isleworth TW7 5PT (081-560 8134). *Location:* situated off the A4 near Gillette Corner. Flat, wooded course. 18 holes, 6242 yards, 5706 metres. S.S.S. 69. *Green Fees:* weekdays £22.00, weekends £33.00 (half price with member). *Eating facilities:* bar snacks available daily, main meals bookable in advance. *Visitors:* welcome with reservation weekdays, and Saturdays after 3pm. *Society Meetings:* catered for on Tuesdays and Thursdays by arrangement, minimum 20. Professional: Tony Fisher (081-847 0685). Secretary: Trevor Glover (081-560 8777).

LONDON. **Lime Trees Park Golf Club,** Ruislip Road, Northolt, Middlesex UB5 6QZ (081-845 3180). *Location:* just off A40 at the Polish War Memorial roundabout. Undulating parkland with interesting water hazards. 9 holes, 5906 yards. S.S.S. 70/71. Driving range. *Green Fees:* weekdays £2.75 for 9 holes, weekends £3.50 for 9 holes. *Eating facilities:* two bars/bistro. *Visitors:* welcome at all times. *Society Meetings:* catered for. General Manager: Simon Keep.

LONDON. **London Scottish Golf Club,** Windmill Enclosure, Wimbledon Common SW19 5NQ (081-788 0135). *Location:* just off A3 – Tibbetts Corner – just south of Putney SW15. Parkland (no bunkers). 18 holes, 5438 yards. S.S.S. 67/68. *Green Fees:* £10.00 per round, £16.00 per day. *Eating facilities:* bar and catering. *Visitors:* welcome weekdays only. Check with Professional recommended. Red top must be worn, no jeans or sweatshirts. *Society Meetings:* minimum 20 players. Professional: Matthew Barr (081-789 1207). Secretary: Jack Johnson (081-789 7517).

LONDON. **Mill Hill Golf Club,** 100 Barnet Way, Mill Hill, London NW7 3AL (081-959 2282). *Location:* A1, south half a mile before Apex Corner left into clubhouse car park – signposted. Flat wooded parkland. 18 holes, 6232 yards, 5697 metres. S.S.S. 70. Practice ground. *Green Fees:* weekdays £18.00 per round, weekends £30.00. *Eating facilities:* restaurant and bar. *Visitors:* welcome Monday to Friday, weekends and Bank Holidays bookings only. Two snooker tables. *Society Meetings:* catered for Mondays, Wednesdays and Fridays with prior booking. Professional: Mr A. Daniel (081-959 7261). Secretary: Mr F.H. Scott (081-959 2339).

LONDON. **Trent Park Golf Club,** Bramley Road, Southgate, London N14 (081-366 7432). *Location:* opposite Oakwood Tube Station. Undulating parkland. 18 holes, 6008 yards. S.S.S. 69. Large practice area. *Green Fees:* weekdays £4.10, weekends £5.60. *Eating facilities:* bar and snacks. *Visitors:* open to public at all times. Bookings necessary at weekends. *Society Meetings:* welcome Monday to Thursday. Professional: Craig Easton. Secretary: F.L. Montgomery.

NORTHWOOD. **Northwood Golf Club Ltd,** Rickmansworth Road, Northwood, Middlesex HA6 2QW (Northwood (09274) 25329). *Location:* on A404 between Pinner and Rickmansworth. Parkland/wooded course. 18 holes, 6493 yards. S.S.S. 71. *Green Fees:* weekdays £16.00 to £24.00. *Eating facilities:* lunches served. *Visitors:* welcome weekdays only. *Society Meetings:* by arrangement. Professional: C.J. Holdsworth (09274 20112). Secretary: C.W. Pipe (09274 21384).

NORTHWOOD. **Sandy Lodge Golf Club,** Sandy Lodge Lane, Northwood, Middlesex HA6 2JD (Northwood (09274) 25429). *Location:* adjacent Moor Park Underground Station. Inland links. 18 holes, 6340 yards. S.S.S. 70. *Green Fees:* weekdays £22.00. *Eating facilities:* full catering and bar service available. *Visitors:* not weekends – telephone first. Handicap Certificate required. *Society Meetings:* catered for by prior arrangement. Professional: Alex M. Fox (09274 25321). Secretary: J.N. Blair (09274 25429).

ORPINGTON. **Lullingstone Park Golf Club,** Park Gate, Chelsfield, Near Orpington, Kent (Knockholt (0959) 32928). *Location:* M25 Junction 4, signposted. Undulating parkland. 18 holes, 6779 yards. S.S.S. 72. 9 holes, 2432 yards. S.S.S. 33. Putting nets and pitch and putt. *Green Fees:* weekdays £7.00, weekends £10.50. *Eating facilities:* cafeteria and bar. *Visitors:* welcome any day, must have proper golf attire and recognised golf shoes only. *Society Meetings:* catered for weekdays only. Professional: Dave Comford (0959 34542). Secretary: G.S. Childs.

PINNER. **Grim's Dyke Golf Club,** Oxhey Lane, Hatch End, Pinner, Middlesex HA5 4AL (081-428 4093). *Location:* on A4008 Watford to Harrow (2 miles west of Harrow). Parkland, tree lined, testing greens. 18 holes, 5598 yards. S.S.S. 67. Practice area. *Green Fees:* weekdays £25.00. No weekend fees unless guest of a member. *Eating facilities:* lunches, teas, snacks except Monday. *Visitors:* must produce Certificate of Handicap. *Society Meetings:* catered for. Professional: Carl Williams (081-428 7484). Amateur record J. Thornton, 65. Secretary: P. Payne (081-428 4539).

PINNER. **Pinner Hill Golf Club,** Southview Road, Pinner Hill HA5 3YA (081-866 0963). *Location:* one mile west Pinner Green. 18 holes, 6280 yards. S.S.S. 70. *Green Fees:* £22.00 weekdays, £30.00 weekends by prior arrangement only, Public Days (no access to clubhouse) Wednesdays and Thursdays £6.50 per round, £9.00 per day. *Eating facilities:* light refreshments served at all times (except Wednesdays and Thursdays). *Visitors:* welcome with Handicap Certificate or letter of introduction. *Society Meetings:* Mondays, Tuesdays and Fridays. Professional: Mark Grieve (081-866 2109). Secretary: Jeremy Devitt (081-868 4817).

ROEHAMPTON. **Roehampton Club Ltd,** Roehampton Lane, London SW15 5LR (081-876 5505). *Location:* South Circular Road between Sheen and Putney. Parkland. 18 holes, 6011 yards. S.S.S. 71. *Green Fees:* weekdays £10.00, weekends £12.00. *Eating facilities:* bar and full restaurant available all week. *Visitors:* welcome if introduced by member, and must play with member at weekends. *Society Meetings:* catered for by arrangement, if introduced by member. Professional: Alan L. Scott (081-876 3858). Cheif Executive: Martin Yates (081-876 5505).

RUISLIP. **Ruislip Golf Club,** King's End, Ickenham Road, Ruislip, Middlesex HA4 7OQ (Ruislip (0895) 638081). *Location:* two and a half miles from Junction 1, M40, first left after M40/A40 merge, onto B467, then left at T-Junction onto B466. Parkland course. 18 holes, 5405 yards. S.S.S. 66. Driving range (40 bays). *Green Fees:* £5.60 weekdays, £8.70 weekends. *Eating facilities:* full restaurant facilities. *Visitors:* welcome mid-week, no booking; booking necessary at weekends. *Society Meetings:* welcome by arrangement. Professional: Derek Nash (0895 632004). Secretary: B.J. Channing (0895 638835).

SHOOTERS HILL. **Shooters Hill Golf Club Ltd,** "Lowood", Eaglesfield Road, Shooters Hill, London SE18 3DA (081-854 1216). *Location:* off A207 between Blackheath and Welling. Hilly wooded course. 18 holes, 5736 yards. S.S.S. 68. *Green Fees:*

weekdays £18.00. *Eating facilities:* bar and dining-room. *Visitors:* members of other clubs welcome weekdays on production of letter of introduction, or official Handicap Certificate. Jacket, collar and tie required in clubhouse. *Society Meetings:* catered for Tuesdays and Thursdays only. Professional: M. Ridge (081-854 0073). Secretary: B.R. Adams (081-854 6368).

SOUTHALL. **West Middlesex Golf Club,** Greenford Road, Southall, Middlesex UB1 3EE (081-574 0166). *Location:* junction of Uxbridge Road (A4020) and Greenford Road. 18 holes, 6242 yards. S.S.S. 70. *Green Fees:* weekdays £10.50 per round, £20.00 per day; weekends £20.00 after 1.30pm in the winter, 3.00pm summer. *Visitors:* welcome without reservation. *Society Meetings:* catered for by prior arrangement. Professional: L. Farmer. Secretary: P.J. Furness (081-574 3450).

SOUTHWARK. **Aquarius Golf Club,** Marmora Road, Honor Oak, Southwark SE22 (081-693 1626). The course is situated on and around a reservoir, testing first and eighth holes. 9 holes, 5034 yards. S.S.S. 65. *Green Fees:* £6.00. *Eating facilities:* limited. *Visitors:* welcome with member only. Professional: F. Private. Secretary: Peter Mutton.

STANMORE. **Stanmore Golf Club,** 29 Gordon Avenue, Stanmore, Middlesex HA7 2RL (081-954 4661). *Location:* nearest roads A41, Uxbridge Road. Wooded, undulating course. 18 holes, 5639 yards. S.S.S. 68. *Green Fees:* weekdays £20.00 per round. *Eating facilities:* lunchtime snacks, evening meals by prior arrangement. *Visitors:* welcome Tuesdays, Wednesdays and Thursdays, Handicap Certificates required on Wednesday and Thursday. *Society Meetings:* catered for Wednesday and Thursday by prior booking only. Professional: Vivian Law (081-954 2646). Secretary: P. Wise (081-954 2599).

TOTTERIDGE. **South Herts Golf Club,** Links Drive, Totteridge N20 (081 445 2035/0117). *Location:* off Totteridge Lane one mile from Whetstone, nearest station Totteridge. 18 holes, 6465 yards. S.S.S. 71. *Green Fees:* on application. *Eating facilities:* lunch, high tea (Dinner served by arrangement). *Visitors:* welcome with reservation Wednesday, Thursday, Friday, lunch, high tea, dinner. Professional: R. Livingston. Secretary: A.A. Dogan.

TWICKENHAM. **Strawberry Hill Golf Club,** Wellesley Road, Twickenham (081-894 1246). *Location:* near Strawberry Hill Station. 9 holes, 2381 yards. S.S.S. 62. *Green Fees:* £10.00 per round, £12.00 per day. *Eating facilities:* light lunches, bar snacks. *Visitors:* welcome with reservation, only with a member at weekends. No ladies before 1.30 p.m. at weekends. *Society Meetings:* small numbers catered for. Professional: P. Buchan. Secretary: R.C. Meer.

TWICKENHAM. **Twickenham Golf Course,** Staines Road, Twickenham (081-979 2758). *Location:* just off A316. Parkland. 9 holes, 3050 yards. S.S.S 35. Practice area. *Green Fees:* £3.00 weekdays per round, £4.00 with 50p booking fee per round weekends. Senior Citizens and Juniors £1.50 weekdays. *Eating facilities:* Pavillion Bar and cafe. *Visitors:* welcome, public course. Function room available. *Society Meetings:* welcome, full banqueting facilities. Golf Director: Suzy Baggs (081-783 1698). Secretary: Ted Eldridge (081-783 1748).

UPMINSTER. **Upminster Golf Club,** Hall Lane, Upminster (Upminster (04022) 22788). *Location:* one mile from Upminster Station. 18 holes, 5951 yards. S.S.S. 68. *Green Fees:* £18.00 per round, £22.00 per day. *Eating facilities:* full catering at club, bookable. *Visitors:* welcome on weekdays. *Society Meetings:* catered for. Professional: Neil Carr (04022 20000).

UXBRIDGE. **Uxbridge Golf Course,** The Drive, Harefield Place, Uxbridge UB10 8PA (Uxbridge (0895) 37287). *Location:* two miles north of Uxbridge off A40. 18 holes, 5660 yards. S.S.S. 67 par 68. *Green fees:* information not provided. *Eating facilities:* cafeteria facilities, bar. *Visitors:* welcome. Snooker club. *Society Meetings:* welcome anytime. Professional: Phil Howard. Caterer: P. Howard. Municipal course (Hillingdon Borough Council).

WANSTEAD. **Wanstead Golf Club,** Overton Drive, London E11 2LW (081-989 0604). *Location:* one mile from junction of A12 and A406. Parkland bordering Epping Forest with featured lake. 18 holes, 6109 yards. S.S.S. 69. *Green Fees:* on request. *Eating facilities:* dining room and bars. *Visitors:* welcome Mondays, Tuesdays and Fridays with Handicap Certificate (booking essential). Weekends with member only. *Society Meetings:* welcome, apply Secretary. Professional: Gary Jacom (081-989 9876). Secretary: Keith Jones (081-989 3938).

WEMBLEY. **Sudbury Golf Club Ltd,** Bridgewater Road, Wembley, Middlesex HA0 1AL (081-902 3713). *Location:* junction of A4005 (Bridgewater Road) and A4090 (Whitton Ave East). Undulating parkland. 18 holes, 6282 yards. S.S.S. 70. Practice ground. *Green Fees:* weekdays £18.00 per round, £27.00 two rounds. *Eating facilities:* dining room and bars. *Visitors:* welcome weekdays, weekends must play with member. *Society Meetings:* catered for. Professional: Neil Jordan (081-902 7910). Secretary: J.A. Smith (081-902 3713).

WIMBLEDON. **Royal Wimbledon Golf Club,** 29 Camp Road, Wimbledon SW19 4UW. *Location:* one mile west of War Memorial in Wimbledon Village. 18 holes, 6300 yards. S.S.S. 70. *Green Fees:* weekdays only, £40.00. *Eating facilities:* lunch served except Mondays. *Visitors:* welcome weekdays only, 48 hours' notice required and production of Handicap Certificate or Introduction Card. *Society Meetings:* Wednesdays, Thursdays and Fridays only, by arrangement. Professional: Hugh Boyle (081-946 4606). Secretary: Maj. G.E. Jones (081-946 2125). Caddiemaster (081-946 1118).

WIMBLEDON. **Wimbledon Common Golf Club,** 19 Camp Road, Wimbledon Common, Wimbledon SW19 4UW (081-946 0294). Links type wooded course. 18 holes, 5438 yards. S.S.S. 66. *Green Fees:* weekdays £10.00 per round, £16.00 per day. *Eating facilities:* light lunches available every day; bar. *Visitors:* welcome weekdays, but only with a member at weekends. *Society Meetings:* not catered for. Professional: J.S. Jukes (081-946 0294). Secretary: B.K. Cox (081-946 7571).

WIMBLEDON. **Wimbledon Park Golf Club,** Home Park Road, Wimbledon, London SW19. *Location:* Church Road, Arthur Road and Home Park Road from Wimbledon High Street, or by District Line to Wimbledon Park Station where signposted. 18 holes, 5465 yards. *Green Fees:* £20.00 per day. *Eating Facilities:* dining room and bar snacks each day except Monday. *Visitors:* welcome weekdays, occasional weekends after 3.30 pm (check with Professional). *Society Meetings:* catered for. Professional: D. Wingrove (081-946 4053). Secretary: M.K. Hale (081-946 1250).

WINCHMORE HILL. **Bush Hill Park Golf Club,** Bush Hill, Winchmore Hill N21 2BU (081-360 5738). *Location:* nine miles north of City. Parkland. 18 holes, 5809 yards. S.S.S. 68. *Green Fees:* weekdays £20.00 per day, £17.00 per round (with member £8.50). *Eating facilities:* full catering available on request. *Visitors:* welcome weekdays. *Society Meetings:* catered for Monday, Tuesday, Thursday and Friday. Professional: G. Low. Secretary/Manager: D.J. Clark.

WOOD GREEN. **Muswell Hill Golf Club,** Rhodes Avenue, Wood Green, London N22 4UT (081-888 2044). *Location:* one mile Bounds Green Underground Station. 18 holes, 6474 yards. S.S.S. 71. *Green Fees:* information on request. *Eating facilities:* available in Clubhouse. *Visitors:* welcome weekdays, weekends pre-booked by Professional. *Society Meetings:* catered for, charges on request. Professional: I. Roberts (081-888 8046). Secretary: J.A.B. Connors (081-888 1764).

Avon

BATH. **Bath Golf Club,** Sham Castle, North Road, Bath BA2 8JG (Bath (0225) 425182). *Location:* off A36, one mile south-east of Bath City Centre. 18 holes, 6369 yards, 5824 metres. S.S.S. 70. *Green Fees:* weekends and Bank Holidays £22, weekdays £18. *Eating facilities:* catering every day. *Visitors:* with bona fide handicap welcome. *Society Meetings:* catered for Wednesday and Friday. Professional: Peter Hancox (0225 466953). Secretary: P.B. Edwards (0225 463834).

BATH. **Entry Hill Golf Club,** Entry Hill, Bath BA2 5NA (0225 834248). *Location:* one mile south of city centre, off A367 road to Wells. Hilly parkland course with many young trees. 9 holes, 2103 yards, 1922 metres. S.S.S. 61 (18 holes). Practice net. *Green Fees:* £4.00 for 9 holes, £6.00 for 18 holes. *Visitors:* unrestricted but pre booking one week in advance essential. Well equipped Pro Shop. *Society Meetings:* by arrangement with Professional. Professional: T. Tapley (0225 834248). Secretary: J. Sercombe (0272 834248).

BATH. **Fosseway Country Club and Centurion Hotel,** Charlton Lane, Midsomer Norton, Bath BA3 4BD (0761 412214). *Location:* off A367 ten miles south of Bath. Parkland course. 9 holes, 4246 yards. S.S.S. 61. *Green Fees:* weekdays and Sunday afternoons £8.00, Saturday afternoons and Bank Holidays £12.00. *Eating facilities:* full three star restaurant and bar snacks always available. *Visitors:* welcome except Saturday and Sunday mornings and Wednesday evenings. 17 bedroom three star hotel, all rooms en-suite. Secretary: R.F. Jones.

BATH. **Lansdown Golf Club,** Lansdown, Bath BA1 9BT (Bath (0225) 425007). *Location:* four miles from M4 junction 18 adjoining Bath Racecourse. Flat, parkland. 18 holes, 6299 yards, 5759 metres. S.S.S. 70. *Green Fees:* weekdays £18.00, weekends £22.00. *Eating facilities:* snacks at all times, lunch or dinner by arrangement with Steward. *Visitors:* welcome. *Society Meetings:* welcome weekdays only. Professional: T. Mercer (0225 420242). Secretary: J. Prosser (0225 422138).

BRISTOL. **Bristol and Clifton Golf Club,** Beggar Bush Lane, Failand, Bristol BS8 3TH (0272 393117). *Location:* two miles west of the Suspension Bridge or three miles south of the M5-Junction 19 access. 18 holes, 6294 yards. S.S.S. 70. Parkland course. *Green Fees:* weekdays £17, weekends £22. *Eating facilities:* available. *Visitors:* welcome weekdays without reservation. *Society Meetings:* welcome. Professional: Peter Mawson (0272 393031. Managing Secretary: Cdr P.A. Woollings (0272 393474).

Please mention this guide when you write or phone to enquire about accommodation.

If you are writing, a stamped, addressed envelope is always appreciated.

BRISTOL. **Chipping Sodbury Golf Club,** Chipping Sodbury, Bristol BS6 6YE (Chipping Sodbury (0454) 312024). *Location* 12 miles north of Bristol, nine miles from Junction No. 14 on M5 and three miles from Junction No. 18 on M4. 18 hole course 6912 yards, 9 hole 3076 yards. S.S.S. 73. *Green Fees:* 18-hole course weekdays £14.00, weekends £18.00. 9 hole course £2.50 any day. *Eating facilities:* full catering available. *Visitors:* welcome except Saturday/Sunday morning and Bank Holidays. *Society Meetings:* catered for by prior arrangement weekdays only. Professional: Steve Harris (0454 314087). Secretary: K.G. Starr (0454 319042).

BRISTOL. **Filton Golf Club,** Golf Course Lane, Filton, Bristol BS12 7QS (Bristol (0272) 692021). *Location:* off A38 north of Bristol. Parkland. 18 holes, 6277 yards. S.S.S. 70. Two practice fields. *Green Fees:* weekdays £14.00, £9.00 with member. *Eating facilities:* meals available all day. *Visitors:* accepted daily subject to programme. *Society Meetings:* all catered for, subject to programme – must book well in advance. Professional: J.C.N. Lumb (0272 694158). Secretary: D.F. O'Leary (0272 694169).

BRISTOL. **Henbury Golf Club,** Henbury Hill, Westbury-on-Trym, Bristol BS10 7QB (Bristol (0272) 500660). *Location:* north M5 Junction 17 A4018 to Westbury-on-Trym. Wooded parkland, 18 holes, 6039 yards. S.S.S. 70. *Green Fees:* weekdays £16.00, £8.00 with member, weekends £15 with member only. *Eating facilities:* dining room and bar snacks. *Visitors:* welcome, restricted at weekends and Bank Holidays. *Society Meetings:* Tuesdays and Fridays by prior arrangement. Professional: Peter Stow (0272 502121). Secretary: J.W. Estill (0272 500044).

BRISTOL. **Knowle Golf Club,** Fairway, off West Town Lane, Brislington, Bristol BS4 5DF (Bristol (0272) 776341). *Location:* three miles south east City centre, left off Wells Road. A4 – Bath. Parkland course. 18 holes, 6073 yards. S.S.S. 69. *Green Fees:* weekdays £16.00 per round, £20.00 per day; weekends £20.00 per round, £25.00 per day. *Eating facilities:* Bar-dining-room, dinners by arrangement with Stewardess. *Visitors* welcome with Handicap Certificate. *Society Meetings:* Thursday only with Handicap Certificate. Professional: Mr Gordon M. Brand (0272 779193). Secretary: Mrs J.D. King (0272 770660).

BRISTOL. **Long Ashton Golf Club,** The Clubhouse, Long Ashton, Bristol BS18 9DW (Long Ashton (0272) 392229). *Location:* three miles south-west of Bristol on the B3129 Clevedon/Bristol Road. Wooded parkland. 18 holes, 6219 yards, 5532 metres. S.S.S. 70. Practice ground. *Green Fees:* weekdays £18.00, weekends £22.00. *Eating facilities:* full catering daily, bar open Monday to Saturday (11am – 11pm). *Visitors:* welcome, must have current Handicap Certificate. *Society Meetings:* by arrangement with Secretary. Professional: Denis Scanlan (0272 392265). Secretary: B. Manning (0272 392316).

BRISTOL. **Mangotsfield Golf Club,** Carsons Road, Mangotsfield, Bristol (Bristol (0272) 565501). *Location:* four miles M32 via Downend. Caravan park Golf Club on course, one mile Warmley A420. Parkland course. 18 holes, 5337 yards. S.S.S. 66. *Green Fees:* informa-

tion not available. *Eating facilities:* no restriction on food and drink. *Visitors* welcome, no restrictions. *Society Meetings:* up to 100 catered for weekdays only. Professional: Craig Trewin. Secretary: Jim Hill.

BRISTOL. **Shirehampton Park Golf Club,** Park Hill, Shirehampton, Bristol BS11 0UL (Bristol (0272) 823059). *Location:* one mile from Junction 18 on M5 on B4054 to Shirehampton. Parkland course. 18 holes, 5493 yards. S.S.S. 67. *Green Fees:* weekdays £15.00, weekends with member only £10.00. *Eating facilities:* lunches, snacks, teas, etc available daily. *Visitors:* welcome weekdays, with reservation (check with Secretary), not weekends and Public Holidays. *Society Meetings:* catered for on Mondays, applications to Secretary. Secretary: John Godsell (0272 822083).

BRISTOL. **Tracy Park Golf and Country Club,** Bath Road, Wick, Bristol BS15 5RN (Abson (027 582) 2251). *Location:* M4 junction 18, A46 towards Bath, A420 towards Bristol. Turn left at bottom of steep hill for Lansdown/Bath. Wooded parkland with water hazards. 27 holes, 6800, 6800, 6200 yards. S.S.S. 73, 73, 70. Practice ground. *Green Fees:* weekdays £15/£22, weekends £20/£30. *Eating facilities:* full catering available. *Visitors:* welcome – telephone ahead. *Society Meetings:* welcome. Tennis, swimming, squash, croquet, snooker available. Professional: Grant Aitken (027 582 3521). Secretary: Mr John Seymour-Williams (027 582 2251).

CLEVEDON. **Clevedon Golf Club,** Castle Road, Clevedon BS21 7AA (0272) 873140). *Location:* two miles from M5 Junction 20. Picturesque course, looking down onto River Severn. 18 holes, 5887 yards. S.S.S. 69. *Green Fees:* weekdays £16.00, weekends and Bank Holidays £24.00. *Eating facilities:* meals from 11 am daily (Tuesdays snacks only). *Visitors:* welcome (afternoons only on Wednesdays). Must be member of a Golf Club in possession of Handicap Certificate. *Society Meetings:* catered for on Mondays only. Professional: Christine Langford (0272 874704). Secretary: Capt. M. Sullivan (0272 874057).

SALTFORD. **Saltford Golf Club,** Golf Club Lane, Saltford, Bristol BS18 3AA (Saltford (0225) 873220). *Location:* off A4 between Bristol and Bath. Wooded parkland course. 18 holes, 6081 yards. S.S.S. 69. Practice ground. *Green Fees:* weekdays £16.00 single round, £20.00 more than one round; weekends £20.00 single round summer only. *Eating facilities:* restaurant bar service. *Society Meetings:* welcome. Professional: D. Millensted (0225 872043). Secretary: Valerie Radnedge (0225 873513).

WESTON-SUPER-MARE.   **Weston-Super-Mare Golf Club,** Uphill Road North, Weston-Super-Mare BS23 4NQ (Weston-Super-Mare (0934) 621360). *Location:* on the sea front next to Royal Hospital, M5. Seaside links course. 18 holes, 6220 yards. S.S.S. 70. Practice facilities. *Green Fees:* weekdays £14.00, weekends £18.00. Weekly £45.00. *Eating facilities:* full bar and catering facilities. *Visitors:* welcome weekdays, restriction weekends to small numbers. *Society Meetings:* catered for weekdays. Professional: Terence Murray (0934 633360). Secretary: K.J.W. Josling (0934 626968).

WESTON-SUPER-MARE. **Worlebury Golf Club,** WMonks Hill, Weston-Super-Mare BS22 8BE (Weston-Super-Mare (0934) 623214). *Location:* from the M5 then A370 main road to the town for two miles, turn right into Baytree Road and continue to top of hill. Club situated at crossroads Milton Hill/Worlebury Hill Road. Hill top with extensive views of the Severn Estuary and Wales. 18 holes, 5921 yards. S.S.S. 69.

Limited practice area. *Green Fees:* weekdays £15.00 including VAT, weekends and Bank Holidays £25.00 including VAT. *Eating facilities:* bar and restaurant. *Visitors:* welcome without reservation. *Society Meetings:* catered for by arrangement with Secretary. Professional: Gary Marks (0934 418473). Secretary: Ralph Bagg (0934 625789).

Bedfordshire

AMPTHILL. **Millbrook Golf Club,** Millbrook, Ampthill MK45 2JB (0525 840252). *Location:* one mile from town centre, M1 Junction 12 from south, Junction 13 from north, towards Ampthill, located on A418. Hilly tree-lined parkland, one of the longest courses in Britain. 18 holes, 6865 yards. S.S.S. 73. Practice area. *Green Fees:* weekdays £14.00 per day, £7.00 with member; weekends £10.00 with member. *Eating facilities:* bar snacks and meals available at all reasonable times. Booking required for meals. *Visitors:* no visitors weekends or Bank Holidays unless guest of member. *Society Meetings:* by arrangement with Professional or Secretary. Professional: T. Devine (0525 402269). Secretary: M.R. Brackley (0525 840252).

BEDFORD. **Bedford and County Golf Club,** Green Lane, Clapham, Bedford (Bedford (0234) 54010). *Location:* off A6 north of Bedford before Clapham Village. Parkland. 18 holes, 6290 yards. S.S.S. 70. *Green Fees:* weekdays £20.00, with member £8.00; weekends and Bank Holidays £12.00. *Eating facilities:* full catering facilities and bar. *Visitors:* welcome without reservation except weekends. *Society Meetings:* catered for Tuesdays, Thursdays and Fridays. Professional/Manager: Eddie Bullock (0234 59189/52617).

BEDFORD. **Bedfordshire Golf Club,** Biddenham, Bedford MK40 4AF (Bedford (0234) 53241). *Location:* one mile west of Bedford town centre on the A428. Flat parkland. 18 holes, 6185 yards. S.S.S. 69. *Green Fees:*

on application. *Eating facilities:* catering 7 days, evenings by arrangement. *Visitors:* welcome on weekdays, must be members of registered golf clubs. Ladies Day Tuesday. *Society Meetings:* catered for weekdays. Professional: G. Buckle (0234 53653). Secretary: T.A. Nutt (0234 261669).

BEDFORD. **Mowsbury Golf Club,** Kimbolton Road, Bedford (0234 771042). *Location:* on B660 at northern limit of city boundary. 18 holes, 6510 yards. S.S.S. 71. *Green Fees:* information not provided. Professional: Paul Ashwell.

DUNSTABLE. **Dunstable Downs Golf Club,** Whipsnade Road, Dunstable LU6 2NB (Dunstable (0582) 604472). *Location:* on B4541; from the south, leave M1 at Markyate, A5 to centre of town, turn left at roundabout into West Street, turn left into Whipsnade Road at third roundabout, club half a mile on left. Downland course, 18 holes, 6184 yards. S.S.S. 70. *Green Fees:* on application. *Eating facilities:* catering Tuesday to Sunday. *Visitors:* weekdays if members of recognised Golf Club, weekends with member only. *Society Meetings:* Tuesdays and Thursdays. Professional: M. Weldon (0582 62806). Secretary: P.J. Nightingale (0582 604472).

DUNSTABLE. **Tilsworth Golf Centre,** Dunstable Road, Tilsworth, Leighton Buzzard LU7 9PU (Leighton Buzzard (0525) 210722). *Location:* two miles north of Dunstable off A5, Tilsworth turn-off. Parkland. 9 holes, 5437 yards. S.S.S. 67. 30 bay floodlit driving range.

Green Fees: weekdays £4.25 for 18 holes; weekends £5.25 for 18 holes. *Eating facilities:* bar snacks and restaurant available. *Visitors:* welcome any time (except Sundays before 11.45 am). Bookings taken up to seven days in advance. *Society Meetings:* welcome by prior arrangement. Professional: Nick Webb (0525 210721).

LEIGHTON BUZZARD. **Leighton Buzzard Golf Club,** Plantation Road, Leighton Buzzard LU7 7JF (Leighton Buzzard (0525) 373811). *Location:* two miles north-east of Leighton Buzzard Station. Wooded parkland course, sandy soil. 18 holes, 5454 yards. S.S.S. 68. Practice ground. *Green Fees:* weekdays £15.00 per round, £20.00 per day weekends only with member. *Eating facilities:* breakfast on request, lunches and dinner served daily. *Visitors:* welcome weekdays, Tuesday Ladies' Day, 1st and 8th tees reserved 12 noon to 3.00 pm; weekends and Bank Holidays with member only. *Society Meetings:* catered for weekends only. Professional: Lee Muncey (0525 372143). Secretary: F.J. Clements (0525 373812).

LEIGHTON BUZZARD Near. **Ivinghoe Golf Club,** Ivinghoe, Near Leighton Buzzard (Cheddington (0296) 668696). *Location:* three miles from Tring and from Dunstable. 9 holes, 4602 yards. S.S.S. 62. *Green Fees:* weekdays £5.00, weekends £6.50. *Eating facilities:* bar and catering. *Visitors:* welcome without reservation. *Society Meetings:* small, catered for. Professional: P.W. Garrad. Secretary: Mrs S. Garrard.

LUTON. **South Beds. Golf Club,** Warden Hill Road, Luton LU2 7AA (Luton (0582) 591500).*Location:* on east side A6, two and a half miles north of Luton. Undulating downland course. 18 holes, 6342 yards. S.S.S. 70. Also 9 holes, 4914 yards. S.S.S. 64. Practice fairway, huts and chipping area. *Green Fees:* 18 holes weekdays £22.00 per day, £15.00 per round; weekends £33.00 per day, £22.00 per round (not on Competition Days). 9 holes (twice round) weekdays £7.00, weekends £10.00. *Eating facilities:* full course meals (must be booked), snacks at all times. *Visitors:* welcome weekdays with reservation. Handicap Certificate essential. Tuesday afternoon is Ladies' Day. *Society Meetings:* catered for by arrangement. Professional: Eddie Cogle (0582 591209). Secretary: A.J. Messing (0582 591500).

LUTON. **Stockwood Park Golf Club,** Golf Pavilion, Stockwood Park, London Road, Luton LU1 4LX (Luton (0582) 31421). *Location:* near Junction 10 of M1 exit Luton Airport, left at first traffic lights towards Luton. Parkland. 18 holes, 5973 yards. S.S.S. 69. Driving range and pitch and putt. *Green Fees:* weekends £5.50, weekdays £3.70. *Eating facilities:* bar and catering facilities. *Visitors:* welcome at all times without reservation, although at weekends prior booking is necessary, telephone Pro shop. *Society Meetings:* catered for Mondays to Thursdays. Pro-

fessional: D. Hunt (0582 413704). Secretary: D.W. Thompson (0582 585549).

MILTON KEYNES. **Aspley Guise and Woburn Sands Golf Club,** West Hill, Aspley Guise MK17 8DX (Milton Keynes (0908) 582264). *Location:* two miles west of Junction 13 M1, between Aspley Guise and Woburn Sands. Undulating parkland, 18 holes, 6248 yards. S.S.S. 70. *Green Fees:* weekdays £13.00 per round, £17.00 per day. *Eating facilities:* full catering except Mondays. *Visitors* welcome weekdays with bona fide handicaps - check with Secretary; only with a member at weekends. *Society Meetings:* Wednesdays and Fridays. Professional: Glyn McCarthy (0908 583974). Secretary: T.E. Simpson (0908 583596).

SANDY.**John O'Gaunt Golf Club,** Sutton Park, Sandy SG19 2LY (Potton (0767) 260252). *Location:* on B1040 off A1 two miles north of Biggleswade. Parkland courses. Two 18 hole courses, John O'Gaunt Course 6513 yards S.S.S. 71 and Carthagena Course 5869 yards. S.S.S. 68. Small practice area. *Green Fees:* weekdays £25.00, weekends £40.00. *Eating facilities:* restaurant and bar. *Visitors:* welcome. Handicap Certificate required at weekends. *Society Meetings:* welcome weekdays, with some limitations on Thursdays and Fridays. Professional: P. Round (0767 260094). Secretary: I.M. Simpson (0767 260360).

SHEFFORD Nr. **Beadlow Manor Hotel, Golf and Country Club,** Beadlow, Near Shefford SG17 5PH (Silsoe (0525) 60800). *Location:* six miles east of J12 M1, two miles west of Shefford on A507 from A1 (M) at Baldock. 27 hole parkland course, 10 holes with water hazards. The Manor Course 18 holes, 6374 yards. S.S.S. 70; *Green Fees:* weekdays from £14.00, weekends from £18.00. The Priory Course 9 holes, 2962 yards. S.S.S. 69. *Green Fees:* weekdays £7.00, weekends £10.00. *Eating facilities:* restaurant and bar snacks, two bars. *Visitors:* welcome with members also on production of handicap certificate also on Golf and Health breaks. *Society Meetings:* most welcome by prior arrangement through Sales and Marketing department, choice of special society menus. Health and Beauty centre with steam, sauna, solarium, jacuzzi and full gym. Residential accommodation available. Professional: Gary Carver (0525 61292, Fax 0525 61345).

WYBOSTON. **Wyboston Lakes Golf Club,** Wyboston Lakes, Wyboston MK44 3AL (Huntingdon (0480) 218411). *Location:* just off A1, south of St. Neots and north of Sandy. Flat parkland with play round four lakes. 18 holes, 5711 yards. S.S.S. 69. Large practice area. *Green Fees:* weekdays £8.50 18 holes, weekends £12.50 18 holes, £15.00 36 holes weekends only. *Eating facilities:* Berni Inn. *Visitors:* Pay and Play course. Handicaps by Social Club. Start times required for weekends. Motel on site. *Society Meetings:* catered for weekdays only. Professional: P. Ashwell (0480 212501). Secretary: B. Chinn (0480 219200).

Berkshire

ASCOT. **Berkshire Golf CLub,** Swinley Road, Ascot (Ascot (0990) 21495). *Location:* off A332. Heathland course. 36 holes. Red 6356 yards. Blue 6258 yards. S.S.S. both 70. Practice facilities. *Green Fees:* £45.00 weekdays. *Eating facilities:* dining room open every day except Monday. *Visitors:* welcome weekdays by application to the Secretary only. *Society Meetings:* catered for by prior bookings. Professional: K.A. Mac-Donald (0990 22351). Secretary: Major P.D. Clarke (0990 21496).

ASCOT. **Lavender Park,** Swinley Road, Ascot (Winkfield Row [0344] 407488). 9 holes, 1,104 yards. S.S.S. 28. *Green Fees:* information not provided. Professional: Tony Bowers.

ASCOT. **Royal Ascot Golf Club (ex Ascot Heath),** Winkfield Road, Ascot SL5 7LJ (Ascot (0344) 22923). *Location:* Ascot Race Course. 18 holes, 5653 yards. S.S.S. 67. *Green fees:* information not provided. *Eating facilities:* full catering available except Tuesdays. *Visitors:* welcome without reservation. *Society Meetings:* catered for, maximum 40. Professional: Clive Dell. Secretary: R.J. Young (0344 25175).

ASCOT. **Swinley Forest Golf Club,** Ascot (0990 20197). *Location:* between Ascot and Bagshot. 18 holes, 6001 yards. *Green Fees:* information not provided. *Eating facilities:* lunches served. *Visitors:* welcome only with a member. *Society Meetings:* catered for. Professional: R.C. Parker. Secretary: I.L. Pearce.

CROWTHORNE. **East Berkshire Golf Club,** Ravenswood Avenue, Crowthorne RG11 6BD (Crowthorne (0344) 772041). *Location:* M3 Junction 3 – Bracknell turn off follow signs to Crowthorne, Ravenswood Avenue opposite Railway Station. Heathland course. 18 holes, 6315 yards. S.S.S. 70. *Green Fees:* £30.00 per round. *Eating facilities:* meals a la carte except Monday. *Visitors:* welcome weekdays only by prior arrangement, Handicap Certificate essential. *Society Meetings:* Thursdays and Fridays only. Professional: Arthur Roe (0344 774112). Secretary: W.H. Short.

MAIDENHEAD. **Hawthorn Hill Golf Centre,** Drift Road, Hawthorn Hill, Near Maidenhead (Maidenhead (0628) 26035). *Location:* A330 five miles from Windsor, five from Ascot Racecourse. Parkland. 18 holes, 6212 yards. S.S.S. 70. 36-bay floodlit range. *Green Fees:* weekdays £8.00; weekends £10.00. *Eating facilities:* Hawthorns Restuarant. *Visitors:* no restrictions. *Society Meetings:* welcome, telephone 0628 771030. Professional: Mr Gary Edmunds (0628 75588).

MAIDENHEAD. **Maidenhead Golf Club,** Shoppen-hangers Road, Maidenhead SL6 2PZ (Maidenhead (0628) 20545). *Location:* adjacent to Maidenhead Station (south side), one mile from M4. Flat course. 18 holes, 6360 yards. S.S.S. 70. *Green Fees:* weekdays £25.00. *Eating facilities:* restaurant (except Mondays) plus bar lunches (Mondays to Fridays). *Visitors:* wel-come weekdays, no visitors after 12 noon Fridays, Handicap Certificate required. *Society Meetings:* weekdays except Fridays. Professional: (0628 24067). Secretary: Iain Lindsay (0628 24693).

MAIDENHEAD. **Temple Golf Club,** Henley Road, Hurley, Near Maidenhead SL6 5LH (Littlewick Green (062 882) 4248). *Location:* on the A423 between M4 (Junction 8/9 turn off) and Henley. Parkland. 18 holes, 6200 yards. S.S.S. 70. *Green Fees:* £25.00 for the day, £8.00 if playing with a member. *Eating facilities:* always available except Mondays, snacks only. *Visitors:* wel-come (except weekends) with reservation, letter of introduction or Handicap Certificate. *Society Meetings:* catered for. Professional: Alan Dobbins (062 882 4254). Secretary: D.W. Kirkland (062 882 4795).

MAIDENHEAD. **Winter Hill Golf Club,** Grange Lane, Cookham (Bourne End (06285) 27810). *Location:* M4/M40, Maidenhead nearest town approxi-mately four miles. Parkland. 18 holes, 6408 yards. S.S.S. 71. Large practice ground and putting green. *Green Fees:* £18.00 weekdays. *Eating facilities:* lunches/teas only – no casual evening meals. *Visitors:* welcome weekdays – confirmatory telephone enquiry advisable. *Society Meetings:* by appointment and in writing only. Professional: Mr. Paul Hedges (06285 27610). Secretary: Mr G.B. Charters-Rowe (06285 27613).

NEWBURY. **Newbury and Crookham Golf Club Ltd,** Bury's Bank Road, Greenham, Newbury. *Location:* on south side of Newbury off A34 opposite American Air Base. 18 holes, 5843 yards. S.S.S. 68. *Green Fees:* information not provided. No visitors weekends or Bank Holidays, unless with member. *Eating facilities:* catering available, coffee, lunch, tea, etc. *Visitors:* welcome with reservation, not weekends or Bank Holidays without member. *Society Meetings:* welcome by prior arrangement, not weekends. Pro-fessional: D. W. Harris. (0635 31201).

NEWBURY. **West Berkshire Golf Club,** Chaddle-worth, Newbury RG16·0HS (Chaddleworth (04882) 574). *Location:* M4 Junction 14 SP R.A.F. Welford OS Map Ref SU411 762. Downland. 18 holes, 7053 yards. S.S.S. 74. *Green Fees:* £10.00 per day weekdays, £15.00 per day weekends. *Eating facilities:* full catering available. *Visitors:* welcome with reservation. *Society Meetings:* catered for. Professional: D. Sheppard. Sec-retary: W. Richardson.

READING. **Calcot Park Golf Club,** Bath Road, Calcot, Reading (0734 427124). *Location:* three miles west of Reading on A4 Exit 12, M4 one mile. 18 holes, 6283 yards. S.S.S. 70. *Green Fees:* information not provided. *Eating facilities:* lunches, teas except Mon-day, bar snacks every day. *Visitors:* welcome excluding weekends and Bank Holidays. Handicap Certificate required. *Society Meetings:* catered for Tuesday, Thursday, Friday. Professional: Albert MacKenzie (0734 427797). Secretary: S.D. Chisholm.

READING. **Hurst Golf Club,** Sandford Lane, Hurst, Reading (Twyford (0734) 345143). *Location:* five miles Reading. 9 holes. *Green Fees:* £3.75. *Visitors:* unrestricted, bookings accepted. Professional: G. Legouix. Course Manager: D. Burton.

READING. **Reading Golf Club,** 17 Kidmore End Road, Emmer Green, Reading RG4 8SG (Reading (0734) 472169). *Location:* two miles north of Reading off the Peppard Road (B481). Parkland. 18 holes, 6204 yards. S.S.S. 70. Practice facilities. *Green Fees:* £23.00 per day, £10.00 with member. *Eating facilities:* available. *Visitors:* welcome without reservation Monday to Thursday, Friday to Sunday with member only. *Society Meetings:* catered for by arrangement Tuesdays and Thursdays. Professional: Tim Morrison (0734 476115). Secretary: J. Weekes (0734 472909).

READING. **Sonning Golf Club,** Duffield Road, Sonning (Reading (0734) 693332). *Location:* left off A4 at Sonning roundabout, then left again. 18 holes, 6349 yards. S.S.S. 70. *Green Fees:* on application. *Eating facilities:* lunches served – advance booking necessary. *Visitors:* welcome Monday to Friday, must be member of a recognised golf club with an official handicap. *Society Meetings:* catered for. Professional: R.T. McDougall (0734 62910). Secretary: P.F. Williams.

SINDLESHAM. **Bearwood Golf Club,** Mole Road, Sindlesham (Arborfield Cross (0734) 760060). *Location:* on B3030 from Winnersh to Arborfield. Flat wooded course. 9 holes, 2814 yards. S.S.S. 67 (18 holes). 9 hole Pitch and Putt. *Green Fees:* (for 9 holes) weekdays £5.00, weekends £5.50 as member's guest only. *Eating facilities:* food available all day. *Visitors:* welcome weekdays, weekends with members only. *Society Meetings:* maximum of 18 catered for. Professional/Manager: Barry Tustin. Secretary: C. Dyer OBE.

SLOUGH. **Datchet Golf Club,** Buccleuch Road, Datchet (Slough (0753) 43887). *Location:*within two miles of both Windsor and Slough. 9 holes, 5978 yards. S.S.S. 69. *Green Fees:* £10.00 per round, £15.00 per day. *Visitors:* welcome without reservation during week up to 3pm. Lessons and club repairs for non members. *Society Meetings:* small societies welcome. Professional: Max Taylor (0753 42755). Secretary: G.S. East (0753 41872).

STREATLEY ON THAMES. **Goring and Streatley Golf Club,** Streatley on Thames (Goring (0491) 872688). *Location:* 10 miles north west of Reading on A329. 18 holes, 6255 yards. S.S.S. 70. *Green Fees:* £20.00 per day (not weekends unless with a member). *Eating facilities:* full restaurant. *Visitors:* welcome on weekdays by telephone booking. *Society Meetings:* catered for. Professional: Roy Mason. Secretary: J. Menzies (0491 873229).

SUNNINGDALE. **Sunningdale Ladies' Golf Club,** Cross Road, Sunningdale (Ascot (0990) 20507). *Location:* second left going west on A30, past Sunningdale level crossing. Heathland. 18 holes, 3622 yards. (Designed for Ladies' Golf). S.S.S. 60. *Green Fees:* £13.00/16.00 weekdays; £15.00/18.00 weekends. *Eating facilities:* snack lunches available at all times. *Visitors:* welcome, telephone first. *Society Meetings:* catered for (Ladies only). Secretary: Bryan Ford.

WOKINGHAM. **Downshire Golf Course,** Easthampstead Park, Wokingham (Bracknell (0344) 424066). *Location:* between Bracknell and Crowthorne off Nine Mile Ride. 18 holes, 6395 yards. 9 hole pitch and putt, driving range and putting green. *Green Fees:* £7.50. *Eating facilities:* bar meals, grills, free house. *Visitors:* welcome. Director of Golf/Professional: Geoffrey Legouix (0344 424066).

Buckinghamshire

AYLESBURY. **Chiltern Forest Golf Club,** Aston Hill, Halton, Aylesbury (Steward: Aylesbury (0296) 630899). *Location:* five miles south-east of Aylesbury, signposted St. Leonards. Wooded. 12 holes, 6140 yards. S.S.S. 70. *Green Fees:* £15.00 per day weekdays, £10.00 with a member weekends. *Visitors:* weekdays unrestricted, weekends with a member. Professional: Christopher Skeet (0296 631817). Secretary: L.E.A. Clark (0296 631267).

AYLESBURY. **Ellesborough Golf Club,** Butlers Cross, Aylesbury HP17 0TZ (Wendover (0296) 622375). *Location:* on B4010 one and a half miles from Wendover. Chiltern Hills course. Undulating links. 18 holes, 6271 yards. S.S.S. 70. Practice net/ground. *Green Fees:* £25.00 per day, £20.00 per round weekdays. *Eating facilities:* available. *Visitors:* except weekends, Tuesday mornings and competition days, must provide Handicap Certificate. *Society Meetings:*

catered for Wednesdays and Thursdays only by arrangement with Secretary. Professional: S. Watkins (0296 623126). Secretary: K.M. Flint (0296 622114).

AYLESBURY. **Weston Turville Golf & Squash Club,** New Road, Weston Turville, Near Aylesbury HP22 5OT (Aylesbury (0296) 24084). *Location:* two miles south east of Aylesbury off A41. Flat course with Chiltern Hills in background. 18 holes, 6002 yards. S.S.S. 69. *Green Fees:* weekdays £10.00, weekends £12.00. *Eating facilities:* meals, snacks and visitors' bar. *Visitors:* welcome, but Saturday and Sunday booking. Squash courts available. *Society Meetings:* by arrangement. Professional: Gary George (0296 25949). Secretary: Mr A.K. Holden (0296 24084).

BEACONSFIELD. **Beaconsfield Golf Club Ltd,** Seer Green, Near Beaconsfield HP9 2UR (Beaconsfield (0494) 676545/6). *Location:* from A40 at Beaconsfield, A355 Amersham Road. one mile turn right to Jordans, one mile signposted. Parkland course. 18 holes, 6469 metres. S.S.S. 71. Large practice ground. *Green Fees:* £30 per day, £25 per round. *Eating facilities:* dining room or bar menu; 2 bars. *Visitors:* welcome weekdays with accredited introduction – check with Pro. *Society Meetings:* catered for Tuesdays and Wednesdays. Professional: Mike Brothers (0494 676616). Secretary: P.I. Anderson (0494 676545/6).

BUCKINGHAM. **Buckingham Golf Club,** Tingewick Road, Buckingham MK18 4AG (0280 813282). *Location:* one and a half miles south west of Buckingham on A421. Undulating parkland – eight holes affected by river. 18 holes, 6082 yards. S.S.S. 69. Practice ground. *Green Fees:* weekdays £18.00, weekends as members' guests only. *Eating facilities:* seven day catering – bars, lunch and evening. *Visitors:* welcome weekdays only. *Society Meetings:* pre-booked on Tuesdays or Thursdays. Professional: Tom Gates (0280 815210). Secretary: David Rolph (0280 815566).

BURNHAM. **Burnham Beeches Golf Club,** Green Lane, Burnham, Slough SL1 8EG (Burnham (0628) 661150 or 661448). *Location:* on M4 for Slough. Wooded parkland course. 18 holes, 6415 yards. S.S.S. 71. *Green Fees:* weekdays £19.50 per round, £29.25 per day, with a member £14.55 per day. *Eating facilities:* bar and restaurant, full catering available. *Visitors:* welcome; at weekends only with a member. *Society Meetings:* April/October Wednesdays, Thursdays and Fridays. Professional: A.J. Buckner (0628 661661). Manager: A.J. Buckner.

CHALFONT ST. GILES. **Harewood Downs Golf Club,** Cokes Lane, Chalfont St. Giles HP8 4TA (Little Chalfont (024-04) 2308). *Location:* Cokes Lane from Little Chalfont or from A413, one mile south of Amersham. Parkland. 18 holes, 5958 yards. S.S.S. 69. Practice ground. *Green Fees:* £20.00 per day. *Eating facilities:* lunches served at club. *Visitors:* welcome on weekdays with current handicap, weekends by prior arrangement only. *Society Meetings:* catered for by arrangement. Professional: G. Morris (042-04 4102). Secretary: R.M. Lennard (042-04 2185).

CHESHAM. **Chesham and Ley Hill,** Ley Hill, Chesham HP5 1UZ (Chesham (0494) 784541). *Loca-*

tion: A41, turn off at Boxmoor to Bovingdon on B4505, follow signs to Ley Hill. Wooded heathland. 9 holes, 5240 yards. S.S.S. 66. *Green Fees:* weekdays £12.00 per round, £17.00 per day. *Eating facilities:* light meals and snacks during bar opening hours (not Mondays). *Visitors:* welcome Mondays and Thursdays all day; Wednesdays pm; Fridays till 1.00pm; all other days with member only. *Society Meetings:* Thursdays by prior arrangement with Committee. Clubhouse Managers: Mr and Mrs K. Brown. Secretary: J.R. Taylor (0494 784541).

DENHAM. **Denham Golf Club,** Tileshouse Lane, Denham UB9 5DE (Denham (0895) 832079). *Location:* one and a half miles from Uxbridge off the left hand side of the A412 on route to Watford. Parkland – undulating. 18 holes, 6451 yards, 6159 metres. S.S.S. 71. Practice ground. *Green Fees:* £21.00 per round, £33.00 per day weekdays. *Eating facilities:* dining-room, bar snacks. *Visitors:* welcome Monday to Thursday by prior arrangement only. Handicap Certificate. *Society Meetings:* catered for Tuesdays, Wednesdays and Thursdays. Professional: John Sheridan (0895 832801). Secretary: Wg Cdr. D. Graham (0895 832022).

GERRARDS CROSS. **Gerrards Cross Golf Club,** Chalfont Park, Gerrards Cross SL9 0QA (Gerrards Cross (0753) 883263). *Location:* alongside A413 (to Amersham) about one mile from junction with A40 (London to Oxford road). Wooded parkland course. 18 holes, 6295 yards. S.S.S. 70. *Green Fees:* £27.00 per day or per round. £20.00 per round starting after 3 pm *Eating facilities:* lunch available to order, bar snacks at all times. *Visitors:* welcome except at weekends and Public Holidays but must produce a letter of introduction or current Handicap Certificate. *Society Meetings:* catered for Thursdays and Fridays, maximum number 50. Professional: A.P. Barr (0753 885300). Secretary/Manager: P.H. Fisher.

HIGH WYCOMBE. **Flackwell Heath Golf Club Limited,** Treadaway Hill, Flackwell Heath, High Wycombe HP10 9PE (Bourne End (06285) 20027). *Location:* M4 Exit 3 from London, Exit 4 from Oxford. 2 miles High Wycombe. Heath and woodland, some hills. 18 holes, 6150 yards. S.S.S. 69. *Green Fees:* weekdays £19.00 per day (£9.00 with member); weekends £9 with member only. *Eating facilities:* restaurant and bars daily (limited catering Mondays). *Visitors:* welcome weekdays only with Handicap Certificate. Weekends with member only. *Society Meetings:* catered for by arrangement Wednesdays and Thursdays. Professional: Brian Plucknett (06285 23017). Secretary: J.J.R. Barton (06285 20929).

HIGH WYCOMBE. **Hazlemere Golf and Country Club,** Penn Road, Hazlemere, Nr. High Wycombe (High Wycombe (0494) 714453). *Location:* on B474 about half a mile from Junction with A404 High Wycombe/Amersham Road – three miles from High Wycombe centre. Undulating parkland course. 18 holes, 5855 yards. S.S.S. 68. *Green Fees:* weekdays £16.00 per round, weekends £20.00 per round. *Eating facilities:* restaurant and bar. *Visitors:* restricted at weekends. Snooker table. *Society Meetings:* by prior arrangement. Professional: Steve Morvell (0494 718098). Secretary: D. Hudson (0494 714722).

IVER. **Iver Golf Course,** Hollow Hill Lane, Off Langley Park Road, Iver SL0 0JJ (Slough (0753) 651114). *Location:* 600 yards from Langley Railway Station. 9 holes, 6214 for 18. S.S.S. 69 for 18. Practice ground available. Flat parkland. *Green fees:* weekdays £4.00 for 9 holes, £6.50 for 18; weekends £5.30 for 9 holes, £9.00 for 18. *Eating facilities:* bar and catering in clubhouse. *Visitors:* welcome, bookings advisable for weekends. Pay and Play Course. *Society Meetings:* accepted. Professional: Terry Notley (0753 655615). Secretary: J. Gedge.

LITTLE CHALFONT. **Little Chalfont Golf Club,** Lodge Lane, Little Chalfont HP8 4AJ (0494 764877). *Location:* junction 18 M25, two miles towards Ambersham on A404, first left past Garnon centre. Undulating parkland. 9 holes, 5852 yards S.S.S. 68. *Green Fees:* weekdays £7.00, weekends £9.00. *Eating facilities:* full bar and eating facilities. *Visitors:* always welcome. *Society Meetings:* welcome mid-week. Professional: B. Woodhouse and A. Philpott (0494 762942). Secretary: J.M. Dunne (0494 764877).

MILTON KEYNES. **Abbey Hill Golf Club,** Abbey Hill, Milton Keynes (Milton Keynes (0908) 562408). *Location:* 2 miles south of Stony Stratford. 18 holes, 5732 metres. S.S.S. 69. Short par 3 course available. Municipal green fees on application. *Eating facilities:* available. *Visitors:* welcome. *Society Meetings:* catered for, apply Professional. Professional: S. Harlock. Secretary: Mr I.D. Grieve.

MILTON KEYNES. **Windmill Hill Golf Course,** Tattenhoe Lane, Bletchley, Milton Keynes MK3 7RB (0908 648149). *Location:* A421 Milton Keynes – Buckingham. Flat course. 18 holes, 6773 yards S.S.S. 72. Floodlit and covered driving ranges. *Green Fees:* weekdays £4.50; weekends and Bank Holidays £6.30. *Eating facilities:* available every day. *Visitors:* welcome. *Society Meetings:* all course bookings through Professional. Professional: C. Clingan (0908 378623). Secretary: Rick Slengelow.

MILTON KEYNES. **Woburn Golf and Country Club,** Bow Brickhill, Milton Keynes MK17 9LJ (Milton Keynes (0908) 370756). *Location:* M1 Junction 13. 36 holes: Duke's Course 6940 yards S.S.S. 74. Duchess' Course 6641 yards, S.S.S. 72. Two practice grounds. *Green Fees:* information on request. *Eating facilities:* two restuarants, breakfasts, lunches and dinners. *Visitors:* welcome on weekdays with prior notice. Tennis and swimming available. *Society Meetings:* catered for, details on application. Professionl/Managing Director: Alex Hay (0908 647987 or 370756).

PRINCES RISBOROUGH. **Whiteleaf Golf Club Ltd,** The Clubhouse, Whiteleaf, Aylesbury HP17 0LY (08444 3097). *Location:* A4010 from Princes Risborough. 9 holes, 5359 yards. S.S.S. 66. *Green Fees:* weekdays £15.00 for 18 holes, £25.00 all day; members only at weekends. *Eating facilities:* bar and food served. *Visitors:* welcome on weekdays only. *Society Meetings:* on application, Thursdays only. Professional: K.S. Ward (08444 5472). Secretary: D.G. Bullard (08444 274058).

SLOUGH. **Farnham Park Municipal Golf Course,** Park Road, Stoke Poges SL2 4PJ (Farnham Common (02814) 3332). *Location:* centrally situated between Stoke Poges and Farnham Royal, off Park Road. Parkland. 18 holes, 5847 yards. S.S.S. 68. *Green Fees:* weekdays £4.80; weekends £7.00. Reduced rates for Senior Citizens and Juniors. *Eating facilities:* available. *Visitors:* welcome. Professional: P. Harrison. Hon. Secretary: Maureen Brooker.

STOKE POGES. **Stoke Poges Golf Club,** North Drive, Park Road, Stoke Poges SL2 4PG (Slough (0753) 26385). *Location:* one mile north of Slough. 18 holes, 6654 yards. S.S.S. 72. *Green Fees:* information not provided. *Eating facilities:* lunch and snack restaurant. *Visitors:* welcome weekdays only with Handicap Certificate or letter of introduction. *Society Meetings:* catered for. Professional: Kim Thomas. Secretary/Manager: R.C. Pickering.

STOWE. **Stowe Golf Club,** Stowe, Buckingham MK18 5EH (0280 816264). *Location:* situated at Stowe School, four miles north of Buckingham. Parkland course with follies and lakes. 9 holes, 2189 yards. S.S.S. 63. *Green Fees:* £5.00. *Visitors:* only as a guest of a member. *Society Meetings:* catered for by appointment. Secretary: Mrs S.A. Cross (0280 813650).

WEXHAM. **Wexham Park Golf Course,** Wexham Street, Slough SL3 6ND (Fulmer (02816) 3271). *Location:* M40 to Beaconsfield, A40 to Gerrards Cross, direction to Fulmer on right hand side, near Wexham Park Hospital. Flat parkland with water hazards. 27 holes, 5836 yards, 5339 metres. S.S.S. 68. From Spring 1990 36 holes open. 20-bay driving range and sports centre. *Green Fees:* weekdays £6.00 for 18 holes, £3.00 for 9 holes; weekends £8.00 for 18 holes, £4.00 for 9 holes. *Eating facilities:* restaurant and bar. *Visitors:* welcome – Pay and Play, open to all. Accomodation available from 1990. *Society Meetings:* weekdays only, minimum 12 people. Professional: David Morgan (02816 3425). Secretary: J.E. Mulley.

PUBLISHER'S NOTE

While every effort is made to ensure accuracy, we regret that FHG Publications cannot accept responsibility for errors, omissions or misrepresentation in our entries or any consequences thereof. Prices in particular should be checked because we go to press early. We will follow up complaints, but cannot act as arbiters or agents for either party.

Cambridgeshire

CAMBRIDGE. **Cambridgeshire Moat House Hotel Golf and Sports Club,** Bar Hill, Cambridge (Crafts Hill (0954) 780555).*Location:* five miles from Cambridge on A604 Huntingdon road. 18 holes, 6734 yards. S.S.S. 72. *Green Fees:* weekdays £15.00, weekends and Public Holidays £25.00. *Eating facilities:* full restaurant and bar snacks available. *Visitors:* welcome by prior phone call. 100 Bedroom Hotel, Squash, Tennis, Health and Fitness Centre, Indoor Heated Swimming Pool. *Society Meetings:* catered for. Professional and Sports Manager: Geoff Huggett.

CAMBRIDGE. **Girton Golf Club,** Dodford Lane, Cambridge (Cambridge (0223) 276169). *Location:* three miles north of Cambridge. 18 holes, 6000 yards. S.S.S. 69. *Green Fees:* £14.00 per day; weekends with a member only. *Eating facilities:* available. *Visitors:* weekdays only. *Society Meetings:* welcomed. Professional: John Sharkey. Secretary: Mrs M.A. Cornwell.

CAMBRIDGE. **Gog Magog Golf Club,** Shelford Bottom, Cambridge CB2 4AB (0223 247626). *Location:* two miles south east of Cambridge on A1307 – Addenbrookes Hospital. Open, undulating. Two courses. 18 holes, 6386 yards. S.S.S. 70. 9 holes, 5805 yards. S.S.S. 68. *Green Fees:* £25.00 weekdays. *Eating facilities:* diningroom, bar meals, mixed and men's bar. *Visitors:* welcome, only with members at weekends and Bank Holidays, Handicap Certificates required, Handicap limit on Old Course 18 and below. *Society Meetings:* catered for Tuesdays and Thurdays. Professional: I. Bamborough (0223 246058). Secretary: John E. Riches (0223 246058).

ELY. **Ely City Golf Course Ltd,** Cambridge Road, Ely CB7 4HX (Ely (0353) 663810). *Location:* on southern outskirts of city on A10 going to Cambridge. Parkland course, slightly undulating, magnificent views of the 12th century cathedral. 18 holes, 6680 yards. S.S.S. 72. Practice area. *Green Fees:* weekdays £15.00, weekends and Bank Holidays £25.00. *Eating facilities:* full bar and restaurant services. *Visitors:* welcome at all times but Handicap Certificates are required. Jeans, T-shirts and trainers not allowed. *Society Meetings:* welcome Tuesday to Friday inclusive. Professional: F.C. Rowden (0353 663317). Secretary: Mr G.A. Briggs (0353 662751)

HUNTINGDON. **Ramsey Golf Club,** 4 Abbey Terrace, Ramsey, Huntingdon (Ramsey (0487) 813573). *Location:* 20 minutes from A1, 12 miles south of Peterborough, 10 miles north of Huntingdon. Parkland, 18 holes, 6136 yards. S.S.S. 70. Two practice grounds. *Green Fees:* weekdays £15.00 round or day with Handicap Certificate. Weekends, Bank Holidays with member only. *Eating facilities:* full catering available. *Visitors:* welcome without reservation. *Society Meetings:* catered for by arrangement, weekdays only. Professional: B.J. Puttick (0487 813022). Secretary: Mr R. Muirhead (0487 812600).

MARCH. **March Golf Club,** Frogs Abbey, Grange Road, March (March (0354) 52364). *Location:* one mile south from town centre on A141. 9 holes, 6210 yards. S.S.S. 70. *Green fees:* information not provided. *Visitors* welcome all week with Handicap Certificate.

PETERBOROUGH. **Orton Meadows Golf Club,** Ham Lane, Orton Waterville, Peterborough PE2 0UU (Peterborough (0733) 237478). *Location:* four miles west of Peterborough on A605. Parkland. 18 holes, 5800 yards. S.S.S. 68. Practice ground. *Green Fees:* weekdays £5.00 per round, weekends and Bank Holidays £7.50 per round. Weekday reductions for Senior Citizens and Juniors. *Eating facilities:* restaurant attached to course. *Visitors:* unrestricted – public course. *Society Meetings:* welcome. Professionals: N. Grant, M.D. Booker. Secretary: K. Boyer.

PETERBOROUGH. **Peterborough Milton Golf Club,** Milton Ferry, Peterborough PE6 7AG (Peterborough (0733) 380204). *Location:* on A47 west of Peterborough, 3 miles east of A1. Parkland. 18 holes, 6431 yards, 5856 metres. S.S.S. 71. *Green Fees:* weekdays £18.00, weekends £21.00. *Eating facilities:* daily except Mondays. *Visitors:* welcome weekdays; as member's guest at weekends. *Society Meetings:* by arrangement with Secretary. Professional: Nigel Bundy (0733 380793). Secretary: P.J. Bishop (0733 380489).

PETERBOROUGH. **Thorpe Wood Golf Course,** Thorpe Wood, Peterborough PE3 6SE (Peterborough (0733) 267701). *Location:* three miles west of town on A47. Parkland. 18 holes, 7086 yards. S.S.S. 74. Practice ground. *Green Fees:* weekdays £5.00, weekends and Bank Holidays £7.50. Weekday reductions for Senior Citizens and Juniors. *Eating facilities:* Public House attached to course. *Visitors:* unrestricted. Public Course. Professionals: D. Fitton, R. Fitton (0733 267701). Secretary: R. Palmer (0733 63758).

ST. IVES. **St. Ives (Hunts) Golf Club,** Westwood Road, St. Ives PE17 4RS (St. Ives (0480) 64459). *Location:* B1040 off A45. 9 holes, 6052 yards. S.S.S. 69. *Green Fees:* weekdays £12.00. *Eating facilities:* lunches at club, except Mondays. Order in advance. *Visitors:* no visitors weekends or Bank Holidays. *Society Meetings:* catered for. Professional: A. Headley (0480 66067). Secretary: Ray Hill (0480 68392).

ST. NEOTS. **Abbotsley Golf and Squash Club,** Eynesbury Hardwicke, St Neots PE19 4XN (Huntingdon (0480) 215153). *Location:* two miles east A1 (M), 12 miles off Junction 13 M11. Undulating meadowland, very challenging golf course especially "The Mousehole". 18 holes, 6217 yards. S.S.S. 72. 20-bay covered driving range with floodlights. *Green Fees:* weekdays £10.00 per round, weekends £15.00 per round. *Eating facilities:* full bar, restaurant facilities. *Visitors:* welcome, weekend starting times – weekend breaks for golfers. Six squash courts. Accommodation available 14 bedroomed hotel. Information on residential/non-residential golf schools available on request. *Society Meetings:* always welcome. Professional: Vivien Saunders (0480 406463). Secretary/Manager: Miss Jenny Wisson (0480 74000).

ST. NEOTS. **St. Neots Golf Club,** Cross Hall Road, St. Neots PE19 4AE (Huntingdon (0480) 74311). *Location:* A45 off A1, eastwards, one mile east of Gt. North Road. 18 holes, 6005 yards. S.S.S. 69. *Green Fees:* on application. *Eating facilities:* full catering facilities except Mondays. *Visitors:* at weekends/Bank Holidays with member only. *Society Meetings:* welcome. Professional: G. Bithrey (0480 76513). Secretary: R.J. Marsden (0480 72363).

Cheshire

ALDERLEY EDGE. **Alderley Edge Golf Club,** Brook Lane, Alderley Edge SK9 7RU (Alderley Edge (0625) 585583). *Location:* off A34. 9 holes, 5836 yards. S.S.S. 68. *Green Fees:* weekends £15.00, weekdays £12.00. *Eating facilities:* meals served in clubhouse. *Visitors:* subject to restrictions on Tuesdays, Wednesdays and weekends. Professional: M. Stewart (0625 584493). Secretary: A.J. Hayes.

ALTRINCHAM. **Hale Golf Club,** Rappax Road, Hale, Altrincham WA15 0NU (061-980 4225). 9 holes (2 rounds), 5780 yards. S.S.S. 68. Pleasant undulating parkland. *Green Fees:* weekdays £12.50, weekends with member only £4.00. *Eating facilities:* by arrangement with Steward. *Visitors:* welcome weekdays (except Thursday) with reservation. *Society Meetings:* by arrangement with Hon. Secretary. Professional: John Jackson (061-904 0835). Hon. Secretary: R.V. Murphy (061-980 1435).

APPLETON. **The Warrington Golf Club,** Hill Warren, London Road, Appleton, Nr. Warrington WA4 5HR (0925 61620). *Location:* M56 exit 11, A49 Warrington one and a half miles. Parkland course. 18 holes, 6217 yards. S.S.S. 70. *Green Fees:* information not provided. *Eating facilities:* available except Monday lunchtime. *Visitors:* welcome with reservation. *Society Meetings:* Wednesdays only. Professional: A.W. Fryer (0925 65431). Secretary: R.O. Francis (0925 61775).

CHEADLE. **Gatley Golf Club Ltd,** Waterfall Farm, Styal Road, Heald Green, Cheadle SK8 3TW (061-437 2091). *Location:* from Gatley village to South down Styal Road and follow directions into Yew Tree Grove, then Motcombe Grove to Club entrance. Parkland course. 9 holes, 5934 yards. S.S.S. 68. *Green Fees:* weekdays £10.00 and £5.00 with member, weekends only if playing with member. Special rates by arrangememt. *Eating facilities:* available except Monday, bar. *Visitors:* welcome Wednesdays and Thursdays. *Society Meetings:* as above. Professional: S. Crake (061-436 2830). Secretary: P. Hannam F.C.A. (061-437 2091).

CHESTER. **Chester Golf Club,** Curzon Park, Chester CH4 8AR (0244 677760). *Location:* one mile from city centre off A55 to North Wales. 18 holes, 6487 yards. S.S.S. 71. *Green Fees:* weekdays £15.00, weekends £20.00. *Eating facilities:* full catering except Mondays. *Visitors:* welcome. *Society Meetings:* catered for by prior arrangement. Professional: George Parton. Secretary: P.M. Pritchard.

CHESTER. **Upton-by-Chester Golf Club,** Upton Lane, Chester CH2 1EE (Chester (0244) 371138). *Location:* off A41, near turn-off Zoo traffic lights. Flat parkland course. 18 holes, 5808 yards. S.S.S. 68. *Green Fees:* £13.00 weekdays, £15.00 weekends. *Eating facilities:* large restaurant and four bars. *Visitors:* no restrictions except Competition Days. *Society Meetings:* welcome except Mondays, Tuesdays and weekends. Minimum number 16. Complete package £24.00. Professional: Peter Gardner (0244 381333). Secretary: John B. Durban (0244 381183).

CHESTER. **Vicars Cross Golf Club,** Tarvin Road, Littleton, Chester (Chester (0244) 335174). *Location:* three miles from Chester on the A51 Manchester road. 18 holes, 6268 yards. S.S.S. 70. *Green Fees:* Mondays to Thursdays £15.00, Fridays, weekends and Bank Holidays must be with a member. *Eating facilities:* full catering except Mondays, two bars. *Visitors:* welcome Monday to Thursday, but restrictions Friday and weekends. *Society Meetings:* catered for Tuesdays and Thursdays. Professional: J.A. Forsythe. Secretary: D.C. Chilton.

CONGLETON. **Astbury Golf Club,** Peel Lane, Astbury, Near Congleton CW12 4RE (Congleton (0260) 272772). *Location:* on A34 Congleton to Newcastle-under-Lyme road. Parkland. 18 holes, 6221 yards. S.S.S. 70. *Green Fees:* £12.00; £6.00 with member. *Eating facilities:* hot or cold meals, licensed bar. *Visitors:* welcome weekdays, weekends with a member. Must be members of recognised golf club with bona fide Handicap. *Society Meetings:* Thursdays only. Professional: S.R. Bassil (0260 272772). Secretary: Tom Williams (0260 279139).

CONGLETON. **Congleton Golf Club,** Biddulph Road, Congleton CW12 3LZ (Congleton (0260) 273540). *Location:* one mile from Congleton Railway Station. 9 holes, 5080 yards. S.S.S. 65. *Green Fees:* information not provided. *Eating facilities:* lunches served, order in advance. *Visitors:* welcome, if members of a bona fide golf club. *Society Meetings:* catered for, one year's notice if accepted. Professional: John Colclough (0260 271083). Secretary: T. Pegg (0260 273540).

CREWE. **Crewe Golf Club Ltd,** Fields Road, Haslington, Crewe CW1 1TB (0270 584227). *Location:* off A534 between Crewe and Sandbach. Parkland course. 18 holes, 6201 yards. S.S.S. 70. *Green Fees:* weekdays £13.00, £11.00 after 1pm; weekends only with members. *Eating facilities:* bar, diningroom. *Visitors:* welcome weekdays only. Snooker room. *Society Meetings:* Tuesdays only. Professional: R.E. Rimmer (0270 585032). Secretary: David G. Elias B.Sc. (0270 584099).

CREWE. **Onneley Golf Club,** Near Crewe (Stoke-on-Trent (0782) 750577). *Location:* one mile from Woore off A51. 9 holes, 5816 yards. S.S.S. 68. *Green Fees:* £10.00 (£5.00 with member). *Eating facilities:* light bar snacks when bar is open in summer. *Visitors:* weekdays unrestricted, Saturdays and Bank Holidays with a member only. *Society Meetings:* welcome, reduced green fees. Hon. Secretary: L.A.C. Kennedy (0270 661842).

CREWE. **Queens Park Golf Course,** Queens Park Drive, Crewe CW2 7SB (0270 666724). *Location:* next to Queens Park, one mile from Crewe Station. Parkland. 9 holes, 4920 yards. S.S.S. 64. *Green fees:* information not available. *Eating facilities:* bar with excellent bar snacks. *Visitors:* welcome, no restrictions. *Society Meetings:* welcome. Professional: H.W. Bilton. Secretary: J. Jones (0270 583478).

HELSBY. **Helsby Golf Club,** Towers Lane, Helsby, Warrington WA6 0JB (Helsby (09282) 2021). *Location:* Junction 14 M56 to Helsby. Through traffic light one mile, first right into Primrose Lane, then first right into Towers Lane (200 yards). Flat parkland course. 18 holes, 6204 yards. S.S.S. 70. Practice area available. *Green Fees:* £12.00 weekdays. *Eating facilities:* full facilities, sandwiches only on Wednesdays. *Visitors:* welcome weekdays, weekends must play with a member. Snooker facilities. *Society Meetings:* welcome Mondays and Thursdays by arrangement. Professional: Ian Wright (09282 5457). Secretary: N. Littler (09282 2021).

HIGHER WALTON. **Walton Hall Golf Club,** Warrington Road, Higher Walton, Warrington WA4 5LU (Warrington (0925) 66775). *Location:* two miles south of Warrington, Exits 10 and 11 M56. Wooded parkland. 18 holes, 6849 yards. S.S.S. 73. Practice ground. *Green Fees:* weekdays £4.00, weekends £5.00. Reduced rates 9-hole evening rounds; Juniors and Senior Citizens. *Eating facilities:* clubhouse, snack bar. *Visitors:* unrestricted. *Society Meetings:* welcome. Secretary: D. Judson (0925 66775). Professional: M.J. Slater (0925 63061). Director of Golf: B. Thomas (0925 444400).

KNUTSFORD. **Knutsford Golf Club,** Mere Heath Lane, Knutsford (Knutsford (0565) 3355). *Location:* one mile east of town centre. 9 holes, 6200 yards. S.S.S. 70. *Green Fees:* information not provided. *Eating facilities:* by prior arrangement with Steward. *Visitors:* welcome with reservation except Tuesdays and Wednesdays. To be introduced by member. *Society Meetings:* catered for by special arrangement with Hon. Secretary. Professional: A. Wilson. Secretary: D. Francis.

KNUTSFORD. **Mere Golf and Country Club,** Chester Road, Knutsford WA16 6LJ (0565 830155). *Location:* two miles east of Junction 19 M6 and three miles west of Junction 7 M56. Regarded as one of the finest Parkland Championship courses in the country. 18 holes, 6849 yards. S.S.S. 73. Practice area with green and bunkers, two 9 holes putting greens, driving range. *Green Fees:* £35.00 weekdays, £45.00 weekends. *Eating facilities:* three private banqueting suites, restaurant and coffee shop. *Visitors:* welcome by prior arrangement only. *Society Meetings:* Mondays, Tuesdays or Thursdays by arrangement. Professional: Eddie Goodwin (0565 830219). Secretary: Alf Turner (0565 830155).

KNUTSFORD. **Wilmslow Golf Club,** Great Warford, Mobberley, Knutsford WA16 7AY (Mobberley (056 587) 2579). *Location:* two miles from Wilmslow off the Knutsford road. Parkland course. 18 holes, 6611 yards. S.S.S. 72. *Green Fees:* weekdays £16.00, weekends £21.00. *Eating facilities:* full catering except Monday, two bars. *Society Meetings:* Tuesdays and Thursdays only. Professional: L.J. Nowicki (056 587 3620). Secretary: C.A. Skelton (056 587 2148).

LYMM. **Lymm Golf Club,** Whitbarrow Road, Lymm WA13 9AN (Lymm (092 575) 2177). *Location:* five miles south east of Warrington. Parkland. 18 holes, 6304 yards. S.S.S. 70. *Green Fees:* £13.00 weekdays. *Eating facilities:* available. *Visitors:* with Handicap Certificates, no visitors on Thursdays, weekends or Bank Holiday. *Society Meetings:* catered for Wednesdays. Professional: Garry Williams (092 575 5054). Secretary: J.M. Pearson (092 575 5020).

MACCLESFIELD. **Macclesfield Golf Club,** The Hollins, Macclesfield SK11 7EA (0625 23227). *Location:* turn left at Windmill Street off the A527 Leek road. Hilly course. 12 holes, 5974 yards, 5462 metres. S.S.S. 69. *Green Fees:* £10.00 weekdays, £12.00 weekends. *Eating facilities:* full catering available except Tuesdays. *Visitors:* welcome without reservation. *Society Meetings:* catered for except weekends. Professional: A. Taylor (0625 616952). Secretary: W. Eastwood (0625 615845).

MACCLESFIELD. **Prestbury Golf Club,** Macclesfield Road, Prestbury, Near Macclesfield (0625 829388). *Location:* on the Macclesfield road leaving Prestbury village. 18 holes, 6359 yards. S.S.S. 71. *Green Fees:* information not provided. *Eating facilities:* lunches, teas and dinners. *Visitors:* welcome on weekdays with official club handicap; Bank Holidays and weekends only with a member. *Society Meetings:* Thursdays only. Professional: Tim Rastall (0625 828242). Secretary/Manager: J.L. Carter (0625 828241).

MACCLESFIELD. **Tytherington Club,** Manchester Road, Macclesfield SK10 2JP (0625 34562). *Location:* one mile north of Macclesfield on A523. New championship course in beautiful parkland setting. Headquarters of the Women Professional Golfers' European Tour and venue for the 1990 European Classic. 6750 yards, par 72. *Green Fees:* Societies: £16 per round, £24 per day; visitors: £18 per round, £26 per day. *Eating facilities:* private dining and bar facilities, gourmet restaurant or bar snacks. *Visitors:* welcome. *Society Meetings:* by arrangement. Country Club facilities include indoor pool, health club, sauna, steam room, gymnasium, beauty salon, squash, tennis, bowls and snooker. Clay shoot by arrangement. Golf carts and trolleys available. Managing Director: Patrick Dawson.

NORTHWICH. **Delamere Forest Golf Club,** Station Road, Delamere, Northwich CW8 2JE (Sandiway (0606) 882807. *Location:* M6, A556. On Frodsham side of A556 between Chester and Northwich. Heathland course. 18 holes, 6305 yards. S.S.S. 70. *Green Fees:* £15.00 weekdays, £20.00 weekends and Bank Holidays. *Eating facilities:* available except Fridays, bar. *Visitors:* welcome any day, but restricted to 2 ball games weekends, Bank Holidays and Competition Days. *Society Meetings:* welcome with prior booking. Professional: D. Comboy (0606 883307). Secretary: L. Parkin (0606 882807).

NORTHWICH. **Sandiway Golf Club,** Sandiway, Northwich CW8 2DJ (Sandiway (0606) 883247). *Location:* off A556. 18 holes, 6435 yards. S.S.S. 72. *Green Fees:* information not provided. *Eating facilities:* lunches and teas served daily at club, order dinners in advance. *Visitors:* welcome on weekdays with letter of introduction from own club. Secretary: V.F.C. Wood. Professional: Iain Clark.

RUNCORN. **Runcorn Golf Club,** Clifton Road, Runcorn WA7 4SU (0928 572093). *Location:* signposted The Heath, A557. High parkland course. 18 holes, 6035 yards. S.S.S. 69. *Green Fees:* weekdays £12.00 per round or day, weekends and Bank Holidays £15.00 per round. *Eating facilities:* by arrangement, bar available. *Visitors:* welcome weekdays except Tuesdays, weekends and Bank Holidays. *Society Meetings:* by arrangement. Professional: Mr Geoff Berry (0928 564791). Secretary: G. E. Povey OBE (0928 574214).

SANDBACH. **Malkins Bank Golf Course,** Betchton Road, Malkins Bank, Sandbach CW11 0XN (0270 767878). *Location:* one mile south of Junction 17 of M6. Reached via Sandbach – Newcastle Road. Countryside course. 18 holes, 6071 yards. S.S.S. 69. Practice area. *Green Fees:* £3.65 weekdays, £4.40 weekends. Special rates for Juniors and Senior Citizens. *Eating facilities:* bar and meals available. *Visitors:* welcome at all times, pre-booking advised weekends. *Society Meetings:* welcome by arrangment. Professional: Dave Wheeler (0270 765931). Secretary: Ken Lea.

SANDBACH. **Sandbach Golf Club,** 117 Middlewich Road, Sandbach CW11 9EA (Crewe (0270) 762117). *Location:* two miles from Junction 17 of M6 on Middlewich Road. Meadowland course. 9 holes, 5600 yards. S.S.S. 67. *Green Fees:* weekdays £15.00 per day, £7.50 with member; weekends and Bank Holidays must be accompanied by a member. *Eating facilities:* available except Mondays and Fridays. *Visitors:* welcome weekdays, weekends by invitation only. *Society Meetings:* catered for only by advance arrangement with Hon. Secretary. Secretary: A.F. Pearson.

SOUTH WIRRAL. **Ellesmere Port Golf Club,** Chester Road, Hooton, South Wirral L66 1QH (051-339 7502). *Location:* approximately six miles north of Chester on main A41 trunk road to Birkenhead. Wooded with a lot of ponds. 18 holes, 6432 yards. S.S.S. 71. *Green fees:* weekdays £2.90, weekends £3.60. Special fees for Junior and OAP golfers, and concessions for unemployed during weekdays. *Eating facilities:* catering is booked through clubhouse. *Visitors:* welcome weekdays, bookable through Professional. *Society Meetings:* catered for Monday and Friday only. Professional: Mr D. Yates (051-339 7689). Secretary: Mr B. Turley (051-335 8800).

STALYBRIDGE. **Stamford Golf Club,** Oakfield House, Huddersfield Road, Heyheads, Stalybridge SK15 3PY (0457 832126). *Location:* on B6175 off A6018. 18 holes, 5619 yards. S.S.S. 67. *Green fees:* information not provided. *Eating facilities:* meals lunchtime and evening (except Monday). *Visitors:* very welcome without reservation. *Society Meetings:* catered for by reservation. Golf Shop: Brian Badger (0457 834829). Secretary: F.E. Rowles.

STOCKPORT. **Davenport Golf Club,** Worth Hall, Middlewood Road, Poynton, Stockport (0625 877321). *Location:* A6 from Stockport, Macclesfield Road at Hazel Grove, left at Poynton Church. Undulating parkland course. 18 holes, 6006 yards. S.S.S. 69. *Green Fees:* weekdays £15.00, weekends £18.00. *Eating facilities:* snacks at all times, full meals by arrangement. *Visitors:* welcome except before 5.15 pm Wednesdays, and before 5.00 pm Saturdays and Sundays. *Society Meetings:* catered for Tuesdays and Thursdays only. Professional: Wyn Harris (0625 877319). Secretary: T.D. Swindells (0625 876951).

WARRINGTON. **Birchwood Golf Club,** Kelvin Close, Birchwood, Warrington WA3 7PB (Warrington (0925) 818819). *Location:* Junction 11, two miles Leigh-Warrington road M62. Parkland with water. 18 holes, 6810 yards. S.S.S. 73. *Green Fees:* weekdays £14.00, weekends £20.00. *Eating facilities:* full restaurant facilities and bar snacks. Must book in advance. *Visitors:* conference and banqueting facilities for 200. *Society Meetings:* catered for weekdays except Fridays.

Package deals available. Professional: Derrick Cooper. Secretary: Alex Jackson (0925 818819).

WARRINGTON. **Leigh Golf Club,** Kenyon Hall, Broseley Lane, Culcheth, Warrington WA3 4BG (Culcheth (092-576) 2943). *Location:* off A580 East Lancs road. Kenyon/Culcheth boundary. Parkland. 18 holes, 5876 yards. Par 69. S.S.S. 68. Three practice areas. *Green Fees:* weekdays £15.00, £6.00 playing with member; weekends and Bank Holidays £20.00. *Eating facilities:* bar and restaurant. *Society Meetings:* catered for on Tuesdays only and some selected Mondays. Professional: Andrew Baguley (092-576 2013). Secretary: G.D. Riley (092-576 2943).

WARRINGTON. **Poulton Park Golf Club Ltd,** Dig Lane, Cinnamon Brow, Warrington (0925 812034/ 825220). *Location:* off A574 (Warrington/Leigh, Crab Lane). 9 holes, 4937 metres. S.S.S. 66. *Green Fees:* £10.00/£12.00 (weekends). *Eating facilities:* except Monday. *Visitors:* welcome. *Society Meetings:* catered for.

WIDNES. **St.Michael's Jubilee Golf Club,** Dundalk Road, Widnes WA8 8BS (051-424 6230). *Location:* five minutes from M56 and M62. Undulating parkland. 18 holes, 5612 yards. S.S.S. 67. Putting and practice areas. *Green Fees:* information not available. *Eating facilities:* bar, meals in restaurant. *Visitors;* unrestricted. *Society Meetings;* by arrangement with Professional. Professional: B. Bilton. Secretary: W. Hughes.

WIDNES. **Widnes Golf Club,** Highfield Road, Widnes WA8 9TD (051-424 2440). *Location:* near town centre. Flat course. 18 holes, 5688 yards. S.S.S. 68. *Green Fees:* weekdays £10.00, weekends £12.00. *Eating facilities:* bar snacks and full menu all day. *Visitors:* welcome with reservation at weekends. *Society Meetings:* catered for Wednesdays only. Professional: F. Robinson. Secretary: Margaret M. Cresswell (051-424 2995).

WIDNES. **Widness Municipal,** Dundalk Road, Widnes (051-424 6230). 18 holes, 5638 yards. S.S.S. 67, Par 69. *Visitors:* unrestricted. Secretary: W. Hughes. Professional: Bob Bilton.

WINSFORD. **Knights Grange Golf Course,** Knights Grange Sports Centre, Grange Lane, Winsford (0606 552780). *Location:* signposted "Sports Complex" from traffic lights Winsford Town Centre. 9 holes, 3105 yards. S.S.S. 36. Practice area. *Green Fees:* £1.80 per round, £2.30 for two rounds weekdays; £2.30 per round, £3.00 for two rounds weekends. *Eating facilities:* snacks only and hot drinks, public house adjacent. *Visitors:* unrestricted (Municipal Course). Bowls, tennis, football, athletics and crazy golf. *Society Meetings:* welcome by arrangement. Professional: Mr G. Moore.

Cleveland

BILLINGHAM. **Billingham Golf Club,** Sandy Lane, Billingham TS22 5NA (Stockton (0642) 554494). *Location:* off A19 trunk road, one mile west of Billingham town centre. Undulating parkland. 18 holes, 6460 yards. S.S.S. 71. Practice area including pitching green and putting greens. *Green Fees:* weekdays £15.00, £7.50 with member; weekends £20.00, £10.00 with member. Visiting parties £8.00 per person per day. *Eating facilities:* full catering Monday to Saturday. No hot meals on Mondays. *Visitors:* welcome weekdays. *Society Meetings:* catered for with prior booking. Professional: P.S. Bradley (0642 557060). Secretary: D.J. Bruce OBE (0642 554494).

EAGLESCLIFFE. **Eaglescliffe Golf Club Ltd,** Yarm Road, Eaglescliffe, Stockton-on-Tees TS16 0DQ (Eaglescliffe (0642) 780098). *Location:* two miles north of Yarm, A135 (Yarm road), off A19. Hilly parkland course. 18 holes, 6275 yards. S.S.S. 70. Practice area and putting green. *Green Fees:* weekdays £14.00, weekends and Bank Holidays £20.00. *Eating facilities:* full menu service except Mondays, two bars. *Visitors:* welcome weekdays, restriction on Tuesdays, Fridays and ladies' day. *Society Meetings:* catered for except weekends. Professional: J. Munro (0642 780588). Secretary: A.H. Painter.

HARTLEPOOL. **Castle Eden and Peterlee Golf Club,** Castle Eden, Hartlepool (Wellfield (0429) 836220). *Location:* two miles south of Peterlee, use exits from A19. Picturesque parkland course. 18 holes, 6297 yards. S.S.S. 70. Practice ground. *Green Fees:* weekdays £10.00 per day, weekends and Bank Holidays £16.00. *Eating facilities:* restaurant, lounge and bars. *Visitors:* welcome, Tuesday Ladies' day. *Society Meetings:* weekdays only with reservation. Professional: Tim Jenkins (0429 836689). Secretary: Peter Robinson (0429 836510).

HARTLEPOOL. **Hartlepool Golf Club,** Hart Warren, Hartlepool (Hartlepool (0429) 274398). *Location:* Off A1086. Seaside links course. 18 holes, 6255 yards. S.S.S. 70. *Green Fees:* weekdays £13.00 per day, £7.00 with member; weekends £20.00 per day, £10.00 with member; reduced fees for parties of 8 or more by arrangement. *Eating facilities:* meals and snacks available. *Visitors:* welcome excluding Sunday without reservation. *Society Meetings:* catered for by arrangement. Professional: M. E. Cole (0492 267473). Hon. Secretary: W.E. Storrow (0492 870282).

HARTLEPOOL. **Seaton Carew Golf Club,** Tees Road, Seaton Carew, Hartlepool (Hartlepool (0429) 266249). *Location:* two miles south of Hartlepool on A178. Old Course: 6604 yards. S.S.S. 72. Brabazon Course: 6802 yards. S.S.S. 73. *Green Fees:* weekdays £16.00 per day, weekends and Bank Holidays £20.00 per day. *Eating facilities:* available. *Visitors:* welcome without reservation. *Society Meetings:* catered for at weekends. Professional: W. Hector. Secretary: T. Waite.

MIDDLESBROUGH. **Middlesbrough Golf Club,** Brass Castle Lane, Marton, Middlesbrough TS8 9EE (Middlesbrough (0642) 316430). *Location:* five miles south of Middlesbrough west of the A172. Parkland course. 18 holes, 6106 yards. S.S.S. 69. *Green Fees:* weekdays £14.50 per day, weekends £17.50. *Eating facilities:* lunches, teas and dinners. *Visitors:* welcome with reservation. *Society Meetings:* catered for. Professional: D.J. Jones (0642 311766). Secretary: J.M. Jackson (0642 311515).

MIDDLESBROUGH. **Middlesbrough Municipal Golf Club,** Ladgate Lane, Middlesbrough TS5 7YZ (Middlesbrough (0642) 315533). *Location:* two miles south of Middlesbrough on A174. Parkland course with featured streams. 18 holes, 6314 yards. Par 71. S.S.S. 70. Floodlit driving range. *Green Fees:* weekdays £4.00 per day, weekends £6.00. *Eating facilities:* bar meals and functions. *Visitors:* welcome, but starting times must be booked in advance. *Society Meetings:* by prior arrangement. Professional: Mike Nutter (0642 315361). Golf Centre Manager: N.B.J. Fick (0642 315533).

REDCAR. **Cleveland Golf Club,** Queen Street, Redcar TS10 1BT (Redcar (0642) 483693). *Location:* south down River Teesmouth by A174 then A1042 into Redcar. 18 holes, 6685 yards, 6117 metres. S.S.S. 72. *Green Fees:* weekdays £10.00 two rounds, £7.50 one round; weekends £15.00 per day, £10.00 one round. *Eating facilities:* all week except Monday. *Visitors:* welcome but not on weekends or Bank Holidays. *Society Meetings:* catered for by prior arrangement weekdays only. Professional: D. Masey (0642 483462). Secretary: L.R. Manley (0642 471798).

REDCAR. **Wilton Golf Club,** Wilton Castle, Redcar (Cleveland (0642) 454626). *Location:* eight miles east of Middlesbrough A174, four miles west of Redcar. Wooded parkland course. 18 holes, 6104 yards. S.S.S. 69. Small practice area. *Green Fees:* weekdays £10.00, £6.00 with member; Sundays and Bank Holidays £15.00. *Eating facilities:* lunches, except Sundays; evening meals by arrangement. *Visitors:* not on Saturdays. *Society Meetings:* by arrangement. Secretary: D.W. Lewis (0642 465265).

SALTBURN BY THE SEA. **Saltburn by the Sea Golf Club Ltd,** Hob Hill, Saltburn by the Sea TS12 1NJ (Guisborough (0287) 22812). *Location:* from Saltburn take Guisborough Road, one mile out of town on left. 18 holes, 5846 yards. S.S.S. 68. *Green Fees:* weekdays £12.00 per day, weekends and Bank Holidays £13.50 per day. *Eating facilities:* available except Mondays. *Visitors* welcome. limited Sundays and Thursdays and no visitors Saturdays. *Society Meetings:* catered for by arrangement. Professional: R. Broadbent (0287 24653). Secretary: David Becker.

STOCKTON-ON-TEES. **Teesside Golf Club,** Acklam Road, Thornaby, Stockton-on-Tees TS17 7JS

(Stockton (0642) 676249). *Location:* take A1130 from the A19 to Stockton, signposted on right after quarter of a mile. Parkland. 18 holes, 6472 yards. S.S.S. 71. Professional teaching. *Green Fees:* weekdays £10.00, £7.00 with member, parties of 10 or more £6.50; weekends £14.00 (subject to starting sheet), £8.00 with member. *Eating facilities:* catering and bar except Mondays. *Visitors:* welcome, not after 4.30pm unless with member; weekends with member only. *Society Meetings:* catered for. Professional: K.W. Hall (0642 6738222). Secretary: Mr W. Allen (0642 616516).

Cornwall

BUDE. **Bude and North Cornwall Golf Club,** Burn View, Bude EX23 8BY (Bude (0288) 353176). *Location:* Seaside links course situated in the centre of the town and adjacent to beaches. 18 holes, 6202 yards. S.S.S. 70. Practice net and grounds. *Green Fees:* weekdays £12.00 per round or day; weekends £15.00. *Eating facilities:* catering and bar snacks. *Visitors:* welcome without reservation. Snooker, billiards and pool. *Society Meetings:* catered for. Professional: John Yeo (0288 353635). Secretary: Kevin Brown (0288 352006).

CAMBORNE. **Tehidy Park Golf Club,** Camborne TR14 0HH (Portreath (0209) 842208). *Location:* A30 via Blackwater and Camborne by-passes to sign for Portreath. Parkland, wooded, 3 new lakes. 18 holes, 6241 yards. S.S.S. 70. *Green Fees:* weekdays £15.00 per round, £20.00 per day, weekends £20.00 per round, £25.00 per day. *Eating facilities:* à la carte restaurant except Mondays. *Visitors:* welcome with Handicap Certificate except Tuesdays and Thursdays. *Society Meetings:* by arrangement; early booking

essential. Professional: J. Dumbreck (0209 842914). (Acting) Manager: F.C. Thomas (0209 842208).

FALMOUTH. **Budock Vean Golf and Country House Hotel,** Near Mawnan Smith, Falmouth TR11 5LG (Mawnan Smith (0326) 250281). *Location:* between Helford and Falmouth, area of Helford River. 9 holes/18 tees 5222 yards. Par 68. S.S.S. 65. *Green Fees:* weekdays £9.00, weekends £12.00 for non-residents, Hotel Guests free. *Eating facilities:* catering and bars available. *Visitors:* daily only for outside visitors who are most welcome, but must have Handicap Certificate. Hotel accommodation. Secretary: F.G. Benney. Golf Manager: A. Ramsden.

FALMOUTH. **Falmouth Golf Club,** Swanpool Road, Falmouth TR11 5BQ (0326 311262).*Location:* quarter-of-a-mile west of Swanpool Beach, Falmouth, on the road to Maenporth. Wooded parkland course with magnificent views. 18 holes, 5581 yards, 5104 metres. S.S.S. 67. *Green Fees:* £10.00 per round or £12.00 per day. Six acres of practice grounds. *Eating facilities:* catering and bar all year round. *Visitors* welcome at all times, except during major competitions. *Society Meetings:* are always welcome, four weeks' notice required. Professional: David Short (0326 316229). Secretary: D.J. de C. Sizer (0326 40525).

HELSTON. **Mullion Golf Club,** Cury, Helston TR12 7BP (Mullion (0326) 240276). *Location:* from Helston on the A3083 past Culdrose Air Station, turn right after three miles. Cliff top and links. 18 holes, 5616 yards.

S.S.S. 67. *Green Fees:* £16.00 flat rate. *Eating facilities:* snacks and meals available, except Tuesday, full bar facilities. *Visitors:* welcome. Golfers with handicap only. *Society Meetings:* welcome on prior booking. Professional: M.F. Singleton (0326 240276). Secretary/Treasurer: D. Watts, F.C.A. (0326 240685).

LAUNCESTON. **Launceston Golf Club,** St. Stephens, Launceston PL15 8HF (0556 773442). *Location:* one mile north of town on Bude road (B3254). Parkland. 18 holes, 6407 yards. S.S.S. 71. *Green Fees:* weekdays £14.00, weekends £16.00. *Eating facilities:* available. *Visitors:* welcome without reservation. *Society Meetings:* catered for. Professional: J. Tozer (0566 5359). Secretary: B.J. Grant (0566 773442).

LOOE. **Looe Golf Club,** Bin Down, Looe PL13 1PX (Widegates (05034) 239). *Location:* three miles from Looe on A387. Downland, fabulous views of Devon, Cornwall and the coast. 18 holes, 5940 yards. S.S.S. 68. Large practice ground. *Green Fees:* weekdays £12.00, weekends £14.00. Reduction for Juniors. *Eating facilities:* two bars, bar snacks and grills. *Visitors:* welcome at all times except club open days. *Society Meetings:* welcome by arrangement. Professional: Alister MacDonald. Secretary: John Rowe.

NEWQUAY. **Newquay Golf Club,** Tower Road, Newquay TR7 1LT (0637 872091). *Location:* 400 yards from Newquay Town Centre. Seaside links with 107 bunkers. 18 holes, 6140 yards, 5526 metres. S.S.S. 69. *Green Fees:* weekdays £13.00 per round,

weekends £15.00 per round. £48.00 per week, £60.00 per fortnight. *Eating facilities:* lunches and bar snacks. *Visitors:* welcome at all times. *Society Meetings:* catered for except Sundays. Professional: P. Muscroft (0637 874830). Secretary: G. Binney (0637 874354).

PADSTOW. **Trevose Golf and Country Club,** Constantine Bay, Padstow PL28 8JB (Padstow (0841) 520208). *Location:* off B3276, four miles west of Padstow at Constantine Bay. Links course. Main course: 18 holes, 6461 yards. S.S.S. 71. Short course: 9 holes, 1357 yards. Par 29. *Green Fees:* Range £15-£30, short course £8-£15. *Eating facilities:* restaurant open daily, bar. *Visitors:* welcome with reservation, must be members of a recognised club and hold a Handicap Certificate. Starting times for 3 & 4 balls restricted all year, phone beforehand. *Society Meetings:* by application. Professional: G. Alliss (0841 520261). Manager: L. Grindley. Owner: P. Gammon. Apply to Manager for starting times. Self catering accommodation in Bungalow, Chalets, Flats and Dormy Suites available at the club, details from Manager.

PENZANCE. **Praa Sands Golf Club,** Germoe Crossroads, Near Penzance TR20 9TQ (0736 763445). *Location:* midway between Helston and Penzance on A394. Seaside, parkland – beautiful sea views from all holes. 9 holes, 4036 yards. S.S.S. 62 (Ladies 64). Practice area and net. *Green fees:* £8.00 per round, weekly £40.00, fortnightly £70.00. *Visitors:* welcome every day except Sunday mornings and Friday evenings after 5.00pm. *Society Meetings:* catered for. Professional: P. Atherton. Secretary: B. Bradford. Proprietors: Kate and David Phillips.

PERRANPORTH. **Perranporth Golf Club,** Budnick Hill, Perranporth (Truro (0872) 572454). Seaside course overlooking Perranporth and beach. 18 holes, 6208 yards. S.S.S. 70. Par 72. *Green Fees:* information on request. *Eating facilities:* lunch and dinner. *Visitors:* welcome without reservation. Concessionary rates from selected holiday accommodation. *Society Meetings:* catered for with advance notice; concessionary rates. Professional: D. Michell. Secretary: P.D.R. Barnes (0872 573701).

REDRUTH. **Radnor Golf Centre,** Radnor Road, Treleigh, Redruth TR16 5EL (Redruth (0209) 211059). *Location:* two miles north east of Redruth, signposted from A3047 at Treleigh and North Country crossroads. Purpose-built Par 3 – interesting layout. 9 holes, 1312 yards. S.S.S. 27. Covered floodlit 18-bay driving range. *Green fees:* £3.25 for 9 holes. *Eating facilities:* planned for late 1990. *Visitors:* welcome, public facility. Professional: Gordon Wallbank.

SALTASH. **St. Mellion Golf and Country Club,** Nr. Saltash PL12 6SD (Liskeard (0579) 50101). *Location:* Tamar Bridge. Old Course: 18 holes, 5927 yards, par 70. S.S.S. 68. Nicklaus Course. 18 holes, 6626 yards, par 72, S.S.S. 72. *Green fees:* on application. *Eating facilities:* many within club complex. *Visitors:* welcome, Handicap Certificate required. *Society Meetings:* welcome. Hotel accommodation: 24 rooms, full facilities (badminton, squash, swimming, tennis, sauna, solarium, multi-gym). Golf Director: D.M. Webb. Professional: Tony Moore (0579 50724).

ST. AUSTELL. **Carlyon Bay Hotel Golf Course,** Carlyon Bay, St. Austell (072681 2340 extension 411). *Location:* on the coast in the centre of the Cornish Riviera. Clifftop, spectacular views, undulating. 18 holes, 6505 yards. S.S.S. 71. Two practice grounds. *Green Fees:* weekdays £13.50, weekends £15.50. *Eating facilities:* bar and restaurant open 11.30am to 11.00pm. *Visitors:* welcome, starting times bookable by phoning Professional. Accommodation available in four star hotel. *Society Meetings:* catered for, playing times bookable by phoning Professional. Professional: Nigel Sears (072681 4228).

ST. AUSTELL. **St. Austell Golf Club,** Tregongeeves, Tregongeeves Lane, St. Austell PL26 7DS (St. Austell (0726) 72649). *Location:* one mile west of St. Austell on A390 St. Austell to Truro road. Parkland course. 18 holes, 5981 yards. S.S.S. 69. *Green Fees:* Information on request. *Eating facilities:* full service; arrange for Hot Meals before play. *Visitors:* welcome with reservation, must be club members and hold Handicap Certificate. *Society Meetings:* catered for weekdays by arrangement. Professional: M. Rowe (0726 68621). Secretary: S.H. Davey (0726 74756).

ST. IVES. **West Cornwall Golf Club,** Lelant, St. Ives TR26 3DZ (0736 753319). *Location:* two miles from St. Ives. 18 holes, 5854 yards. S.S.S. 68. Practice ground. *Green Fees:* weekdays £12.00 round, £18.00 per day; weekends £18.00. Weekly £50.00. *Eating facilities:* bar and restaurant. *Visitors:* must be golf club members with Handicap Certificate. Professional: P. Atherton (0736 753177). Secretary: W.S. Richards (0736 753401).

TORPOINT. **Whitsand Bay Hotel Golf Club,** Portwrinkle, Torpoint (St. Germans (0503) 30470). *Location:* on coast six miles from Torpoint. Clifftop course. 18 holes, 5796 yards. S.S.S. 68. *Green Fees:* weekdays £10.00, weekends £12.00. *Eating facilities:* clubhouse and hotel. *Visitors:* welcome at all times with Handicap Certificate. Swimming, etc on application to Hotel. *Society Meetings:* catered for on application to Hotel or Secretary. Professional: D.S. Poole (0503 30778). Secretary: G.G. Dyer (0503 30418). Hotel: (0503 30276).

TRURO. **Truro Golf Club,** Treliske, Truro TR1 3LG (Truro (0872) 72640). *Location:* two miles west of Truro on A390 to Redruth. Undulating parkland. 18 holes, 5357 yards. S.S.S. 66. *Green Fees:* weekdays £15.00 per day or round, weekends and Bank Holidays £18.00 per day or round. *Eating facilities:* available. *Visitors:* welcome with Handicap Certificates but restrictions on competition days, Tuesdays and weekends. *Society Meetings:* catered for on weekdays. Professional: N.K. Bicknell (0872 76595). Secretary: B.E. Heggie (0872 78684).

WADEBRIDGE. **St. Enodoc Golf Club,** Rock, Wadebridge (Trebetherick (020 886) 3216). *Location:* B3314 from Wadebridge. Left at St. Minver to Rock. Two 18 hole courses, 6207 yards and 4165 yards. S.S.S. 70 and 61. *Green Fees:* information not provided. *Eating facilities:* sandwiches and lunches by arrangement. *Visitors:* members of recognised golf clubs welcome. Handicap certificates will be required for main course. *Society Meetings:* catered for by arrangement. Professional: N.J. Williams. Secretary: L. Guy.

Isles of Scilly

ST MARY'S. **Isles of Scilly Golf Club,** St. Mary's, Isles of Scilly (0720 22692). *Location:* one mile from Hugh Town. 9 holes, 2987 yards. Par 72. S.S.S. 69. Moorland course by the sea, with magnificent views. *Green Fees:* information not available. *Eating facilities:* lunches and evening meals available. *Visitors:* welcome; Sunday play with member only. Professional: Mary Holway. Hon Secretary: P.H. Holway (0720 22050).

Cumbria

ALSTON. **Alston Moor Golf Club,** The Hermitage, Middleton Teesdale Road, Alston (0434 381675). *Location:* one-and-three-quarter miles from Alston on B6277 to Barnard Castle. Parkland (highest golf course in England). 9 holes, 6400 yards. S.S.S. 64. Practice ground. *Green Fees:* weekdays £4.00, weekends £5.00. £1.00 discount with member. *Eating facilities:* bar – food available by prior notice. *Visitors:* welcome without reservation. *Society Meetings:* welcome by arrangement. Secretary: A. Dodd (0434 381242).

APPLEBY. **Appleby Golf Club,** Brackenber Moor, Appleby-in-Westmorland (Appleby (07683) 51432). *Location:* off A66 at Coupland Beck, two miles south of Appleby. Moorland course. 18 holes, 5914 yards. S.S.S. 68. *Green Fees:* information not provided. *Eating facilities:* available except Tuesdays. *Visitors:* welcome without reservation. *Society Meetings:* catered for by prior arrangement. Secretary: B.W. Rimmer.

ASKAM-IN-FURNESS. **Dunnerholme Golf Club,** Duddon Road, Askam-in-Furness (Dalton (0229) 62675). *Location:* A590; over crossing gates at Askam, towards the beach, turn right over cattle grid. Seaside links. 10 holes, 6181 yards. S.S.S. 69. *Green fees:* information not provided. *Eating facilities:* bar snacks every day during season. *Visitors:* welcome without reservation, excluding competition days. *Society Meetings:* catered for. Secretary: J.H. Mutton.

BARROW-IN-FURNESS. **Barrow Golf Club,** Rakesmoor, Hawcoat, Barrow-in-Furness LA14 4QB (Barrow (0229) 25444). *Location:* one mile from Barrow town centre, turn right first traffic lights into town then one mile. 18 holes, 6209yards, 5679 metres. S.S.S. 70. *Green Fees:* £10.00 per day, £6.00 if playing with a member. *Eating facilities:* available; bar. *Visitors:* welcome without reservation, must be members of recognised golf club. *Society Meetings:* catered for up to 40. Professional: M. Booth (0229 31212). Secretary: I. Booth (0229 35213).

BARROW-IN-FURNESS. **Furness Golf Club,** Central Drive, Walney Island, Barrow-in-Furness LA14 3LN (Dalton (0229) 41232). *Location:* A590 into Barrow, follow sign to Walney Island Bridge crossing. Proceed straight ahead towards the shore. Seaside links. 18 holes, white 6363, yellow 5965 yards. S.S.S. 71. Practice area. *Green Fees:* £10.00 daily (£8.00 with member); Societies £6.00 per head for parties numbering over 12. *Eating facilities:* by arrangement with Steward. *Visitors:* welcome without reservation. Ladies' Day – Wednesdays, Competition Days – Saturdays or Sundays throughout summer, March/October. *Society Meetings:* catered for by arrangement by letter to Secretary. Professional: K. Bosward. Secretary: W.T. French.

BRAMPTON. **Brampton Golf Club,** Talkin Tarn, Brampton CA8 1HN (Brampton (06977) 2255). *Location:* situated on the Brampton-Castle Carrock road (B6413), approximately one-and-a-half miles from Brampton. Rolling fell countryside, excellent views. 18 holes, 6420 yards. S.S.S. 71. *Green fees:* weekends £14.00, midweek £10.00. Practice facilities available plus snooker and pool tables. *Eating facilities:* catering available every day during playing season and on most days during winter period. *Visitors:* welcome without reservation, but should avoid Sunday, Monday, Wednesday and Thursday mornings. *Society Meetings:* catered for, limited numbers at weekends. Contact for visiting societies, J.F. Swift (0228 36699). Professional: S. Harrison (06977 2000). Secretary: Ian J. Meldrum (0228 23155).

CARLISLE. **Carlisle Golf Club,** Aglionby, Carlisle CA4 8AG (Scotby (0228) 513303). *Location:* Exit M6 at Junction 43, turn east for half-a-mile, course on right. 18 holes, 6278 yards. S.S.S. 70. *Green fees:* £15.00 per day. *Eating facilities:* snacks, lunches, dinners and high teas. *Visitors:* welcome Mondays, Wednesdays and Fridays. *Society Meetings:* catered for Mondays, Wednesdays and Fridays. Professional: John S. More (0228 513241). Administrator/Secretary: J. Hook.

CARLISLE. **Stoneyholme Municipal Golf Club,** St. Aidans Road, Carlisle (Carlisle (0228) 33208). *Location:* off A69 between M6 junction 42 and town. Parkland course, 18 holes, 6000 yards. S.S.S. 68. Large practice area, changing rooms. *Green fees:* information not available. *Eating facilities:* bar and restaurant. *Visitors:* welcome without reservation, but booking advisable weekends and Bank Holidays. *Society Meetings:* welcome by prior arrangement. Professional: Stephen Ling (0228 34856).

CARNFORTH. **Silverdale Golf Club,** Redbridge Lane, Silverdale, Carnforth LA5 0SP (Silverdale (0524) 701300). *Location:* M6 to Carnforth, then two miles west, adjacent to railway station. 9 holes, 5256 yards. S.S.S. 67. *Green Fees:* weekdays £6.00, weekends and Bank Holidays £10.00. *Eating facilities:* limited. *Visitors:* welcome with restrictions on Wednesdays, Ladies' Day and Sundays, competitions. *Society Meetings:* welcome by arrangement with Secretary. Secretary: E.F. Wright (05395 63782).

EMBLETON. **Cockermouth Golf Club,** The Clubhouse, Embleton, Near Cockermouth CA13 9SG (Bassenthwaite Lake (059-681) 223). *Location:* second exit A66 to Embleton across Old Road and up 1:5 hill. Scenic fell land course. 18 holes, 5457 yards. S.S.S. 67. *Green Fees:* weekdays £6.00, weekends and Bank Holidays £8.00. *Eating facilities:* meals by arrangement with Stewardess. *Visitors:* welcome with restrictions at weekends. *Society Meetings:* catered for if members of bona fide golf clubs. Secretary: R.D. Pollard (0900 822650).

GRANGE-OVER-SANDS. **Grange Fell Golf Club,** Fell Road, Grange-over-Sands (05395 32536). *Location:* Cartmel Road from Grange one mile. 9 holes, 4826 metres. S.S.S. 66. *Green Fees:* weekdays £10.00, weekends and Bank Holidays £15.00. *Visitors:* welcome without reservation. *Society Meetings:* not catered for. Secretary: J.B. Asplin.

GRANGE-OVER-SANDS. **Grange-Over-Sands Golf Club,** Meathop Road, Grange-over-Sands LA11 6QX (Grange-over-Sands (05395) 33180). *Location:* leave the A590 at roundabout signposted Grange, take the B5277 for approximately three miles. Flat parkland. 18 holes, 5670 yards, 5183 metres. S.S.S. 68. Practice area. *Green Fees:* weekdays £10.00, weekends and Bank Holidays £13.00. *Eating facilities:* diningroom, bar open every day except Tuesdays. *Visitors:* welcome without reservation weekdays and most weekends. *Society Meetings:* by arrangement. Secretary: J.R. Green (05395 32039).

KENDAL. **Kendal Golf Club,** The Heights, Kendal (0539 724079). *Location:* off A6 at Town Hall, signposted. 18 holes, 5483 yards. S.S.S. 67. *Green Fees:* £12.00 (£6.00 with member), weekends £16.00 (£8.00 with member). *Eating facilities:* meals available any day except Mondays. *Visitors:* welcome without reservation. Professional: D.J. Turner. Secretary: E.F. Millar.

KESWICK. **Keswick Golf Club,** Threlkeld Hall, Keswick CA12 4HH (Threlkeld (07687) 83324). *Location:* four miles from Keswick on A66 road to Penrith. Scenic fell and parkland course. 18 holes, 6175 yards. S.S.S. 72, Par 71. Extensive practice area. *Green Fees:* weekdays £10.00, weekends £12.00. *Eating facilities:* by arrangement; bar. *Visitors:* welcome. *Society Meetings:* welcome, by arrangement. Professional: Harry Waller. Hon. Secretary: Donald S. Cowen (07687 72147 or 83324).

KIRKBY LONSDALE. **Kirkby Lonsdale Golf Club,** Casterton Road, Kirkby Lonsdale (Kirkby Lonsdale (05242) 72085). *Location:* one mile on Sedbergh road. 9 holes, 4058 yards. *Green Fees:* information not provided. *Visitors:* unrestricted. Secretary: P. Jackson.

MARYPORT. **Maryport Golf Club,** Bankend, Maryport (Maryport (0900) 812605). *Location:* adjacent to beach. Links course. 11 holes, 18 tees. 6272 yards. S.S.S. 71. *Green Fees:* weekdays £8.00, weekends £10.00. *Eating facilities:* by arrangement. *Visitors:* welcome without reservation. *Society Meetings:* catered for. Secretary: N.H. Cook (0900 815652).

MILLOM. **Silecroft Golf Club,** Silecroft, Millom (0657 774250). *Location:* junction of A595 and A5093, eight miles north of Broughton-in-Furness. 9 holes, 18 tees, 5712 yards. S.S.S. 68. *Green Fees:* £5.00, at all times. *Visitors:* welcome without reservation except Bank Holidays. Secretary: M.O'N. Wilson (0657 774160).

PENRITH. **Penrith Golf Club,** Salkeld Road, Penrith CA11 8SG (Penrith (0768) 62217). *Location:* one mile from A6 to east of town. 18 holes, 6026 yards, 5510 metres. S.S.S. 69. *Green Fees:* weekdays £12.00, weekends and Bank Holidays £15.00. *Eating facilities:* new dining facilities, excellent cuisine. *Visitors:* welcome with Handicap Certificate. Tee reservation is required at weekends and telephone inquiries advisable weekdays. No visitors to start after 4 pm during the week. *Society Meetings:* catered for, parties unlimited weekdays, up to 30 at weekends. Professional: C.B. Thomson. Secretary: J. Carruthers (0768) 62217).

SEASCALE. **Seascale Golf Club,** The Banks, Seascale (Seascale (09467) 28202). *Location:* B5344 off A595. 18 holes, 6416 yards. S.S.S. 71. *Green Fees:* £12.00 per day, £15.00 weekends and Bank Holidays. *Eating facilities:* daily except Tuesday when limited only. *Visitors:* welcome without reservation. *Society Meetings:* catered for. Secretary: C. Taylor.

SEDBERGH. **Sedbergh Golf Club,** The Riggs, Sedbergh (05396 20993). *Location:* one mile south of Sedbergh on road to Dent. Very hilly course, with panoramic views. 9 holes, 4134 yards. S.S.S. 61. *Green Fees:* £3.00 any day. *Eating facilities:* not available on course. *Visitors:* welcome at all times, no trolleys. Secretary: A.D. Lord (05396 20993).

SILLOTH. **Silloth on Solway Golf Club,** The Clubhouse, Silloth (Silloth (0965) 31179). *Location:* travelling north on M6, leave motorway at Junction 41. Wigton to Silloth. Links course with beautiful greens. 18 holes, 6343 yards. S.S.S. 71. *Green Fees:* weekdays £14.00, weekends and Bank Holidays £20.00. Restriction, only one round allowed per day at weekends. *Eating facilities:* excellent catering. *Visitors:* welcome without reservation. Special package deals including accommodation in local hotels. Professional: John Burns. Secretary: G.S. Hartley (0965 31304).

ULVERSTON. **Ulverston Golf Club Ltd,** Bardsea Park, Ulverston LA12 9QJ (Ulverston (0229) 52824). *Location:* Exit 36, M6. A590 to Barrow then A5087 to Bardsea village. Wooded parkland. 18 holes, 6142 yards. S.S.S. 69. Large practice ground. *Green Fees:* weekdays £12.00, weekends and Bank Holidays £15.00 November to February; weekdays £15.00, weekends and Bank Holidays £18.00 March to October. Juniors half price. *Eating facilities:* lunch and bar snacks (excluding Mondays). *Visitors:* welcome except Saturdays (Competition Day), and Tuesdays, Ladies' day. Must be members of accredited golf club. *Society Meetings:* welcome with reservation. Professional: M.R. Smith (0229 52806). Secretary: Mr D. Weston.

WHITEHAVEN. **St. Bees Golf Club,** Whitehaven (Whitehaven (0946) 822695). *Location:* four miles south of Whitehaven. 9 holes, 5079 yards. S.S.S. 65. *Green Fees:* information not provided. *Visitors:* unrestricted. Secretary: J.B. Campbell, Rhoda Grove, Rheda, Frizington CA26 3TE (0946 812105).

WINDERMERE. **Windermere Golf Club,** Cleabarrow, Windermere LA23 3NB (Windermere (09662) 3123). *Location:* one mile from Bowness-on-Windermere on Crook road, B5284. Idyllic National Park setting. 18 holes, 5006 yards. S.S.S. 65. Practice ground. *Green Fees:* weekdays £15.00, weekends £20.00. *Eating facilities:* catering provided daily except Mondays; lounge/bar daily. *Visitors:* welcome with bona fide handicaps and if members of recognised golf clubs. *Society Meetings:* catered for by prior arrangement with Secretary, numbers from twelve to 50. Professional: W.S.M. Rooke (09662 3550). Secretary: K.R. Moffat (09662 3123).

WORKINGTON. **Workington Golf Club Ltd,** Branthwaite Road, Workington (Workington (0900) 3460). *Location:* on A596, two miles east of town. Meadowland. 18 holes, 6252 yards. S.S.S. 70. *Green Fees:* weekdays £10.00, weekends and Bank Holidays £15.00. *Eating facilities:* lunches and dinners except Mondays and Thursdays. *Visitors:* welcome without reservation, must be members of recognised golf club. *Society Meetings:* welcome by prior arrangement. Professional: N. Summerfield (0900 67828). Secretary: J.K. Walker.

Derbyshire

ALFRETON. **Alfreton Golf Club,** Wingfield Road, Alfreton (Alfreton (0773) 832070). *Location:* B6024 (Matlock Road) one mile from Alfreton. 9 holes, 5012 yards. S.S.S. 65. *Green Fees:* £8.50 per round, £10.00 per day. *Eating facilities:* lunches except Mondays. *Visitors:* welcome with reservation. *Society Meetings:* catered for. Secretary: D. Tomlinson.

ASHBOURNE. **Ashbourne Golf Club Ltd,** Clifton, Ashbourne (Ashbourne (0335) 42078). *Location:* on A515 Ashbourne to Lichfield. 9 holes, 5388 yards. S.S.S. 66. *Green Fees:* weekdays £6.00, weekends and Bank Holidays £10.00. *Eating facilities:* catering available by prior arrangement with Steward; bar. *Visitors:* welcome. *Society Meetings:* small groups catered for. Secretary: N.P.A. James (0335 42077).

BAKEWELL. **Bakewell Golf Club,** Station Road, Bakewell (Bakewell (062-981) 2307). 9 holes, 5600 yards. S.S.S. 66. *Green Fees:* information not provided. *Eating facilities:* meals available during bar opening times. *Visitors:* welcome all week. Professional: T.E. Jones. Secretary: T.P. Turner.

BUXTON. **Buxton and High Peak Golf Club,** Town End, Buxton (Buxton (0298) 3453). *Location:* on A6 to Chapel-en-le-Frith. 18 holes. S.S.S. 69. *Green Fees:* information not provided. *Eating facilities:* full catering available. *Visitors:* welcome without reservation. *Society Meetings:* catered for. Professional: A. Wardle. Secretary: B. Webb.

BUXTON. **Cavendish Golf Club Ltd,** Gadley Lane, off Watford Road, Buxton SK17 6XD (0298 23494). *Location:* one mile west of town centre, north of A53 and south of A5002, both signposted. Parkland, designed by Dr McEnzie who designed Augusta. 18 holes, 5833 yards. S.S.S. 68. *Green Fees:* £15.00 per round, £17.00 per day weekdays; £24.00 per round weekends. *Eating facilities:* restaurant and bar snacks. *Visitors:* welcome anytime but always ring before coming. *Society Meetings:* catered for weekdays only (contact Professional). Professional: John Nolan (0298 25052). Secretary: S. Doyle-Davidson (0298 23494).

CHAPEL-EN-LE-FRITH. **Chapel-en-le-Frith Golf Club,** The Cockyard, Manchester Road, Chapel-en-le-Frith SK12 6UH (0298 812118). *Location:* midway between Sheffield and Manchester, 25 miles from each on the B5470. Parkland, scenic. 18 holes, 6065 yards.

S.S.S. 69. Practice ground. *Green Fees:* weekdays £10.00, weekends £15.00. *Eating facilities:* all meals daily except Mondays. *Visitors:* welcome, small numbers without reservation. *Society Meetings:* catered for by arrangement. Professional: D. Cullen (0298 812118). Secretary: J.W. Dranfield (0298 813943).

CHESTERFIELD. **Chesterfield Golf Club Ltd,** The Clubhouse, Walton, Chesterfield S42 7LA (Chesterfield (0246) 232035). *Location:* two miles from town centre on Chesterfield to Matlock road (A632). Parkland. 18 holes, 6326 yards. S.S.S. 70. Practice ground. *Green Fees:* weekdays £15.00 per round, £20.00 per day; weekends £10.00 with member only. *Eating facilities:* full catering, two bars. *Visitors:* weekdays only. *Society Meetings:* catered for on application except weekends. Professional: Michael McLean (0246 276297). Secretary: A. Bonsall (0246 279256).

CHESTERFIELD. **Stanedge Golf Club,** Walton Hay Farm, Walton, Chesterfield S45 0LW (Chesterfield (0246) 566156). *Location:* five miles south-west of Chesterfield, off B5057 near "Red Lion" public house. 9 holes, 4867 yards. S.S.S. 64. *Green Fees:* weekdays £8.00, £4.00 with member; Saturdays and Bank Holidays £5.00, must be playing with member. *Visitors:* welcome by prior arrangement. No visitors on Sundays until 4 p.m. and they must be with member. *Society Meetings:* catered for by prior arrangement. Secretary: W.C. Tyzack (0246 276568).

CHESTERFIELD. **Tapton Park Golf Club,** Murray House, Crow Lane, Chesterfield (0246 273887). *Location:* into Chesterfield turn left at railway station. Parkland course. 18 holes, 5982 yards. S.S.S. 69. Also 9 hole course, 2478 yards. *Green Fees:* weekdays £3.00, weekends £4.00. *Eating facilities:* meals and bar all day, closed 3pm-7pm on Sundays. *Visitors:* welcome without reservation. *Society Meetings:* welcome with reservations. Municipal course, open to general public. Professional: John Delaney (0246 273887). Secretary: H. Longdon (0246 235503).

CODNOR. **Ormonde Fields Golf & Country Club,** Clubhouse, Nottingham Road, Codnor, Ripley DE5 9RG (0773 744157). *Location:* five miles M1 Junction 26 towards Ripley on A610. Parkland. 18 holes, 6000 yards. S.S.S. 69. Practice area. *Green Fees:* £10.00 weekdays, £15.00 weekends. *Eating facilities:* full catering available. *Visitors:* unrestricted. *Society Meetings:* catered for; book through Secretary. Professional: Simon Illingworth (0773 742987). Secretary: R.N. Walters (0773 744157).

DERBY. **Allestree Park Golf Club,** Derby (Derby (0332) 550616). *Location:* 2 miles north of Derby on A6. Municipal course, parkland. 18 holes, 5749 yards. S.S.S. 68. *Green Fees:* £3.50 weekdays, £4.60 weekends. Professional: R. Brown. Secretary: R.S. Hill.

DERBY. **Breadsall Priory Golf and Country Club,** Moor Road, Morley DE7 6DL (0332 832534). *Location:* when turning off the A61 towards Breadsall proceed on Croft Lane, turn left into Rectory Lane, then bear right onto Moor Road, continue past the Church for approximately one mile. Undulating parkland. 18 holes, 5963 yards. S.S.S. 69. *Green Fees:* £18.00. *Eating facilities:* restaurant and poolside grill room. *Visitors:* welcome by prior arrangement, starting times MUST be booked in advance. *Society Meetings:* catered for by prior arrangement. Accommodation, leisure club and conference facilities. Professional: Andrew Smith (0332 834425). Secretary: Thelma Mortimer (0332 832235).

DUFFIELD. **Chevin Golf Club,** Golf Lane, Duffield DE6 4EE (0332 840497). *Location:* five miles north of Derby on A6 at Duffield village. Hilly course. 18 holes, 6057 yards, 5451 metres. S.S.S. 69. Two practice areas. *Green Fees:* £20.00 per day. *Eating facilities:* full catering and bar. *Visitors:* welcome weekdays, Handicap Certificates required. *Society Meetings:* welcome weekdays, but never Saturdays, very limited on Sundays. Professional: W. Bird (0332 841112). Secretary: C.P. Elliott (0332 841864).

GLOSSOP. **Glossop and District Golf Club,** Glossop (Glossop (045-74) 3117). Location: off A57, one mile from town centre. Moorland course, 9 holes, 5726 yards. S.S.S. 68. *Green Fees:* information not provided. *Eating facilities:* arranged with Steward. *Visitors:* welcome with reservation. Professional: L. Turner. Secretary: J. Dickson.

ILKESTON. **Erewash Valley Golf Club,** Stanton-by-Dale, Near Ilkeston (Ilkeston (0602) 322984). *Location:* from M1 Junction 25 follow signs to Sandiacre. 18 holes, 6487 yards. S.S.S. 71 plus par 3 course. *Green Fees:* £15.00 weekdays, £18.00 weekends and Bank Holidays. *Eating facilities:* dining room service available with advance booking (0602 323258), bar snacks at all times. *Visitors:* welcome all week. *Society Meetings:* by arrangement. Professional: Mike Ronan. Secretary: D. Knowles.

ILKESTON. **Ilkeston Borough Golf Club,** Peewit Municipal Golf Course, West End Drive, Ilkeston (0602 304550). *Location:* one mile west of Ilkeston market place. Slightly hilly meadowland. 9 holes, 4116 yards. S.S.S. 60. *Green Fees:* £4.00 per round. *Eating facilities:* not available. *Visitors:* welcome, no restrictions. Secretary: S.J. Rossington (0602 320304).

MATLOCK. **Matlock Golf Club Ltd,** Chesterfield Road, Matlock DE4 5LF (Matlock (0629) 582191). *Location:* Matlock-Chesterfield road, A632, one mile out of Matlock, left hand side main road. 18 holes,

yellow tees, 5756 yards. S.S.S. 68. *Green Fees:* weekdays £15.00 per round or day; weekends and Bank Holidays £10.00 with a member only. *Eating facilities:* snacks, luncheons and evening meals by arrangement (except on Mondays). *Visitors:* welcome weekdays. *Society Meetings:* catered for Tuesday to Friday. Professional: M. Deeley (0629 584934). Secretary: A.J. Box.

MICKLEOVER. **Mickleover Golf Club,** Uttoxeter Road, Mickleover, Derby (Derby (0332) 513339). *Location:* three miles west of Derby on the A516/B5020 to Uttoxeter. Undulating course. 18 holes, 5708 yards. S.S.S. 68. *Green Fees:* weekdays £13.00, weekends and Bank Holidays £15.00. *Eating facilities:* coffee, lunches and dinners. *Visitors:* welcome, no restrictions – telephone Professional before arrival. *Society Meetings:* Tuesdays and Thursdays. Professional: Paul Wilson (0332 518662). Secretary: Doug Rodgers (0332 512092).

MICKLEOVER. **Pastures Golf Club,** Pastures Hospital, Mickleover (0332 513921 extension 419). *Location:* four miles west of Derby. Undulating meadowland. 9 holes, 5005 yards. S.S.S. 64. Practice area. *Green Fees:* £7.00 weekdays and Saturdays, no green fees Sundays. *Eating facilities:* bar facilities/snacks. *Visitors:* welcome everyday except Sundays and must be with a member. *Society Meetings:* by arrangement. Secretary: S. McWilliams (0332 513921 extension 348).

QUARNDON. **Kedleston Park Golf Club,** Kedleston, Quarndon, Derby DE6 4JD. *Location:* four miles north of Derby on Kedleston Hall Estate – National Trust. Parkland with lakes. 18 holes, 6636 yards, 6068 metres. S.S.S. 72. *Green Fees:* weekdays £20.00 per round, £25.00 per day. *Eating facilities:* full catering, bars. *Visitors:* welcome Monday to Friday. *Society Meetings:* welcome Monday to Friday. Professional: J. Hetherington (0332 841685). Secretary: K. Wilson (0332 840035).

SHEFFIELD. **Renishaw Park Golf Club,** Golf House, Renishaw, Sheffield S31 9UZ (Eckington (0246) 432044). *Location:* A616 Barlborough (Junction 30 M1) to Sheffield. Parkland/meadowland. 18 holes, 6253 yards. S.S.S. 70. Practice net. *Green Fees:* weekdays £13.50 round, £15.50 day without member; with member £6.00 round, £8.00 day. Weekends: without member £17.00 round, £21.00 day; with member £8.50 round, £11.00 day. *Eating facilities:* bar meals, full restaurant, full bar available. *Visitors:* welcome without reservation (advisable to ring Pro prior to arrival). *Society Meetings:* by prior arrangement. Full day package available. Professional: S. Elliott (0246 435484). Secretary: D.G. Rossington (0246 432044).

SHEFFIELD. **Sickleholme Golf Club,** Bamford, Sheffield S30 2BH (Hope Valley (0433) 51306). *Location:* A625 west of Sheffield, right at Marquis of Granby, Bamford. 18 holes, 6064 yards. S.S.S. 69. *Green Fees:* weekdays £15.00, weekends £20.00. *Eating facilities:* by arrangement. *Visitors:* must be members of a recognised Golf Club. *Society Meetings:* catered for by arrangement. Professional: P. H. Taylor (0433 51252). Secretary: W.T.N. Scott (0433 51306).

SHIRLAND. **Shirland Golf Club,** Lower Delves, Shirland DE5 6AU (Alfreton (0773) 834969/834935). *Location:* 1 mile North of Alfreton off A61, three miles from M1 junction 28 via A38. Tree-lined rolling parkland, 18 holes, 5948 yards. S.S.S. 68. Par 71. Two practice grounds. *Green Fees:* £10.00 per round, £18.00 per day weekdays; £15.00 per round weekends. *Eating facilities:* full restaurant, bar meals. Conference and banquet rooms. *Visitors:* unrestricted weekdays, but must book through Professional at weekends. County standard bowling green avialble. *Society Meetings:* welcome. Secretary: Mrs. C. S. Fincham (0773 832515). Professional: N.B. Hallam (0773 834935).

SINFIN. **Derby Golf Club,** Sinfin, Derby (Derby (0332) 766323). *Location:* two miles town centre. 18 holes, 6223 yards. S.S.S. 70. *Green Fees:* information not provided. *Eating facilities:* light meals only. *Visitors:* welcome without reservation. Professional: R. Brown. Secretary: P. Davidson.

STOCKPORT. **New Mills Golf Club,** Shaw Marsh, New Mills (New Mills (0663) 743485). *Location:* off A6015. 9 holes, 5633 yards. S.S.S. 67. *Green Fees:* £8 weekdays only. *Eating facilities:* catering except Thursdays. *Visitors:* welcome weekdays with reservation, weekends with members. No visitors competition days. *Society Meetings:* no catering Thursdays, catered for by appointment. Professional: Andrew Hoyles. Secretary: R. Tuson.

Devon

AXMOUTH. **Axe Cliff Golf Club,** Squires Lane, Axmouth, Seaton EX12 2BJ (0297) 20499). *Location:* A35 from Lyme Regis, turn left on to B3172 at junction with A358 Seaton. Seaside wooded course. 18 holes, 5111 yards. S.S.S. 65. *Green Fees:* weekdays £10.00, weekends £12.00. *Eating facilities:* dining room. Hot meals/snacks, etc. *Visitors:* welcome without reservation, some restrictions Wednesdays and weekends. *Society Meetings:* catered for, apply Secretary. Secretary: Y.G. Keep (0297 24371).

BIGBURY. **Bigbury Golf Club Ltd,** Bigbury, Kingsbridge TQ7 4BB (Bigbury on Sea (0548) 810207). *Location:* off main Plymouth to Kingsbridge road, turn right at Harraton Cross. two courses: No 1 – 18 holes, 5793 yards. S.S.S. 68. No. 2 (Comp) – 18 holes, 6076 yards. S.S.S. 69. *Green Fees:* £15.00 per person per day. *Eating facilities:* buffet catering always available: medium to full catering order in advance. *Visitors:* welcome. *Society Meetings:* catered for by prior arrangement. Professional: Simon Lloyd. Secretary: B.J. Perry (0548 810557).

BRAUNTON. **Saunton Golf Club,** Saunton, Braunton (0271 812436). *Location:* eight miles west of Barnstaple on Linksland at north side of Barnstaple Bay. East course 18 holes, 6703 yards. S.S.S. 73. West course 18 holes, 6356 yards. S.S.S. 71. *Green Fees:* weekdays £17.00, weekends £20.00. Weekly £85.00. *Eating facilities:* Full catering available. *Visitors:* welcome with reservation, must be members of another golf club and must be able to produce Handicap Certificate. *Society Meetings:* catered for by arrangement. Professional: J.A. McGhee (0271 812013). Secretary: W.E. Geddes (0271 812436).

BRIXHAM. **Churston Golf Club,** Churston, Brixham (0803 842218). *Location:* situated between Paignton and Brixham on the main road. 18 holes, 6243 yards. S.S.S. 70. Seaside course overlooking Torbay. *Green Fees:* weekdays £20.00, weekends £25.00. *Eating facilities:* available all day. *Visitors:* welcome, must be members of recognised club. *Society Meetings:* catered for by arrangement. Professional: Richard Penfold (0803 842894). Secretary: A.M. Chaundy (0803 842751).

BUDLEIGH SALTERTON. **East Devon Golf Club,** North View Road, Budleigh Salterton EX9 6DQ (Budleigh Salterton (03954) 2018). *Location:* three miles from Exmouth. Heathland, 18 holes, 6214 yards. S.S.S. 70. *Green Fees:* weekdays £20.00, weekends £25.00. *Eating facilities:* meals and snacks available every day except Mondays. *Visitors:* welcome with letter of introduction, Handicap Certificate or Devon County card. *Society Meetings:* catered for by arrangement. Professional: Trevor Underwood (03954 5195). Secretary: J.C. Tebbet (03954 3370).

CHULMLEIGH. **Chulmleigh Golf Course,** Leigh Road, Chulmleigh (Chulmleigh (0769) 80519). *Location:* midway between Barnstaple and Exeter on A377. Undulating course. 18 holes, 1450 yards. 6214 yards. Mid December to end of March 9 holes x 2, 2352 yards. *Green Fees:* £3.50 per round, 2 rounds £5.00. Day ticket £7.00. *Eating facilities:* snacks, bar. *Visitors:* welcome. *Society Meetings:* welcome by prior arrangement. Owner/Secretary: P.N. Callow.

CREDITON. **Downes Crediton Golf Club,** Hookway, Crediton (Crediton (03632) 3991). *Location:* off Crediton-Exeter road. Part flat, part hilly course featuring woods and water. 18 holes, 5758 yards. S.S.S. 68. *Green Fees:* £12.00 weekdays, £15.00 weekends. *Eating facilities:* available from 11.30am to one hour before bar closes. *Visitors:* welcome, advisable to phone first. *Society Meetings:* by arrangement. Professional: Howard Finch (03632 4464). Secretary: W.J. Brooks (03632 3025).

DAWLISH. **Warren Golf Club,** Dawlish (0626 862255). *Location:* 12 miles from Exeter off A379. Typical flat links course lying on split between sea and Exe estuary. 18 holes, 5576 yards. Par 69, S.S.S. 69. *Green Fees:* weekdays £12.00, weekends £14.00. *Visitors:* welcome with reservation. *Society Meetings:* welcome by arrangement. Professional: Geoff Wicks. Secretary: T. Allen.

EXETER. **Exeter Golf and Country Club,** Countess Wear, Exeter EX2 7AE (0392 874139). *Location:* near M5, exit Junction 30. Parkland course. 18 holes, 5993 yards. S.S.S. 69. Practice ground. *Green Fees:* £17.00 weekdays. *Eating facilities:* sports bar, lounge bar, diningroom. *Visitors:* welcome except Tuesdays (Ladies Day) and weekends (very busy with members), booking number 0392 876303). *Society Meetings:* catered for Thursdays only. Professional: Mike Rowett (0392 875028). Secretary: C.H.M. Greetham (0392 874139).

HOLSWORTHY. **Holsworthy Golf Club,** Kilatree, Holsworthy (Holsworthy (0409) 253177). *Location:* leave Holsworthy on Bude road, A3072; one mile on left. Parkland, 18 holes, 6025 yards. S.S.S. 69. *Green Fees:* £10.00. *Eating facilities:* snacks at bar. *Visitors:* welcome without reservation (after 12 noon on Sundays). *Society Meetings:* catered for by arrangement. Secretary: Barry Megson (0409 253701).

HONITON. **Honiton Golf Club,** Middlehills, Honiton (0404 42943). *Location:* one mile south of town proceed from New Street to Farway. Flat parkland. 18 holes, 5931 yards. S.S.S. 68. Small practice ground. *Green Fees:* weekdays 14.00 per day, weekends and Bank Holidays £17.00. *Eating facilities:* bar and restaurant. *Visitors:* bona fide members of other clubs welcome, with restrictions on Wednesdays (Ladies' day) and weekends (club competitions). *Society Meetings:* bookable on Thursdays only. Professional: Adrian Cave (0404 42943). Secretary: D. Holloway (0404 44422).

ILFRACOMBE. **Ilfracombe Golf Club,** Hele Bay, Ilfracombe EX34 9RT (0271 862050). *Location:* on main coastal road between Ilfracombe and Combe Martin. Parkland and undulating with spectacular views from every tee and green. 18 holes, 5857 yards. S.S.S. 68. Practice area and green. *Green Fees:* £12.00. *Eating facilities:* full catering available; normal club bar hours. *Visitors:* welcome (Handicap/membership Certificate preferred). Weekends until 10 a.m. and then between 12–2 p.m. with members only. *Society Meetings:* catered for, with some time restrictions. Professional: David Hoare (0271 863328). Secretary: Rodney C. Beer (0271 862176).

MORETONHAMPSTEAD. **Manor House Hotel and Golf Course,** Moretonhampstead TR13 8RE (Moretonhampstead (0647) 40355). *Location:* Junction 31 from M5, B3212 for two miles. Parkland with rivers. 18 holes, 6016 yards. S.S.S. 69. Extensive practice facilities. *Green Fees:* on application. *Eating facilities:* brunch service, cream teas, two bars. *Visitors:* welcome. Please book in advance. *Society Meetings:* by prior arrangement. Professional/Golf Manager: Richard Lewis (0647 40355).

NEWTON ABBOT. **Newton Abbot (Stover) Golf Club,** Bovey Road, Newton Abbot TQ12 6QQ (Newton Abbot (0626) 52460). *Location:* A382 three miles north of Newton Abbot. Wooded parkland with river. 18 holes, 5852 yards. S.S.S. 68. *Green Fees:* £17.00 weekdays, weekends and Bank Holidays. *Eating facilities:* full catering daily from 11.00 a.m. *Visitors:* welcome if members of recognised club. *Society Meetings:* catered for on Thursdays, parties of 24 and over. Professional: M. Craig (0626 62078). Secretary: R. Smith (0626 52460).

OKEHAMPTON. **Okehampton Golf Club,** Off Tors Road, Okehampton EX20 1EF (0837 2113) *Location:* from A30 take turning from centre of Okehampton then follow the signposts. 18 holes, 5300 yards. S.S.S. 67. *Green Fees:* weekdays £11.00, weekends £15.00. *Eating facilities:* by arrangement; bar. *Visitors:* welcome. *Society Meetings:* catered for. Professional: Philip Blundell (0837 3541). Secretary: S. Chave (0837 52113).

PLYMOUTH. **Elfordleigh Hotel, Golf and Country Club,** Near Colebrook, Plympton, Plymouth PL7 5EB (0752 336428). *Location:* one mile from Plympton. Woodland course in picturesque countryside. 9 holes, 5470 yards (twice round). S.S.S. 67. Practice area. *Green Fees:* £12.00 weekdays, £15.00 weekends. Special rates available on request. *Eating facilities:* bar meals available from Country Club bar. *Visitors:* welcome. Hotel accommodation available. *Society Meetings:* catered for by arrangement. Secretary: A.W. Dunstan (0752 703824). FAX: 0752 344581.

PLYMOUTH. **Staddon Heights Golf Club,** Staddon Heights, Plymstock, Plymouth PL9 9SP (0752 41998). *Location:* from Plymouth city follow signs to Plymstock. Seaside links. 18 holes, 5861 yards. S.S.S. 68. Practice area. *Green Fees:* weekdays £12.00, weekends £15.00. *Eating facilities:* diningroom open daily. *Visitors:* welcome except when tee booked for club competitions. *Society Meetings:* by arrangement with Secretary. Professional: John Cox (0752 492630). Secretary: Mike Holliday (0752 402475).

SIDMOUTH. **Sidmouth Golf Club,** Cotmaton Road, Peak Hill, Sidmouth EX10 8SX (0395 513023). *Location:* half a mile from town centre, 12 miles south east of M5 Junction 30. Parkland with breathtaking views over Sid Valley and Lyme Bay. 18 holes, 5800 yards. S.S.S. 65. *Green Fees:* weekdays £12.00, weekends £15.00. *Eating facilities:* catering except Tuesday, all-day bar Saturdays. *Visitors:* welcome, by arrangement with Secretary. *Society Meetings:* catered for, contact Secretary. Professional: M. Kemp (0395 516407). Secretary: I.M. Smith (0395 513451).

SOUTH BRENT. **Wrangaton (South Devon) Golf Club,** Golf Links Road, Wrangaton, South Brent TQ10 9HJ (South Brent (0364) 73229). *Location:* driving south, take next exit from A38 after South Brent. Parkland/moorland course 18 holes, 6000 yards. S.S.S 69. Practice ground and net. *Green Fees:* weekdays £10.00, weekends £15.00. *Eating facilities:* full catering and bar facilities available. *Visitors:* welcome, restricted during club competitions, Sundays until 4.30pm. *Society Meetings:* can be catered for, three months notice required. Secretary/Manager: Richard R. Hine.

TAVISTOCK. **Tavistock Golf Club,** Down Road, Tavistock PL19 9AQ (0822 612049) *Location:* Whitchurch Down one mile from Tavistock. 18 holes, 6250 yards. S.S.S. 70. *Green Fees:* £12.00 weekdays, £15.00 weekends and Bank Holidays. *Eating facilities:* full catering facilities. *Visitors:* welcome with reservation. *Society Meetings:* catered for. Professional: Richard Hall (0822 612316). Secretary: B. G. Steer (0822 612344).

TEIGNMOUTH. **Teignmouth Golf Club,** Haldon Moor, Teignmouth (Teignmouth (0626 773614). *Location:* two miles north of Teignmouth on the Exeter road. Level heathland course, panoramic views. 18 holes, 6200 yards. S.S.S. 69. *Green Fees:* information not available. *Eating facilities:* full catering service midday to 7pm. *Visitors:* welcome with reservation if members of another club with Handicap Certificate. *Society Meetings:* catered for weekdays only. Professional: P. Ward (0626 722894). Secretary: (0626 774194).

THURLESTONE. **Thurlestone Golf Club,** Thurlestone, Kingsbridge TQ7 3NZ (0548 560221). *Location:* turn off A379 near Kingsbridge. Downland with superb views. 18 holes, 6303 yards, 5818 metres. S.S.S. 70. Practice area. *Green Fees:* £15.00 per day. *Eating facilities:* catering available from 10.00 a.m. until 5.30 p.m. daily. *Visitors:* must produce Handicap Certificate, please telephone in advance. *Society Meetings:* not catered for. Professional: Neville Whitley (0548 560715). Secretary: R.W. Marston (0548 560405).

TIVERTON. **Tiverton Golf Club,** Post Hill, Tiverton EX16 4NE (Tiverton (0884) 252114). *Location:* three miles east of Tiverton, Junction 27 of M5, proceed through Sampford Peverell and Halberton. Parkland, tree lined fairways. 18 holes, 6263 yards. S.S.S. 71. *Green Fees:* on application. *Eating facilities:* snacks, lunches and teas, evening meals by arrangement. *Visitors:* welcome with reservation, Handicap Certificate or introduction required. Professional: R.E. Freeman (0884 254836). Secretary: M. Crouch (0884 252187).

TORQUAY. **Torquay Golf Club,** 30 Petitor Road, St Marychurch, Torquay (0803 314591). 18 holes, 6192 yards. S.S.S. 69. *Green Fees:* on application. *Eating facilities:* lunches and teas available. *Visitors:* welcome if members of golf clubs. *Society Meetings:* catered for. Professional: M. Ruth. Secretary: B.G. Long.

TORRINGTON. **Torrington Golf Club,** Weare Trees, Torrington EX38 7EZ (Torrington (0805) 22229). *Location:* one mile north of Torrington on Torrington to Weare Giffard road. Exposed common land with excellent views. 9 holes, 4418 yards, 4044 metres. S.S.S. 62. *Green Fees:* weekdays £8.00 per round/day; weekends £10.00 per round/day. Half green fee if with member. *Eating facilities:* light meals and bar snacks available during bar hours. *Visitors:* welcome except on Sunday mornings and during competitions. *Society Meetings:* catered for by arrangement. Secretary: Geoffrey S.C. Green (0237 472792).

WESTWARD HO!. **Royal North Devon Golf Club,** Golf Links Road, Westward Ho!, Bideford EX39 1HD (0237 473824). *Location:* A386. B3236 Bideford to Northam. Seaside links. 18 holes, 6662 yards, 6089 metres. S.S.S. 72. Practice area. *Green Fees:* weekdays £14.00, weekends £16.00. *Eating facilities:* full catering available. *Visitors:* welcome with no restrictions. *Society Meetings:* catered for. Professional: G. Johnston (0237 477598). Secretary: Capt. E.J. Davies (0237 473817).

YELVERTON. **Yelverton Golf Club,** Golf Links Road, Yelverton PL20 6BN (Yelverton (0822 853618). *Location:* eight miles north of Plymouth on A386 road. Moorland course. 18 holes, 6293 yards. S.S.S. 70. Practice ground. *Green Fees:* £14.00 weekdays, £18.00 weekends. *Eating facilities:* full catering available. *Visitors:* welcome if member of a recognised golf club or golf society. Handicap Certificate required. *Society Meetings:* catered for, welcome by arrangement with Secretary. Professional: Ian Parker (0822 853593). Secretary: Major D.R. Bettany (0822 852824).

Dorset

BLANDFORD. **Ashley Wood Golf Club,** Wimborne Road, Tarrant Rawston, Blandford (Blandford (0258) 452253). *Location:* one-and-a-half miles south of Blandford on B3082. 9 holes, 6227 yards, 5692 metres. S.S.S. 70. Practice ground. *Green Fees:* weekdays: 18 holes £12.00, with member £6.00; 36 holes £18.00, with member £9.00; weekends: 18 holes £14.00, with member £9.00; 36 holes £21.00, with member £13.50. *Eating facilities:* bar and dining area. *Visitors:* welcome without reservation except on Tuesday mornings, weekends before noon, competition and match days. *Society Meetings:* welcome by arrangement with Secretary. Professional: Spencer Taylor (0258 480379). Secretary: Peter Fry (0258 452253).

BOURNEMOUTH. **Boscombe Golf Club,** Queens Park, West Drive, Bournemouth (0202 34466). *Location:* adjacent to Wessex Bay. Ringwood/Bournemouth Spin. Three miles from town centre. Play over Queens Park course. Wooded parkland course, undulating. 28 holes, 6505 yards. S.S.S. 72. Practice area. Changing rooms. *Green Fees:* information on application. *Eating facilities:* restaurant and bar. *Visitors:* unrestricted, except Sunday p.m. *Society Meetings:* on application to Borough Parks Dept. Professional: R. Hill (0202 36817). Secretary/Manager: Joseph Burdett (0202 483017).

BOURNEMOUTH. **Bournemouth & Meyrick Park Golf Club, (Playing over Municipal course),** Meyrick Park, Bournemouth BH2 6LH (Bournemouth (0202) 290307). *Location:* one mile from town centre. Beautiful woodland. 18 holes, 5878 yards. S.S.S. 69. Practice and putting. *Green Fees:* £6.50. *Eating facilities:* clubhouse – restaurant and bar; public cafe – bar and cafe. *Visitors* welcome with a member. *Society Meetings:* catered for. Professional: (0202 290862). Secretary: Mr R. Pike.

BOURNEMOUTH. **Knighton Heath Golf Club,** Francis Avenue, Bournemouth BH11 8NX (Bournemouth (0202) 577870). *Location:* A348 and A3049 roundabout exit Francis Avenue. Undulating heathland, 18 holes, 6206 yards. S.S.S. 70. *Green Fees:* on application. *Eating facilities:* meals and bar snacks available daily, except Monday. *Visitors:* welcome with reservation, after 9.30 a.m. weekdays, 10.30 a.m. weekends with Handicap Certificate. Restrictions on competition days. *Society Meetings:* catered for if arranged in advance. Professional: M.D. Torrens (0202 578275). Secretary: R.C. Bestwick (0202 572633).

BOURNEMOUTH. **Queens Park Municipal Golf Course,** Bournemouth (Bournemouth (0202) 36198). *Location:* adjacent to Ringwood, Bournemouth Spur, three miles from town centre. 18 holes, 6250 yards. S.S.S. 70. *Green Fees:* information not provided. *Eating facilities:* lunches available daily. *Society Meetings:* catered for. Professional: J. Sharkey.

BRIDPORT. **Bridport and West Dorset Golf Club,** East Cliff, West Bay, Bridport DT6 4EP (Bridport (0308) 22597). *Location:* one and a half miles south of Bridport, east of West Bay harbour. Clifftop links course. 18 holes, 5246 yards, 4795 metres. S.S.S. 66. Practice area. *Green Fees:* weekdays £12.00, weekends £18.00. *Eating facilities:* lounge and dining-room. *Visitors:* welcome. 1991 is our Centenary Year. *Society Meetings:* catered for by prior arrangement. Professional: John Parish (0308 421491). Hon. Secretary: P.J. Ridler (0308 421095).

BROADSTONE. **Broadstone (Dorset) Golf Club,** Wentworth Drive, Off Station Approach, Broadstone BH18 8DQ (Broadstone (0202) 692595). *Location:* off A349 to B3072 to Broadstone. Heathland. 18 holes, 6183 yards. S.S.S. 70. *Green Fees:* weekdays £18.00 per round, £22.00 per day. *Eating facilities:* full catering available. *Visitors:* welcome, after 9.30 a.m. weekdays, current Handicap Certificate required. No visitors weekends. *Society Meetings:* welcome by arrange-

ment. Professional: Nigel Tokely (0202 692835). Secretary: J.M. Cowan (0202 692595).

CHRISTCHURCH. **Christchurch Golf Club,** Iford Bridge, Barrack Road (0202 473817). *Location:* boundary of Bournemouth on road to Christchurch. 9 holes, 4654 yards. S.S.S. 63. *Green Fees:* weekdays £3.80, weekends £4.30. Driving range 50 balls £1.50. *Eating facilities:* snack bar and bar. *Visitors:* welcome. (Car park.) Secretary: P.H. Miller. Professional: P. Troth.

CHRISTCHURCH. **Highcliffe Castle Golf Club,** 107 Lymington Road, Highcliffe on Sea, Christchurch BH23 4LA (Highcliffe (0425 272953). *Location:* on the coastal road linking Lymington and Christchurch. Flat, wooded course. 18 holes, 4657 yards, 4259 metres. S.S.S. 63. *Green Fees:* £14.00 weekdays; weekends before noon £20.00; after noon £16.00. Must be in possession of Handicap Certificate.*Eating facilities:* full catering available. *Visitors:* welcome after 9.30am if member of recognised golf club after 3.00pm on competition days. *Society Meetings:* catered for, all must be members of recognised golf clubs. Professional: R.E. Crockford (0425 26640). Secretary: D.W. Blakeman (0425 272210).

DORCHESTER. **Came Down Golf Club,** Higher Came Down, Dorchester DT2 8NR (Dorchester (0305) 812531). *Location:* two miles south of Dorchester. Downland course. 18 holes, 6244 yards, 5709 metres. S.S.S. 71. Practice facilities. *Green Fees:* £14.00 weekdays, £20.00 weekends and Bank Holidays. *Eating facilities:* full catering available; bar. *Visitors* welcome without reservation except am Sundays and competition days – phone in advance. *Society Meetings:* wednesday only. Professional: R. Preston (0305 812670). Secretary: David E. Matthews (0305 813494).

FERNDOWN. **Ferndown Golf Club,** 119 Golf Links Road, Ferndown BH22 8BU (Ferndown (0202) 872022). *Location:* off A31. 18 holes, 6442 yards.

S.S.S. 71. 9 holes, 5604 yards. S.S.S. 68. Practice ground. *Green Fees:* Old Course: £25.00 weekdays, £30.00 weekends. New Course: £15.00 weekdays, £20.00 weekends. Societies £38.00 for the day. *Eating facilities:* available. *Visitors:* welcome but prior permission recommended. Handicap Certificate required from a recognised golf club. Professional: D.N. Sewell (0202 873825). Secretary: (0202 874602).

LYME REGIS. **Lyme Regis Golf Club,** Timber Hill, Lyme Regis DT7 3HQ (Lyme Regis (02974) 2043). *Location:* just off A35, one mile north of town centre. Seaside links. 18 holes, 6262 yards. S.S.S. 70. *Green Fees:* weekdays £16.00, weekends £18. *Eating facilities:* restaurant (closed Mondays) and bar. *Visitors:* welcome, but not before 9.30am and restrictions Thursday and Sundays; best to check with Professional. *Society Meetings:* minimum for Tee Booking 12. Professional: Andrew Black (02974 3822). Secretary: R.G. Fry (02974 2693).

POOLE. **Parkstone Golf Club,** Links Road, Parkstone, Poole BH14 9JU (Canford Cliffs (0202) 707138). *Location:* off A35 Bournemouth to Poole. Wooded heathland. 18 holes, 6250 yards. S.S.S. 70. *Green Fees:* £20.00 per round, £25.00 per day weekdays; £25.00 per round, £30.00 per day weekends and Bank Holidays. *Eating facilities:* catering available daily. *Visitors:* welcome with reservation and Handicap Certificate. *Society Meetings:* catered for as above. Professional: Nigel Blenkarne (0202 708092). Secretary: A.S. Kinnear (0202 707138).

SHERBORNE. **Sherborne Golf Club,** Higher Clatcombe, Sherborne DT9 4RN (Sherborne (0935) 812475). *Location:* one mile north of town on B3145 to Wincanton. Parkland. 18 holes, 5949 yards. S.S.S. 68. Practice facilities. *Green Fees:* £14.00 weekdays, £18.00 weekends. *Eating facilities:* snacks, lunches, teas; dinners to order. *Visitors:* as commitment allow, telephone in advance, Thursday is Ladies Day. *Society Meetings:* catered for Tuesday and Wednesdays. Pro-

fessional: A. Pakes (0935 812274). Secretary/Manager: Mrs J.M.C. Guy (0935 814431).

STUDLAND. **Isle of Purbeck Golf Course,** Studland BH19 3AB (Studland (092 944) 361). Heathland courses with wonderful views. Purbeck – 18 holes, 6248 yards, 5823 metres. S.S.S. 71. Dene – 9 holes, 2022 yards. S.S.S. 30. *Green Fees:* Purbeck £19.50 weekdays, weekends and Bank Holidays £24.00. Dene weekdays £8.50, weekends and Bank Holidays £10.00. *Eating facilities:* full catering, bar and snacks. *Visitors:* welcome. *Society Meetings:* catered for by arrangement, minimum 12. Professional: Paul Sowerby (092 944 354). Managing Director: Mrs J. Robinson (092 944 361).

WAREHAM. **East Dorset Golf Club,** Hyde, Wareham BH20 7NT (0929 471706). *Location:* take A352 off Wareham by-pass, enter Puddletown Road, Wargret Heath. Proceed 4 miles to ARC Blockworks, turn right immediately before Blockworks (signposted). 200 yards to clubhouse. Parkland. 18 holes, 6108 yards. S.S.S. 69. Driving range and Pro shop. *Green Fees:* £15 per round; £18 per day weekdays; £18 per round, £21 per day weekends. *Eating facilities:* excellent bar and restaurant. *Visitors:* welcome with prior reservation. *Society Meetings:* welcome (not weekends). Professional: G. Packer (0929 472272). Secretary: I. Mullins (0929 472244). General Manager: D. Thomas.

WAREHAM. **Lakey Hill Golf Club,** Hyde, Nr. Wareham BH20 7NT (Bere Regis (0929) 471776/ 471941). FAX 471941. *Location:* take Wool road from Bere Regis for three miles and turn left (golf club signposted). Parkland with back 9 through rhododendron woodland. 18 holes, 6108 yards. S.S.S. 69. *Green fees:* information not provided. *Eating facilities:* light refreshments all day, carvery available. *Visitors:* welcome. *Society Meetings:* welcome by arrangement (not weekends) with Club Secretary. Professional: Graham Packer (0929 471574). Secretary: Ivor Mullins (0929 471776).

WAREHAM. Wareham Golf Club, Sandford Road, Wareham BH20 4DH (Wareham [0929] 554156). *Location:* adjoining A351 near railway station. Partly wooded course. 18 holes, 5332 yards. S.S.S. 66. *Green Fees:* weekdays £12.00 per round, £15.00 per day; weekends with a member only £8.00. *Eating facilities:* bar with light refreshments. *Visitors:* welcome, weekdays only. *Society Meetings:* catered for by arrangement. Secretary: Major J.L. Holloway (0929 554147).

WEYMOUTH. Wessex Golf Centre, Rapipole Lane, Weymouth (Weymouth (0305) 784737). *Location:* on bypass road by Weymouth Football Club. Flat public course. 9 holes, 1385 yards. Par 3. Driving range. *Green Fees:* £2.30. *Visitors:* public course.

WEYMOUTH. Weymouth Golf Club Ltd, Links Road, Weymouth DT4 0PF (0305 784994). *Location:* A354 from Dorchester, take last exit at Manor roundabout then follow signs. Parkland, gradually undulating. 18 holes, 5985 yards. S.S.S. 69. Practice area. *Green Fees:* weekdays £15.00, weekends £20.00. Juniors half price. *Eating facilities:* food and drink always available. *Visitors:* welcome, but only with Handicap Certificate. *Society Meetings:* catered for (except weekends), arrange with Secretary. Professional: Mr Des Lochrie (0305 773997). Secretary: Mr Colin Robinson (0305 773981).

County Durham

BARNARD CASTLE. Barnard Castle Golf Club, Harmire, Barnard Castle, (Barnard Castle (0833) 37237). *Location:* one mile north of Barnard Castle Town Centre on the B6278. Open parkland. 18 holes, 5382 yards, 4919 metres. S.S.S. 68. *Green Fees:* weekdays £10.00, weekends and Bank Holidays £16.00, five days £25.00. *Eating facilities:* available. *Visitors:* welcome. *Society Meetings:* catered for by prior arrangement. Professional: J. Harrison (0833) 37237). Secretary: A.W. Lavender (club – 0833 38355, home – 0325 730615).

BISHOP AUCKLAND. Bishop Auckland Golf Club, High Plains, Durham Road, Bishop Auckland DL14 8DL. (Bishop Auckland (0388) 602198). *Location:* A689 west off A1 at Rushyford then six miles. Parkland, 18 holes, 6420 yards. S.S.S. 71. *Green Fees:* weekends £15.00 per round, weekdays £12.00 per round. *Eating facilities:* Full catering facilities. *Visitors:* welcome. Ladies' day Tuesday. *Society Meetings:* catered for on application, not weekends. Professional: Mr D. Skiffington (0388 661618). Secretary: Mr G. Thatcher (0388 663648).

BRANCEPETH VILLAGE. Brancepeth Castle Golf Club, Brancepeth Village DH7 8EA (Durham (091) 3780075). *Location:* four miles south of Durham city on A690 Durham to Crook road. Parkland. 18 holes, 6415 yards. *Green Fees:* weekdays £16.00 per day, weekends by prior booking £20.00. *Eating facilities:* available. *Society Meetings:* catered for at negotiable rates. Monday to Friday only. Professional: D. Howdon (091-3780183). Secretary: D.C. Carver (091-3780075).

CHESTER-LE-STREET. Chester-le-Street Golf Club, Lumley Park, Chester-le-Street DH3 4NS (Chester-le-Street (091) 3883218). *Location:* off A1 adjacent to Lumley Castle, half a mile east of Chester-le-Street. Parkland. 18 holes, 6054 yards, 5535 metres. S.S.S. 69. *Green Fees:* weekdays £10.00, weekends and Public Holidays £15.00. *Eating facilities:* lunches, snacks, dinners, bar. *Visitors:* welcome weekdays with letter of introduction or Handicap Certificate, but some restrictions weekends and Public Holidays. *Society Meetings:* catered for but not weekends and Public Holidays. Professional: M.A. Strong (091-3890157). Secretary: W.B. Dodds (091-3883218).

CHESTER-LE-STREET. Roseberry Grange Golf Club, Grange Villa, Chester-le-Street DH9 0UT (091 3700670). *Location:* three miles west of Chester-le-Street on A693. Parkland course. 18 holes, 5809 yards. S.S.S. 68. Driving range. *Green Fees:* weekdays £5.00 per round, £6.50 per day; weekends £6.00 per round, £7.50 per day. Half price weekdays for Juniors and Senior Citizens. *Eating facilities:* bar meals 12 noon to 2.00pm and 7.00pm to 9.30pm. *Visitors:* welcome, no restrictions. Professional: A. Hartley (091 3700660). Secretary: J. Turnbull (091 3702047).

CONSETT. Consett and District Golf Club, Elmfield Road, Consett DH8 5NN (Consett (0207) 502186). *Location:* A691 from Durham (12 miles) A692 from Gateshead (12 miles). 18 holes, 6001 yards. S.S.S. 69. *Green Fees:* weekdays £8.00, weekends £12.00. *Eating facilities:* Full catering available. *Visitors:* most welcome without reservation. *Society Meetings:* catered for by arrangement, enquiries welcomed. Secretary: Mr. J. Horrill (0207 562261). Professional: S. Corbally (0207 580210).

CROOK. Crook Golf Club, Low Jobs Hill, Crook DL15 9AA (Bishop Auckland (0388) 762429). *Location:* six miles west of Durham City on A689. Hilly demanding parkland course. 18 holes, 6075 yards. S.S.S. 69. Practice fairway. *Green Fees:* weekdays

£6.00, weekends £10.00. *Eating facilities:* all meals catered for. *Visitors:* at any time other than when club competitions are held. Caravan Club Site (4 Vans) adjacent clubhouse. *Society Meetings:* catered for by arrangement with Secretary. Secretary: R. King (0388 746400).

DARLINGTON. **Blackwell Grange Golf Club,** Briar Close, Blackwell, Darlington DL3 8QX (0325 464464). *Location:* one mile south of Darlington on A66 turn into Blackwell. Signposts to Club. Parkland course. 18 holes, 5621 yards. S.S.S. 67. *Green Fees:* £10.00 weekdays, £12.00 weekends and Bank Holidays. *Eating facilities:* full menu except Mondays. *Visitors:* welcome without reservation except weekends. *Society Meetings:* catered for except Wednesday and weekends. Professional: Ralph Givens (0325 462088). Secretary: F. Hewitson (0325 464458).

DARLINGTON. **Dinsdale Spa Golf Club,** Middleton-St-George, Darlington DL2 1DW (Dinsdale (0325) 332222). *Location:* Darlington to Teesside, Airport Road, right at Middleton-St-George, one mile on Neasham Road. 18 holes, 6078 yards. S.S.S. 69. *Green Fees:* information not available. *Eating facilities:* full catering available. *Visitors:* welcome weekdays except Tuesday. *Society Meetings:* catered for Monday to Friday by arrangement. Professional: D. Dodds (0325 332515). Secretary: Mr P.J. Wright (0325 332297).

DARLINGTON. **Stressholme Golf Club,** Snipe Lane, Darlington (0325 353073). *Location:* one mile south of Darlington town centre near junction of A66 and A167. 18 holes, 6511 yards, 5953 metres. S.S.S. 71. Practice ground. *Green Fees:* £5.50 weekdays, £6.50 weekends and Bank Holidays (children £3.75 after 12 noon). *Eating facilities:* two bars, three course meals to snacks. *Visitors:* always welcome anytime. *Society Meetings:* welcome, book through Professional. Professional: Fred Thorpe (0325 461002). Secretary: Graham A. Patrick (0325 466587).

DARLINGTON. **The Darlington Golf Club (Members) Ltd,** Haughton Grange, Darlington DL1 3JD (0325 463936). *Location:* northern outskirts of town A1150 off A167, approximately 800 yards. Parkland, 18 holes, 6271 yards. S.S.S. 70. Large practice ground. *Green Fees:* weekdays £12.00. *Eating facilities:* first class catering, Men's Bar, lounge bar available. *Visitors:* welcome weekdays with reservation, must be members of recognised golf club. *Society Meetings:* by arrangement with Secretary, no more than 40 members. Professional: I. Todd (0325 462955). Secretary: J. Welsh (0325 355324).

DURHAM. **Durham City Golf Club,** Littleburn, Langley Moor, Durham DH7 8HL (Durham (091) 3780806). *Location:* from Durham City take A690 to Crook – course signposted in Langle Moor. Parkland. 18 holes, 6211 yards. S.S.S. 70. Large practice area. *Green Fees:* weekdays £12.00, weekends £16.00. £10.00 for parties of 20 or more. *Eating facilities:* no catering Mondays or Thursday evenings. *Visitors:* visiting parties not accepted at weekends. *Society Meetings:* very welcome – please write. Professional: S. Corbally (091 3780029). Secretary: I. Wilson (091 3780069).

DURHAM. **Mount Oswald Golf Club,** South Road, Durham DH1 3TQ (091-386 7527). *Location:* A1 (M) Durham City, A177 – A1050. Parkland. 18 holes, 6101 yards. S.S.S. 69. *Green Fees:* weekdays £6.00 per round, weekends and Bank Holidays £7.00 per round. *Eating facilities:* bar meals; large parties catered for. *Visitors:* welcome, no restrictions except Sunday mornings before 10 am. Bookings only at weekends. *Society Meetings:* welcome, same restrictions as visitors. Manager: S.E. Reeve (091-386 7527).

NEWTON AYCLIFFE. **Aycliffe Golf Course and Driving Range,** Sports and Leisure Complex, School Aycliffe Lane, Newton Aycliffe TL5 6QZ (0325 310820). *Location:* between A167 – A68, near School Aycliffe, five minutes off A1. Rolling parkland. 9 holes, 5962 yards, 5150 metres. S.S.S. 69. Driving range, squash, indoor bowls, indoor cricket, badminton, five-a-side. *Green Fees:* information not provided. Reduced rates for Senior Citizens and under 16's. *Eating facilities:* restaurant and bar. *Visitors:* no restrictions. *Society Meetings:* all welcome. Professional: Robert Lister (0325 310820).

NEWTON AYCLIFFE. **Woodham Golf and Country Club,** Burnhill Way, Newton Aycliffe DL5 4PM (Darlington (0325) 320574). *Location:* A167, one mile north of Newton Aycliffe on the Shildon road. Parkland, with lakes, trees and water hazards. 18 holes, 6727 yards. S.S.S. 72. Practice grounds. *Green Fees:* weekdays £10.00 per round, £12.00 per day; weekends £9.00 per round, £12.00 per day. *Eating facilities:* diningroom and bar available. *Visitors:* unlimited weekdays; starting sheet at weekends and Bank Holidays. *Society Meetings:* welcome by arrangement. Professional: Jim Graham. Secretary: G.E. Golightly.

SEAHAM. **Seaham Golf Club,** Dawdon, Seaham (091-5812354). *Location:* off A19 to Dawdon, Seaham. Heathland, 18 holes, 5972 yards, 5459 metres. S.S.S. 69. Practice area. *Green Fees:* weekends, Bank Holidays £12.00, weekdays £8.00, with member £6.00 and £4.00. *Eating facilities:* meals and snacks available. *Visitors:* welcome with bookings through Secretary. Restricted weekend booking. *Society Meetings:* welcome, catering on request. Secretary: Vincent Smith (091-5815413).

STANLEY. **Beamish Park Golf Club,** Stanley (Durham (091) 3701133). *Location:* follow directions to Beamish Museum. Parkland, 18 holes, 6205 yards. S.S.S. 70. Two practice areas. *Green Fees:* £11.00 weekdays, £15.00 weekends. *Eating facilities:* bar and a la carte menu. *Visitors:* welcome, Monday to Friday. Professional: Mr. C. Cole (091-370 1984). Secretary: Mr. A. Curtis (091-370 1382).

STANLEY. **South Moor Golf Club,** The Middles, Craghead, Stanley DH9 6AG (Stanley (0207) 232848). *Location:* eight miles north-west of Durham, seven miles north-west of A1 (M) from Chester-le-Street. Parkland and moorland. 18 holes, 6445 yards, 5891 metres. S.S.S. 71. *Green Fees:* £12.00 per day weekdays, £15.00 per day weekends and Bank Holidays. *Eating facilities:* available. *Visitors:* welcome without reservation, except on Club competition days. *Society Meetings:* catered for. Secretary: R. Harrison (0207 283525).

Essex

BASILDON. **Basildon Golf Club,** Clay Lane, Basildon (Basildon (0268) 533297). *Location:* off A176 from A13 or A127 Kingswood Roundabout. Undulating parkland. 18 holes, 6122 yards. S.S.S. 69. Practice ground. *Green Fees:* £5.00 weekdays, £10.50 weekends. *Eating facilities:* lunches served at club. *Visitors:* welcome. Municipal course. *Society Meetings:* catered for – book through Professional. Professional: W. Paterson (0768 533532). Secretary: A. M. Burch (0268 533849).

BASILDON. **Pipps Hill Golf Club,** Pipps Hill Country Club, Cranes Farm Road, Basildon (Basildon (0268) 23456). 9 hole course, 5658 yards. *Green Fees:* information not provided. *Eating facilities:* comprehensive eating facilities. *Visitors:* unrestricted at all times.

BRAINTREE. **Braintree Golf Club,** Kings Lane, Stisted, Braintree CM7 8DA (Braintree (0376) 24117). *Location:* one mile from A120, 300 yards east of Braintree by pass, signposted Stisted – golf club. Parkland, gentle slopes, near stream. 18 holes, 6123 yards, S.S.S. 70. Two practice areas. *Green Fees:* £18.00 weekdays, £30.00 Saturdays only. *Eating facilities:* available. *Visitors:* welcome Monday to Saturdays; Fridays and Sundays must have Handicap Certificate. *Society Meetings:* catered for Wednesday and Thursday. Professional: A.K. Parcell (0376 43465). Secretary: H.W. Hardy (0376 46079).

BRAINTREE. **Towerlands Golf Club,** Panfield Road, Braintree CM7 5BJ (Braintree (0376) 26802). *Location:* off A120 in Braintree. Undulating course. 9 holes, 2703 yards. S.S.S. 66. Golf range. *Green Fees:* weekdays £6.00 for 9 holes, £7.50 for 18 holes; weekends and Bank Holidays £10.00 for 18 holes after 12 noon. *Eating facilities:* full bar and restaurant. *Visitors:* welcome. Wide range of other sports facilities. *Society Meetings:* by arrangement. Secretary: K. Cooper (0376 513519).

BRENTWOOD. **Hartswood Golf Club, (Play on Brentwood Municipal),** King George's Playing Fields, Ingrave Road, Brentwood (Brentwood (0277) 217128). *Location:* one mile south of Brentwood on A128. Parkland, 18 holes, 6238 yards. S.S.S. 70. *Green fees:* information not provided. *Eating facilities:* Full catering available. *Visitors:* welcome without reservation. *Society Meetings:* limited number of society bookings. Professional: J. Stanion (0277 230474). Secretary: J. Turner (0277 218850).

BRENTWOOD. **The Warley Park Golf Club,** Magpie Lane, Little Warley, Brentwood CM13 3DX (Brentwood (0277) 224891). *Location:* leave M25 at intersection 29. A127 towards Southend. Turn left three-quarters-of-a-mile Little Warley, Hall Lane. Turn left into Magpie Lane. Parkland, 3 Courses, (27 holes) S.S.S. 70-70-69. Large practice area, putting greens. *Green Fees:* £18.50 per round, £25.00 per day. *Eating*

facilities: lounge bar and restaurant/spike bar. *Visitors:* welcome Monday to Friday, must produce club Handicap. *Society Meetings:* minimum 20. Professional: P. O'Connor (0277 212552). Secretary: S. Greene (0277 231352).

BRENTWOOD. **Thorndon Park Golf Club Ltd,** Thorndon Park, Ingrave, Brentwood CM13 3RH (Brentwood (0277) 811666). *Location:* three miles south of Brentwood on A128. 18 holes, 6403 yards. S.S.S. 71. *Green Fees:* £35.00 per day, £25.00 per round. *Eating facilities:* lunches served at club. *Visitors:* welcome with reservation, weekdays subject to prior permission. *Society Meetings:* catered for. Professional: Brian White. Secretary: J.E. Leggitt.

BRENTWOOD. **Bentley Golf Club,** Ongar Road, Brentwood CM15 9SS (Coxtie Green (0277) 373179). *Location:* situated on A128 approximately five miles from Junction 28 of M25. Flat course. 18 holes, 6709 yards, 6136 metres. S.S.S. 72. Practice field. *Green Fees:* weekdays £15.00 per round, £20.00 day ticket. *Eating facilities:* snacks and bar available all day. *Visitors:* welcome weekdays with Handicap Certificate or letter of introduction. Restrictions Bank Holidays; weekends with member only. *Society Meetings:* welcome by prior arrangement. Professional: Keith Bridges (0277 372933). Secretary: J.A. Vivers (0277 373179).

BURNHAM-ON-CROUCH. **Burnham-on-Crouch Golf Club Ltd,** Ferry Road, Creaksea CM0 8PQ (Maldon (0621) 782282). *Location:* one mile west of Burnham-on-Crouch, turn right off B1010. Undulating meadowland. 9 holes, 5918 yards, 5410 metres. S.S.S. 68. *Green Fees:* £12.00 weekdays. *Eating facilities:* teas, evening meals except Monday. *Visitors:* no visitors weekends and Bank Holidays, must commence play Mondays to Fridays (except Thursdays) 9.30am to 2pm. Thursdays 12 noon to 2pm. *Society Meetings:* catered for Tuesdays and Wednesdays by arrangement. Secretary: A.S. Hill.

CANVEY ISLAND. **Castle Point Golf Course,** Somnes Avenue, Canvey Island SS8 9FG (0268 510830). *Location:* just off A13, follow signs to Canvey Island. Seaside links course. 18 holes. Large practice area. *Green Fees:* weekdays £6.00, weekends £10.00. Juniors and OAPs £3.00 weekdays. *Eating facilities:* restaurant and bar available. *Visitors:* welcome anytime. *Society Meetings:* welcome, catered for. Professional: Mr John Hudson.

CHELMSFORD. **Channels Golf Club,** Belsteads Farm Lane, Little Waltham, Chelmsford (0245 440003). *Location:* A12 – Chelmsford A130. Old sand and gravel quarry, incorporating water, hills, etc. 18 holes, 6000 yards. S.S.S. 69. *Green Fees:* £16.00 weekdays, weekends only with a member £8.00. *Eating facilities:* excellent restaurant and bar in 13th century clubhouse. *Visitors:* welcome weekdays only. *Socity Meetings:* catered for weekdays except Thursday mornings. Professional: I.B. Sinclair (0245 441056). Secretary: R.J. Slubbings (0245 440005).

CHELMSFORD. **Chelmsford Golf Club,** Widford Road, Chelmsford. Manager (0245 256483). Members (0245 250555). *Location:* close to Widford roundabout on A1016. 18 holes, 5912 yards. S.S.S. 68. *Green Fees:* information not provided. *Eating facilities:* dining room and bar. *Visitors:* welcome Monday to Friday with reservation. Professional: D. Bailey. Manager: Wg. Cdr. B.A. Templeman-Rooke DSO, DFC, AFC, RAF (Retd.).

CHIGWELL. **Chigwell Golf Club,** The Clubhouse, High Road, Chigwell IG7 5BH (081-500 2059). *Location:* on A113, 14 miles from London. Undulating parkland course. 18 holes, 6279 yards. S.S.S. 70. *Green Fees:* £20.00 weekdays, weekends only with member. *Eating facilities:* lunches served, snack bar. *Visitors:* weekdays by prior arrangement, Handicap Certificate required and club membership. *Society Meetings:* for a limited number Wednesdays and Thursdays. Professional: R. Beard (081-500 2384). Secretary: G. Kitson (081-500 2059).

CHIGWELL. **Hainault Forest Golf Club,** Romford Road, Chigwell IJ7 4QW (01-500 2097). *Location:* off A12 towards Chigwell-Hainault. Flat wooded course with several lakes. 18 holes, 6600 yards. S.S.S. 71. 18 holes, 5754 yards. S.S.S. 67. Practice field and putting green. *Green Fees:* weekdays £5.00, weekends £7.00. *Eating facilities:* course restaurant; bars in private club. *Visitors:* public course. *Society Meetings:* weekdays by arrangement with Secretary. Professional: E. Frost (01-500 2131). Secretary: H.G. Richards (01-500 0385 or (home) 04023 44435).

CLACTON. **Clacton Golf Club,** West Road, Clacton (0255 421919). Seaside course. 18 holes, 6244 yards. S.S.S. 70. *Green Fees:* £15.00 weekdays, £23.00 weekends and Bank Holidays. *Eating facilities:* full catering by prior arrangement. *Visitors:* welcome with reservation and current Handicap Certificate. Weekends and Bank Holidays not before 11.00a.m. *Society Meetings:* Monday to Friday catered for by arrangement. Professional: S.J. Levermore. Secretary: I.M. Simpson.

COLCHESTER. **Birch Grove Golf Club,** Layer Road, Colchester (Layer de la Haye (020 634) 276). *Location:* two miles south of town. 9 holes, 4138 yards. S.S.S. 60. *Green Fees:* £7.00 weekdays, £10.00 weekends and Bank Holidays for 18 holes. *Eating facilities:* hot meals and snacks are available during opening hours. *Visitors:* welcome without reservation Monday to Saturday and after 12 noon Sundays. *Society Meetings:* catered for weekdays. Secretary: Mrs M. Marston.

COLCHESTER. **Colchester Golf Club,** Braiswick, Colchester CO4 5AU (Colchester (0206) 852946). *Location:* one mile north-west of Colchester North Station, on A133. Parkland. 18 holes, 6319 yards. S.S.S. 70. *Green Fees:* £14.00 per round, £18.00 per day, Handicap Certificates required. *Eating facilities:*

available. *Visitors:* welcome except Saturday and Sunday mornings. *Society Meetings:* catered for except Tuesdays, Saturdays and Sundays. Professional: Paul Hodgson (0206 853920). Secretary: Mrs J. Boorman (0206 853396).

COLCHESTER. **Stoke by Nayland Golf Club,** Keepers Lane, Leavenheath, Colchester CO6 4PZ (Nayland (0206) 262836). *Location:* just off A134 on B1068 towards Stoke by Nayland. Undulating parkland with water hazards. Two courses (1) Gainsborough – 18 holes, 6516 yards. S.S.S. 71. (2) Constable – 18 holes, 6544 yards. S.S.S. 71. *Green Fees:* weekdays £15.00; weekends £18.00 (handicap golfers only). *Eating facilities:* full catering and bar. *Visitors:* welcome weekdays, phone call advisable; weekends after 10.30am, must produce Handicap Certificate. Squash courts also available. *Society Meetings:* welcome weekdays, book well in advance. Professional: Kevin Lovelock (0206 262769). Secretary: Jonathan Loshak (0206 262836).

COLD NORTON. **Three Rivers Golf and Country Club,** Stow Road, Cold Norton (Maldon (Essex) (0621) 828631). *Location:* 12 miles Chelmsford and 5 miles from Maldon at Cold Norton Village. 18 and 9 holes, 6609 yards. S.S.S. 72. *Green Fees:* on application. *Eating facilities:* comprehensive. *Visitors:* welcome Monday to Friday without reservation. En suite accommodation available (inc. gymnasium, swimming pool, snooker, saunas, sun beds, 8 squash courts, 5 tennis courts). *Society Meetings:* catered for mainly Tuesdays and Thursdays. Professional: Lionel Platts. General Manager: Glen Stafford.

EPPING. **Theydon Bois Golf Club,** Theydon Road, Epping CM16 4EH (037881 2279). *Location:* M25 Waltham Abbey/Epping A11 London to Cambridge, turn right at Bell Hotel. Wooded course. 18 holes, 5472 yards. S.S.S. 68. Practice nets. *Green Fees:* £16.00 per day, £24.00 at weekends. *Eating facilities:* restaurant and bar. *Visitors:* welcome except Wednesday and Thursday morning. Not available December to March. *Society Meetings:* Monday and Tuesday £21 plus catering per day. Professional: R.T. Joyce (037881 2460). Secretary: Ian McDonald (037881 3054).

FRINTON-ON-SEA. **Frinton Golf Club,** 1 Esplanade, Frinton-on-Sea CO13 9EP (Frinton-on-Sea (0255) 674618). *Location:* east of Colchester, B1033 to Frinton. Seaside links 18 and 9 holes, 6259 yards, 5777 metres. S.S.S. 70. *Green Fees:* £20.00. *Eating facilities:* lunches and dinners each day except Mondays. *Visitors:* welcome with reservation, must produce proof of membership of a club. *Society Meetings:* catered for weekdays only. Professional: Peter Taggart. Secretary: Paul B. Stokes.

GREENFORD. **Perivale Park Golf Club,** Ruislip Road East, Greenford, Middlesex (081-578 1693). *Location:* off A40, Ealing. Flat. 9 holes, 2667 yards. S.S.S. 34. Excellent practice ground. *Green Fees:* information not provided. *Eating facilities:* available. *Visitors:* welcome without any restrictions. *Society Meetings:* catered for. Professional: John Hamlin (081-575 8655). Secretary: Richard Sivers.

HARLOW. **Canons Brook Golf Club,** Elizabeth Way, Harlow CM19 5BE (Harlow (0279) 25142). *Location:* A414. 18 holes, 6745 yards. S.S.S. 73. *Green Fees:* £20.00 per weekday. *Eating facilities:* full catering except Mondays. *Visitors:* welcome weekdays. *Society Meetings:* catered for except Mondays. Professional: Roger Yates (0279 418357). *Secretary:* G.E. Chambers (0279 21482).

HARWICH. **Harwich Dovercourt Golf Club,** Parkeston Road, Harwich (Harwich (0255) 3616). *Location:* A604 thence to sign Parkeston Quay. Course marked on left hand side of Parkeston Road. 9 holes, 5862 yards. S.S.S. 68. *Green Fees:* information not provided. No visitors Saturdays, Sundays and Bank Holidays unless playing with a member. *Eating facilities:* order before playing. *Visitors:* welcome with Handicap Certificates. *Society Meetings:* catered for. Secretary: Mr B. Q. Dunham.

ILFORD. **Fairlop Waters,** Forest Road, Barkingside, Ilford IG6 3JA (081 500 9911). *Location:* two miles north of Ilford, half a mile from A12, one and a half miles from southern end of M11. Parkland course. 18 holes, 6281 yards. S.S.S. 70. *Green Fees:* £5.25 weekdays, £7.25 weekends. *Eating facilities:* bar food (all day), full a la carte restuarant. *Visitors:* welcome all week. Banqueting for 250 and conferences. Professional: Tony Bowers (081-501 1881). Manager: John Topping.

ILFORD. **Ilford Golf Club,** 291 Wanstead Park Road, Ilford RG1 3TR (081-554 5174). *Location:* at end of M11. Parkland with winding river. 18 holes, 5702 yards. S.S.S. 68. *Green Fees:* weekdays £7.00, weekends £9.00. *Eating facilities:* restaurant and bar. *Visitors:* welcome weekdays, restricted times at weekends. *Society Meetings:* welcome. Professional: K. Ashdown (081-554 0094). *Secretary:* J.A. Smith (081-554 2930).

LEIGH-ON-SEA. **Belfairs Golf Club,** Eastwood Road North, Leigh-on-Sea SS9 4LR (Southend (0702) 526911). Park front 9, heavy woodland back 9; easy walking but challenging golf. Play over Belfairs municipal course, 18 holes, 5857 yards. S.S.S. 68. *Green Fees:* weekdays £6.00, weekends and Bank Holidays £9.00. *Eating facilities:* public restaurant. *Visitors:* unrestricted but bookings required for weekends and Bank Holidays. Secretary: B.J. Orr. Professional: Roger Foreman (0702 520202).

LOUGHTON. **Loughton (Loughton Golf Centre),** Clay's Lane, Debden, Loughton IG10 2RZ (01 502 2923). *Location:* just north of Loughton, on edge of Epping Forest. Parkland. 9 holes, 4700 yards. S.S.S. 63. *Green Fees:* for 9 holes: weekdays £2.50, weekends £4.00. *Eating facilities:* bar, snacks available. *Visitors:* public course, telephone to book. *Society Meetings:* welcome. Professional/Manager: Jon Payne.

MALDON. **Bunsay Downs Golf Club,** Little Baddow Road, Woodham Walter, Maldon CM9 6RW (Danbury (024 541) 2369 or 2648). *Location:* 7 miles east of Chelmsford off A414 at Woodham Walter, left onto Little Baddow Road. Undulating landscaped course. 9 holes, 2913 yards. S.S.S. 68. Par 3 course, indoor range. *Green Fees:* Information not supplied. *Eating facilities:* bar/grill restaurant. *Visitors:* welcome at all times. Gift shop. *Society Meetings:* small societies welcome. Professional: Mickey Walker (024 541 2648).

MALDON. **Forrester Park Golf and Tennis Club,** Forrester Park, Beckingham Road, Great Totham, Near Maldon CM9 8EA (Maldon (0621) 891903). *Location:* three miles off A12 Rivenhall turn-off, on B1022 in Great Totham, near Witham between Compasses and Bull. Parkland course. 18 holes, 6050 yards, S.S.S. 69. *Green Fees:* weekdays £10.00, weekends £15.00. *Eating facilities:* two bars, meals or bar snacks. *Visitors:* welcome weekdays but not after 4pm Wednesdays nor Saturdays, Sundays and Bank Holidays before 1.00pm. *Society Meetings:* welcome with prior reservation. Secretary: Tim Forrester-Muir (0621 891406).

MALDON. **Maldon Golf Club,** Beeleigh, Langford, Maldon CM9 7SS (Maldon (0621) 853212). *Location:* B1019 two miles north west of Maldon, turn off at the Essex Waterworks. Parkland, 9 holes, 6197 yards, 5667 metres. S.S.S. 69. *Green Fees:* 18 holes £10.00, all day £12.00. *Eating facilities:* light lunches except Tuesday. No evening meals, bar. *Visitors:* welcome, must produce Handicap Certificate from established club unless playing with a member. Ladies' morning Tuesdays. *Society Meetings:* catered for by arrangement. Secretary: J.C. Rigby.

MALDON. **Quietwaters Club,** Colchester Road, Tolleshunt D'Arcy, Maldon (Maldon (0621) 860410). *Location:* B1026 south of Colchester. European Tour Course. 18 holes, 6201 yards, 5671 metres. S.S.S. 70. Links type course 1-18 holes, 6855 yards S.S.S. 72. *Green Fees:* £16.00 per round weekdays; £14.00 per round weekends. *Eating facilities:* dining room and bars. Evening meals by arrangement. *Visitors:* welcome at most times. *Society Meetings:* catered for. Professional: Gary Pike (0621 860576). General Manager: P.D. Keeble.

MALDON. **Warren Golf Club,** Woodham Walter, Maldon CM9 6RW (Danbury (024-541) 3198/3258). *Location:* close to Chelmsford. A414 turn off to Maldon. Undulating wooded course. 18 holes, 6211 yards. S.S.S. 70. Large practice area. *Green Fees:* £17.00 per round, £20.00 per day weekdays. *Eating facilities:* restaurant, bar, bar snack menu. *Visitors:* welcome with reservation weekdays except Wednesdays am. Handicap Certificate required. *Society Meetings:* catered for weekdays – up to 40 players. Professional: Mickey Walker (0245-41 4662). Manager: M.L.F. Durham.

OCKENDON. **Thurrock Belhus Park Golf Club,** South Ockendon RM15 4QR (0708 852248). *Location:* on A13 London Southend road approximately one mile north. 18 holes, 5701 yards. S.S.S. 68. *Green Fees:* weekdays £4.00 per round, weekends £9.00 per round: day tickets and reductions for Senior Citizens and Juniors available. *Eating facilities:* cafe and bar at clubhouse. *Visitors:* no booking required except weekends and Public Holidays. *Society Meetings:* by arrangement with Manager (0708 852248). Professional: Steve Wimbleton (0708 854260). Secretary: D. A. Faust (04024 46224).

ORSETT. **Orsett Golf Club,** Orsett (Grays Thurrock (0375) 891226). *Location:* A13 junction roundabout with A128. South towards Orsett Depot on A128. Heathland, parkland course. 18 holes, 6619 yards. S.S.S. 72. *Green Fees:* £20.00 per round or day. *Eating facilities:* full catering available. *Visitors:* welcome on weekdays only. Must be members of a club and have handicap. Proof must be produced. *Society Meetings:* welcome on Mondays, Tuesdays and Wednesdays, maximum 40. Professional: Robert Newberry (0375 891797). Secretary: R.A. Bond (0375 891352).

ROCHFORD near. **Ballards Gore Golf Club,** Gore Road, Canewdon, Near Rochford SS4 2DA (0702 258917). *Location:* Southend Airport three miles, London via A127, club two miles from Rochford. Parkland with lakes. 18 holes, 7062 yards. S.S.S. 74. Practice area. *Green Fees:* £18.00 weekdays. *Eating facilities:* diningroom (80 covers). *Visitors:* welcome weekdays only. *Society Meetings:* catered for by arrangement. Professional: Mr Mark Pierce (0702 258924). Secretary: N.G. Patient (0702 258917).

ROCHFORD. **Rochford Hundred Golf Club,** Hall Lane, Rochford SS4 1NW (Southend-on-Sea (0702) 544302). *Location:* B1013 four miles north of Southend. Parkland course. 18 holes, 6132 yards. S.S.S. 69. *Green Fees:* Information not provided. *Eating facilities:* full restaurant and snack facilities and bars. *Visitors:* welcome with reservation. *Society Meetings:* catered for. Professional: Mr Gary Shipley (0702 548968). Secretary: Mr T.J. Ager.

ROMFORD. **Havering Municipal Golf Course,** Risebridge Chase, Lower Bedfords Road, Romford. *Location:* Gallows Corner, straight road, left turn at junction, Collier Row. 18 holes, 6342 yards. S.S.S. 70. *Green fees:* information not provided. *Visitors:* welcome without reservation. *Society Meetings:* catered for. Professional: Paul Jennings. Pro Shop: (0708 741429).

ROMFORD. **Maylands Golf and Country Club,** Colchester Road, Harold Park, Romford RM3 0AZ (Ingrebourne (040-23) 73080). *Location:* directly on A12 between Romford and Brentwood. 18 holes, 6182 yards. S.S.S. 70. *Green Fees:* £20.00 per round, £30.00 per day. *Eating facilities:* by arrangement. *Visitors:* welcome with reservation. *Society Meetings:* catered for. Professional: John Hopkin (042-23 46466). Secretary/Proprietor: P. S. Taylor.

ROMFORD. **Risebridge Golf Club,** Risebridge Chase, Lower Bedfords Road, Romford (Romford (0708) 41429). *Location:* Gallows Corner, straight road, left turn at junction, Collier Row. 18 holes, 6342 yards. S.S.S. 70. *Green Fees:* weekdays £4.65, weekends £6.10. *Eating facilities:* available. *Visitors:* welcome without reservation. *Society Meetings:* catered for. Professional: Paul Jennings. Secretary: Mrs Joan Simper (0708 765084).

SAFFRON WALDEN. **Saffron Walden Golf Club,** Windmill Hill, Saffron Walden CB10 1BX (Saffron Walden (0799) 22786). *Location:* End of town on A130 to Cambridge. 18 holes, 6617 yards. S.S.S. 72. *Green Fees:* £17.00 per day or round (weekdays only). *Eating*

facilities: lunches and snacks available. *Visitors:* welcome with current Handicap Certificate. *Society Meetings:* catered for Mondays, Wednesdays and Thursdays. Professional: Philip Davis. General Manager: K.W. Reddall.

SOUTH BENFLEET. **Boyce Hill Golf Club Ltd,** Vicarage Hill, South Benfleet SS7 1PD (Benfleet (0268) 793625). *Location:* one-and-a-half-miles from A13 or A127. Hilly course, 18 holes. S.S.S. 68. *Green Fees:* weekdays £18.00. *Eating facilities:* full dining facilities. *Visitors:* welcome, except Tuesday mornings. *Society Meetings:* catered for Thursdays only. Professional: G. Burroughs (0268 752565). Secretary: J.E. Atkins (0268 793625).

SOUTHEND-ON-SEA. **Southend-on-Sea Golf Club,** Belfairs Park, Southend-on-Sea (0702 524836). Play over Belfairs Municipal. *Green fees:* information not available. Secretary: N.A. Dye (0702 340472).

SOUTHEND-ON-SEA. **Thorpe Hall Golf Club,** Thorpe Hall Avenue, Thorpe Bay, Southend-on-Sea. *Location:* one mile east of Southend-on-Sea. 18 holes, 6286 yards. S.S.S. 71. *Green Fees:* £20.00 per day or round. *Eating facilities:* restaurant open every day except Mondays. *Visitors:* welcome if members of recognised golf club. *Society Meetings:* catered for. Professional: Gary Harvey (0702 588195). Secretary: R.C.P. Hunter (0702 582205).

STAPLEFORD ABBOTTS. **Stapleford Abbotts Golf Club,** Horsemans Side, Tysea Hill, Stapleford Abbotts RM4 1JU (Ingrebourne (04023) 81278/81108). *Location:* M25 off Main Romford Ongar road, B175 at Stapleford Abbotts, Essex. Parkland. 18 holes, Par 72, 6481 yards. S.S.S. 72. 9 hole Par 3 course, 1140 yards. *Green fees:* 18 holes: weekdays £15; weekend after 12 noon £20; Par 3 course: weekdays £5; weekends £5 per round, £10 day ticket. *Eating facilities:* full catering available. *Visitors:* welcome, group and individual tuition. *Society Meetings:* catered for. Professional/Manager: Scott Cranfield (04023 81278).

STAPLEFORD TAWNEY. **Abridge Golf and Country Club,** Epping Lane, Stapleford Tawney RM4 1ST (Stapleford (Essex) (04028) 396 and 397). *Location:* A113 from London through Chigwell to Abridge, left at White Hart, right after 200 yards. Two miles on. 18 holes, 6609 yards. S.S.S. 72. *Green Fees:* information not provided. *Eating facilities:* Lunch and teas served at club except Fridays. *Visitors:* welcome but must be a member of a recognised golf club and produce evidence of current handicap, weekdays only. Tennis courts and heated swimming pool. *Society Meetings:* catered for on Mondays and Wednesdays only. Professional: Bernard Cooke (04028 333). Secretary: P.G. Pelling.

WOODFORD GREEN. **Woodford Golf Club,** Sunset Avenue, Woodford Green (01-504 0553). Woodland with gorse. Centenary 1990. 18 holes, 5806 yards. S.S.S. 68. *Green Fees:* £9.00 per round, £12.00 per day. *Eating facilities:* available. *Visitors:* no green fees Tuesday or Thursday mornings or after 3.00pm weekdays. *Society Meetings:* welcome. Professional: A. Johns (01-504 4254). Secretary: G.J. Cousins (01-504 3330).

Gloucestershire

BROADWAY. **Broadway Golf Club**, Willersey Hill, Broadway WR12 7LG (Broadway (0386) (858997). *Location:* one-and-a-half-mile east Broadway (A44). 18 holes, 6211 yards. S.S.S. 70. *Green fees:* on application. *Eating facilities:* available daily (except Monday). *Visitors:* welcome; reservation advised. Handicap Certificates required. Saturdays (April/September) with member only before 4 pm. October/March no restrictions. *Society Meetings:* by arrangement (Wednesday, Thursday and Friday). Secretary: B. Carnie (0386 853683). Professional: John Freeman (0386 853275).

CHELTENHAM. **Cleeve Cloud Golf Club,** Nr. Prestbury, Cheltenham (Bishops Cleeve (024-267) 2592. *Location:* three miles north of Cheltenham on A46. 18 holes, 6217 yards. S.S.S. 70. *Green Fees:* information not provided. *Eating facilities:* full restaurant and bar snack facilities available every day. *Society Meetings;* catered for by arrangement. *Visitors:* welcome without reservation. Professional: D. Finch. Secretary: R. East.

CHELTENHAM. **Lilley Brook Golf Club,** Cirencester Road, Charlton Kings, Cheltenham GL53 8EG (Cheltenham (0242) 526785). *Location:* two miles south-east of Cheltenham on main Cirencester road (A435). Parkland. 18 holes, 6226 yards, 5979 metres. S.S.S. 70. Practice field. *Green Fees:* weekdays £18.00, weekends £25.00 (Handicap Certificates required). *Eating facilities:* full catering available. *Visitors:* welcome weekdays and weekends, Handicap Certificates required. *Society Meetings:* Wednesdays and Thursdays catered for by arrangement. Professional: Forbes E. Hadden (0242 525201). Secretary: K.A. Skeen (0242 526785).

CHELTENHAM near. **Cotswold Hills Golf Club Ltd,** Ullenwood, Near Cheltenham GL53 9QT (Cheltenham (0242) 522421). *Location:* between A436 and B4070. Approach from Roundabout A417, A436 and B4070, proceeding north east along A436 for one mile. 18 holes, 6650 yards. S.S.S. 72. *Green fees:* weekdays

£16.00 per round, £20.00 per day; weekends £20.00 per round, £25.00 per day. *Eating facilities:* lunch every day (not Monday). Evening meal by arrangement. *Visitors:* welcome without reservation, must be members of a golf club. *Society Meetings:* catered for by arrangement. Professional: Noel Boland (0242 515263). Secretary: Andrew O'Reilly (0242 515264).

CIRENCESTER. **Cirencester Golf Club,** Cheltenham Road, Cirencester (Cirencester (0285) 653939). *Location:* one mile north of Cirencester on A435 Cheltenham road. 18 holes, 6108 yards. S.S.S. 69. *Green Fees:* weekdays £18.00, weekends and Bank Holidays £25.00. *Eating facilities:* lunches and suppers by arrangement. Hot and cold snacks always available. *Visitors:* welcome, Handicap Certificate required. *Society Meetings:* catered for Tuesday, Wednesday and Friday only. Professional: M. Thomas. Secretary: N.D. Jones (0285 652469).

COLEFORD. **Royal Forest of Dean Golf Club,** Lords Hill, Coleford GL16 8BD (Dean (0594) 32583). *Location:* 10 miles from Severn Bridge. M4, M5 and M50. Parkland course in Forest of Dean. 18 holes, 5519 yards. S.S.S. 67. Practice area. *Green Fees:* weekdays £12.00, weekends £14.00. Bargain Daily Break – golf, snack lunch, three course dinner only £22.00. *Eating facilities:* restaurant, bar snacks, bar open all day. *Visitors:* welcome without reservation. *Society Meetings:* welcome on special Bargain Daily Break, Monday-Thursday £22.00. Professional: John Nicol (0594 33689). Secretary: Roy Sanzen-Baker (0594 33606). Other facilities include: Hotel, all bedrooms en suite. Bowling green, outdoor swimming pool, new all-weather tennis court, conference facilities for up to 150.

DURSLEY. **Stinchcombe Hill Golf Club,** Stinchcombe Hill, Dursley GL11 6AQ (Dursley (0453) 542015). *Location:* M5 between Junctions 13 and 14, A38 to Dursley. At traffic lights in centre of Dursley enter May Lane, continue to top of hill and turn right onto Golf Course. A gently undulating course situated on a hilltop at the southern edge of the Cotswolds, extensive views. 18 holes, 5723 yards. S.S.S. 68. Practice and teaching areas. *Green Fees:* £13.00 weekdays, £15.00 weekends and Bank Holidays. Reduced by £5.00 when playing with a member. *Eating facilities:* full catering and bar service available. *Visitors:* welcome with recognised handicaps, time restrictions at weekends and Bank Holidays. *Society Meetings:* catered for by arrangement. Professional: Anthony Valentine (0453 543878). Secretary: John R. Clarke (0453 542015).

GLOUCESTER. **Gloucester Hotel and Country Club,** Matson Lane, Gloucester GL4 9EA (Gloucester (0452) 25653 Ext.316). *Location:* one-and-a-half-miles from Gloucester city centre off Painswick Road B4073. Parkland. 18 holes, 6135 yards, 5614 metres. S.S.S. 69. *Green Fees:* weekdays £15.00 per round, weekends £19.00 per round. *Eating facilities:* full catering available. *Visitors:* welcome any time but booking recommended by telephoning Secretary. Professional: P. Darnell. Secretary: R. Jewell (0452 411331).

LYDNEY. **Lydney Golf Club,** The Links, off Lakeside Avenue, Lydney GL15 5QA (Dean (0594) 842614). *Location:* on front left-hand side of town when entering on A48 Cardiff road from Gloucester. Meadowland. 9 holes, 5382 yards. S.S.S. 66. Small practice area. *Green Fees:* on application. *Eating facilities:* snack meals only. *Visitors:* welcome, but only with a member at weekends/Bank Holidays. *Society Meetings:* welcome by prior arrangement (maximum 30/36). Hon. Secretary: D.A. Barnard (0594 843940).

MINCHINHAMPTON. **Minchinhampton Golf Club,** New Course, Minchinhampton, Stroud (Nailsworth (045-383) 3858). *Location:* New Course between Minchinhampton and Avening. Old Course between Minchinhampton and Stroud. Both courses 18 holes. New Course 6675 yards. Old Course 6295 yards. S.S.S. New Course 72, Old Course 70. *Green Fees:* New Course: weekdays £15.00 day, weekends and Bank Holidays £20.00 day. Old Course: weekdays £8.00 day, weekends and Bank Holidays £10.00 day. *Eating facilities:* normal catering at both New Course and Old Course Clubhouses. *Visitors:* New Course: welcome, must have handicap. Old Course: welcome. *Society Meetings:* both courses cater for groups by arrangement. Professional: New and Old Courses C. Steele (045-383 3860). Secretary: D.R. Vickers (045-383 3866). Old Course Golf Shop (045-383 2642).

PAINSWICK. **Painswick Golf Club,** Painswick, Near Stroud (Painswick (0452) 812180. *Location:* three miles north-east of Stroud on A46. 18 holes, 4900 yards. S.S.S. 64. *Green Fees:* weekdays £6.00, Saturdays £7.00. *Eating facilities:* lunches at Club (prior notice requested). *Visitors:* welcome weekdays and Saturday mornings. Saturday afternoons and Sunday mornings only with member. Saturday morning without reservation. *Society Meetings:* catered for, welcome most days. Secretary: R.J. May.

TETBURY. **Westonbirt Golf Course,** c/o Bursar. Westonbirt School Ltd, Near Tetbury (Westonbirt (066 688) 242). *Location:* turn off A433, 3 miles south-west of Tetbury through Westonbirt Village. Parkland. 9 holes, 4504 yards. S.S.S. 61. *Green Fees:* weekdays £5.00 per day, weekends and Bank Holidays £5.00 per round £10.00 per day. *Visitors:* welcome without reservation. *Society Meetings:* catered for. Secretary: c/o Bursar, Westonbirt School, Nr. Tetbury.

TEWKESBURY. **Tewkesbury Park Hotel Golf and Country Club,** Lincoln Green Lane, Tewkesbury GL20 7DN (Tewkesbury (0684) 295405). *Location:* two miles Tewkesbury Exit Junction 9 M5. South of Tewkesbury on A38 to Cheltenham/Gloucester. Parkland. 18 holes, 6781 yards. S.S.S. 72. 6 hole Par 3 course. *Green Fees:* weekdays £18.00, weekends £20.00. *Eating facilities:* full catering available. *Visitors:* welcome without reservation weekdays. Handicap Certificate required. Other facilities include 85 en-suite rooms, squash courts, heated indoor pool, sauna, steam room, multi gym, beauty salon, snooker, tennis, conference and meeting rooms. *Society Meetings:* catered for. Professional: Peter Cane (0684 29492). Secretary: Major John McCarthy (0684 299452).

WOTTON-UNDER-EDGE. **Cotswold Edge Golf Club,** Upper Rushmire, Wotton-under-Edge GL12 7PT (Dursley (0453) 844167). *Location:* eight miles from Junction 14 M5, on B4058 Tetbury road. Fairly flat course with magnificent views. 18 holes, White Tees – 6170 yards. S.S.S. 70; Yellow Tees – 5816 yards. S.S.S. 68. *Green Fees:* weekdays £12.00. *Eating facilities:* good catering service, usual bar facilities. *Visitors:* welcome weekdays. Telephone call in advance advisable. *Society Meetings:* by arrangement with Secretary. Professional: David Gosling (0453 844398). Secretary: N.J. Newman (0453 844167).

Hampshire

ALDERSHOT. **Army Golf Club,** Laffan's Road, Aldershot GU11 2HF (Farnborough (0252) 540638). Clubhouse (0252 541104). Pro's Shop (0252 547232). *Location:* access from Eelmoor Bridge off A323 Aldershot Fleet Road. 18 holes, 6533 yards. S.S.S. 71. *Green Fees:* no casual green fees for civilians, only with member. Special rates for servicemen. *Eating facilities:* a range of catering is available by arrangement with the Secretary. *Visitors:* must be members' guests or servicemen. *Society Meetings:* catered for. Professional: Mr. Peter Thompson. Secretary/Manager: R.T. Crabb.

ALRESFORD. **Alresford Golf Club,** Cheriton Road, Tichborne Down, Alresford S024 0PN (Alresford (0962) 733746). *Location:* one mile south of A31 (Winchester/Alton). Two miles north A272 (Winchester/Petersfield). Undulating parkland, wooded. 12 holes, 6038 yards. S.S.S. 69. *Green Fees:* £11.50 per round, £16.50 per day (18 holes) weekdays, £20.00 per round weekends (18 holes). *Eating facilities:* every day except Mondays. *Visitors:* welcome but not before 12 noon weekends/Bank Holidays. Handicap Certificate required. *Society Meetings:* catered for by arrangement. Professional: Malcolm Scott (0962 733998). Secretary: Peter Kingston (0962 733746).

ALTON. **Alton Golf Club,** Old Odiham Road, Alton GU34 4BU (Alton (0420) 82042). *Location:* off A32, two miles north of Alton. Odiham six miles. Undulating wooded course. 9 holes, alternate tees. 5744 yards. S.S.S. 68. *Green Fees:* weekdays £10.00, weekends £15.00. *Visitors:* weekdays welcome without reservation, except on competition days. Sundays with member. *Society Meetings:* catered for. Professional: Martin Smith (0420 86518). Secretary: Mrs M.J. Woodhead (0420 82042).

AMPFIELD. **Ampfield Par Three Golf and Country Club,** Ampfield, Near Romsey (Braishfield (0794) 68480). *Location:* main A31 Winchester to Romsey road, approximately two miles west of Hursley Village. 18 Par threes, 2478 yards. S.S.S. 53. *Green Fees:* on application. *Eating facilities:* light meals and snacks except Tuesday. *Visitors:* welcome, but best to phone first. *Society Meetings:* catered for. Professional: Richard Benfield (0794 68750). Secretary: Mrs Stella Baker.

ANDOVER. **Andover Golf Club,** 51 Winchester Road, Andover SP10 2EF (Andover (0264) 23980). *Location:* half-mile south of town centre on the A3057 Winchester/Stockbridge road. Parkland. 9 holes, 5933 yards. S.S.S. 68. *Green Fees:* £10.00 weekdays, £20.00 weekends. *Eating facilities:* full catering available. *Visitors:* welcome, Handicap Certificate required. *Society Meetings:* catered for by prior arrangement. Professional: A. Timms (0264 24151). Secretary: Major B.F. Gerhard, M.B.E. (0264 58040). Clubhouse Manager: (0264 23980).

BARTON-ON-SEA. **Barton-on-Sea Golf Club,** Marine Drive, Barton-on-Sea, New Milton BH25 7DY (0425 639092). *Location:* one mile from New Milton. Seaside course. 18 holes, 5650 yards. S.S.S. 67. *Green Fees:* on request. *Eating facilities:* full catering available. *Visitors:* welcome but not before 11.15 a.m. at weekends and Bank Holidays. *Society Meetings:* catered for with three months notice in writing. Professional: P. Coombs (0425 611210). Secretary: C.J. Wingfield (0425 615308).

BASINGSTOKE. **Basingstoke Golf Club,** Kempshott Park, Basingstoke RG23 7LL (Basingstoke (0256) 465990). *Location:* on A30, three miles west of town on road to Winchester; from Winchester leave M3 at Exit 7. Parkland course. 18 holes, 6259 yards. S.S.S. 70. *Green Fees:* information not provided. *Eating facilities:* lunches and teas in clubhouse. *Visitors:* welcome on weekdays if member of a golf club, at weekends and Bank Holidays only if playing with a member. *Society Meetings:* Wednesdays and Thursdays. Professional: I. Hayes (0256 51332). Secretary: J.E. Osborough.

BASINGSTOKE. **Bishopswood Golf Club,** Bishopswood Lane, Tadley, Basingstoke RG26 6AT (Tadley (0734) 815213). *Location:* six miles north of Basingstoke off the A340. Floodlit driving range open 7 days a week. 9 holes, 6440 yards. S.S.S. 71. *Green Fees:* £4.50 per round, weekdays. *Eating facilities:* available 7 days a week. *Visitors:* welcome Tuesdays, Thursdays and Fridays only. Not weekends. *Society Meetings:* catered for with prior arrangement. Professional: K. Pickett. Manager: M.W. Phillips.

BASINGSTOKE. **Tylneypark Golf Club,** Rotherwick (Hook (0256) 762079). *Location:* one mile Hook, A30. 18 holes, 6135 yards. S.S.S. 69. Par 70. *Green Fees:* weekdays £13.00, weekends £20.00 with handicap. *Visitors:* weekdays unrestricted, weekends with member. Secretary: A.D. Bewley. Professional: C. DeBruin.

BORDON. **Blackmoor Golf Club,** Whitehill, Bordon GU35 9EH (Bordon (04203) 2775). *Location:* lies midway between Petersfield and Farnham on A325. 18 holes, 6213 yards. S.S.S. 70. *Green Fees:* £27.50, after 1pm £20.00. *Eating facilities:* dining room. *Visitors:* welcome with reservation, handicaps necessary. *Society Meetings:* catered for all day. Morning coffee, lunch, evening meal. Professional: A. Hall. Secretary: Major (Retd.) H. R. G. Spiller.

BORDON near. **Kingsley Golf Club,** Main Road, Kingsley, Near Bordon GU35 9NG. *Location:* B3004 off A325 (Farnham to Petersfield Road). Parkland public course, a challenging short course. 18 holes, 2956 yards. S.S.S. 54. *Green Fees:* £5.00 weekdays (Juniors £2.50), £6.50 weekends (Juniors £3.50). *Eating facilities:* bar and restaurant. *Visitors:* course closed to visitors third Sunday in month, must book tee on Sundays. Driving range, indoor computerised driving bay, equipment superstore, golf school for tuition. *Society Meetings:* can be arranged. Professional/ Acting Secretary: Richard Adams (04203 88195).

BROCKENHURST. **Brockenhurst Manor Golf Club,** Sway Road, Brockenhurst SO47SG (Lymington (0590) 22383). *Location:* from M27 take A337 to Brockenhurst then B3055 (to Sway). Approximately one mile to golf club. Beautiful New Forest course – wet in winter. 18 holes, 6222 yards. S.S.S. 70. *Green Fees:* on application. *Eating facilities:* available all day; to 5.00pm in winter. *Visitors:* enquiries for play recommended. Club Handicap Certificate required. *Society Meetings:* play may be restricted in wet periods. Thursdays only, small groups catered for by arrangement. Professional: C. Bonner (0590 23092). Secretary: C.F. Mackintosh (0590 23332).

CRONDALL. **Crondall Golf Course,** Oak Park, Heath Lane, Crondall, Near Farnham, Surrey GU10 5PB (0252 850880). *Location:* one and a half miles off A287 Farnham-Odiham road, five miles from Junctions 4 and 5 of M3. Gently undulating parkland course. 18 holes, 6278 yards. S.S.S. 70. Putting green and driving range. *Green Fees:* weekdays £12.50 per round (reductions for Juniors); weekends £17.50 per round. Twilight ticket £12.50 weekends, £7.50 weekdays. *Eating facilities:* restaurant open 5 days a week and bar snacks available daily. *Visitors:* must book through Professional; reserved tee system weekends and Public Holidays. *Society Meetings:* by arrangement, welcome every day subject to availability. Professional: Peter Rees (0252 850066). Secretary: Mrs R. Smythe (0252 850880).

DIBDEN. **Dibden (Municipal) Golf Course,** Dibden, Southampton (Hythe (0703) 845596). *Location:* half-mile off A326 Totton to Fawley road at Dibden very close to New Forest. 18 holes, 6206 yards. S.S.S. 70. *Green Fees:* summer rate: weekdays £4.30, weekends £6.30; winter: weekdays £3.60, weekends £5.30. *Eating facilities:* available. *Visitors:* welcome without reservation. *Society Meetings:* catered for. Professional: Alan Bridge. Course administration by Professional.

EASTLEIGH. **Fleming Park Golf Club,** Fleming Park, Eastleigh (Eastleigh (0703) 2797). *Location:* two miles off M27 Eastleigh Airport turning. Parkland. 18 holes, 4494 yards. S.S.S. 65. *Green Fees:* information not provided. *Eating facilities:* available plus bar. *Visitors:* welcome, book at least one week in advance. *Society Meetings:* all welcome. Professional: D. Miller. Secretary: R.L. Peddle.

FAREHAM. **Southwick Park Golf Club,** Pinsley Drive, Southwick, Fareham PO17 6EL. *Location:* Near Southwick village, within HMS Dryad. Parkland. 18 holes, 5855 yards. S.S.S. 68. Practice area, pitch and putt. *Green Fees:* weekdays £10.00 per round. *Eating facilities:* bar and snacks available. *Visitors:* weekdays only. *Society Meetings:* Tuesdays only, book through Manager. Professional: J. Green (0705 380442). Manager: N.W. Price (0705 380131).

FARNBOROUGH. **Southwood Golf Course,** Ively Road, Cove, Farnborough GU14 0LJ (0252 515139). Location: approximately half a mile west of A325. Flat parkland. 18 holes, 5553 yards. S.S.S. 67. Putting green. *Green Fees:* £7.00, Juniors and Senior Citizens half price. *Eating facilities:* bar and diningroom available. *Visitors:* welcome, bookable at all times. *Society Meetings:* catered for by arrangement. Professional: Bob Hammond (0252 548700). Secretary: Bob Smith (0276 22279).

FLEET. **Hartley Wintney Golf Club,** London Road, Hartley Wintney, Basingstoke RG27 8PT (Hartley Wintney (025-126) 2214). *Location:* on A30 between Camberley and Basingstoke. Parkland. 9 holes, 6096 yards. S.S.S. 69. *Green Fees:* under review. Jeans and trainers not permitted. *Eating facilities:* full catering facilities available. *Visitors:* restricted Wednesdays; weekends and Bank Holidays with member only. *Society Meetings:* catered for Tuesdays and Thursdays on application. Secretary: B.D. Powell (025-126 4211). Professional: T. Barter (025-126 3779).

FLEET. **North Hants Golf Club,** Minley Road, Fleet GU13 8RE (Fleet (0252) 616443). *Location:* B3013 off A30. 400 yards from railway station. 18 holes, 6257 yards. S.S.S. 70. *Green Fees:* information not provided. *Eating facilities:* lunch daily, snacks only on Mondays. *Visitors:* welcome with reservation. Handicap Certificates required. *Society Meetings:* Tuesdays and Wednesdays only. Professional: Steve Porter (0252 616655). Secretary: I.R. Goodliffe.

GOSPORT. **Fleetland Golf Club,** Rnay Fleetland, Fareham Road, Gosport PO13 0AW. *Location:* two miles south of Fareham on Fareham/Gosport road. Flat course. 9 holes, 4367 yards, 4777 metres. S.S.S. 63. *Green Fees:* £1.50 weekdays, £3.00 weekends. *Eating facilities:* bar. *Visitors:* by appointment with member only. *Society Meetings:* by appointment with member only. Secretary: Mr A. Eade (0705 822351 extension 44384).

GOSPORT. **Gosport and Stokes Golf Club,** Haslar, Gosport (Gosport (0705) 81625). *Location:* A32 to Gosport, course is one mile east of Stokes Bay, Near Gilkicker Point. Links course. 9 holes, 5668 yards.

S.S.S. 69. Nets and pitch and putt. *Green Fees:* £8.00 per day weekdays, £10.00 per day Sundays. *Eating facilities:* one bar, food available. *Visitors:* welcome all week except Sundays. *Society Meetings:* small meetings catered for. Secretary: T.W. Jopling (0705 27941).

HAVANT. **Rowlands Castle Golf Club,** 31 Links Lane, Rowlands Castle PO9 6AE (Rowlands Castle (0705) 412216). *Location:* four miles north of Havant or Horndean/Rowlands Castle Junction from A3M. 18 holes, 6627 yards White Tees, 6381 yards Yellow Tees. S.S.S. 72 (White), 70 (Yellow). *Green Fees:* weekdays £18.00 per round or day, £22.00 per round or day Sundays and Bank Holidays. *Eating facilities:* full catering available except Mondays. *Visitors:* welcome, except Saturdays. Advisable to telephone prior to playing. *Society Meetings:* catered for. Professional: Peter Klepacz (0705 412785). Secretary: Captain A.W. Aird (0705 412784).

HAYLING ISLAND. **Hayling Golf Club,** Ferry Road, Hayling Island PO11 0BX (Hayling Island (0705) 463777). *Location:* A3023 five miles south of Havant. Seaside Links. 18 holes, 6489 yards. S.S.S. 71. *Green Fees:* £20.00 per day, weekends £28.00. *Eating facilities:* lunches and afternoon teas available. *Visitors:* welcome with bona fide handicaps and must be members of recognised clubs. *Society Meetings:* Tuesdays and Wednesdays only by arrangement with the Secretary. Professional: Ray Gadd (0705 464491). Secretary: R.C.W. Stokes (0705 464446).

LEE-ON-THE-SOLENT. **Lee-On-The-Solent Golf Club,** Brune Lane, Lee-on-the-Solent PO13 9PB (Lee-on-the-Solent (0705) 551170 (Manager). *Location:* three miles south of Fareham on the B3385 then signposted. Parkland course. 18 holes, 5793 yards. S.S.S. 69. *Green Fees:* £16.00 per day. *Eating facilities:* bar snacks, lunches and afternoon teas, except Tuesdays; dinner by arrangement. *Visitors:* welcome weekdays with Handicap Certificate, weekend with member only. *Society Meetings:* Thursday by arrangement. Professional: Mr John Richardson (0705 551181).

LIPHOOK. **Liphook Golf Club,** Wheatsheaf Enclosure, Liphook GU30 7EH (Liphook (0428) 723271). *Location:* one mile south of Liphook off A3. Heathland. 18 holes, 6250 yards. S.S.S. 70. *Green Fees:* on application. *Eating facilities:* bar and restaurant. *Visitors:* welcome, Handicap Certificate required, check with Secretary. *Society Meetings:* catered for. Professional: Ian Large (0428 723271). Secretary: Major J.B. Morgan MBE (0428 723785).

LIPHOOK. **Old Thorns Golf Course & Hotel,** Longmoor Road, Liphook GU30 7PE (Liphook (0428) 724555). *Location:* A3 to Liphook, then one mile down Longmoor Road (B2131). Parkland, wooded, with natural streams and lakes. 18 holes, 6447 yards. S.S.S. 72. Practice ground and putting green. *Green Fees:* £18.00 per round, £27.00 per weekday: £28.00 per round weekends. Telephone to arrange a starting time.

Eating facilities: full catering available. Choice of European or Japanese cuisine. *Visitors:* welcome at all times. *Society Meetings:* welcome all week. Society days £45.00. Company days £60.00. Facilities: 33 en suite bedrooms, indoor heated swimming pool, sauna, solarium, massage, 2 tennis courts, conference and banqueting rooms. Professional: Philip Loxley. General Manager: G.M. Jones.

LYNDHURST. **Bramshaw Golf Club,** Brook, Lyndhurst (Soton (0703) 813433). *Location:* M27 (Interchange 1) one mile from M27 (north) at Brook. Two courses: one parkland, one woodland. Both 18 holes. Forest Course 5774 yards, S.S.S. 68. Manor Course 6233 yards. S.S.S. 70. Practice facilities. *Green Fees:* £20.00 weekdays, weekends with member only. *Eating facilities:* clubhouse and restaurant, also Bell Inn close by. *Visitors:* welcome Monday to Friday. No visitors at weekends unless playing with a member or Bell resident, Handicap Certificates required. 22 bedroomed hotel. *Society Meetings:* catered for by arrangement. Professional: Alan Edford (0703 813434). Manager: Bob Tingey (0703 813433).

LYNDHURST. **New Forest Golf Club,** Southampton Road, Lyndhurst SO43 7BU (Lyndhurst (042128) 2450). *Location:* on the A35 Southampton to Bournemouth road, on the Southampton side of Lyndhurst. Heathland course. 18 holes, 5742 yards. S.S.S. 68. Practice ground and net available. *Green Fees:* £9.00 weekdays, £12.00 weekends and Bank Holidays. *Eating facilities:* 11.00am to 3.00pm snacks and light meals. Bar open from 11.00am. *Visitors:* welcome after 9.30am Saturdays and after 1.00pm Sundays. No jeans, shorts or trainers allowed in the clubhouse. *Society Meetings:* catered for; maximum number 30 booked and confirmed in advance. Professional: Ken Gilhespy (042128 2450). Proprietor: Mickey Swann. Secretary: Wendy Swann (042128 2752).

PETERSFIELD. **Petersfield Golf Club,** Heath Road, Petersfield GU31 4EJ (Petersfield (0730) 63725). *Location:* turn off A3 in town centre, clubhouse one mile east. Heathland and parkland. 18 holes, 5720 yards. S.S.S. 69. *Green Fees:* £12.00 weekdays, £18 weekends. *Eating facilities:* available Tuesday to Saturday. *Visitors:* welcome weekdays, also Saturdays after 11.00am and Sundays after noon. *Society Meetings:* welcome except at weekends. Professional: Stephen Clay (0730 67732). Secretary: Lt Cdr P. Heraud RN (0730 62386).

PORTSMOUTH. **Great Salterns Municipal Golf Course,** Great Salterns, Portsmouth (Portsmouth (0705) 664549). *Location:* half a mile from M27 Exit A2030 Southsea. 18 holes, 6058 yards. S.S.S. 69. Floodlit driving range. *Green Fees:* information not provided. *Eating facilities:* available. *Visitors:* welcome. Professional: Terry Heally.

PORTSMOUTH. **Waterlooville Golf Club,** Cherry Tree Avenue, Cowplain, Portsmouth PO8 8AP (0705 252661). *Location:* off A3 or A3 (m), 10 miles north of Portsmouth. Parkland course. 18 holes, 6647 yards. S.S.S. 72. *Green Fees:* £17.00 per round, £20.00 per day, weekends only. *Eating facilities:* full catering service available, bar facilities. *Visitors:* welcome with

reservation Monday to Friday, weekends as members' guests only. *Society Meetings:* catered for by prior arrangement. Professional: John Hay (0705 256911). Secretary: Mr C. Chamberlain (0705 263388).

PURBROOK. **Portsmouth Municipal Golf Course,** Crookhorn Lane, Widley, Portsmouth PO7 5QL (Cosham (0705) 372210). *Location:* two thirds of a mile from junction of B2177 and A3. 18 holes, 6081 yards. S.S.S. 70. Practice area. *Green Fees:* £5.80. *Eating facilities:* available. *Visitors:* welcome, tee bookings required. *Society Meetings:* as arranged with Pro Shop. Professional: R. Brown (0705 372210). Portsmouth Golf Club (1926) play over the above course. Secretary: D. Houlihan (0705 381640 evenings).

RINGWOOD. **Burley Golf Club,** Burley, Ringwood BH24 4BB (Burley (04253) 2431). *Location:* A31 from Ringwood and turn right at Picket Post and on through Burley Street. Downland course, 9 holes, 6149 yards. S.S.S. 69. *Green Fees:* £10.00. *Visitors:* welcome but restrictions on Wednesday mornings and Saturday play. Handicap Certificates required. *Society Meetings:* not catered for. Secretary: G.R. Kendall.

ROMSEY. **Dunwood Manor Country Club,** Shootash Hill, Near Romsey SO51 0GF (0794 40549). *Location:* four miles from Romsey off A27. Undulating parkland. 18 holes, 6004 yards. S.S.S. 69. Practice area. *Green Fees:* £15.00 round, £20.00 day weekdays; £25.00 per round weekends. Society rates £13 per round, £18 per day. *Eating facilities:* full catering facilities. *Visitors:* welcome, by arrangement. *Society Meetings:* welcome, by arrangement. Professional: Gary Stubbington (0794 40663). Secretary: Mrs Hazel Johnson (0794 40549). Golf Manager: Patrick Dawson. Food and Beverage Manager: Nick Penny.

SOUTHAMPTON. **Corhampton Golf Club,** Sheeps Pond Lane, Droxford, Southampton SO3 1QZ (Droxford (0489) 877279). *Location:* one mile from Corhampton on the Bishops Waltham – Corhampton road (B3135). 18 holes, 6088 yards. S.S.S. 69. *Green Fees:* £15.00 per round, £25.00 per day. *Eating facilities:* full catering, except Tuesdays. *Visitors:* welcome Monday to Friday; weekends and Bank Holidays with a member. *Society Meetings:* Mondays and Thursdays. Professional: John Harris (0489 877638). Secretary: P. Taylor.

SOUTHAMPTON. **Meon Valley Hotel, Golf and Country Club,** Sandy Lane, Shedfield SO3 2HQ (Wickham (0329) 833455). *Location:* two miles northwest of Wickham north off A334. 18 holes, 6519 yards. S.S.S. 71. *Visitors:* Handicap Certificate required. 84 twin-bedded rooms with bathroom, three squash courts, three tennis courts, three snooker tables, gymnasium, indoor swimming pool, solarium, sauna, steam room and spa bath. Conference and meeting rooms. Professional: John Stirling.

SOUTHAMPTON. **Southampton Golf Club** (Play over the Municipal Golf Course), Municipal Golf Course Pavilion, Golf Course Road, Southampton. 18 holes, 6218 yards, S.S.S. 70. 9 holes separate course also. S.S.S. 33. *Green fees:* 18 holes weekdays £4.80 plus £1 booking fee, weekends and Bank Holidays £7.00 plus £1 booking fee; 9 holes weekdays £2.40, weekends and Bank Holidays £3.50. OAP and Junior 9 holes. *Eating facilities:* bar and full catering. *Visitors:* welcome but must book at weekends. *Society Meetings:* by arrangement with Sports Centre Manager's Office (0703 790732). Professional: John Cave (0703 768407). Hon. Secretary: K.G. Kennard (0703 760472).

SOUTHAMPTON. **Stoneham Golf Club,** Bassett Green Road, Bassett, Southampton SO2 3NE (Southampton (0703) 768151). *Location:* A33/M27 north of Southampton find Chilworth roundabout, take road to Airport (A27), half mile on left. Hilly heathery course. 18 holes, 6310 yards. S.S.S. 70. *Green Fees:* £21.00 per round or day, no green fees at weekends. *Eating facilities:* full catering, bar open all day. *Visitors:* welcome, except weekends and competition days. *Society Meetings:* catered for. Professional: Ian Young (0703 768397). Secretary: Mrs A. M. Wilkinson (0703 769272).

TIDWORTH. **Tidworth Garrison Golf Club,** Bulford Road, Tidworth (Stonehenge (0980) 42321). *Location:* A338, seven miles north-east of Amesbury, Wilts. on border of Hants. and Wilts. Superb scenic course. 18 holes, 5806 yards. S.S.S. 69. *Green Fees:* weekdays £15.00, weekends £20.00 per round or day. *Eating facilities:* full meal service can now be provided.

Visitors: welcome, but advisable to telephone in advance. *Society Meetings:* catered for Tuesdays, Thursdays and Fridays. Professional: T. Gosden (0980 42393). Secretary: Lt. Col. D.F.T. Tucker R E (0980 42301).

WINCHESTER. **Hockley Golf Club,** Twyford, Near Winchester SO21 1PL (Winchester (0962) 713461). *Location:* on A333 (Twyford road), two miles south east of Winchester off M3. Parkland course. 18 holes, 6279 yards. S.S.S. 70. Practice areas. *Green Fees:* £20.00 per day or round. *Eating facilities:* restaurant and bar available. *Visitors:* welcome weekdays, weekends with members only. Check first with Professional. *Society Meetings:* welcome, catered for Wednesdays and Thursdays only. Professional: Terry Lane (0962 713678). Secretary: (0962 713165).

WINCHESTER. **Royal Winchester Golf Club,** Sarum Road, Winchester (Winchester (0962) 51694). *Location:* one mile west of Winchester, left off A272, right at A31. 18 holes, 6218 metres. S.S.S. 70. *Green Fees:* weekdays £20.00. Weekends with member only. *Eating facilities:* full catering available except Thursdays. *Visitors:* welcome with Handicap Certificate. *Society Meetings:* by prior booking. Professional: D.P. Williams (0962 62473). Manager: (0962 52462).

Hereford & Worcester

BELMONT. **Belmont House Golf Course,** Belmont House, Belmont HR2 9SA (0432 277445). Riverside and parkland. 18 holes, 6448 yards. S.S.S. 71. *Green Fees:* on application. Discounts for groups over 10. *Eating facilities:* restaurant and bar. *Visitors:* welcome with advance booking. 30 en-suite bedrooms, tennis, fishing, meeting rooms. *Society Meetings:* catered for. Professional: Mike Welsh (0432 277445). General Manager: P. Bridges.

BEWDLEY. **Little Lakes Golf Club,** Lye Head, Bewdley, Worcester (Rock (0299) 266385). *Location:* two miles west of Bewdley off A456, turn left opposite Alton Glasshouses. 9 holes, 6247 yards. S.S.S. 72. *Green Fees:* weekdays £9.00 per round, £12.00 per day, weekends only by invitation of a member. *Eating facilities:* full restaurant service. *Visitors:* no restrictions weekdays. *Societies:* welcome by prior arrangement. Secretary: R.A. Norris (0562 67495). Professional: M. Laing.

BLACKWELL. **Blackwell Golf Club,** Blackwell, Near Bromsgrove B60 1PY (021-445 1470). *Location:* approximately 10 miles south of Birmingham and three miles east of Bromsgrove. Parkland. 18 holes, 6202 yards. S.S.S. 71. *Green Fees:* £20.00 per day. *Eating facilities:* full catering by prior arrangment. *Visitors:* welcome Monday to Friday without reservation. *Society Meetings:* catered for by arrangement through Secretary. Professional: H. MacDonald (021-445 3113). Secretary: S. Allen (021-445 1994).

BLAKEDOWN. **Churchill and Blakedown Golf Club,** Churchill Lane, Blakedown, Nr. Kidderminster. (Kidderminster (0562) 700200). *Location:* off A456 Birmingham/Kidderminster road at Blakedown. 9 holes, 5399 yards. S.S.S. 67. *Green Fees:* £10.00. *Eating facilities:* Snacks and full meals except Monday. *Visitors:* welcome with reservation. *Society Meetings:* weekdays only by arrangement through the Secretary. Secretary: J.H. Lidstone.

DROITWICH. **Droitwich Golf and Country Club Ltd,** Westford House, Ford Lane, Droitwich WB9 0BQ (Droitwich (0905) 770129). *Location:* between junction 5 of M5 and Droitwich just off A38. Parkland – undulating – wooded. 18 holes, 6040 yards. S.S.S. 69. Practice area. *Green Fees:* £16.50 weekdays, with a member only £5.00; £6.00 weekends playing with a member only. *Eating facilities:* full catering available. *Visitors:* welcome without reservation Mondays to Fridays, weekends with member only. *Society Meetings:* catered for Wednesdays or Fridays. Professional: C.S. Thompson (0905 770207). Secretary: M.J. Taylor (0905 774344).

EVESHAM. **Evesham Golf Club,** Craycombe Links, Fladbury Cross, Pershore WR10 2QS (Evesham (0386) 860395). *Location:* M5 at Junction 6, A4538 and B4084 to Evesham. Approximately 10 miles from M5 and three miles from Evesham. 9 holes, 6418 yards. S.S.S. 71. Small practice area. *Green Fees:* £10.00. *Eating facilities:* catering available. *Visitors:* only allowed at weekends if playing with a member. Ladies' day – Tuesday. *Society Meetings:* catered for by prior arrangement. Professional: Raymond J. Gray (0386 860395). Secretary: Frank G. Vincent (0386 552373). Steward: J.A. Webber (0386 860822).

HAGLEY. **Hagley Country Club Golf Club,** Wassell Grove, Hagley (Hagley (0562) 883701). *Location:* Wassell Grove is off A456 Birmingham to Kidderminster Road. 18 holes, 6353 yards. S.S.S. 72. *Green fees:* £14.00 per round per person, £20.00 per day Monday to Friday. *Eating facilities:* a la Carte Restaurant and bar snacks, Tuesday to Saturday. Secretary: Graham F. Yardley.

HEREFORD. **Herefordshire Golf Club,** Ravens Causeway, Wormsley, Hereford HR4 8LY (0432 71219). *Location:* six miles north-west of Hereford on a B road to Weobley. Undulating parkland course. 18 holes, 6036 yards. S.S.S. 69. *Green Fees:* £15.00 weekends, £11.00 during week, reduced to £9.00 and £7.00 respectively for members' guests. *Eating facilities:* catering available, except Monday. *Visitors:* welcome. *Society Meetings:* catered for on weekdays, restricted at weekends. Professional: David Hemming (0432 71465). Secretary: Cyril Jones.

KIDDERMINSTER. **Habberley Golf Club,** Habberley, Kidderminster DY13 0RB (Kidderminster (0562) 822381). *Location:* north west side of Kidderminster. Hilly parkland course. 18 holes, 5481 yards. S.S.S. 68. Practice area. *Green Fees:* £9.00 weekdays, £5.00 weekends with member. *Eating facilities:* food and bar

available. *Visitors:* welcome weekdays, without reservation, weekends with member only. *Society Meetings:* by negotiation. Secretary: Mr D.B. Lloyd (0562 745756).

KIDDERMINSTER. **Kidderminster Golf Club,** Russell Road, Kidderminster DY16 3HT (Kidderminster (0562) 822303). *Location:* signposted off A449 Worcester-Wolverhampton Road. 18 holes, 6223 yards. S.S.S. 70. Practice ground. *Green Fees:* £18.00 weekdays. *Eating facilities:* available. *Visitors:* welcome weekdays only if member of another club, weekends by guest of member. Snooker room with bar. *Society Meetings:* catered for Thursdays only. Professional: N.P. Underwood (0562 740090). Secretary/Manager: W. Wiltshire.

KINGTON. **Kington Golf Club,** Bradnor Hill, Kington (Kington (0544) 8230340). *Location:* one mile out of Kington, on B4355 to Presteigne. Hill course, with views of seven counties. Highest 18 hole course in England and Wales. 18 holes, 5820 yards. S.S.S. 68. *Green Fees:* £11.00 weekdays, £16.00 weekends and Bank Holidays. *Eating facilities:* meals at club. *Visitors:* welcome. *Society Meetings:* catered for by arrangement. Hon. Secretary: F.H. Bradley.

LEOMINSTER. **Leominster Golf Club,** Ford Bridge, Leominster HR6 0LE (Leominster (0568) 2863). *Location:* three miles south of Leominster on A49 on bypass, Club marked. Undulating parkland. 9 holes, 6084 yards. S.S.S. 69. Practice area. *Green Fees:* weekdays £10.00, weekends £13.00. Special rates for groups of

12 or more. *Eating facilities:* all meals available except Mondays. *Visitors:* welcome daily, weekends by appointment. *Society Meetings:* catered for by prior arrangement. Professional: Mr Russell Price (0568 2863). Secretary: J.A. Ashcroft (043-272 493).

MALVERN WELLS. **The Worcestershire Golf Club,** Wood Farm, Malvern Wells WR14 4PP (Malvern (0684) 573905). *Location:* two miles south of Great Malvern, near junction of A449 and B4209. Exceptionally scenic – Malvern Hills and Vale of Evesham. 18 holes, 6449 yards. S.S.S. 71. *Green Fees:* £16.00 weekdays, £20.00 weekends. With member £6.00. *Eating facilities:* available. *Visitors:* visitors unaccompanied by a member must provide evidence of Golf Club Membership. Weekends after 10.00am. *Society Meetings:* catered for Thursday and Fridays only on application. Professional: G.M. Harris (0684 564428). Secretary: G.R. Scott (0684 575992).

REDDITCH. **Abbey Park Golf and Country Club,** Abbey Park, Dagnell End Road, Redditch B98 7BD (Redditch (0527) 63918). *Location:* leave M42 at A435 Evesham – through Bedley towards Redditch or off A441 Birmingham to Redditch. Parkland. 18 holes, 6411 yards, 5827 metres. S.S.S. 71. Driving range. *Green Fees:* weekdays £5.00, weekends £6.00. *Eating facilities:* bars, restaurant and bar snacks. *Visitors:* welcome, no restrictions. Booking usually necessary at weekends and Bank Holidays. Accommodation available, special rates for Weekend Breaks. Snooker room available. *Society Meetings:* welcome. Professional: R.K. Cameron. Secretary: M.E. Bradley.

REDDITCH. **Redditch Golf Club,** Lower Grinsty Green Lane, Callow Hill, Redditch B97 5PJ (Redditch (0527) 43309). *Location:* three miles west of Redditch town centre, off Redditch to Bromsgrove road (A448), or Astwood Bank to Redditch (A441), take Windmill Drive, look for Callow Hill signs. Frist 9 holes parkland, second 9 holes wooded. 18 holes, 6671 yards. S.S.S. 72. Two practice areas. *Green Fees:* £15.00 weekdays, weekends £4.00 with member. *Eating facilities:* restaurant and bar. *Visitors:* welcome, weekends with member. *Society Meetings:* catered for by arrange-

ment. Professional: Mr F. Powell (0527 46372). Secretary: Mr C. Holman.

ROSS-ON-WYE. **Ross-on-Wye Golf Club,** Two Park, Gorsley, Ross-on-Wye HR9 7UT (098982 660). *Location:* off Junction 3, M50, midway Ross-on-Wye and Newent. Parkland course. 18 holes, 6500 yards. S.S.S. 73. Practice area. *Green fees:* weekdays £17.00, weekends £20.00. Member's guest £8.00. *Eating facilities:* full catering, diningroom. *Visitors:* welcome, Handicap Certificate advised. Must be members of recognised golf club. Book in advance with Professional. *Society Meetings:* two per week, booking well in advance with Professional. Minimum number 16, maximum 60. Snooker tables also available. Professional: Adrian Clifford (098982 439). Secretary: G.H. Cason (098982 267).

WORCESTER. **Tolladine Golf Club,** The Fairway, Tolladine Road, Worcester WR4 9BA (Worcester (0905) 21074). *Location:* M5, exit 6. Warndon turn off, one mile. 9 holes, 18 holes, 5630 yards. S.S.S. 67, Par 68. *Green Fees:* £10.00 weekdays, £4.00 with member. £5.00 weekends with member only. *Visitors:* welcome weekdays. Secretary: A.J. Wardle.

WORCESTER. **Worcester Golf and Country Club,** Boughton Park, Worcester WR2 4EZ (Worcester (0905) 421132). *Location:* one-and-a-quarter miles west of city on A4103 (to Hereford). Parkland. 18 holes, 5946 yards. S.S.S. 68. *Green Fees:* £18.00 per weekday. Weekends only with a member. *Eating facilities:* full catering available. Caterers: S and T. Fletcher (0905 421132).*Visitors:* welcome with reservation. *Society Meetings:* catered for. Handicap golfers by arrangement. Professional: Colin Colenso (0905 422044). Secretary: J.M. Kennedy (0905 422555).

WYTHALL. **Fulford Heath Golf Club Ltd,** Tanners Green Lane, Wythall (Wythall (0564) 822806). *Location:* one mile from Alcester Road, via Tanners Green Lane. 18 holes, 6256 yards. S.S.S. 70. *Green Fees:* on application. *Visitors:* welcome weekdays with reservation. *Society Meetings:* catered for on application. Professional: Mr K. Hayward. Secretary: R. Bowen.

Hertfordshire

BARNET. **Arkley Golf Club,** Rowley Green Road, Barnet EN5 3HL (081-449 0394). *Location:* A1000 from London, turn by Elstree Moat House, two miles from Barnet. Parkland. 9 holes, 6045 yards. S.S.S. 69. *Green Fees;* weekdays £15.00 per round, £20.00 per day; weekends only with a member. *Eating facilities:* available, no catering Mondays. *Visitors:* welcome weekdays please phone, weekends with member only. *Society Meetings:* catered for Wednesdays, Thursdays and Fridays. Professional: M. Squire (081-440 8473). Secretary: G.D. Taylor (081-499 0394).

BARNET. **Hadley Wood Golf Club,** Beech Hill, Near Barnet (081-449 4328). *Location:* off the exit from M25 at Junction 24 on to A111 Cockfosters. Down hill, third turning on the right. 18 holes, 6473 yards. S.S.S. 71. *Green Fees:* £22.00 per round, £30.00 per day weekdays except Tuesday a.m. *Eating facilities:* available Tuesday to Friday. *Visitors:* welcome weekdays, (not Tuesday a.m.), with club Handicap Certificate or letter of introduction. *Society Meetings:* catered for Wednesday to Friday. Professional: Alan McGinn (081-449 3285). Secretary/General Manager: J.E. Linaker (081-449 4486).

BERKHAMSTED. **Ashridge Golf Club,** Little Gaddesden, Berkhamsted (Little Gaddesden (044284) 2244). *Location:* five miles north west of Berkhamsted. 18 holes, 6508 yards. S.S.S. 71. *Green Fees:* on application. *Eating facilities:* daily. *Visitors:* welcome with reservation. Professional/Golf Manager: Geoffrey Pook. Secretary: Mrs Maggie West.

BERKHAMSTED. **Berkhamsted Golf Club,** The Common, Berkhamsted HP4 2QB (Berkhamsted (0442) 863730). *Location:* A41 to Berkhamsted, up Raven's Lane to top of hill, turn left. Heathland, no sand bunkers. 18 holes, 6605 yards, 6040 metres. S.S.S. 72. *Green Fees:* weekdays £27.50 all day, £20.00 half day, weekends £40.00 (1990). *Eating facilities:* daily although limited on Mondays. *Visitors:* welcome weekdays (ring Secretary first). Handicap Certificate required. *Society Meetings:* catered for Wednesdays and Fridays. Professional: B.J. Proudfoot (0442 865851). Secretary: J.F. Robinson (0442 865832).

BISHOP'S STORTFORD. **Bishop's Stortford Golf Club,** Dunmow Road, Bishop's Stortford CM23 5HP (Bishop's Stortford (0279) 54027). *Location:* M11 Junction 8, follow signs to town centre/hospital. Golf Club entrance one mile on left. Parkland. 18 holes, 6440 yards. S.S.S. 71. *Green Fees:* weekdays £18.00; weekends £12.00 (with full member only). *Eating facilities:* restaurant and bar. *Visitors:* welcome weekdays; weekends with member only. *Society Meetings:* catered for weekdays except Tuesdays (maximum 40). Professional: Vince Duncan (0279 651324). Secretary: Major C. Rolls (0279 654715).

BUNTINGFORD. **East Herts Golf Club Ltd,** Hamels Park, Buntingford SG9 9NA (Ware (0920) 821978). *Location:* one mile north of Puckeridge on A10. 18 holes, 6416 yards. S.S.S. 71. *Green Fees:* details on application. *Eating facilities:* no catering Tuesdays. *Visitors:* welcome with members only at weekends. *Society Meetings:* catered for weekdays. Professional: J. Hamilton. Secretary: J.A. Harper.

BUSHEY. **Bushey Hall Golf Club,** Bushey Hall Drive, Bushey (Watford (0923) 225802). *Location:* Bushey Hall Road, Aldenham Road roundabout, one mile from M1. 18 holes, 6099 yards. S.S.S. 70. *Green Fees:* on application. *Eating facilities:* full catering available. *Visitors:* welcome with reservation. *Society Meetings:* catered for weekdays. Professional: D. Fitzsimmons. Secretary: C.A. Brown.

BUSHEY HEATH. **Hartsbourne Golf and Country Club,** Hartsbourne Avenue, Bushey Heath WD2 1JW. *Location:* five miles south east of Watford. Parkland. 18 holes, 6305 yards. S.S.S. 70. 9 holes, 5342 yards. S.S.S. 66. *Green Fees:* weekdays £12.50, weekends £15.00. *Eating facilities:* restaurant and snack bar available. *Visitors:* guests of members only. *Society Meetings:* catered for Mondays, Wednesdays and Fridays. Professionals: Geoff Hunt and Martin Hattam (01-950 2836). Secretary: R.J.H. Jourdan (01-950 1133 or 4346).

CHORLEYWOOD. **Chorleywood Golf Club Ltd.,** Common Road, Chorleywood (Chorleywood (09278) 2009). *Location:* half a mile off A404, three miles from Rickmansworth. Flat common land with woods. 9 holes, 5676 yards. S.S.S. 67. *Green Fees:* £8.00 weekdays, £10.00 weekends. *Eating facilities:* meals served if ordered by phone. *Visitors:* welcome weekdays except Tuesday and Thursday mornings, restricted at weekends. Hon. Secretary: L.W. Turner.

DAGNALL. **Whipsnade Park Golf Club,** Studham Lane, Dagnall HP4 1RH (Little Gaddesden (044-284) 2330/2331). *Location:* between Dagnall and Studham. Junction 11 M1 (from north), Junction 9 (from south). Parkland. 18 holes, 6800 yards. S.S.S. 72. Large practice area. *Green Fees:* £15.00 per round, £20.00 per day weekdays, weekends with member only. *Eating facilities:* restaurant open daily, 2 bars. *Visitors:* welcome weekdays with reservation. *Society Meetings:* welcome with reservation. Professional: Mike Lewendon (044284 2331). Secretary: Andrea King (044284 2330).

HARPENDEN. **Harpenden Common Golf Club,** East Common, Harpenden AL5 1BL (0582 712856). *Location:* on A1081 between Harpenden and St. Albans. Flat heathland. 18 holes, 5613 yards, 5133 metres. S.S.S. 67. *Green Fees:* weekdays £14.00 per round, £18.00 per day. *Eating facilities:* daily except

Mondays. *Visitors:* welcome weekdays only with reservation (not Tuesdays). Weekends with member only. *Society Meetings:* Thursday and Friday only. Professional: Nigel Lawrence (0582 460655). Secretary: H.N. Hobbs (0582 715959).

HARPENDEN. **Harpenden Golf Club**, Hammonds End, Redbourn Lane, Harpenden (Harpenden (0582) 712580). *Location:* turn off A1081, four miles after St. Albans on B487. Parkland course. 18 holes, 6363 yards. S.S.S. 70. *Green Fees:* £24.00 per day. *Eating facilities:* lunches at club, order in advance. *Visitors:* welcome by arrangement. *Society Meetings:* by arrangement only. Professional: Doug Smith. Secretary: H. Pitcock.

HATFIELD. **Brookmans Park Golf Club**, Golf Club Road, Brookmans Park, Hatfield AL9 7AT (Potters Bar (0707) 52459). *Location:* between A1 and A1000, also just off M25, exit for Potters Bar. Parkland. 18 holes, 6454 yards, 5901 metres. S.S.S. 71. Practice ground and putting green. *Green Fees:* weekdays £20.00 per round, £25.00 per day. Handicap Certificate required. *Eating facilities:* bar snacks and lunches weekdays. *Visitors:* welcome weekdays; weekends with member only. *Society Meetings:* catered for Wednesdays and Thursdays. Professionals: M.M.R. Plumbridge and I. Jelley (0707 52468). Secretary: P.A. Gill (0707 52487).

HATFIELD. **Hatfield London Country Club**, Bedwell Park, Essendon, Hatfield AL9 6JA (Potters Bar (0707) 42624/42626). *Location:* B158, 5 miles north east of Potters Bar, one mile south of Essendon village. 18 holes and 9 holes Pitch and Putt. 6878 yards. S.S.S. 72. *Green Fees:* information not provided. *Eating facilities:* lunch except Mondays. *Visitors:* welcome with advance booking only. *Society Meetings:* catered for. Professional: Norman Greer.

HATFIELD. **Hatfield London Country Club**, Bedwell Park, Essendon, Hatfield AL9 6JA (Potters Bar (0707) 42624 or 42626). *Location:* B158, five miles north east of Potters Bar, one mile south of Essendon village. 18 holes and 9 holes Pitch and Putt. 6878 yards. S.S.S. 72. *Green Fees:* information not provided. *Eating facilities:* lunch except Mondays. *Visitors:* welcome, advance bookings only. *Society Meetings:* catered for. Professional: Norman Greer.

HEMEL HEMPSTEAD. **Boxmoor Golf Club**, 18 Box Lane, Hemel Hempstead (Hemel Hempstead (0442) 42434). *Location:* two miles from Hemel Hempstead, three-quarters of a mile from Hemel Hempstead Station on A41. Hilly/moorland course, 9 holes, 4112 yards. S.S.S. 62. *Green Fees:* Information not provided. *Eating facilities:* snacks by arrangement. *Visitors:* welcome without reservation, except on Sundays. *Society Meetings:* catered for with 4 weeks notice. Secretary: E. Duell (0442 62427).

HEMEL HEMPSTEAD. **Little Hay Golf Course**, Box Lane, Bovingdon. *Location:* just off A41, along Chesham Road from Hemel Hempstead. 18 hole golf course, 9 hole pitch & putt course, 18 hole putting green. *Visitors:* all members of the public welcome. Professional: David S. Johnson.

HERTFORD. **Brickendon Grange Golf and Country Club**, Brickendon, Near Hertford SG13 8PD (Bayford (099286) 228). *Location:* 3 miles south of Hertford, one mile from Bayford Railway Station. Undulating parkland with specimen trees. 18 holes, 6315 yards. S.S.S. 70. *Green Fees:* £25.00 day ticket, £20.00 half day ticket weekdays, weekends only with a member. *Eating facilities:* bar and restaurant, snack meals available lunchtimes. *Visitors:* welcome weekdays only, Handicap certificate required. *Society Meetings:* catered for by arrangement. Professional: J. Hamilton (099286 218). Secretary: N. Martin (099286 258).

KNEBWORTH. **Knebworth Golf Club**, Deards End Lane, Knebworth SG3 6NL (Stevenage (0438) 814681). *Location:* one mile south of Stevenage. Parkland. 18 holes, 6428 yards. S.S.S. 70. *Green Fees:* details on application. *Eating facilities:* available. *Visitors:* welcome (with members only at weekends). *Society Meetings:* welcome weekdays. Professional: R.Y. Mitchell (0438 812757). Secretary: J.C. Wright (0438 812752).

LETCHWORTH. **Letchworth Golf Club**, Letchworth Lane, Letchworth SG6 3NQ (Letchworth (0462) 683203). *Location:* two miles from A1 (M) near village of Willian, adjacent to Letchworth Hall Hotel. Parkland course. 18 holes, 6181 yards. S.S.S. 69. Practice ground. *Green Fees:* £25.00 per day. *Eating facilities:* bars and restaurant except Mondays. *Visitors:* weekdays Handicap Certificate required, weekends accompanied only. *Society Meetings:* catered for Wednesdays, Thursdays and Fridays. Professional: John Mutimer (0462 682713). Secretary: Basil M. Barber.

POTTERS BAR. **Potters Bar Golf Club**, Darkes Lane, Potters Bar EN6 1DF (0707 52020). *Location:* exit 24 from M25 north orbital road, turn to Potters Bar. Through one set of traffic lights, turn right at second set into Darkes Lane, clubhouse on left at end of village (one mile M25). Parkland course, well wooded and undulating. 18 holes, 6273 yards, 5736 metres. S.S.S. 71. Small practice ground, nets and putting green. *Green Fees:* weekdays £25.00. *Eating facilities:* luncheons and buffet served (except Wednesday am) from 11.30am. *Visitors:* weekdays only, must produce Handicap Certificate. Members only at weekends. *Society Meetings:* Mondays or Fridays only, corporate days by arrangement. Professional: Kevin Hughes (0707 52987). Secretary/Manager: A. St.J. Williams (0707 52020).

RADLETT. **Porters Park Golf Club**, Shenley Hill, Radlett WD7 7AZ (Radlett (0923) 856262). *Location:* approximately 3 miles south-west of Junction 22 (M25), 3 miles north-east Junction 5 (M1). Watford 5 miles, St. Albans 8 miles. Park-type course with fine trees and a brook. 18 holes, 6313 yards. S.S.S. 70. Two practice areas. *Green Fees:* weekdays £25.00 per round, £35.00 per day; weekends with members only (£10 per round with member). *Eating facilities:* men's bar, mixed lounge and diningroom. *Visitors:* welcome weekdays by appointment only, Handicap Certificate required. *Society Meetings:* catered for Wednesday and Thursday only. Professional: David Gleeson (0923 854366). Manager: J.H. Roberts (0923 854127).

RICKMANSWORTH. **Moor Park Golf Club,** Moor Park, Rickmansworth WD3 1QN (Rickmansworth (0923) 773146). *Location:* A404 to Northwood Hills, Batchworth Heath. Course no. 1: 18 holes, 6695 yards. S.S.S. 72. Course no. 2: 18 holes, 5823 yards. S.S.S. 68. *Green Fees:* information not provided. *Eating facilities:* full catering always available at club. *Visitors:* welcome on weekdays by prior arrangement, and on weekends with a member. Professional: E.R. Whitehead. Secretary: J.A. Davies.

RICKMANSWORTH. **Rickmansworth Golf Club,** Moor Lane, Rickmansworth WD3 1QL (Rickmansworth (0923) 773163). *Location:* from town centre along A404 to Waterworks, left along B4504, then first right. Testing, undulating parkland course. 18 holes, 4500 yards, 4115 metres. S.S.S. 62. *Green Fees:* £5.50 weekdays, £7.60 weekends. *Eating facilities:* bars, restaurant. *Visitors:* no restrictions. *Society Meetings:* catered for. Professional: Ian Duncan (0923 775278). Secretary: G.P. Harrison (0923 260703).

ROYSTON. **Royston Golf Club,** Baldock Road, Royston SG8 5BG (Royston (0763) 242177). *Location:* on the outskirts of Royston on A505 between Royston and Baldock. Undulating heathland. 18 holes, 6032 yards. S.S.S. 69. Practice fairway. *Green Fees:* £15.00 weekdays. *Eating facilities:* bar and restaurant meals – two bars. *Visitors:* welcome weekdays; weekends only with member. *Society Meetings:* catered for weekdays with 12 or more members. Professional: M. Hatcher (0763 243476). Secretary: Mrs S. Morris (0763 242696).

ST. ALBANS. **Batchwood Hall Golf Club,** Batchwood Drive, St. Albans (St. Albans (0727) 33349). *Location:* north west corner of town. 18 holes, 6463 yards. S.S.S. 71. *Green Fees:* on application. *Eating facilities:* private caterers. *Visitors:* welcome without reservation except 0630 to 1000 hours weekends. *Society Meetings:* not catered for. Professional: J. Thomson (0727 52101). Secretary: B.R. Mercer.

ST. ALBANS. **Mid-Herts Golf Club,** Gustard Wood, Wheathampstead, St. Albans (Wheathampstead (058 283) 3118). *Location:* B651, six miles north of St. Albans. Heathland, short and tight course. 18 holes, 6094 yards. S.S.S. 69. Course record 67. *Green Fees:* weekdays £20.00 per day or round; weekends and Bank Holidays with member only. *Eating facilities:* by arrangement. *Visitors:* welcome weekdays with reservation; Handicap Certificate required. *Society Meetings:* catered for by arrangement. Professional: N. Brown (058 283 2788). Secretary: J. Bowen. (058 283 2242).

ST. ALBANS. **Redbourn Golf Club,** Luton Lane, Redbourn, Near St. Albans AL3 7QA (0582 793493). *Location:* 4 miles north of St. Albans, 4 miles south of Luton, 1 mile south off M1 Junction 9. Parkland. 18 holes, 6407 yards. S.S.S. 71. 9 holes, 1361 yards. S.S.S. 27. Driving range. *Green Fees:* for visitors – £10.00 weekdays, £12.00 weekends and Bank Holidays. *Eating facilities:* licensed bar; snacks and hot

meals readily available. *Visitors:* welcome weekdays; weekends and Bank Holidays after 3.00pm. *Societies:* catered for by arrangement. Professional: Steve Baldwin (0582 793493). Secretary: W.M. Dunn (0582 792150).

ST. ALBANS. **Verulam Golf Club,** 226 London Road, St. Albans AL1 1JG (St. Albans (0727) 53327). *Location:* Junction 22 M25, then A1081 St. Albans. Parkland. 18 holes, 6432 yards. S.S.S. 71. Practice ground. *Green Fees:* weekdays £15.00 per round, £18.00 per day (Mondays £12.00 per round, £16.00 per day). *Eating facilities:* bar snacks, lunches. *Visitors:* welcome except weekends and Bank Holidays. *Society Meetings:* catered for by arrangement. Professional: Paul Anderson (0727 61401). Secretary: G.D. Eastwood (0727 53327).

STEVENAGE. **Stevenage Golf Centre,** Aston Lane, Stevenage SG2 7EL (Shephall (043888) 424). *Location:* turn off A1(M) at Stevenage South Junction onto A602 to Hertford. 18 holes, 6451 yards. S.S.S. 71. Par 72. 20-bay driving range. *Green Fees:* telephone the Professional for details. *Eating facilities:* restaurant and bar. *Visitors:* welcome, advance booking system available to reserve tee-off times. Shower facilities. *Society Meetings:* catered for by arrangement. Professional: K. Bond. Manager: S. Robb.

WALTHAM CROSS. **Cheshunt Golf Club,** The Clubhouse, Park Lane, Cheshunt (Waltham Cross (0992) 29777). *Location:* M25 Junction 25 then A10 towards Hertford, second set of traffic lights to Flanstead End. Flat parkland course. 18 holes, 6608 yards. S.S.S. 71. Practice area. *Green Fees:* weekdays £4.50, weekends and Bank Holidays £6.00. OAPs £2.25 weekdays only. *Eating facilities:* public cafe. *Visitors:* welcome any time. For tee-off times phone Pro's Shop (0992 24009). *Society Meetings:* catered for by arrangement. Professional: C. Newton (0992 24009). Secretary: J.G. Duncan (0992 29777).

WARE. **Chadwell Springs Golf Club,** Hertford Road, Ware SG12 9LE (Ware (0920) 463647). *Location:* midway between Ware and Hertford on A119. 9 holes, 3027 yards. S.S.S. 69. *Green Fees:* weekdays £12.00, weekends with member only £8.00. *Eating facilities:* food available in bars lunchtime. *Visitors:* welcome weekdays; weekends with member only. *Society Meetings:* by arrangement. Professional: Adrian Shearn (0920 462075). Secretary: J.E. Moughton (0920 461447).

WATFORD. **Aldenham Golf and Country Club,** Church Lane, Aldenham, Near Watford WD2 8AL (Watford (0923) 853929). *Location:* Junction 5 on M1, take A41 to South Watford, turn left at 1st roundabout, 2nd right. Flat parkland. 18 holes, 6500 yards. S.S.S. 71. Practice area. *Green Fees:* £15.00 per round weekdays, £22.00 per round weekends. *Eating facilities:* bars, snack bar, restaurant. *Visitors:* welcome but not before 1pm weekends. *Society Meetings:* by arrangement. Professional: Alistair McKay (0923 857889). Secretary: D.W. Phillips (0923 853929).

WELWYN GARDEN CITY. **Panshanger Municipal Golf Club,** Old Herns Lane, Panshanger, Welwyn Garden City (Welwyn Garden (0707) 333350). *Location:* A1 (M) Clock Motel exit Welwyn. 2 miles off A1 (A1000 towards Hertford). Parkland. 18 holes, 6624 yards. S.S.S. 72. Practice area. *Green fees:* information not available. *Eating facilities:* restaurant, cafeteria and licensed bar available. *Visitors:* welcome any time without reservation. 9 hole pitch and putt, 3 squash courts. *Society Meetings:* catered for in advance except weekends. Professionals: Bryan Lewis and Mick Corlass (0707 333350). Secretary: John Travers (0707 332837).

WELWYN GARDEN CITY. **Welwyn Garden City Golf Club Ltd.,** Mannicotts, High Oaks Road, Welwyn Garden City AL8 7BP (Welwyn Garden (0707) 322722). *Location:* from north Junction 5 on A1M and take B197 to Valley Road. From south Junction 4 on A1M to Lemsford Lane and Valley Road. Undulating parkland. 18 holes, 6200 yards. S.S.S. 69. Practice ground. *Green Fees:* £20.00 weekdays. *Eating facilities:* by order for lunches; sandwiches available. *Visitors:* welcome weekdays with Handicap Certificate; weekends with member only. *Society Meetings:* Wednesdays and Thursdays only. Professional: H. Arnott (0707 325525). Secretary/Manager: J.L. Carragher (0707 325243).

Humberside

BEVERLEY. **Beverley and East Riding Golf Club,** Westwood, Beverley, North Humberside (0482 868757). *Location:* one mile from Beverley town centre. 18 holes, 6164 yards. S.S.S. 69. *Green Fees:* £7.00 weekdays, £10.00 Sundays and Bank Holidays. *Eating facilities:* Lunch and high teas, prior ordering. *Visitors:* welcome with reservation. *Society Meetings:* catered for, prior notice for approval of committee. Professional: Ian Mackie. Secretary: A. Walker.

BEVERLEY. **Hainsworth Park Golf Club,** Brandesburton, Near Driffield YO25 8RQ (Hornsea (0964) 542362). *Location:* A165 between Beverley and Bridlington, eight miles north of Beverley. Parkland with mature trees. 9 holes, 5450 yards, 4844 metres. S.S.S. 66. Small practice area. *Green Fees:* weekdays £5.00, weekends £7.50. *Eating facilities:* bar and catering. *Visitors:* welcome. Hotel accommodation on the course. *Society Meetings:* welcome. Secretary: R. Hounsfield (0377 43751). Any enquiries to B. Atkin at club address.

BRIDLINGTON. **Bridlington Golf Club,** Belvedere Road, Bridlington YO15 3NA (0262 672092). *Location:* one mile south from Bridlington Station, adjacent A165. Flat parkland. 18 holes, 6330 yards. S.S.S. 70. *Green Fees:* weekdays £10.00 per round/day, weekends and Bank Holidays £15.00 per round/day. Reductions for parties over 20 in number. *Eating facilities:* full catering. *Visitors:* welcome most days but limited on Sundays. Advisable to book in advance. *Society Meetings:* catered for. Professional: D.M. Rands (0262 674721). Hon. Secretary: Clive Wilson (0262 606367).

BRIDLINGTON. **Flamborough Head Golf Club,** Flamborough, Bridlington (Bridlington (0262) 850333). *Location:* five miles north-east of Bridlington on B1255. 18 holes, 5438 yards. S.S.S. 66. *Green Fees:* weekdays £10.00 per day; weekends and Bank Holidays £13.00 per day. *Visitors:* welcome. *Society Meetings:* catered for, apply to Secretary. Secretary: W.R. Scarle.

BRIGG. **Elsham Golf Club,** Barton Road, Elsham Brigg, South Humberside (0652 688382). *Location:* off Junction 5 M180. Parkland. 18 holes, 6411 yards. S.S.S. 71. *Green Fees:* £15.00 weekdays. Only with member at weekends. *Eating facilities:* full catering. *Visitors:* welcome. *Society Meetings:* catered for on weekdays on application to Manager. Steward (0652 688382). Professional: Stuart Brewer (0652 680432). Secretary: B.P. Nazer (0652 680291).

BROUGH. **Brough Golf Club,** Cave Road, Brough HU15 1HB (0482-667374). *Location:* 10 miles west of Hull off A63. Parkland. 18 holes, 6153 yards. S.S.S. 69. Practice facilities. *Green Fees:* £15.00 per round, £20.00 per day. *Eating facilities:* snacks etc. *Visitors:* welcome Monday to Friday subject to club events, not weekends or Bank Holidays. Wednesdays only after 2pm. *Society Meetings:* catered for. Professional: G. Townhill (0482 667483). Secretary: H.J. Oldroyd (0482 667291).

CLEETHORPES. **Cleethorpes Golf Club Ltd,** Golf House, Kings Road, Cleethorpes DN35 0PN (Grimsby (0472) 812059). *Location:* approximately one mile south of Cleethorpes. Flat meadowland crossed by large dykes. 18 holes, 6018 yards, 5503 metres. S.S.S. 69. Restricted practice area. *Green Fees:* weekdays £10.00 day/round, weekends and Bank Holidays £13.00 day/round. £3.00 reduction if playing with a member. *Eating facilities:* bar snacks always available; evening meals by prior arrangement. *Visitors:* welcome except Wednesdays, but must be members of another golf club. *Society Meetings:* weekdays only by arrangement with the Secretary. Ladies do not play Saturday afternoon and Sunday morning. Men do not play Wednesday afternoon. Professional: E. Sharp (0472 814060) Secretary: G.B. Standaloft (0472 814060).

CONISTON. **Ganstead Park Golf Club,** Longdales Lane, Coniston, Near Hull HU11 4LB (Hull (0482) 811280). *Location:* east of Hull, A165. Flat parkland. 18 holes, 6495 yards. S.S.S. 71. *Green Fees:* weekdays £9.00 per day, weekends £12.00 per day. *Eating facilities:* full catering facilities. *Visitors:* welcome without reservation except Wednesday 9.00 – 11.00am and Sunday 8.00am – 1.00pm. *Society Meetings:* catered for subject to availability. Professional: Mike Smee (0482 811121). Secretary: (0482 874754).

COTTINGHAM. **Hessle Golf Club,** Westfield Road, Raywell, Cottingham (Hull (0482) 659187). *Location:* three miles south west of Cottingham. Parkland. 18 holes, 6290 yards, S.S.S. 70. Two practice areas. *Green Fees:* £12.00 per round, £15.00 per day weekdays; weekends and Bank Holidays £20.00. *Eating facilities:* full eating facilities except Mondays in the Winter months. *Visitors:* mid-week unrestricted except at Professionals discretion, Tuesdays 9.15am – 1pm, weekends after 11am. *Society Meetings:* catered for subject to availability. Professional: G. Fieldsend (0482 650190). Secretary: R. L. Dorsey (0482 650171).

DRIFFIELD. **Driffield Golf Club,** Sunderlandwick, Driffield (Driffield (0377) 43116). *Location:* one mile south of Driffield off the A161. 9 holes, 6202 yards. S.S.S. 70. 18 holes to open during 1990. *Green Fees:* information not provided. *Eating facilities:* meals available except Monday. Bar and Steward. *Visitors:* welcome except on competition days. *Society Meetings:* catered for. Secretary: J.W. Finch.

GRIMSBY. **Grimsby Golf Club Ltd,** Littlecoats Road, Grimsby DN34 4LU (Grimsby (0472) 342823). *Location:* one mile west of Grimsby town centre off A18. 18 holes, 6058 yards. S.S.S. 69. Practice area. *Green Fees:* weekdays £13.00, weekends £16.00 per day. Reduction with member. *Eating facilities:* snack lunches most days, set lunches by arrangement, afternoon teas most days, evening meals by arrangement with Steward. *Visitors:* welcome weekdays, must be members of golf clubs. Ladies do not play Saturday between 1.00pm – 5.00pm and Sunday mornings.

Society Meetings: catered for Mondays and Fridays by arrangement with Secretary (Club ladies' day Tuesday, club ladies have priority). Professional: Steve Houltby (0472 356981). Secretary: A.D. Houlihan (0472 342630).

HORNSEA. **Hornsea Golf Club,** Rolston Road, Hornsea HU18 1XG (Hornsea (0964) 535488). *Location:* Follow signs for Hornsea Pottery – Golf Course 200 yards past Pottery. Parkland. 18 holes, 6475 yards. S.S.S. 71. Large practice area. *Green Fees:* weekdays £13.00 per round, £18.00 per day; weekends £15.00 per round, £20.00 per day. *Eating facilities:* available every day. *Visitors:* welcome, please ring Professional for a time. Ladies Day Tuesdays. *Society Meetings:* catered for by arrangement with the Secretary. Professional: B. Thompson (0964 534989). Secretary: B.W. Kirton (0964 532020).

HOWDEN. **Boothferry Golf Club,** Spaldington Lane, Howden, Near Goole DN14 7NG (Howden (0430) 430371). *Location:* M62 Junction 36 B1228 towards Bubwith. Flat meadowland, with bunkers, ditches and ponds. 18 holes, 6651 yards. S.S.S. 72. Two large practice areas. *Green Fees:* weekdays £5.00 per round, weekends £10.00 per round. Special rates for parties of 12 or more and for visitors accompanied by members. *Eating facilities:* bar and catering facilities. *Visitors:* welcome seven days a week, must book times; dress restrictions. *Society Meetings:* welcome all week, numbers over 12. Professional: Stewart Wilkinson (0430 430364). Secretary: A. Atkin (0430 430364).

HULL. **Hull Golf Club (1921) Ltd.,** The Hall, 27 Packman Lane, Kirk Ella, Hull HU10 7TJ (Hull (0482) 653026). *Location:* five miles west of Hull. Parkland and wooded. 18 holes, 6242 yards. S.S.S. 70. *Green Fees:* on application. *Eating facilities:* available. *Visitors:* welcome weekdays except Wednesday. *Society Meetings:* by prior arrangement. Professional: D. Jagger (0482 653074). General Manager: R. Toothill (0482 658919).

HULL. **Springhead Park Golf Club,** Willerby Road, Hull (Hull (0482) 656309). *Location:* west boundary. 18 holes, 6439 yards. S.S.S. 71. *Green Fees:* weekdays £2.85 per round, weekends £4.00 per round. *Visitors:* unrestricted. Professional: B. Herrington. Secretary: F. Coggrave.

HULL. **Sutton Park Municipal Golf Club,** Saltshouse Road, Hull HU8 9HF (Hull (0482) 74242). *Location:* three miles east of city centre on A164. Parkland course. 18 holes, 6295 yards 5719 metres. S.S.S. 70. *Green Fees:* weekdays £3.25, weekends £4.50. Reductions for Juniors and Senior Citizens. *Eating facilities:* available, parties by pre-booking.

Visitors: no restrictions except Sunday mornings. *Society Meetings:* by application to Hull Corporation Leisure Services Dept. Professional: Paul Rushworth (0482 711450). Secretary: C.D. Smith (0482 781039).

IMMINGHAM. **Immingham Golf Club,** Church Lane, Immingham DN40 2EU (Immingham (0469) 575298). *Location:* two miles off A180, behind St. Andrews Church, Immingham. Flat-ridge and furrow, wide and deep dykes. 18 holes, 5809 yards, 5312 metres. S.S.S. 68. *Green Fees:* weekdays £8.00, weekends £12.00. *Eating facilities:* full catering facilities, normal bar. *Visitors:* welcome anytime except Thursday pm, Saturday pm and Sunday am or other competition days. *Society Meetings:* catered for if booked in advance. Professional: (0469 575493). Secretary: Mr E.W. Cowton (0469 573633 or 0469 572000).

SCUNTHORPE. **Holme Hall Golf Club,** Holme Lane, Bottesford, Scunthorpe DN16 3RF (Scunthorpe (0724) 840909). *Location:* M180 Exit 4 (Scunthorpe East). Heathland with sandy subsoil. 18 holes, 6475 yards. S.S.S. 71. *Green Fees:* £10.00 per round, £13.00 per day. With member £6.00 per round, £8.00 per day. Weekends only with member, full rate before 3.30pm. *Eating facilities:* daily except Fridays. *Visitors:* welcome if members of affiliated clubs, not Saturdays or Sundays. *Society Meetings:* catered for by arrangement with Secretary. Professional: Richard McKiernan (0724 851816). Secretary: A.H.F. Holtby (0724 862078).

SCUNTHORPE. **Normanby Hall Golf Club,** Normanby Park, Near Scunthorpe (Scunthorpe (0724) 720252). *Location:* five miles north of Scunthorpe on B1130. Follow signs for Normanby Hall Country Park. Parkland. 18 holes, 6548 yards. S.S.S. 71. Practice area. *Green Fees:* weekdays £7.00 per round, £9.50 per day; weekends £9.50 per round. *Eating facilities:* fully licensed Clubhouse with restaurant, Societies should notify Catering Manager in advance. *Visitors:* welcome on most occasions, check times in advance with golf professional. *Society Meetings:* bookings taken for weekdays, except Bank Holidays. Professional: C. Mann (0724 720226). Hon. Secretary: I.D. Reekie (0724 280444 ext 850).

SCUNTHORPE. **Scunthorpe Golf Club,** Burringham Road, Scunthorpe DN17 2AB (Scunthorpe (0724) 842913. *Location:* M181 – Burringham Road opposite Asda Superstore. Flat wooded course. 18 holes, 6281 yards. S.S.S. 71. *Green Fees:* weekdays £12.00. *Eating facilities:* full catering and bar available. *Visitors:* welcome weekdays only. *Society Meetings:* catered for weekdays. Professional: G. Bailey (0724 868972). Secretary: E. Willsmore (0724 866561).

WITHERNSEA. **Withernsea Golf Club,** Chestnut Avenue, Withernsea HU19 2PG (0964 612258). *Location:* 25 miles north-east of Kingston-upon-Hull. Seaside links. 9 holes, 5112 yards. S.S.S. 64. *Green Fees:* £5.00 per day. Weekday ticket £20.00; 7-day ticket £25.00. *Eating facilities:* bar and meals available. *Visitors:* welcome any day except weekends unless playing with a member. *Society Meetings:* by reservation. Special rates. Professional: G. Harrison. Secretary: F. Buckley (0964 612214).

Isle of Wight

COWES. **Cowes Golf Club,** Crossfield Avenue, Cowes (Cowes (0983) 292303). 9 holes, 5880 yards. S.S.S. 68. *Green Fees:* £12.00 per round/day. *Eating facilities:* snack meals available in bar in summer. Bar open 11.00am to 2.00pm summer months. *Visitors:* welcome except Sunday before 1.00pm and Thursday, Ladies' Day (10.30am to 3.00pm). *Society Meetings:* by arrangement with Secretary. Society rates by arrangement. Secretary: R.E. Wootton.

EAST COWES. **Osborne Golf Club,** Osborne House, East Cowes PO32 6JX (Cowes (0983) 295421). *Location:* off A3027 north east Cowes, in Osborne Estate. Parkland. 9 holes, 6286 yards. S.S.S. 70. Practice area. *Green Fees:* £12.00 weekdays, £15.00 weekends and Bank Holidays. *Eating facilities:* bar and catering. *Visitors:* welcome except on Saturdays and Sundays before 12.00 noon and Tuesdays before 3.00pm. *Society Meetings:* catered for (24 maximum). Professional: Ian Taylor (0983 295649). Secretary: Mrs M. Butler.

If you are writing, a stamped, addressed envelope is always appreciated.

FRESHWATER. Freshwater Bay Golf Club, Afton Down, Freshwater (Freshwater (0983) 752955). *Location:* western end of Island, approximately half-a-mile east of Freshwater Bay on coast road to Ventnor. 18 holes, 5379 yards. S.S.S. 67. Also separate 18 hole pitch and putt course. *Green Fees:* £12.00 per day, £14.00 weekends and Bank Holidays. *Eating facilities:* licensed bar, limited catering. *Visitors:* welcome without reservation. *Society Meetings:* by arrangement. Secretary: H.G.V. Gordon.

NEWPORT. Newport (Isle of Wight) Golf Club, St. Georges Down, Near Shide, Newport, Isle of Wight (Newport (0983) 525076). *Location:* one mile south east of Newport. 9 holes, 5704 yards. S.S.S. 68. *Green Fees:* £10.00 per day, £12.00 Saturday and Sunday afternoons. *Eating facilities:* licensed bar, catering facilities. *Visitors:* welcome, except Saturday and Sunday mornings. *Society Meetings:* welcome. Secretary: J. Ambrose (0983 525076).

RYDE. Ryde Golf Club, Binstead Road, Ryde, Isle of Wight PO33 3NF (Ryde (0983) 614809). *Location:* on A3054 very close to town. Parkland course. 9 holes, 5220 yards. S.S.S. 66. Practice area. *Green Fees:* weekdays £10.00 per day; weekends and Bank Holidays £12.50. *Eating facilities:* available. *Visitors:* welcome. *Society Meetings:* catered for. Professional: S. Ward (0983 62088). Secretary: F. Cockayne (0983 64388).

SANDOWN. Shanklin and Sandown Golf Club, The Fairway, Lake, Sandown, Isle of Wight PO36 9PR (0983 403170). *Location:* Within 12 minutes' walk of Sandown Railway Station. Readily accessible by car. Car Park. Seaside links/parkland. 18 holes, 6058 yards. S.S.S. 69. *Green Fees:* weekdays £16.00, weekends and Public Holidays, £18.00. Five days (Mon.-Fri.) £65.00. *Eating facilities:* available. Bar facilities. *Visitors:* welcome, restrictions weekends. Handicap Certificate preferred. Bona fide golfers only. *Society Meetings:* catered for, not weekends. Professional: Paul Warner (0983 404424). Secretary: G.A. Wormald (0983 403217).

UPPER VENTNOR. Ventnor Golf Club, Steephill Down Road, Upper Ventnor (Ventnor (0938) 853326). *Location:* north-west boundary of Ventnor. Downland. 9 holes, 5910 yards. S.S.S. 68. *Green Fees:* £8.00. *Eating facilities:* bar snacks only. *Visitors:* welcome except on Sundays and Bank Holidays before 11.30. Secretary: R. Hose (0983 853198).

Kent

ASHFORD. **Ashford (Kent) Golf Club,** Sandyhurst Lane, Ashford TN25 4NT (Ashford (0233) 620180). *Location:* just off A20, one and a half miles west of Ashford. Parkland – stream cutting through course. 18 holes, 6246 yards. S.S.S. 70. *Green Fees:* weekdays £16.00, weekends and Bank Holidays £20.00. *Eating facilities:* every day. *Visitors:* welcome. Handicap Certificate required. *Society Meetings:* catered for by arrangement. Professional: Hugh Sherman (0233 629644). Secretary: A.H. Story (0233 622655).

BECKENHAM. **Beckenham Place Park Golf Club,** Beckenham Hill Road, Beckenham. *Location:* on A222 north of Bromley. Parkland. 18 holes, 5672 yards. S.S.S. 68. Practice ground, nets, putting green. *Green Fees:* weekdays £7.00, weekends £11.00, £9.50 after 10am. *Eating facilities:* bar and cafeteria. *Visitors:* welcome without reservation on weekdays, but must book for weekends. *Society Meetings:* not catered for. Other facilities include tennis courts and putting green. Professional: B. Woodman (081-658 5374). Secretary: K. Tregunno (081-778 4116).

BECKENHAM. **Braeside Golf Club,** Beckenham Place Park, Beckenham Hill, Beckenham (081 650 2292). Parkland course. 18 holes, 5722 yards, 5230 metres. S.S.S. 68. Practice area and nets. *Green Fees:* £4.60 weekdays, £8.40 plus £1.50 booking fee/£11.00 plus £2.50 booking fee weekends. *Eating facilities:* cafe and bar. *Visitors:* welcome any time. Professional: Bill Woodman (081 658 5374). Secretary: R. Oliver (081 304 3818).

BECKENHAM. **Langley Park Golf Club,** Barnfield Wood Road, Beckenham BR3 2SZ (01-650 2090). *Location:* one mile from Bromley South station. Flat parkland. 18 holes, 6488 yards, 5931 metres, S.S.S. 71. Practice nets. *Green Fees:* weekdays £25.00, weekends with member only, £12.00. *Eating facilities:* bar snacks, restaurant/dining room. *Visitors:* welcome by arrangement with Professional. *Society Meetings:* by arrangement with Secretary. Professional: George Ritchie (01-650 1663). Secretary: J.L. Smart (01-658 6849).

BEXLEY HEATH. **Bexley Heath Golf Club,** Mount Row, Mount Road, Bexley Heath DA6 8JS (01-303 6951). *Location:* adjacent to A2. Hilly parkland. 9 holes, 5239 yards, 4788 metres. S.S.S. 66. *Green Fees:* £8.00 (approximately). Weekends with member only. *Eating facilities:* catering available. *Visitors:* weekdays only. Professional: To be appointed. Secretary: S.E. Squires.

BIGGIN HILL. **Cherry Lodge Golf Club,** Jail Lane, Biggin Hill, Nr. Westerham TN16 3AX (Biggin Hill (0959) 72250). *Location:* from Bromley, A233 to Westerham, Jail Lane on left. Parkland. Two courses. One course, yellow, Par 75. 18 holes, 6522 yards. S.S.S. 73. Practice ground. *Green Fees:* weekdays £18.00 per round, £25.00 per day; weekends with

member only £12.50 per round, £18.00 per day. *Eating facilities:* a la carte restaurant and lounge bar. *Visitors:* weekdays only. *Society Meetings:* welcome. Professional: Nigel Child (0959 72989). Manager/Secretary: David Downard (0959 72250).

BROADSTAIRS. **North Foreland Golf Club,** The Clubhouse, Convent Road, Broadstairs CT10 3PU (Thanet (0843) 62140). *Location:* outside Broadstairs, near North Foreland Lighthouse. Seaside downland. 18 holes, 6382 yards. S.S.S. 71. Short Course: 18 holes, 1752 yards. Par 3. *Green Fees:* £15.00 per round, £20.00 per day weekdays; £20 per round weekends. Short Course: £4.50 weekdays, £5.00 weekends and Public Holidays. *Eating facilities:* bar and dining room. *Visitors:* weekdays and weekend afternoons with current Handicap Certificate. Tennis. *Society Meetings:* Wednesdays and Fridays by prior arrangement with Secretary. Professional: Mike Lee (0843 69628). Secretary: B.J. Preston (0843 62140).

BROMLEY. **Shortlands Golf Club,** Meadow Road, Shortlands, Bromley BR2 0PB (081-460 2471). *Location:* car park and entrance in Ravensbourne Avenue, off the main Beckenham to Bromley road. 9 holes, 5261 yards. S.S.S. 65. *Green Fees:* no green fees allowed except when introduced and playing with a member. Professional: J. Bates. Assts: D. Wyborn and W. Hodgkin. Hon. Secretary: Mrs Leah Burrows (081-460 8828).

BROMLEY. **Sundridge Park Golf Club,** Garden Road, off Plaistow Lane, Bromley BR1 3NE (081-460 1822). *Location:* five minutes walk from Sundridge Park station. Wooded parkland. 36 holes. East 6410 yards. West 6027 yards. S.S.S. 71 and 69. Two practice grounds. *Green Fees:* £30.00 per day weekdays. *Eating facilities:* restaurant, spike bar. lounge bar, members bar. *Visitors:* welcome weekdays only, with Handicap Certificate. *Society Meetings:* catered for by arrangement. Professional: Bob Cameron (081-460 5540). Secretary: Derek Lowton (081-460 0278).

BROMLEY. **Magpie Hall Lane Municipal Golf Club,** Magpie Hall Lane, Bromley (081-462 7014). *Location:* off Bromley Common on A21. 9 holes, 5538 yards. S.S.S. 67. *Green fees:* information not provided. *Visitors:* welcome without reservation. Professional: A. Hodgson (081-462 7014). Clubhouse (081-462 8001).

CANTERBURY. **Broome Park Golf and Country Club,** Broome Park Estate, Barham, Near Canterbury CT4 6QX (Canterbury (0227) 831701). *Location:* off the A2 at the A260, half a mile on right hand side. Parkland, undulating, lake in front of 18th green. 18 holes, 6610 yards, S.S.S. 72. *Green Fees:* £19.00 weekdays, £21.00 weekends. *Eating facilities:* available all week. *Visitors:* weekdays. *Society Meetings:* weekdays. Professional: Tienie Britz (0227 831701 extension 264). Hon. Secretary: Don Lees (0227 831701 extension 298).

CANTERBURY. **Canterbury Golf Club,** Scotland Hills, Littlebourne Road, Canterbury CT1 1TW (0227 463586). *Location:* one mile from town centre on the A257 road to Sandwich. 18 holes, 6209 yards. S.S.S. 70. *Green Fees:* weekdays £18.00 per round, £24.00 per day. Weekends £25.00 per round. Saturday only. *Eating facilities:* snacks, sandwiches, lunches, dinners each day. *Visitors:* welcome without reservation. *Society Meetings:* catered for Tuesday and Thursday. Professional: Paul Everard (0227 462865). Secretary: G. Good (0227 453532).

CHISLEHURST. **Chislehurst Golf Club,** Camden Park Road, Chislehurst BR7 5HJ (01-467 3055). *Location:* between Bromley and junction of A222 and Sidcup bypass. Parkland. 18 holes, 5128 yards. S.S.S. 65. *Green Fees:* £20.00 weekdays, £7.00 weekends with member only. *Eating facilities:* catering available. Large parties by prior arrangement. *Visitors:* welcome but restricted to weekdays (except Wednesday mornings) and only with a member at weekends. *Society Meetings:* catered for by arrangement. Professional: S. Corstorphine (01-467 6798). Secretary: N.E. Pearson (01-467 2782).

CRANBROOK. **Cranbrook Golf Club Ltd.,** Benenden Road, Cranbrook TN17 4AL (Cranbrook (0580) 712833). *Location:* situated between Sissinghurst and Benenden. Parkland. 18 holes, 6216 yards. S.S.S. 70. Practice area. *Green Fees:* weekdays £10.00 with member, weekends and Bank Holidays £15.00 with member. *Eating facilities:* clubhouse facilities available all day. *Visitors:* welcome only with a member. *Society*

Meetings: group bookings accepted mid week. Secretary: Miss R. Banister (0580 712833).

DARTFORD. **Corinthian Golf Club,** Fawkham Road, Fawkham, Dartford DA3 8LY (04747 7559). *Location:* off the A2 east of Dartford. Wooded with astroturf greens and tees. 9 holes. S.S.S. 70. Practice area. *Green Fees:* £7.50, with a member £5.00. *Eating facilities:* bar with snacks, catering by arrangement. *Visitors:* welcome except weekends and Bank Holiday mornings. *Society Meetings:* welcome. Secretary: Stephen Billings.

DARTFORD. **Dartford Golf Club Ltd.,** The Clubhouse, Dartford Heath, Dartford DA1 2TN (Dartford (0322) 223616). *Location:* backing on to A2, one mile from Dartford Tunnel and M25. Flat parkland. 18 holes, 5914 yards. S.S.S. 68. *Green Fees:* weekdays £25.00. *Eating facilities:* catering available. *Visitors:* welcome on weekdays with reservation, must be member of another golf club. *Society Meetings:* welcome on Mondays and Fridays by prior arrangement with Secretary. Professional: A. Blackburn (0322 226409). Secretary: R.J.H. Smith (0322 226455).

DEAL. **Royal Cinque Ports Golf Club,** Golf Road, Deal (Deal (0304) 374328). *Location:* A258 from Sandwich. In Upper Deal leave for Middle Deal Road, left turn into Albert Road, Western Road, on to Golf Road (or from Dover, A258 via seafront and Godwin Road). 18 holes, Championship 6744 yards, Medal 6409 yards. S.S.S. 72. *Green Fees:* weekdays £32.00 per day, £22.00 per round. No fees accepted at weekends. *Eating facilities:* hot snacks provided Mon-

day to Saturday, through bar. Dining room Sunday. *Visitors:* welcome with reservation, introduction preferred. *Society Meetings:* catered for on application. Professional: A.W. Reynolds (0304 374170). Secretary: N.S. Phillips (0304 374007).

DEAL. **Walmer and Kingsdown Golf Club,** The Leas, Kingsdown, Deal CT14 8ER (Deal (0304) 373256). *Location:* on A258 from Dover (A2) to Deal, club signposted at village of Ringwood. Seaside links on clifftop near Dover. 18 holes, 6451 yards. S.S.S. 71. Practice ground. *Green Fees:* weekdays £18.00 per day, £20.00 weekends after 12 noon. *Eating facilities:* full catering and bar service. *Visitors:* welcome without reservation if members of another club. *Society Meetings:* catered for except Saturdays and Sundays. Professional: Tim Hunt (0304 363017). Secretary: B.W. Cockerill.

DEANGATE. **Deangate Ridge Golf Club,** Hoo, Rochester (Medway (0634) 250374). *Location:* three miles from Rochester off A228 towards Isle of Grain. Wooded. 18 holes, 6300 yards. S.S.S. 70. 18 hole Pitch and Putt. *Green Fees:* £3.50 weekdays, £4.90 weekends. *Eating facilities:* available. *Visitors:* welcome without reservation, bookings required for weekends. *Society Meetings:* catered for. Professional: Barry Aram (0634 251180). Secretary: R. Worthington (0634 271749).

EAST GRINSTEAD. **Holtye Golf Club,** Holtye Common, Cowden, Near Edenbridge TN8 7ED (0342 850635). *Location:* four miles east of East Grinstead on A264, seven miles west of Tunbridge Wells. Undulating forest course; alternate tees. 9 holes, 5265 yards. S.S.S. 66. Large practice ground. *Green fees:* available on request. *Eating facilities:* available by arrangement. *Visitors:* welcome, restrictions Thursday and weekend mornings. *Society Meetings:* catered for. Professional: Kevin Hinton (0342 850635). Secretary: J. P. Holmes (0342 850576).

EDENBRIDGE. **Edenbridge Golf and Country Club,** Crouch House Road, Edenbridge TN8 5LQ (Edenbridge (0732) 865097). *Location:* from M25 take A25, at Limpsfield take B2026 to Edenbridge. Parkland. 18 holes, 6643 yards. S.S.S. 73. Driving range with 16 bays covered and floodlit. New 18 holes opening Spring 1991. *Green Fees:* weekdays £10.00 per round, weekends and Bank Holidays £12.00 round. *Eating facilities:* bar and restaurant available. *Visitors:* welcome weekdays, call for start time weekends. *Society Meetings:* welcome by arrangement. Professionals: B. Hemsley, Tony Noble (0732 865202). Secretary: Gay Hayward (0732 865097).

FARNBOROUGH. **High Elms Golf Club,** High Elms Road, Downe, Kent (0689 58175). *Location:* two miles from Farnborough Hospital on A21, turn right at Shire

Lane, second left. 18 holes, 5626 metres. S.S.S. 70. *Green fees:* information not available. *Eating facilities:* food by arrangement with publican, ring (0689 50177). Professionals: Alan Hodgson, John Kane and Peter Remy. Secretary: Mrs P. O'Keeffe (081-300 2734).

FAVERSHAM. **Faversham Golf Club Ltd.,** Belmont Park, Faversham. *Location:* M2 Faversham Exit (A251) to A2 junction, left to Brogdale Road, left to Belmont. 18 holes, 6021 yards. S.S.S. 69. *Green Fees:* weekdays £15.00 per round, £21.00 all day; weekends £18.00 per round, £25.00 all day. *Eating facilities:* by arrangement with Steward (079 589 251). *Visitors:* normally welcome weekdays with reservation. Handicap Certificate required. *Society Meetings:* Tuesday, Wednesday and Friday catered for. Professional: G. Nixon (079 589 275). Secretary: D.B. Christie (079 589 561).

FOLKESTONE. **Sene Valley, Folkestone and Hythe Golf Club Ltd.,** Blackhouse Hill, Folkestone CT18 8BZ (0303 66726). *Location:* A20 then B2065 by Channel Tunnel initial works. Downland course overlooking sea. 18 holes, 6287 yards. S.S.S. 70. Practice ground. *Green Fees:* weekdays £16.00, weekends and Bank Holidays £20.00. *Eating facilities:* bar and restaurant (no catering Mondays). *Visitors:* welcome with Handicap Certificate (preferably not weekends or Bank Holidays). *Society Meetings:* welcome. Professional: Trevor Dungate (0303 68514). Secretary: G. Hills (0303 268513).

GILLINGHAM. **Gillingham Golf Club Ltd.,** Woodlands Road, Gillingham ME7 2BX (Medway (0634) 50999). *Location:* M2 to Gillingham turn off, left to A2. Turn left towards Gillingham, course on right hand side. Parkland. 18 holes, 5863 yards, 5364 metres. S.S.S. 68. *Green Fees:* weekdays with a member £8.00 per round, £12.00 per day; without a member £18.00 round or day. Weekends only with a member. *Eating facilities:* available Wednesday – Sunday. *Visitors:* not weekends; must hold Handicap Certificate and be member of a golf club. *Society Meetings:* welcome, maximum 30 players. Professional: Stanley Barrow (0634 55862). Secretary: L.P. O'Grady (0634 53017).

GRAVESEND. **Mid-Kent Golf Club,** Singlewell Road, Gravesend DA11 7RB (Gravesend (0474) 352387). *Location:* A227 off A2. Parkland. 18 holes, 6206 yards. S.S.S. 70. *Green Fees:* weekdays £20.00 per round, £25.00 per day; weekends with member only. *Eating facilities:* lunch and dinner by arrangement, bar 11am to 11pm. *Visitors:* welcome weekdays except competition days, with Handicap Certificate. *Society Meetings:* catered for Tuesdays only. Professional: R. Lee (0474 332810). Secretary: A.F. Reid (0474 568035).

HAWKHURST. **Hawkhurst Golf Club,** Hawkhurst. (Hawkhurst (0580) 752396). *Location:* on A268 from

Hawkhurst to Flimwell. 9 holes, 5769 yards. S.S.S. 68. *Green Fees:* £14.00 weekdays; weekends only with member. *Eating facilities:* snacks available. *Visitors:* welcome. *Society Meetings:* weekdays, catered for with prior notice. Professional: Tony Collins. Secretary: A.W. Shipley.

HERNE BAY. **Herne Bay Golf Club,** Canterbury Road, Herne Bay (Herne Bay (0227) 373964). 18 holes, 5466 yards. S.S.S. 67. *Green Fees:* weekdays £13.00 per round, £18.00 per day; weekends and Bank Holidays £18.00 per round. *Eating facilities:* available except Monday. *Visitors:* welcome with reservation, Handicap Certificate required. Weekends and Bank Holidays p.m. only. *Society Meetings:* catered for weekdays. Professional: D. Lambert. Secretary: B. Warren.

HYTHE. **Hythe Imperial Golf Club,** Princes Parade, Hythe CT21 6AE. *Location:* come off M20 Junction 11 directions for Hythe A261. Flat seaside course. 9 holes, 5533 yards. S.S.S. 67. *Green Fees:* information not provided. Reductions if playing with a member. *Eating facilities:* available at the hotel. *Visitors:* welcome weekdays, no fees weekends up to 1pm. *Society Meetings:* welcome weekdays only. Professional: Gordon Ritchie (0303 267441). Secretary: Mr I. Kaye (0303 267554).

MAIDSTONE. **Bearsted Golf Club,** Ware Street, Bearsted, Maidstone ME14 4PQ (0622 38198). *Location:* one minute from Bearsted station, three miles east of Maidstone, between A20 and M20. Secluded parkland course with view of North Downs. 18 holes, 6253 yards, 5715 metres. S.S.S. 70. Practice ground and putting green. *Green Fees:* £18.00 per round, £25.00 per day, weekdays only. *Eating facilities:* prior notice is required for lunch or dinner, sandwiches usually available. *Visitors:* welcome on proof of membership of another golf club and with a current handicap (weekends with member only). *Society Meetings:* catered for weekdays only by prior arrangement. Professional: T. Simpson (0622 38024). Secretary: Mrs L.M. Siems (0622 38198).

MAIDSTONE. **Cobtree Manor Park Golf Club,** Chatham Road, Sandling, Maidstone ME14 3AZ (0622 681560). *Location:* M20, A229 Chatham (not Maidstone). Undulating course with trees, and interesting 6th hole over lake. 18 holes, 5716 yards. S.S.S. 68. Tuition, practice, putting. *Green Fees:* weekdays £6.00 per round, weekends £9.00 per round. Weekday reductions Juniors and Senior Citizens. *Eating facilities:* restaurant and bar. *Visitors:* welcome, book one week in advance through Professional. *Society Meetings:* weekdays by arrangement only. Professional: Martin Drew (0622 53276).

MAIDSTONE. **Leeds Castle Golf Course,** Leeds Castle, Leeds, Maidstone ME17 1PL (0622 880467). *Location:* M20-A20 near Maidstone. Situated in the grounds of Leeds Castle. 9 holes, 2910 yards. Practice nets and putting green. *Green Fees:* £6.95 for 9 holes. Reductions Juniors and Senior Citizens weekdays, and also available after 2.00pm weekends. *Eating facilities:* Park Gate Inn (situated in golf course car park). *Visitors:* welcome, bookings must be made six days in advance. Correct dress mandatory, no denim jeans allowed.

Society Meetings: bookings at least six weeks in advance. Professional: Chris Miller PGA. Secretary: Jill Skinner.

MAIDSTONE. **Tudor Park Hotel, Golf and Country Club,** Ashford Road, Bearsted, Maidstone ME14 4NQ (Maidstone (0622) 35891). *Location:* east of Maidstone, on A20 at Bearsted. Off Junction 8 of M20. Parkland. 18 holes, 6041 yards. S.S.S. 69. *Green Fees:* weekdays £25.00, weekends £30.00 (£12.50 with member). *Eating facilities:* restaurants and bars. *Visitors:* current Handicap Certificate required. Hotel, leisure and conference facilities. *Society Meetings:* welcome midweek. Professional: Marc Boggia (0622 34334).

MAIDSTONE. **West Malling Golf Club,** London Road, Addington, Maidstone (West Malling (0732) 844785). *Location:* A229 turn off M20. Parkland, 18 holes, 6142 yards. S.S.S. 70 (Spitfire Course). 18 holes, 6300 yards. S.S.S. 70 (Hurricane Course). *Green Fees:* weekdays £14.00 per round, £20.00 per day; weekends £18.00 per round. *Eating facilities:* restaurant available. *Visitors:* welcome except Bank Holidays or before 11.30am weekends. *Society Meetings:* catered for. Professional: P. Foston (0732 844022). Secretary: Mike Ellis (0732 844785).

NEW ROMNEY. **Littlestone Golf Club,** St. Andrews Road, Littlestone, New Romney TN28 8RB (New Romney (0679) 62310). *Location:* A20 to Ashford, B2070 to New Romney, one mile from New Romney. Seaside links course. 18 holes, 6417 yards. S.S.S. 71. Also 9 hole course, 1998 yards. S.S.S. 32. Driving range. *Green Fees:* £18.00 per round, £25.00 per day weekdays; £20.00 per round, £30.00 per day weekends. 9 hole course £6.50 weekdays, £8.00 weekends. *Eating facilities:* available. *Visitors:* Handicap Certificate required, visitors not allowed at weekends in Winter, in Summer only after 3pm. Weekdays by prior arrangement with Secretary. *Society Meetings:* catered for weekdays by arrangement with the Secretary. Professional: Stephen Watkins (0679 62231). Secretary: J.D. Lewis (0679 63355).

ORPINGTON. **Cray Valley Golf Club,** Sandy Lane, St. Mary Cray, Orpington BR5 3HY (Orpington (0689) 31927). *Location:* Ruxley roundabout A20; turn off into Sandy Lane, half-a-mile on left. Parkland. 18 holes, 5624 yards. S.S.S. 67. *Green Fees:* weekdays £7.00, weekends £10.50. Also 9 hole course: weekdays £4.00, weekends £5.50. *Eating facilities:* hot meals available lunchtimes, also bar. *Visitors:* welcome all week. *Society Meetings:* welcome any day, please phone (0689 31927). Professional: Tudor Morgan (0689 37909). Secretary: Ron Hill (0689 39677).

ORPINGTON. **Ruxley Golf Centre,** Sandy Lane, St. Paul's Cray, Orpington BR5 3HY (Orpington (0689) 71490). *Location:* off Ruxley roundabout on the old A20. Undulating parkland. 18 holes, 4466 yards. S.S.S. 65. Floodlit driving range. *Green Fees:* weekdays £8.00, weekends £10.00. *Eating facilities:* bar and catering facilities. *Visitors:* welcome, except weekends before 11.00am. *Society Meetings:* welcome. Professional: R. Cornwell. Secretary: D. Simpson.

ORPINGTON. **West Kent Golf Club,** Downe, Near Orpington (Farnborough (Kent) (0689) 51323). *Loca-*

tion: six miles from Orpington. 18 holes, 6392 yards. S.S.S. 70. *Green Fees:* £20.00 per round, £30.00 per day. *Eating facilities:* meals by arrangement. *Visitors:* welcome with letter of introduction and recognised handicap. *Society Meetings:* catered for. Professionals: R.S. Fidler and G. Ryan. Secretary: A.M. Watt.

RAMSGATE. **St. Augustine's Golf Club,** Cottington Road, Cliffsend, Ramsgate CT12 5JN (Thanet (0843) 590333). *Location:* two miles south-west of Ramsgate - approaching from A253 or A256 follow signs to St. Augustine's Cross. Entrance 75 yards beyond Cross by railway bridge. Mainly parkland, flat - tight and challenging course. 18 holes, 4999 yards, 4572 metres. S.S.S. 64. *Green Fees:* £16.00 weekdays, £18.00 weekends. Weekly £50.00, monthly £150. *Eating facilities:* full catering except Mondays when sandwiches and beverages only, usual bar facilities. *Visitors:* welcome, proof of Handicap required, advisable to ring Professional the day before to check periods booked for competitions, societies, etc. *Society Meetings:* catered for, book through Secretary. Professional: D. Scott (0843 590222). Secretary: R. James (0843 590333).

ROCHESTER. **Rochester and Cobham Park Golf Club,** Park Pale, By Rochester ME2 3UL (Shorne (047 482) 3411). *Location:* on A2, 2 miles east of Gravesend turn off. 18 holes, 6467 yards. S.S.S. 71. *Green Fees:* on application. *Eating facilities:* lunch, tea, dinner and snacks available, lunches should be ordered in advance. *Visitors:* with Handicap Certificates – welcome without reservation on weekdays. *Society Meetings:* catered for on Tuesdays and Thursdays. Professional: Matt Henderson (047 482 3658). Manager: J.W. Irvine (047 482 3411).

SANDWICH BAY. **Prince's Golf Club,** Sandwich Bay. (Sandwich (0304) 611118). *Location:* four miles from Sandwich through the Sandwich Bay Estate. 27 holes, arranged as 3 loops of 9 holes named "Dunes", "Himalayas", "Shore". D & H 6262 – 6776 yds, par 71, S.S.S. 70-73. H & S 6238 – 6813 yds, Par 71, S.S.S. 70-73, S & D 6466-6947 yds, Par 72, S.S.S. 71-73. *Green Fees:* weekdays £24.00 round, £26.00 day; Saturdays £29.00 round, £31.00 day; Sundays £32.00 round, £34.00 day. *Eating facilities:* breakfast, lunch, dinner available every day (pre-booking advisable); bar buffet/Ploughman's lunchtime & evenings; light snacks throughout the day. *Visitors & Societies:* welcome without restriction, Company days and private parties our speciality. Dormy House accommodation available for groups. Brochure available on request. *Starting Times:* Phillip Sparks (Professional) (0304 613797). *Information & Bookings:* Geoff Ramm (0304 611118).

SANDWICH. **Royal St. Georges Golf Club,** Sandwich CT13 9PB (0304 617308). *Location:* one mile from Sandwich on the road to Sandwich Bay. From Canterbury A257, from Dover A258. Links. 18 holes, Championship 6903 yards, Medal 6534 yards. S.S.S. Championship 74, Medal 72. *Green Fees:* £28.00 per round, £40.00 per day weekdays. *Eating facilities:* snack bar and dining room. *Visitors:* welcome on most weekdays only, but it is advisable to write in advance. *Society Meetings:* catered for by arrangement. Professional: Niall Cameron (0304 615236). Secretary: Captain R.J. Hitchen, R.N. (0304 613090).

SEVENOAKS. **Darenth Valley Golf Course,** Station Road, Shoreham, Near Sevenoaks TN14 7SA (Otford (095-92) 2944). *Location:* A225 between Otford and Eynsford, approximately four miles north of Sevenoaks. Parkland course. 18 holes, 6356 yards. S.S.S. 70. Practice areas, putting greens. *Green Fees:* £8.50 per 18 holes weekdays, weekends and Bank Holidays £11.00 per 18 holes. *Eating facilities:* bar snacks, diningroom, functions up to 100 cover. *Visitors:* welcome without reservation except weekends and Bank Holidays. *Society Meetings:* catered for by arrangement. Professional: P. Edwards (095-92 2922). Steward: Neil Morgan.

SEVENOAKS. **Knole Park Golf Club,** Seal Hollow Road, Sevenoaks TN15 0HJ (Sevenoaks (0732) 452709). *Location:* one mile south-east of Sevenoaks town. Parkland. 18 holes, 6249 yards, 5711 metres. S.S.S. 70. *Green Fees:* weekdays only, £20.00 per round, £30.00 for two rounds. *Eating facilities:* full catering and bar. *Visitors:* by appointment only, must have a club handicap. *Society Meetings:* catered for by arrangement only. Professional: P.E. Gill (0732 451740). Secretary: D.J.L. Hoppe (0732 452150).

SEVENOAKS. **Wildernesse Golf Club,** Seal, Sevenoaks (Sevenoaks (0732) 61526). *Location:* three miles east of Sevenoaks on A25. 18 holes, 6448 yards. S.S.S. 72. *Green Fees:* on application. *Eating facilities:* by arrangement. *Visitors:* welcome, weekdays only by prior arrangement. *Society Meetings:* catered for, limited. Professional: Bill Dawson (0732 61527). Secretary: (0732 61199).

SEVENOAKS. **Woodlands Manor Golf Club,** Tinkerpot Lane, Woodlands, Near Otford, Sevenoaks TN15 6AB (Otford (09592) 3805). *Location:* junction 3, M25 take "Brands Hatch" sign on A20, seven miles. Parkland. 18 holes, 6000 yards. S.S.S. 68. Six acre practice ground. *Green fees:* on application. *Eating facilities:* restaurant and bar daily. *Visitors:* welcome weekdays, Handicap Certificate required at weekends after 1pm. *Society Meetings:* welcome by arrangement Monday to Friday. Professional: Nick Allen (09592 4161). Secretary: E.F. Newman (09592 3806).

SEVENOAKS. **Wrotham Heath Golf Club,** Seven Mile Lane, Comp, Sevenoaks TN15 8QZ (Borough Green (0732) 884800). *Location:* on B2016 half-a-mile south of junction with A20. Woods and heather. 9 holes with alternative tees for 18. 5851 yards. S.S.S. 68. *Green Fees:* £22.00 per day, £17.00 per round. Weekends only with a member. *Eating facilities:* bar and snacks, meals by arrangement, except Mondays. *Visitors:* welcome on weekdays with Handicap Certificate, but not Bank Holidays. *Society Meetings:* catered for Fridays only. Professional: H. Dearden (0732 883854). Secretary: T.J. Fenson (0732 884800).

SHEERNESS. **Sheerness Golf Club,** Power Station Road, Sheerness ME12 3AE (Sheerness (0795) 662585). *Location:* follow A249 then A250 towards Sheerness. 18 holes, 6500 yards. S.S.S. 71. Practice area. *Green Fees:* weekdays £10.00 (£8.00) per round, £15.00 (12.00) per day; weekends £15.00 (£12.00) per round. (Weekends only if playing with a member or by arrangement with Secretary). *Eating facilities:* available. *Society Meetings:* catered for by previous arrangement. Professional: P.B. King. Secretary/Manager: J.W. Gavins.

SIDCUP. **Sidcup Golf Club (1926) Ltd,** 7 Hurst Road, Sidcup DA15 9AE (081-300 2150). *Location:* 3 minutes walk from Sidcup Station. Parkland. 9 holes, 5692 yards. S.S.S. 68. *Green Fees:* weekdays £15.00. *Eating facilities:* meals and snacks during bar opening hours or by arrangement at other times. *Visitors:* welcome without reservation Monday to Friday (not Bank Holidays). *Society Meetings:* (up to 30 members) catered for by arrangement. Professional: Ross Taylor (081-309 0679). Secretary: Sandy Watt (081-300 2150).

SITTINGBOURNE. **Sittingbourne and Milton Regis,** Wormdale, Newington, Sittingbourne ME9 7PX (Newington (0795) 842261). *Location:* Junction M2 and A249 three-quarters of a mile. Undulating course with trees. 18 holes, 6121 yards. S.S.S. 69. *Green Fees:* £13.00 (18 holes), £23.00 (36 holes) weekdays. No green fees weekends. *Eating facilities:* available. *Visitors:* welcome weekdays, Handicap Certificate or letter of introduction required. *Society Meetings:* catered for Tuesdays and Thursdays by arrangement. Professional: J. Hearn (0795 842775). Manager: H.D.G. Wylie.

TENTERDEN. **Tenterden Golf Club,** Woodchurch Road, Tenterden TN30 7DR (Tenterden (058 06) 3987). *Location:* one mile south east of Tenterden on B2067. Parkland course. 18 holes, 6000 yards. *Green Fees:* information not given. *Eating facilities:* catering available. *Visitors:* welcome except weekends and Bank Holidays. *Society Meetings:* by prior arrangement. Professional: Garry Potter (05806 2409). Secretary: D.F. Hunt.

TONBRIDGE. **Poult Wood Public Golf Course,** Higham Lane, Tonbridge (Tonbridge (0732) 364039 - Golf Shop). *Location:* A227, two miles north of town centre. Wooded, 18 holes, 5569 yards. S.S.S. 67. Practice ground. *Green Fees:* £5.50 per round (£3.10 Juniors/Senior citizens) weekdays; £8.00 per round weekends. Day ticket (Society) £14.00. *Eating facilities:* full catering available. *Visitors:* all welcome. *Society Meetings:* by arrangement with Clubhouse Manager. Other facilities, squash courts, meeting room, showers, toilets, changing, lockers. Non-Resident Professional: Ken Adwick. Club House Manager: (0732 366180).

TUNBRIDGE WELLS. **Lamberhurst Golf Club,** Church Road, Lamberhurst (Lamberhurst (0892) 890241). *Location:* A21 from Tonbridge, Pembury, Hastings Road, left at Church Road prior to descending hill to Lamberhurst. 18 holes, 6249 yards. S.S.S. 70. *Green Fees:* £20 per weekday, £25.00 weekends and Bank Holidays after 12.00 noon. *Eating facilities:* full

catering by arrangement. *Visitors:* welcome with reservation. *Society Meetings:* catered for by arrangement. Professional: M. Travers. Secretary: Mr P. Gleeson (0892 890591).

TUNBRIDGE WELLS. **Nevill Golf Club,** Benhall Mill Road, Tunbridge Wells (Tunbridge Wells (0892) 25818). *Location:* off Forest Road, follow signs. 18 holes, 6336 yards. S.S.S. 70. *Green Fees:* £24.00 weekdays, £30.00 weekends and Bank Holidays. *Eating facilities:* lunches at club by prior arrangement. *Visitors:* welcome with reservation. Handicap Certificate required. *Society Meetings:* catered for. Professional: Paul Huggett. Secretary: R.A. White.

TUNBRIDGE WELLS. **Tunbridge Wells Golf Club,** Langton Road, Tunbridge Wells (Tunbridge Wells (0892) 23034). *Location:* behind Marchants Garages. 9 holes, 4525 yards. S.S.S. 62. *Green Fees:* weekdays £18.00. *Eating facilities:* snacks at bar or by arrangement. *Visitors:* welcome weekdays except Tuesdays. *Society Meetings:* only by previous arrangement. Professional: K. Smithson. Secretary: E.M. Goulden.

WESTGATE ON SEA. **Westgate and Birchington Golf Club,** Canterbury Road, Westgate on Sea CT8 8LT (Thanet (0843) 33905). *Location:* between Westgate on Sea and Birchington on A28 approx. one mile outside Birchington. Seaside links course. 18 holes, 4926 yards, 4547 metres. S.S.S. 64. *Green Fees:* weekdays £12.00 per day (after 10 a.m.), weekends and Bank Holidays £14.00 (Sat. after 11 am, Sun. after 12 noon). *Eating facilities:* bar with limited snack facilities. *Visitors:* welcome if members of a recognised golf club. *Society Meetings:* by arrangement with Secretary. Professional: R. Game (0843 31115). Secretary: J.M. Wood (0843 31115).

WHITSTABLE. **Chestfield (Whitstable) Golf Club,** 103 Chestfield Road, Chestfield, Whitstable CT5 3LU (0227 792243). *Location:* half a mile south of Thanet Way (A299). Seaside links with woods – slightly hilly. 18 holes, 6126 yards, 5977 metres. S.S.S. 69. *Green Fees:* £22.00 weekdays. *Eating facilities:* full catering facilities. *Visitors:* welcome weekdays with Handicap Certificate, weekends with member only. *Society Meetings:* catered for weekdays. Professional: John Brotherton (0227 793563). Secretary: R.W. Leaver (0227 794411).

WHITSTABLE. **Whitstable and Seasalter Golf Club,** Collingwood Road, Whitstable CT5 1EB (0227 272020). *Location:* course adjoins town centre, take Nelson Road turning off main street. Flat seaside links. 9 holes, 5276 yards. S.S.S. 63. Practice net. *Green Fees:* £10.00, green fees are accepted at weekends only if accompanied by a member. *Eating facilities:* bar snacks. Hon. Secretary: Derek Spratt (0227 272020 or 273589).

Lancashire

ACCRINGTON. **Accrington and District Golf Club**, New Barn Farm, West End, Oswaldtwistle, Accrington (Accrington (0254) 32734). *Location:* on A679, 2 miles from Blackburn. 18 holes, 5954 yards. S.S.S. 69. *Green fees:* weekdays £5.00, weekends £7.00. *Eating facilities:* lunches and evening meals. *Visitors:* welcome without reservation. *Society Meetings:* prior bookings catered for. Professional: Bill Harling (0254 31091). Hon Secretary: J. Pilkington (0254 32734 club).

ACCRINGTON. **Green Haworth Golf Club**, Green Haworth, Accrington (Accrington (0254) 37580). *Location:* off A679, one mile Town Centre, via Willows Lane, turn left 300 yards beyond Red Lion Inn. 9 holes, 5513 yards. S.S.S. 67. *Green Fees:* weekdays £7.00, weekends and Bank Holidays £10.00. *Eating facilities:* meals may be ordered in advance. *Visitors:* welcome, restricted to weekdays and Saturday with reservation. *Society Meetings:* catered for weekdays only. Secretary: D. Jarvis.

BACUP. **Bacup Golf Club**, Bankside Lane, Bacup (Bacup (0706) 3170). *Location:* one mile from Bacup centre. 9 holes, 5656 yards. S.S.S. 67. *Green Fees:* information not provided. *Eating facilities:* by arrangement except Mondays. *Visitors:* welcome without reservation except Mondays. Secretary: J. Garvey (0706 874485).

BLACKBURN. **Blackburn Golf Club**, Beardwood Brow, Blackburn BB2 7AX (Blackburn (0254) 51122). *Location:* off A677 within easy reach of M6 (Junction 31), M61 and M65; west end of Blackburn. Meadowland with superb views of Lancashire coast and Pennine hills. 18 holes, 6100 yards. S.S.S. 70. Outdoor practice ground and indoor net. *Green fees:* weekdays £12.00 (£4.00 with a member); weekends and Bank Holidays £15.00 (£5.00 with a member). Special rates for parties of 12 or more. *Eating facilities:* full catering and bar facilities (restricted Mondays). *Visitors:* welcome without reservation except on competition days. *Society Meetings:* catered for by arrangement (not Tuesdays or weekends). Professional: Alan Rodwell (0254 55942). Secretary: P.D. Haydock (0254 51122).

BLACKBURN. **Great Harwood Golf Club**, Harwood Bar, Great Harwood, Blackburn (Great Harwood (0254) 884391). 9 holes, 6411 yards. S.S.S. 71. *Green Fees:* weekdays £8.00 without member, £5.00 with. Weekends £10.00 without member, £7.00 with. *Eating facilities:* all meals catered for. *Visitors:* welcome without reservation. *Society Meetings:* catered for. Professional: C. Chadwick (0254 876870). Secretary: A. Garraway.

BLACKBURN. **Pleasington Golf Club**, Pleasington, Near Blackburn (Blackburn (0254) 201028). *Location:* M6 north to Junction 31. Blackburn eight miles.

Undulating woodland. 18 holes, 6445 yards. S.S.S. 71. *Green Fees:* weekdays £20.00, weekends and Bank Holidays £25.00. *Eating facilities:* full catering available. *Visitors:* welcome by prior arrangement. *Society Meetings:* Mondays, Wednesdays, Fridays by arrangement. Professional: G.J. Furey (0254 201630). Secretary: L. Ingham (0254 202177).

BLACKBURN. **Rishton Golf Club**, Eachill Links, Rishton (Great Harwood (0254) 884442). *Location:* three miles east of Blackburn. 9 holes, 6094 yards. S.S.S. 69. *Green Fees:* £8.00, £4.00 with member. *Visitors:* welcome on weekdays and with a member at weekends and on Bank Holidays. *Society Meetings:* visiting parties welcome by prior arrangement. Secretary: G. Haworth.

BLACKBURN. **Whalley Golf Club**, Portfield Lane, Whalley, Blackburn (Whalley (025 482) 2236). *Location:* seven miles east of Blackburn on A59. Parkland. 9 holes, 5912 yards, 5406 metres. S.S.S. 69. *Green Fees:* weekdays £9.00, weekends £12.00. Discount for parties over 20. *Eating facilities:* full catering and bar facilities. *Visitors:* welcome except Thursday afternoons and Saturdays April to September. *Society Meetings:* welcome by appointment. Secretary: P.C. Burt (025 482 2367).

BLACKBURN. **Wilpshire Golf Club Ltd**, Whalley Road, Wilpshire, Blackburn (Blackburn (0254) 248260 or 249691). *Location:* A666 three miles north of Blackburn on Blackburn to Whalley road. 18 holes, 5911 yards. S.S.S. 68. *Green Fees:* £13.00 weekdays, £17.00 weekends. *Eating Facilities:* lunch, high tea, dinner except Mondays. *Visitors:* welcome without reservation except competition days. *Society Meetings:* catered for by prior booking through the Secretary. Professional: W. Slaven. Secretary: B. Grimshaw.

BLACKPOOL. **Blackpool North Shore Golf Club**, Devonshire Road, Blackpool FY2 0RD (0253 51017). *Location:* north Blackpool on A587 behind North Prom. Undulating parkland. 18 holes, 6431 yards. S.S.S. 71. *Green Fees:* £17.00 weekdays, £20.00 weekends. Special package rates Mondays, Tuesdays, Wednesdays and Fridays. *Eating facilities:* full catering and bar facilities. *Visitors:* welcome except Saturdays. *Society Meetings:* welcome except Thursdays and weekends. Professional: Brendan Ward (0253 54640). Secretary: D.S. Walker (0253 52054).

BLACKPOOL. **Blackpool Park Golf Club**, North Park Drive, Stanley Park, Blackpool (Blackpool (0253) 33960). *Location:* within the boundary of Stanley Park. Parkland course. 18 holes, 6060 yards. S.S.S. 69. *Green Fees:* £4.50 weekdays, £5.50 weekends. *Eating facilities:* full catering, bar. *Visitors:* welcome. *Society meetings:* catered for. Professional: B. Purdie (0253 31004). Secretary: Terence Lee (0253 37916).

BLACKPOOL. **Knott End Golf Club Ltd,** Wyre Side, Knott-End-on-Sea, Blackpool FY6 0AA (Knott End (0253) 810254). *Location:* M55 Exit 3, A585 Fleetwood Road and A588 to Knott End, or by passenger ferry from Fleetwood. Scenic seaside undulating course. 18 holes, 5852 yards. S.S.S. 68. Practice ground. *Green Fees:* £14.00 weekdays, weekends £18.00. *Eating facilities:* full catering available. *Visitors:* welcome weekdays, restricted weekends. *Society Meetings:* by arrangement weekdays only. Professional: Kevin Short (0253 811365). Secretary: C. Desmond (0253 810576).

BLACKPOOL. **Poulton le Fylde Golf Club,** Breck Road, Poulton le Fylde, Blackpool (Blackpool (0253) 893150 and 892444). *Location:* three miles east of Blackpool. 9 holes, 2972 yards. *Green Fees:* £2.50 weekdays, £3.50 weekends per round. *Eating facilities:* meals at lunch time and light snacks available all day. *Visitors:* welcome without reservation. *Society Meetings:* catered for by prior booking.

BOLTON. **Bolton Municipal Golf Course,** Links Road, Bolton New Road, Bolton BL2 9XX (Bolton (0204) 44170). *Location:* midway between Horwich and Bolton, A673. Fairly flat parkland. 18 holes, 6336 yards, 5570 metres. S.S.S. 70. Practice ground. *Green Fees:* weekdays £3.50, weekends £4.50. *Eating facilities:* snack and meal facilities available and bar. *Visitors:* welcome at any time. *Society Meetings:* advance booking. Mid-week Society package available. Professional: A.K. Holland (0204 42336). Secretary: Mr A. Cunniffe (0204 44170).

BOLTON. **Great Lever and Farnworth Golf Club Ltd.,** Lever Edge Lane, Bolton BL3 3EN (Bolton (0204) 62582). *Location:* A666 or M61, one and a half miles from Bolton town centre. Parkland. 18 holes, 5859 yards. S.S.S. 69. Practice ground. *Green Fees:* weekdays £9.00, weekends £12.50. *Eating facilities:* restaurant and bar every day except Mondays. *Visitors:* welcome weekdays, preferably by appointment. *Society Meetings:* catered for by arrangement weekdays. Professional: (0204 656650). Secretary: P.J. Holt (0204 656137).

BURNLEY. **Burnley Golf Club,** Glen View, Burnley (Burnley (0282) 21045). *Location:* 300 yards from junction of A56 and A646. 18 holes, 5891 yards. S.S.S. 69. *Green Fees:* weekdays £10.00, weekends and Bank Holidays £12.00. *Eating facilities:* available except Wednesdays from lunchtime and Mondays. *Visitors:* welcome except Saturdays. *Society Meetings:* catered for. Professional: R.M. Cade. Secretary: G. Dean.

BURNLEY. **Towneley Golf Club,** Todmorden Road, Burnley (0282 51636). *Location:* east of town centre on road towards Bacup, one and a half miles from Burnley centre. Parkland course, reasonably flat. 18 holes, 5862 yards, 5357 metres. S.S.S. 68. Small practice area. *Green Fees:* £3.70 weekdays, £4.50 weekends. *Eating facilities:* clubhouse with diningroom, lounge bar and games room. *Visitors:* welcome, reservations recommended and tee reservation advisable. New 9 hole course recently opened in addition. *Society Meetings:* contact Steward at clubhouse for catering requirements. Secretary: Bernard Walsh (0282 26459).

CHORLEY. **Chorley Golf Club,** Hall o' the' Hill, Heath Charnock, Chorley PR6 9HX (0257 480263). *Location:* Chorley is between the M6 at Shevington and Charnock Richard and the M61 at Hartwood (Chorley North) and at Blackrod (Chorley South). Scenic course. 18 holes, 6317 yards. S.S.S. 70. *Green Fees:* weekdays £15.00 (£5.00 with a member), weekends £20.00 (£5.00 with a member). *Eating facilities:* restaurant and lounge bar. *Visitors:* welcome weekdays only, with reservation for parties (minimum 12). Excellent changing facilities for ladies. *Society Meetings:* catered for by arrangement. Professional: Paul Wesselingh (0257 481245). Secretary: George Birtill (0254 63024).

CHORLEY. **Duxbury Park Golf Club (Municipal),** Duxbury Hall Road, Duxbury Park, Chorley PR7 4AS (02572 41634). *Location:* one mile south of town centre off A6. Wooded parkland with water hazards on several holes. 18 holes, 6390 yards, 5843 metres. S.S.S. 70. Small practice area. *Green Fees:* weekdays £3.20, weekends £5.20. *Eating facilities:* can be arranged. *Society Meetings:* weekdays. Professional: David Clarke (02572 65380). Secretary: Reg Bleasie (02572 68665).

CHORLEY. **Shaw Hill Hotel Golf and Country Club,** Preston Road, Whittle-le-Woods, Chorley PR6 7PP (Chorley (02572) 69221). *Location:* one mile north of Junction 8 on M61. Championship course in superb parkland with the clubhouse in a beautiful

Georgian mansion. 18 holes, 6470 yards. S.S.S. 72. *Green Fees:* weekdays £16.00, weekends £20.00. *Eating facilities:* top class restaurant and bars. *Visitors:* welcome all week, must hold current Handicap Certificate. Accommodation available, sauna, solarium. Golf trolleys and buggies also available. *Society Meetings:* catered for weekdays only. Professional: Ian Evans (02572) 79222). Club Secretary: Mr Frank Wharton.

CLITHEROE. **Clitheroe Golf Club,** Whalley Road, Pendleton, Clitheroe BB7 1PP (Clitheroe (0200) 22618). *Location:* off A59, two miles south of Clitheroe. Flat parkland course. 18 holes, 6322 yards, 6094 metres. S.S.S. 71. Practice ground and range. *Green Fees:* weekdays £15.00, weekends and Bank Holidays £18.00. *Eating facilities:* full service available. *Visitors:* welcome with reservation. Saturdays some restrictions. No jeans/trainers. Jackets and ties in diningroom after 7pm. *Society Meetings:* catered for by arrangement. Professional: P. Geddes (0200 24242). Secretary: J.B. Kay (0200 22292).

COLNE. **Colne Golf Club,** Law Farm, Skipton Old Road, Colne BB8 7EB (Colne (0282) 863391). *Location:* one-and-a-half miles east of Colne, between A56 and A6068 on Lothersdale road. Flat scenic course. 9 holes, 5961 yards, 5451 metres. S.S.S. 69. Practice area. *Green Fees:* £8.00 weekdays, £10.00 weekends and Bank Holidays. Reduced terms for Societies. *Eating facilities:* available. *Visitors:* welcome except weekends and competition days (phone to check). *Society Meetings:* welcome weekdays by appointment. Secretary: K. Hargreaves.

DARWEN. **Darwen Golf Club,** Winter Hill, Darwen BB3 0LB (0254 701287). *Location:* one and a half miles from Darwen centre. Moorland. 18 holes, 5752 yards. S.S.S. 68. Large practice area. *Green Fees:* weekdays £10.00, weekends and Bank Holidays £15.00. *Eating facilities:* full catering. *Visitors:* welcome, except Saturdays. *Society Meetings:* welcome, except Saturdays. Professional: Wayne Lennon (0254 776370). Secretary: J. Kenyon.

FLEETWOOD. **Fleetwood Golf Club Ltd.,** The Golf House, Princes Way, Fleetwood (Fleetwood (03917) 3661). *Location:* on Fylde Coast, eight miles from Blackpool. 18 holes: White course 6628 yards, S.S.S. 72; Yellow course 6324 yards, S.S.S. 71. *Green Fees:* on request. *Eating facilities:* full catering facilities except Thursday (03917 79300). *Visitors:* welcome without reservation except parties. *Society Meetings:* catered for with reservation. Professional: C.J. Burgess. Secretary: K. Volter.

HEYSHAM. **Heysham Golf Club,** Trumacar Park, Middleton Road, Heysham LA3 3JH (Lancaster (0524) 51011). *Location:* five miles from M6 via Lancaster and Morecambe. Parkland, part-wooded. 18 holes, 6338 yards. S.S.S. 70. Two practice grounds. *Green Fees:* weekdays £10.00 per round, £13.00 per day; Saturdays and Bank Holidays £12.00 per round, £16.00 per day; Sundays £18.00. Special rates for parties on application. *Eating facilities:* full catering seven days. Bar open all day Sunday. *Visitors:* welcome without reservation. Tee reserved for members 1 to 1.45pm. *Society Meetings:* catered for by arrangement with

Secretary. Professional: R. Williamson (0524 52000). Secretary: A. Hesketh (0524 51011).

LANCASTER. **Lancaster Golf and Country Club Ltd,** Ashton Hall, Ashton-with-Stodday, Lancaster LA2 0AJ (Galgate (0524) 751247). *Location:* three miles south of Lancaster on A588. 18 holes, 6282 yards. S.S.S. 71. *Green Fees:* £18.00 per day/round. *Eating Facilities:* available (Caterer: 0524 751105). *Visitors:* welcome with reservation. Club has a Dormy House (part of Ashton Hall) which accommodates 18 persons, 2 night minimum stay. *Society Meetings:* catered for weekdays only. Professional: Robert Head (0524 751802). Secretary: Mrs Judith Hayhurst.

LANCASTER. **Lansil Golf Club,** Caton Road, Lancaster LA1 3PE (Lancaster (0524) 39269). *Location:* A683, towards Lancaster from Junction 34 M6. Parkland, quite hilly. 9 holes, 5608 yards. S.S.S. 67. *Green Fees:* weekends and Bank Holidays £12.00 (£6.00 with a member), weekdays £8.00 (£5.00 with a member). *Eating facilities:* light refreshments only by arrangement. *Visitors:* welcome, not before 1pm Saturday and Sunday. *Society Meetings:* catered for by arrangement weekdays only. Secretary: Derrick Crutchley (0524 418007).

LEYLAND. **Leyland Golf Club Ltd.,** Wigan Road, Leyland (Leyland (0772) 421359). *Location:* leave M6 at Exit 28, turn right to traffic lights, (200 yards) turn right onto the A49, course located one mile on left. 18 holes, 6105 yards. S.S.S. 69. *Green Fees:* £10.00 weekdays. *Eating facilities:* full catering except Mondays. *Visitors:* welcome. *Society Meetings:* catered for weekdays only. Professional: C. Burgess. Secretary: G.D. Copeman (0772 436457).

LYTHAM ST. ANNES. **Fairhaven Golf Club Ltd.,** Lytham Hall Park, Ansdell, Lytham St. Annes FY8 4JU (Lytham (0253) 736741). *Location:* on B5261, two miles from Lytham, eight miles from Blackpool. 18 holes, 6880 yards. S.S.S. 73. Practice ground and net. *Green Fees:* weekdays £20.00 per round, £25.00 per day; weekends £25.00 per round. *Eating facilities:* full catering except Mondays. *Visitors:* welcome with reservation. *Society Meetings:* catered for by arrangement Mondays, Tuesdays, Wednesdays and Fridays. Professional: Mr I. Howieson (0253 736976). Secretary: Brian Hartley.

LYTHAM ST. ANNES. **Lytham Green Drive Golf Club,** Ballam Road, Lytham St. Annes FY8 4LE (Lytham (0253) 234782). *Location:* half mile from Lytham centre. Parkland course. 18 holes, 6175 yards. S.S.S. 69. *Green Fees:* £18.00 weekdays, £22.00 per day weekends. *Eating facilities:* catering available daily. *Visitors:* welcome weekdays. Weekends on application. *Society Meetings:* catered for mid-week. Professional: F.W. Accleton (0253 737379). Secretary: R. Kershaw (0253 737390).

LYTHAM ST. ANNES. **Royal Lytham and St. Annes Golf Club,** Links Gate, Lytham St. Annes FY8 3LQ (0253 724206). *Location:* within one mile of the centre of St. Annes on Sea. Seaside links course. 18 holes, 6673 yards. S.S.S. 73. *Green Fees:* weekdays £30.00 per round, £45.00 per day. *Eating facilities:* restaurant and bar. *Visitors:* welcome weekdays only.

Letter of introduction and Handicap Certificate required. Package deals available in the Dormy House (Gentlemen only), details from the Secretary. *Society Meetings:* by arrangement. Professional: Eddie Birchenough. Secretary: Major A.S. Craven.

LYTHAM ST. ANNES. **St. Annes Old Links Golf Club,** Highbury Road, Lytham St. Annes FY8 2LD (St. Annes (0253) 723597). *Location:* via M6 and M55 to Blackpool off A584, on entering St. Annes. Links course. 18 holes, 6616 yards. S.S.S. 72. Practice ground. *Green Fees:* on application. *Eating facilities:* full dining facilities. *Visitors:* welcome, not weekends or Tuesdays. *Society Meetings:* by arrangement with Secretary (must be club members). Professional: G.G. Hardiman (0253 722432). Secretary: D.J.M. Hemsted (0253 723597).

MORECAMBE. **Morecambe Golf Club Ltd.,** The Club House, Bare, Morecambe LA4 6AJ (Morecambe (0524) 418050). *Location:* five miles from end of M6 via Carnforth or Lancaster (Exits 34 or 35), on sea front. 18 holes, 5766 yards, 5271 metres. S.S.S. 68. *Green Fees:* weekdays £11.00 per round, £13.00 per day; weekends and Bank Holidays £15.00 per round, £17.00 per day. Professional: D. Helmn. Secretary: Major B.C. Hodgson (0524 412841).

NELSON. **Marsden Park Golf Club,** Nelson Municipal Golf Course, Townhouse Road, Nelson BB9 8DG (0282 67525). *Location:* just off M65, heading towards Colne. Hilly parkland. 18 holes, 5806 yards. S.S.S. 68. *Green fees:* information not available. *Eating facilities:* bar, meals to order. *Visitors:* welcome without restriction. *Society Meetings:* by arrangement. Professional: N. Brown (0282 67525). Secretary: D. Manley.

NELSON. **Nelson Golf Club,** King's Causeway, Brierfield, Nelson BB9 0EU (Nelson (0282) 64583). *Location:* on A682 two miles north of Burnley, one mile from Junction 12 M65. Moorland with trees. 18 holes, 5967 yards. S.S.S. 69. *Green Fees:* £12.00 weekdays, £14.00 weekends and Public Holidays. *Eating facilities:* lunches, dinners by arrangement except Mondays. *Visitors:* weekdays except Thursdays, no Saturdays, Sundays by arrangement. *Society Meetings:* weekdays except Thursdays. Professional: R. Geddes (0282 67000). Secretary: R.W. Baldwin (0282 691803).

ORMSKIRK. **Ormskirk Golf Club,** Cranes Lane, Lathom L40 5UJ (Ormskirk (0695) 572112). *Location:* two miles east of Ormskirk. 18 holes, 6358 yards. S.S.S. 70. *Green Fees:* Monday, Tuesday, Thursday, and Friday £20.00; Wednesday, weekends and Bank Holidays £25.00. *Eating facilities:* available except Monday. *Visitors:* welcome, Handicap Certificates required, notice advised with reservation. *Society Meetings:* catered for, book in advance. Professional: J. Hammond. Secretary: P.D. Dromgoole.

PRESTON. **Ashton and Lea Golf Club Ltd,** Tudor Avenue, off Blackpool Road, Lea, Preston PR4 0XA (Preston (0772) 726480). *Location:* on A583, three miles west of Preston, turn right opposite Pig and Whistle Hotel. Parkland with water features. 18 holes, 6289 yards. S.S.S. 70. Practice ground. *Green Fees:* weekdays £12.50, weekends and Bank Holidays

£17.00. Reduced rates if playing with member. *Eating facilities:* full catering except Thursdays. *Visitors:* welcome, restricted competition days. *Society Meetings:* catered for on application Mondays, Tuesdays and Wednesdays only. Professional: Mr P. Laugher (0772 720374). Secretary: M.G. Gibbs (0772 735282).

PRESTON. **Ashton and Lea Golf Club Ltd,** Tudor Avenue, off Blackpool Road, Lea, Preston PR4 0XA (Preston (0772) 726480). *Location:* on A583, three miles west of Preston, turn right opposite Pig and Whistle Hotel. Parkland with water features. 18 holes, 6289 yards. S.S.S. 70. Small practice ground. *Green Fees:* weekdays £12.50, weekends and Bank Holidays £17.00. Reduced rates if playing with member. *Eating facilities:* full catering except Mondays, bars. *Visitors:* welcome but please telephone to reserve tee time. *Society Meetings:* catered for Mondays, Tuesdays and Wednesdays only, apply in writing to the Secretary. Professional: Mr P.G. Laugher (0772 720374). Secretary: Mr M.G. Gibbs (0772 735282).

PRESTON. **Fishwick Hall Golf Club,** Glenluce Drive, Farringdon Park, Preston PR1 5TD (Preston (0772) 798300). *Location:* two minutes from Exit 31 M6, off A49 Blackburn Road. Parkland, part wooded, bounded by river. 18 holes, 6028 yards. S.S.S. 69. Practice ground and net. *Green Fees:* Mondays to Thursdays £12.00, Fridays, weekends and Public Holidays £18.00. Reductions if playing with members. *Eating facilities:* bar, full catering available. *Visitors:* welcome by arrangement. *Society Meetings:* catered for by arrangement. Professional: H. Smith (0772 795870). Secretary: R.R. Gearing (0772 796866).

PRESTON. **Ingol Golf and Squash Club,** Tanterton Hall Road, Ingol, Preston PR1 7BY (Preston (0772) 734556). *Location:* Junction 32 M6 (joins M55). One-and-a-half miles north of Preston. Parkland. 18 holes, 6225 yards. S.S.S. 70. *Green Fees:* weekdays £15.00 (£10.00 with member), weekends and Bank Holidays £18.00 (£10.00 with member). Reductions for parties. *Eating facilities:* full catering available. *Visitors:* welcome all week (please check tee availability). Privately owned club with other leisure facilities. *Society Meetings:* welcome by arrangement. Professional: Mark Cartwright. General Manager: Harold Parker.

PRESTON. **Longridge Golf Club,** Fell Barn, Jeffrey Hill, Longridge, Preston PR3 2TU (Longridge (0772) 783291). *Location:* eight miles north-east of Preston off B6243. Moorland with extensive spectacular views. 18 holes, 5726 yards. S.S.S. 68. *Green Fees:* £12.00 Mondays to Thursdays, £15.00 Fridays, Saturdays, Sundays and Bank Holidays. *Eating facilities:* full catering except Mondays. *Visitors:* welcome at all times. *Society Meetings:* welcome by arrangement. Professional: Neil James. Secretary: J. Greenwood (0772 782765 evenings).

PRESTON. **Penwortham Golf Club Ltd.,** Blundell Lane, Penwortham, Preston PR1 0AX (Preston (0772) 743207). *Location:* one mile west of Preston on main Southport to Liverpool road. 18 holes, 5667 yards. S.S.S. 69. *Green Fees:* £16.00 weekdays, £22.00 weekends. *Eating facilities:* lunches and dinners served at Club. *Visitors:* weekdays only. *Society Meetings:*

catered for by arrangement. Professional: J. Wright (0772 742345). Secretary: J. Parkinson (0772 744630).

PRESTON. **Preston Golf Club,** Fulwood Hall Lane, Fulwood, Preston PR2 4DD (0772 794234). *Location:* exit 32 on M6 marked Preston & Garstang, partway to Preston turning at Watling Street Road. Parkland course. 18 holes, 6267 yards. S.S.S. 70. *Green Fees:* weekdays £15.00 per round, £18.00 per day. Subject to review. *Eating facilities:* first class dining room, bars. *Visitors:* welcome Mondays, Wednesdays and Fridays maximum 48, Tuesdays and Thursdays maximum 16, members have priority up to 9.30am and from 12.30pm to 1.45pm. *Society Meetings:* catered for, Handicap Certificates required. Professional: P. Wells (0772 700022). Secretary: J.B. Dickinson (0772 700011).

ROSSENDALE. **Rossendale Golf Club Ltd.,** Ewood Lane Head, Haslingden, Rossendale BB4 6LH (Rossendale (0706) 213056). *Location:* 14 miles north of Manchester, easy access from M66 and A56. 18 holes, 6260 yards. S.S.S. 70. *Green Fees:* weekdays £11.00, weekends and Bank Holidays £14.00. *Eating Facilities:* full catering except Mondays; bar. *Visitors:* welcome except Saturdays during season. *Society Meetings:*

special terms including full catering. Professional: S.J. Nicholls (0706 213616). Secretary: W.P. Whittaker (0706 216234 or 831339).

SKELMERSDALE. **Beacon Park Golf Club,** Beacon Lane, Dalton, Upholland WN8 7RU (Upholland (0695) 622700). *Location:* near the Beacon at Dalton, Skelmersdale. Parkland/wooded with views of North Wales. 18 holes, 5995 yards. S.S.S. 69. Driving range. *Green Fees:* weekdays £3.00, weekends £4.30. *Eating facilities:* bar/restaurant. *Visitors:* welcome anytime. *Society Meetings:* catered for. Book through Professional. Professional: Ray Peters (0695 622700). Secretary: J.C. McIlroy (0704 892930).

UP HOLLAND. **Dean Wood Golf Club,** Lafford Lane, Up Holland (Up Holland (0695) 622980). *Location:* Exit 26 from M6 signposted for Southport; follow A577 to Up Holland. First right after church. 18 holes, 6097 yards. S.S.S. 70. *Green Fees:* weekdays £14.00, weekends and Bank Holidays £18.00; with a member £6.00 any day. *Eating facilities:* daily catering available. *Visitors:* welcome with reservation, not before 10.30am weekends and Bank Holidays. *Society Meetings:* catered for by prior arrangement. Professional: Tony Coop. Secretary: J. Walls (0695 622219).

Leicestershire

ASHBY DE LA ZOUCH. **Willesley Park Golf Club,** Tamworth Road, Ashby de la Zouch (0530 411532). *Location:* on A453 towards Tamworth, one mile from centre of Ashby. Wooded park, semi-heathland. 18 holes, 6304 yards. S.S.S. 70. *Green Fees:* weekdays £20.00 per round/day, weekends and Bank Holidays £25.00. *Eating facilities:* dining room and bar. *Visitors:* welcome with reservation. *Society Meetings:* catered for Wednesday, Thursday and Friday. Professional: C.J. Hancock (0530 414820). Secretary: N.H. Jones (0530 414596).

BIRSTALL. **Birstall Golf Club,** Station Road, Birstall LE4 3BB (Leicester (0533) 674450). *Location:* 3 miles north of Town just off the A6 Leicester to Derby. Parkland. 18 holes, 5988 yards. S.S.S. 69. Practice ground. *Green fees:* weekdays £12.00. £9.50 for groups of 20 – 45, £9.00 for groups of over 45. *Eating facilities:* bar, diningroom. No catering Mondays. *Visitors:* welcome Wednesdays and Fridays. *Society Meetings:* catered for Wednesdays and Fridays. Professional: D. Clark (0533 675245). Secretary: Miss S. Wells (0533 674322).

COSBY. **Cosby Golf Club,** Chapel Lane, Cosby, Leicester (Leicester (0533) 864759). *Location:* seven miles south of Leicester, 4 miles from Junction 21 M1. Parkland. 18 holes, 6277 yards. S.S.S. 70. *Green Fees:* £12.00 without member, day or round; £5.00 with member. *Eating facilities:* bar and food available by arrangement with the Steward. *Visitors:* welcome

weekdays up to 4.00pm without reservation. No visitors over Easter, Christmas or Bank Holidays. *Society Meetings:* welcome weekdays by arrangement. Special rates for parties over 20 persons. Professional: David Bowring (0533 848275). Secretary: M.D. Riddle (0533 775597 home).

ENDERBY. **Enderby Golf Club,** Enderby Golf Course, Enderby Leisure Centre, Mill Lane, Enderby (0533 849388). *Location:* two miles from M1/M69 junction 21 roundabout. Flat parkland course. 9 holes, 2178 yards. S.S.S. 61. *Green fees:* weekdays 9 holes £2.50, 18 holes £3.50; weekends 9 holes £3.50, 18 holes £4.75. *Eating facilities:* bar open normal bar hours, light snacks available at lunchtime. *Visitors:* welcome at all times. Full range of recreational facilities available swimming, squash, indoor bowls, sauna, solarium, badminton, snooker, etc. Professional: Chris d'Araujo.

HINCKLEY. **Hinckley Golf Club,** Leicester Road, Hinckley LE10 3DR (Hinckley (0455) 615124). *Location:* situated one mile from Hinckley on A47 Leicester-Hinckley road. Parkland with featured lakes. 18 holes, 6592 yards, 6028 metres. S.S.S. 71. Practice area for members. *Green Fees:* weekdays, £15.00 per round or day (reductions if playing with member). *Eating facilities:* bar and meals daily except Sunday evenings. *Visitors:* welcome except Tuesdays, Thursdays and weekends. *Society Meetings:* by appointment. Professional: R. Jones (0455 615014). Secretary: J. Toon (0455 615124).

KIRBY MUXLOE. **Kirby Muxloe Golf Club,** Station Road, Kirby Muxloe LE9 9EP (Leicester (0533) 393107). *Location:* four miles west of Leicester on A47. M1 Exit 21. Undulating parkland with lake. 18 holes, 6303 yards, 5766 metres. S.S.S. 70. Practice area and tuition from Professional. *Green Fees:* weekdays £15.00 per round, £20.00 per day; weekends same with Captain's permission only. *Eating facilities:* bars, dining room. *Visitors:* welcome weekdays (some restrictions). Advisable to phone in advance. *Society Meetings:* Wednesday, Thursday, Friday only. Reduced rates for parties exceeding 20. Professional: R.T. Stephenson (0533 392813). Secretary: S.F. Aldwinckle (0533 393457).

LEICESTER. **Humberstone Heights Golf Club,** Gipsy Lane, Leicester (Leicester (0533) 761905). *Location:* opposite Towers Hospital, Uppingham side of Leicester. Parkland. 18 holes, 6444 yards. S.S.S. 71. Practice area, pitch and putt course. *Green Fees:* weekdays £4.50 per round, weekends £5.50 (reduced rates for Juniors). *Eating facilities:* bar, snacks. *Visitors:* welcome (Municipal Golf Course). Green Fee ticket gains entry to Clubhouse. *Society Meetings:* welcome. Professional: Philip Highfield (0533 764674). Secretary: Stephen Day (0533 674835).

LEICESTER. **Kibworth Golf Club Ltd.,** Weir Road, Kibworth Beauchamp, Leicester LE8 0LP (0533 793201/79230). *Location:* A6, four miles Market Harborough, 12 miles Leicester. Flat wooded course. 18 holes, 6298 yards. S.S.S. 70. *Green Fees:* £16.00. *Eating facilities:* restaurant – book through Steward in advance avoiding Monday. *Visitors:* welcome, Handicap Certificate required or introduction from club member. *Society Meetings:* catered for if booked. Professional: Alan Strange (0533 792283). Secretary: W. Potter (0533 792301).

LEICESTER. **Leicestershire Golf Club,** Evington Lane, Leicester LE5 6DJ (Leicester (0533) 736035). *Location:* two miles from city centre off A6 road. Parkland. 18 holes, 6312 yards. S.S.S. 70. *Green Fees:* weekdays £19.00, weekends £23.00. *Eating facilities:* bar snacks, full catering available by order. *Visitors:* welcome, Handicap Certificate required. *Society Meetings:* by arrangement. Professional: John R. Turnbull (0533 736730). Secretary: J.L. Adams (0533 738825).

LEICESTER. **Scraptoft Golf Club,** Beeby Road, Scraptoft, Leicester LE7 9SJ (Leicester (0533) 419000). *Location:* off A47 Peterborough. Undulating. 18 holes, 6166 yards. S.S.S. 70. *Green Fees:* £16.00 weekdays, £20.00 weekends. Sunday mornings with club member only. *Eating facilities:* full restaurant service except Mondays. *Visitors:* welcome, proof of Handicap required. *Society Meetings:* catered for on application, parties over 20 £14.00 weekdays only. Professional: Simon Sherratt (0533 419138). Secretary: J. White (0533 418863).

LEICESTER. **Western Park Golf Club,** Scudamore Road, Braunstone Frith, Leicester (0533 876158). *Location:* four miles west of junction 21 on M1 motorway. Flat, wooded course. 18 holes, 6532 yards. S.S.S. 71. Practice area. *Green fees:* information not

available. *Eating facilities:* full catering facilities. *Visitors:* contact Professional. *Society Meetings:* contact Professional. Professional: Bruce Whipham (0533 872339). Secretary: Trevor Elliott (0533 874749).

LEICESTER. **Whetstone Golf Club and Driving Range,** Cambridge Road, Cosby (Leicester (0533) 861424). *Location:* south boundary of Leicester. 18 holes, 3106 yards. S.S.S. 69. Driving range, putting green. *Green fees:* information not available. *Eating facilities:* bar serving snacks. *Visitors:* welcome, except Saturday and Sunday mornings. Professional: N. Leatherland. Secretary: B. Bywater.

LOUGHBOROUGH. **Charnwood Forest Golf Club,** Breakback Road, Woodhouse Eaves, Near Loughborough (Woodhouse Eaves (0509) 890259). *Location:* B591 off A6 at Quorn. North of Woodhouse Eaves on the road to Nanpanton. Rocks, bracken, woods – in the heart of Charnwood Forest. 9 holes, 5960 yards. S.S.S. 69. *Green Fees:* weekdays £12.00, weekends £15.00 (£6.00 with member). *Eating facilities:* full catering except Mondays; snacks available. *Visitors:* welcome, but not Tuesdays (Ladies' Day). *Society Meetings:* not more than 40 catered for by prior arrangement. Professional: Mr Lawrence. Secretary: A.G. Stanley (0509 890259).

LOUGHBOROUGH. **Longcliffe Golf Club,** Snell's Nook Lane, Nanpantan, Loughborough. *Location:* two miles west of Loughborough Town Centre, 13 miles north of Leicester. Approximately one mile from Exit 23, M1. 18 holes, 6551 yards. S.S.S. 71. *Green Fees:* £17.00 per day. *Eating facilities:* full catering facilities, except Monday. *Visitors:* restricted, must be introduced and playing with member at weekends and Bank Holidays. *Society Meetings:* by arrangement only accepted on Tuesday, Wednesday, Thursday and Friday. Professional: I. Bailey. Secretary: G. Harle (0509 239129).

LUTTERWORTH. **Lutterworth Golf Club,** Rugby Road, Lutterworth, Leicester LE17 5HN (Lutterworth (0455) 557141). *Location:* Lutterworth is two minutes from M1, Exit 20 on A4114. Hilly parkland-type course – open fairways. 18 holes, 5570 yards. S.S.S. 67. *Green Fees:* £11.00 per day. *Eating facilities:* lunches and evening meals available every day. *Visitors:* welcome on weekdays and with a member at weekends. Professional: N. Melvin (0455 567199). Secretary: Major J.C. Bonfield (0455 552532). Steward: C.D. Sholl (0455 557141).

LUTTERWORTH near. **Ullesthorpe Court Golf Club,** Frolesworth Road, Ullesthorpe, Near Lutterworth LE17 5BZ (0455 209023). *Location:* 10/15 minutes M1, M69, M6, between Leicester and Coventry. 18 holes, 6650 yards. S.S.S. 72. *Green Fees:* £10.50 weekdays. Golf Day Specials from £18.00. *Eating facilities:* restaurant, bar snacks and functions. *Visitors:* welcome weekdays except Bank Holidays. 40 bedroomed Hotel and Leisure Centre. *Society Meetings:* catered for weekdays except Bank Holidays. Professional: N. Warrburton (0455 209150). Secretary: Mrs P. Woolley (0455 202361).

MARKET HARBOROUGH. **Market Harborough Golf Club,** Oxendon Road, Market Harborough (Market Harborough (0858) 63684). *Location:* two

miles south of town on A508. Parkland. 9 holes, 6090 yards. S.S.S. 69. Practice ground. *Green Fees:* £8.00 per day. *Eating facilities:* full catering available. *Visitors:* welcome weekdays; weekends only with a member, with permission. *Society Meetings:* welcome, minimum 10, maximum 30; reduced rates. Professional: N. Gilks. Secretary: J. Lord (0536 771771).

MELTON MOWBRAY. **Melton Mowbray Golf Club,** Thorpe Arnold, Melton Mowbray LE14 4SD (Melton Mowbray (0664) 62118). *Location:* A607 road two miles north-east of Melton Mowbray. 9 holes, 18 tees, 6200 yards, S.S.S. 70. *Green Fees:* weekdays £10.00, weekends £15.00. *Eating facilities:* by arrangement. *Visitors:* welcome. *Society Meetings:* weekdays only. Secretary: E.A. Sallis.

OADBY. **Glen Gorse Golf Club,** Glen Road, Oadby LE2 4RF (Leicester (0533) 712226). *Location:* four and a half miles south of Leicester on the A6. Flat but wooded course. 18 holes, 6641 yards. S.S.S. 72. *Green Fees:* weekdays £17.00, weekends with member only £6.00. *Eating facilities:* bar and meals/snacks (not Mondays). *Visitors:* welcome weekdays without reservation. *Society Meetings:* welcome Tuesday to Friday. Professional: Bob Larratt (0533 713748). Secretary: K. McKay (0533 714159).

OADBY. **Oadby Golf Club,** Leicester Road, Oadby, Leicester LE2 4AB (Leicester (0533) 700215). *Location:* on A6 south of Leicester, one mile from City boundary, at Leicester Racecourse. Parkland. 18 holes, 6228 yards, 5692 metres. S.S.S. 69. Practice ground, coaching. *Green Fees:* £16.00 per round or day. Weekends with members only. *Eating facilities:* snacks always available, bar with meals on prior notice. *Visitors:* welcome on application to the Professional or booked through Oadby and Wigston Borough Council. *Society Meetings:* booking as for Visitors (weekdays only). Professional: Simon Ward (0533 709052). Hon. Secretary: C. Chamberlain (0533 889862 home).

ROTHLEY. **Rothley Park Golf Club,** Westfield Lane, Rothley, Leicester LE7 7LH (Leicester (0533) 302019). *Location:* off A6, north of Leicester. Parkland. 18 holes, 6481 yards. S.S.S. 71. *Green Fees:* £20.00 weekdays, £25.00 weekends and Bank Holidays with member only. *Eating facilities:* available except Mondays. *Visitors:* welcome except Tuesdays, weekends and Bank Holidays, must be members of recognised golf club with handicap. *Society Meetings:* catered for Wednesdays and Thursdays. Professional: P.J. Dolan (0533 303023). Secretary: Bernard Durham (0533 302809).

WOODHOUSE EAVES. **Lingdale Golf Club,** Joe Moore's Lane, Woodhouse Eaves, Near Loughborough (Woodhouse Eaves (0509) 890035). *Location:* on B5300, Ansty-Shepshed road, three miles from Exit 23 on M1. Woodland and parkland – set in Charnwood Forest. 9 holes, 3322 yards. S.S.S. 72. Practice ground. *Green Fees:* weekdays £10.00, weekends £20.00. *Eating facilities:* meals at club except Mondays and competition days. *Visitors:* welcome. *Society Meetings:* catered for Mondays, Wednesdays, Thursdays and Fridays (two weeks notice required). Professional: P. Sellears (0509 890684). Secretary: D A Wardle (0509 890703).

Lincolnshire

BOSTON. **Boston Golf Club Ltd,** Cowbridge, Horncastle Road, Boston PE22 7EL (Boston (0205) 62306). *Location:* two miles north of Boston on B1183. Look for sign to right if travelling north. Parkland with featured water. 18 holes, 5825 yards, 5326 metres. S.S.S. 68. *Green Fees:* weekdays £10.00 per round, £13.00 per day; weekends and Bank Holidays £15.00 per round, £20.00 per day. *Eating facilities:* daily by arrangement with resident Steward. *Visitors:* welcome without reservation. *Society Meetings:* small groups catered for midweek. Professional: T.R. Squires (0205 62306). Secretary: D.E. Smith (0205 350589).

GAINSBOROUGH. **Gainsborough Golf Club,** Gainsborough DN21 1PZ (Gainsborough (0427) 613088). *Location:* one mile north east of Gainsborough, between A159 and A631. Flat parkland. 18 holes, 6551 yards, 5986 metres. S.S.S. 71. Putting green and driving range. *Green Fees:* weekdays £14.00 per round, £17.00 per day. Parties over 20 £16.00 per day. *Eating facilities:* restaurant and coffee shop. *Visitors:* welcome weekdays without reservation; weekends with member only. *Society Meetings:* welcome if booked in advance. Professional: Gary Stafford (0427 612278). Manager: D.J. Garrison (0427 613088).

GRANTHAM. **Belton Park Golf Club,** Belton Lane, Londonthorpe Road, Grantham NG31 9SH (0476 63355). *Location:* two miles from Grantham. 250 acre Deer Park adjacent to the historical Belton House. Three courses as follows: Brownlow Course 6420 yards (Championship). S.S.S. 71. Ancaster Course 6252 yards. S.S.S. 70. Belmont Course 6016 yards. S.S.S. 69. Two large practice areas. *Green Fees:* weekdays £13.00 per round, half price if playing with member; weekends and Bank Holidays £20.00 per round, half price with member. All including VAT, no limit on number of holes played. *Eating facilities:* full restaurant facilities every day; three bars. *Visitors:* welcome without reservation. *Society Meetings:* catered for by arrangement weekdays only (except Tuesday). Special day package. Professional: B. McKee (0476 63911). Secretary and General Manager: T. Measures (0476 67399 – all enquiries).

GRANTHAM. **Stoke Rochford Golf Club,** Stoke Rochford, Near Grantham NG33 5EW (Great Ponton (047 683 275). *Location:* five miles south of Grantham on A1. Entrance at "A.J.S." service area. Parkland. 18 holes, 6209 yards. S.S.S. 70. Small practice ground. *Green Fees:* £14.00 per round, £20.00 per day weekdays (estimated), £23.00 weekends and Bank Holidays (estimated). Reduction if playing with a member. *Eating facilities:* meals available daily, to be booked before playing. *Visitors:* welcome by prior arrangement with Professional. *Society Meetings:* by prior arrangement. Professional: A.E. Dow (047 683 218). Secretary: J.M. Butler (0476 67030).

LINCOLN. **Blankney Golf Club,** Blankney, near Metheringham, Lincoln (0526 20263). *Location:* on B1188, 10 miles south of Lincoln. Parkland, slightly undulating. 18 holes, 6402 yards. S.S.S. 71. Large practice area. *Green Fees:* weekdays £12.00 per round, £16.00 per day. *Eating facilities:* bar snacks, full catering in dining room by prior arrangement. *Visitors:* welcome weekdays except Bank Holidays – telephone beforehand. *Society Meetings:* by advance booking only. Professional: Graham Bradley (0526 20202). Secretary: Ian McIntosh (0526 20263 or 0526 52027 – home).

LINCOLN. **Canwick Park Golf Club,** Canwick Park, Washingborough Road, Lincoln LN4 1EF (Lincoln (0522) 522166). *Location:* one and a half miles approximately east of Lincoln, first left (turning) off Canwick Road from Lincoln is Washingborough Road. Wooded parkland course. 18 holes, 6257 yards, 5726 metres, S.S.S. 70. Practice ground. *Green Fees:* £6.00 Mondays, £8.00 Tuesdays to Fridays (£6.00 with a member), weekends £12.00 (£6.00 with a member). *Eating facilities:* bar snacks and meals to order. *Visitors:* welcome weekdays; weekends after 3.00pm. Professional: Steve Williamson (0522 536870). Secretary: Mr A.C. Hodgkinson (0526 398978).

LINCOLN. **Carholme Golf Club,** Carholme Road, Lincoln (Lincoln (0522) 23725). *Location:* one mile from city centre on A57 to Worksop. 18 holes, 6086 yards. S.S.S. 69. *Green fees:* information not provided. *Eating facilities:* lunches, snacks, sandwiches (not Mondays). *Visitors:* welcome (not Sundays). *Society Meetings:* by prior arrangement only. Professional: G. Leslie (0522 23725). Secretary: B.W. Robinson.

LINCOLN. **Lincoln Golf Club,** Torksey, Lincoln (Torksey (042 771) 210. *Location:* East Lincolnshire, between Lincoln, Gainsborough and Newark. 18 holes, 6438 yards. S.S.S. 71. *Green Fees:* Information not provided. *Eating facilities:* full table, but book in advance. *Visitors:* weekdays by arrangement, weekends with members only. *Society Meetings:* catered for. Professional: Ashley Carter. Secretary: D. Boag.

LOUTH. **Louth Golf Club,** Crowtree Lane, Louth LN11 9LJ (Louth (0507) 602554). *Location:* one mile west of town centre. 18 holes, 6477 yards. S.S.S. 71. *Green Fees:* £10.00 weekdays, £12.00 weekends and Bank Holidays. *Eating facilities:* full catering 10.00am to 10.00pm. *Visitors:* welcome without reservation. *Society Meetings:* catered for. Professional: A.J. Blundell (0507 604648). Secretary/Manager: Major E.G. Coombes (0507 603681).

MABLETHORPE. **Sandilands Golf Club,** Roman Bank, Sandilands, Sutton on Sea LN12 2RJ (0521 41432). *Location:* A52 one mile south of Sutton-on-

Sea. Seaside links adjacent to sea and sand. 18 holes, 5995 yards, 5483 metres. S.S.S. 69. *Green Fees:* weekdays £10.00 round, £12.00 day; weekends and Bank Holidays £15.00 per round. *Eating facilities:* meals and drinks in clubhouse. *Visitors:* welcome. *Society Meetings:* catered for weekdays. Professional: D. Vernon (0521 41600). Secretary: D. Mumby (0521 41617).

MARKET RASEN. **Market Rasen and District Golf Club,** Legsby Road, Market Rasen LN8 3DZ (Market Rasen (0673) 842319). *Location:* A46 to Market Rasen – one mile east of town. Wooded course. 18 holes, 6043 yards, 5527 metres. S.S.S. 69. Practice ground. *Green Fees:* weekdays £15.00 per day, £10.00 per round; weekends only with member. *Eating facilities:* by arrangement with the Steward but not Mondays. *Visitors:* welcome with reservation, must be member of bona fide golf club. Not Wednesdays after 10.30 a.m. Weekends with members only. *Society Meetings:* catered for Tuesdays and Fridays. Professional: A.M. Chester. Hon. Secretary: E. Hill (0673 842416).

SKEGNESS. **North Shore Golf Club,** North Shore Road, Skegness PE25 1DN (Skegness (0754) 3298). *Location:* north of town one mile. Half seaside links, half parkland overlooking the sea. 18 holes, 6010 yards. S.S.S. 69. *Green Fees:* £20.00 weekdays, £25.00 weekends and Bank Holidays. *Eating facilities:* hotel on the course. *Visitors:* welcome, prior notice advisable. *Society Meetings:* weekdays only, by arrangement. Professional: John Cornelius (0754 4822). Secretary: R. Sykes (0754 67280).

SKEGNESS. **Seacroft Golf Club,** Seacroft, Skegness PE25 3AU (Skegness (0754) 3020). *Location:* towards Gibraltar Nature Reserve. Seaside links course. 18 holes, 6490 yards. S.S.S. 71. *Green Fees:* weekdays £18.00 per round, £25.00 per day; weekends and Bank Holidays £25.00 round, £30.00 per day. *Eating facilities:* available on prior booking. *Visitors:* welcome after 9.30am if members of recognised club, Handicap Certificate required; not between 12 noon and 2pm. *Society Meetings:* catered for, limited to 24 at weekends. Professional: R. Lawie (0754 69624). Secretary: H.K. Brader (0754 3020).

SLEAFORD. **Sleaford Golf Club,** Willoughby Road, South Rauceby, Sleaford NG34 8PL (South Rauceby (05298) 273). *Location:* off A153, two miles west of Sleaford. Inland links-type course, fairly flat and lightly wooded. 18 holes, 6443 yards, 5947 metres. S.S.S. 71. Practice field, 6 hole pitch and putt. *Green Fees:* weekdays £14.00, weekends £22.00. *Eating facilities:* full catering except Mondays. Bar open seven days. *Visitors:* welcome without reservation, except winter Sundays. Handicap Certificate required and must be members of a recognised club. *Society Meetings:* catered for weekdays only by prior arrangement. Professional: S.D. Harrison (05298 644). Secretary: D.B.R. Harris. (05298 326).

SPALDING. **Sutton Bridge Golf Club,** New Road, Sutton Bridge, Spalding (Holbeach (0406) 350323). *Location:* off A17, 18 miles east of Spalding. 9 holes, 5804 yards. S.S.S. 68. *Green Fees:* £15.00 weekdays. *Eating facilities:* available. *Visitors:* welcome, except weekends and not on match or competition days. *Society Meetings:* not catered for. Professional: R. Wood (0406 351080). Secretary: K.C. Buckle (0945 870455).

SPALDING. **The Spalding Golf Club,** Surfleet, Spalding PE11 4DG (Surfleet (077-585) 234). *Location:* four miles from Spalding on A16 to Boston. 18 holes, 5847 yards. S.S.S. 68. *Green fees:* information not provided. Handicap Certificates required. *Society Meetings:* catered for on Thursdays only. Professional: John W. Spencer (077-585 474). Secretary: E. Codling (077-585 386).

STAMFORD. **Burghley Park (Stamford) Golf Club,** St. Martins Without, Stamford PE9 3JX (0780 53789). *Location:* leave A1 at roundabout for Stamford, club one mile on right. Flat parkland. 18 holes, 6133 yards. S.S.S. 69. *Green Fees:* weekdays £18.00, weekends as members' guests only. *Eating facilities:* restaurant and bar. *Visitors:* welcome weekdays. Handicap Certificates required. *Society Meetings:* Wednesdays only. Professional: Glenn Davies (0780 62100). Secretary: Howard Mulligan (0780 53789).

STAMFORD. **Luffenham Heath Golf Club,** Ketton, Stamford PE9 3UU (Stamford (0780) 720205). *Location:* one-and-a-half miles south-west of Ketton on A6121. Undulating heathland, in conservation area for flora and fauna. 18 holes, 6254 yards. S.S.S. 70. *Green Fees:* on application. *Eating facilities:* catering available by arrangement. *Visitors:* welcome, advisable to contact Professional first. Changing room/showers.

Society Meetings: catered for by arrangement. Professional: J.A. Lawrence (0780 720298). Secretary: Ian F. Davenport.

WOODHALL SPA. **Woodhall Spa Golf Club,** Woodhall Spa LN10 6PU (Woodhall Spa (0526) 52511). *Location:* 19 miles from Lincoln, Boston, Sleaford; 33 miles from Skegness; 50 miles from Nottingham. Flat, wooded heathland. 18 holes, 6866 yards. S.S.S. 73. Practice ground and driving net. *Green Fees:* weekdays £18.00 per round, £25.00 per day; weekends and Bank Holidays £20.00 per round, £28.00 per day (all fees are estimates). *Eating facilities:* full catering available. *Visitors:* welcome with reservation. Handicap Certificates required (maximum handicap permitted Gents 20, Ladies 30). *Society Meetings:* catered for if booked in advance. Professional: P. Fixter (0526 53229). Secretary: S.R. Sharp.

Greater Manchester

ALTRINCHAM. **Altrincham Golf Course,** Stockport Road, Timperely, Altrinchram, Cheshire (061-928 0761). Course and shop managed by Trafford Borough Council, Altrincham Golf Club play over the course. *Location:* on A560 one mile east of Altrincham. 18 holes, 6162 yards. S.S.S. 69. *Green fees:* information not available. *Visitors:* welcome weekdays without reservation. Weekends, book a day in advance. Professional: R. West. Secretary: F.M. Platt.

ALTRINCHAM. **Dunham Forest Golf and Country Club,** Oldfield Lane, Altrincham WA14 4TY (061-928 2605). *Location:* approximatley 9 miles south of Manchester off A56. Wooded parkland. 18 holes, 6772 yards. S.S.S. 72. *Green Fees:* weekdays £18.00, weekends and Bank Holidays £22.00. *Eating facilities:* clubhouse restaurant and bar open daily. *Visitors:* welcome, but should telephone to check availability. *Society Meetings:* welcome by prior arrangement. Professional: I. Wrigley (061-928 2727). Secretary: Mrs S. Klaus (061-928 2605).

ALTRINCHAM. **The Ringway Golf Club Ltd,** Hale Mount, Hale Barns, Altrincham WA15 8SW (061-904 9609). *Location:* Junction 6, M56 then A538 towards Altrincham for one mile. Parkland. 18 holes, 6494 yards. S.S.S. 71. *Green Fees:* weekdays £20.00, weekends and Bank Holidays £25.00. *Eating facilities:* full diningroom facilities available. *Visitors:* generally not on Tuesdays or Saturdays which are Ladies and Gentlemans Competition Days and Fridays members only. *Society Meetings:* catered for by arrangement. Professional: Nick Ryan (061-980 8432). Secretary: D. Wright (061-980 2630).

ASHTON-IN-MAKERFIELD. **Ashton-in-Makerfield Golf Club Ltd,** Garswood Park, Liverpool Road, Ashton-in-Makerfield (Wigan (0942) 727267). *Location:* M6, Haydock Park roundabout. Wooded course. 18 holes, 6140 yards. S.S.S. 69. *Green fees:* information not available. *Eating facilities:* available. *Visitors:* welcome mid-week only without reservation. *Society Meetings:* catered for, mid-week. Professional: P. Allan (0942 724229). Secretary: F. Moran (0942 725617).

ASHTON-UNDER-LYNE. **Ashton-under-Lyne Golf Club,** Gorsey Way, Ashton-under-Lyne OL6 9HT (061-330 1537). *Location:* three miles from town centre, Mossley Road, left at Queens Road, right at Nook Lane, Clubhouse top of St. Christopher's Road. Wooded course. 18 holes, 6209 yards. S.S.S. 70. *Green Fees:* weekdays £12.00 per day, weekends with member only, £12.00. *Eating facilities:* full catering except Mondays. *Visitors:* members of recognised golf clubs welcome without reservation. *Society Meetings:* catered for on application: special daily rates. Professional: C. Boyle (061-308 2095). Secretary: G.J. Musgrave (061-339 8655).

BOLTON. **Bolton Golf Club Ltd,** Lostock Park, Chorley New Road, Bolton BL6 4AJ (Bolton (0204) 43067). *Location:* off main road half-way between Bolton and Horwich. 18 holes, 6215 yards. S.S.S. 70. *Green Fees:* information not provided. *Eating facilities:* luncheons (evening meals except Monday and Sunday). *Visitors:* welcome with reservation. *Society Meetings:* catered for on Thursdays and Fridays. Professional: R. Longworth. Secretary: H. Cook.

BOLTON. **Breightmet Golf Club,** Red Bridge, Ainsworth, Bolton (Bolton (0204) 27381). *Location:* leave Bolton on main road to Bury, turn left two miles on Milnthorpe road for the bridge. 9 holes, 6418 yards. S.S.S. 71. *Green Fees:* weekdays £8.00, weekends and Bank Holidays £10.00 (half-price with a member). *Eating facilities:* lunches and light refreshments. *Visitors:* welcome, preliminary phone call advisable. *Society Meetings:* catered for on application. Secretary: R. Weir.

BOLTON. **Deane Golf Club,** Broadford Road, Deane, Bolton (Bolton (0204) 61944). *Location:* one mile east of Junction 5 of M61 towards Bolton Centre. Rolling parkland with number of small ravines to cross. 18 holes, 5583 yards, 5105 metres. S.S.S. 67. *Green Fees:* weekdays £10.00, weekends £15.00. *Eating facilities:* lunches and evening meals by arrangement. *Visitors:* welcome. *Society Meetings:* Mondays, Tuesdays, Thursdays and Fridays only. Secretary: P. Flaxman (0204 651808).

BOLTON. **Dunscar Golf Club Ltd,** Longworth Lane, Bromley Cross, Bolton BL7 9QY (Bolton (0204) 53321). *Location:* one and a half miles north of Bolton on A666. Parkland, moorland course. 18 holes, 5977 yards, 5466 metres. S.S.S. 69. *Practice facilities available. Green Fees:* weekdays £12.00, weekends and Bank Holidays £15.00. With a member £7.50. *Eating facilities:* available. *Visitors:* welcome except weekends. *Society Meetings:* catered for by arrangement. Professional: Gary Treadgold (0204 592992). Secretary: Thomas Michael Yates (0204 53321).

BOLTON. **Harwood Golf Club,** Roading Brook Road, Harwood, Bolton BL2 4JD (Bolton (0204) 22878). *Location:* three miles east of Bolton – A58 to Bury, turn left through Ainsworth village. Flat meadowland. 9 holes, 5958 yards. S.S.S. 69. Small practice area. *Green Fees:* weekdays £10.00. *Eating facilities:* bar not open during weekdays, except Wednesdays, catering on request. *Visitors:* welcome any weekday, but not Sundays in golf season. *Society Meetings:* catered for on written application to Secretary. Professional: Max Evans (0204 398472). Secretary: J.S. Fairhurst (0204 28028).

BOLTON. **Old Links (Bolton) Ltd,** Chorley Old Road, Montserrat, Bolton BL1 5SU (0204 40050). *Location:* on B6226, 400 yards north of roundabout on ring road. Championship course, moorland. 18 holes, 6410 yards. S.S.S. 72. Practice facilities. *Green Fees:* weekdays £15.00, weekends £20.00. *Eating facilities:* available except Mondays. *Visitors:* welcome, not Saturdays until 4.00pm. *Society Meetings:* catered for weekdays. Professional: P. Horridge (0204 43089). Secretary: E. Monaghan (0204 42307).

BOLTON. **Regent Park Golf Club Ltd,** Links Road, Chorley New Road, Bolton B12 9XX (Bolton (0204) 42336). *Location:* midway between Bolton and Horwich. 18 holes, 6069 yards. S.S.S. 69. *Green Fees:* information not available. *Eating facilities:* snacks and meals available. *Society Meeetings:* welcome mid-week, book in advance. Professional: K. Holland. Secretary: A. Cunliffe.

BOLTON. **Turton Golf Club,** Wood End Farm, Chapeltown Road, Bromley Cross, Bolton (0204 852235). *Location:* three miles north of Bolton on the A666. Moorland course with extensive views. 9 holes, 5805 yards. S.S.S. 68. Practice area. *Green Fees:* information not provided. *Eating facilities:* to order except Mondays. *Visitors:* welcome except Mondays, Wednesday afternoons or Saturdays. *Society Meetings:* welcome on Thursdays by arrangement. Secretary: H.M. Ainscough (0204 52459).

BRAMHALL. **Bramhall Golf Club,** The Clubhouse, Ladythorn Road, Bramhall, Stockport SK7 2EY (061-439 4057). *Location:* three-quarters of a mile from Bramhall Railway Station, half a mile from Bramhall Moat House Hotel. 18 holes, 6361 yards, 5816 metres. S.S.S. 70. *Green Fees:* information not provided. *Eating facilities:* Steward will provide meals on request, subject to club and visiting party occasions. *Society Meetings:* catered for Wednesdays. Professional: Brian Nield (061-439 1171). Secretary: F. Chadfield (061-439 6092).

BURY. **Bury Golf Club,** Unsworth Hall, Blackford Bridge, Bury (061-766 4897). *Location:* A56 eight miles north of Manchester. 18 holes, 5953 yards. S.S.S. 69. *Green Fees:* information not provided. *Eating facilities:* grill room service except Mondays. *Visitors:* welcome without reservation. *Society Meetings:* catered for. Professional: M. Peel (061-766 2213). Secretary: J. Meikle.

BURY. **Greenmount Golf Club,** Greenhaigh Fold Farm, Greenmount, Bury (Tottington (020-488 3712). *Location:* three miles north of Bury. 9 holes, 4915 yards. S.S.S. 64. *Green Fees:* weekdays £6.00 per day. *Eating facilities:* lunches at club except on Thursdays. *Visitors:* welcome. Tuesday – Ladies' day. *Society Meetings:* not catered for. Hon. Secretary: H.J. Billingham (020-488 3712).

BURY. **Lowes Park Golf Club Ltd,** Hill Top, Walmersley, Bury BL9 6SU (061-764 1231). *Location:* take A56 north from Bury, turn right at Bury General Hospital into Lowes Road. Hilly exposed course. 9 holes, 6009 yards, 5500 metres. S.S.S. 69. *Green Fees:* weekdays £7.00, Sundays by appointment only, £8.00.

Eating facilities: full catering except Mondays. *Visitors:* welcome weekdays except Wednesdays (Ladies' Day); not Saturdays; Sundays by letter to Secretary. *Society Meetings:* catered for as for visitors. Secretary: E. Brierley (0706 67331).

BURY. **Walmersley Golf Club,** Garretts Close, Walmersley, Bury (061-764 1429). *Location:* leave A56 approximately two miles north of Bury at Walmersley Post Office into Old Road, right at Masons Arms Inn. Moorland course. 9 holes, 6114 yards, 5588 metres. S.S.S. 70. *Green Fees:* £8.00 per day, £5.00 with member. *Eating facilities:* lunches and evening meals served except Mondays. *Visitors:* welcome weekdays without reservation. *Society Meetings:* catered for weekdays. Secretary: C. Stock (061-764 5057).

CHEADLE. **Cheadle Golf Club,** Shiers Drive, Cheadle (061-428 2160). *Location:* one-and-a-half miles Junction 11 M63. 9 holes, 5006 yards. S.S.S. 65. *Green Fees:* information not provided. *Eating facilities:* by arrangement. *Visitors:* welcome with reservation and playing with member. *Society Meetings:* catered for by arrangement. Professional: N.R. Harding (061-428 9878). Secretary: P.P. Webster (061-428 2160).

DENTON. **Denton Golf Club,** Manchester Road, Denton M34 2NU (061-336 3218). *Location:* A57, 5 miles from Piccadilly, Manchester. 18 holes, 6290 yards. S.S.S. 70. *Green Fees:* information not provided. *Eating facilities:* meals catered for except all day Monday and Thursday afternoon. *Visitors:* welcome with club members and handicap, without reservation weekdays only. *Society Meetings:* catered for on weekdays except Tuesday by application. Professional: Roger Vere. Secretary: R. Wickham.

DUKINFIELD. **Dukinfield Golf Club,** Lyne Edge, Dukinfield (061-338 2340). *Location:* six miles east of Manchester via Ashton-under-Lyne. Hillside with wooded areas. 16 holes, 5556 yards. S.S.S. 67. *Green Fees:* weekdays £8.00. *Visitors:* welcome except Wednesdays and weekends. *Society Meetings:* catered for by prior arrangement. Secretary: K.P. Parker (061-338 2669).

ECCLES. **Worsley Golf Club,** Stableford Avenue, Monton, Eccles M30 8AP (061-789 4202). *Location:* one mile from Junction 13 M62. Parkland. 18 holes, 6200 yards. S.S.S. 70. *Green Fees:* weekdays £14.00 (£7.00 with member), weekends and Bank Holidays £18.00 (£9.00 with member). *Eating facilities:* snacks, lunches and evening meals. *Visitors:* welcome, if past or present members of recognised golf clubs. *Society Meetings:* catered for Mondays, Wednesdays and Thursdays. Professional: Ceri Cousins. Secretary: B. Dean.

HYDE. **Werneth Low Golf Club,** Werneth Low, Hyde, Cheshire SK14 3AF (061-368 2503). *Location:* one mile from centre of Hyde via Gee Cross. Scenic, hilly course with excellent greens. 9 holes, 6114 yards. S.S.S. 66. *Green Fees:* information not available. *Eating facilities:* light refreshments normally available except Wednesdays. *Visitors:* welcome any time except Sunday mornings and Tuesday evenings; Sundays with member only. *Society Meetings:* catered for by prior arrangement. Professional: T. Bacchus (061-336 6908). Secretary: R. Watson (061-368 7388).

LEIGH. Pennington Golf Club (Municipal), Pennington Golf Course, Pennington Country Park, off St. Helens Road, Leigh. *Location:* junction 17 on M6 to Leigh. Flat parkland with water coursing through. 9 holes, 2919 yards, S.S.S. 34. *Green Fees:* on request. *Eating facilities:* snack bar facilities. *Visitors:* welcome without reservation. Professional: Mr T. Kershaw (0942 607278). Secretary: Mr P.A. Cartwright (061-794 5316).

LITTLEBOROUGH. Whittaker Golf Club, Shore Lane, Littleborough, OL15 0LH (Littleborough (0706) 78310). *Location:* one mile from town centre along Blackstone Edge Old Road. Moorland course. 9 holes, 5632 yards. S.S.S. 67. *Green Fees:* weekdays £6.00, weekends £8.00. *Eating facilities:* none, but bar available. *Visitors:* welcome without reservation, except Tuesday afternoons and Sundays. *Society Meetings:* weekdays and Saturdays only by prior arrangement with Secretary. Secretary: G.A. Smith (0484 428546).

MANCHESTER. Blackley Golf Club, Victoria Avenue East, Manchester M9 2HW (061-643 2980). 18 holes, 6235 yards. S.S.S. 70. *Green fees:* £12.00 weekdays. *Eating facilities:* lunches at club except Monday, order in advance. *Visitors:* welcome, except Saturday and Sunday. Professional: Martin Barton. Secretary: C.B. Leggot (061-643 3812).

MANCHESTER. Brookdale Golf Club Ltd, Ashbridge, Woodhouse, Failsworth, Manchester (061-681 4534). *Location:* five miles north of Manchester. 18 holes, 6040 yards. S.S.S. 68. *Green Fees:* weekdays £8.00 to £10.00 without member, weekends and Bank Holidays £12.00 without member. *Eating facilities:* available with ample notice. *Visitors:* welcome without reservation except Sundays. *Society Meetings:* catered for with one month's notice. Professional: P. Davalle (061-681 2655). Secretary: G. Glass.

MANCHESTER. Chorlton-cum-Hardy Golf Club, Barlow Hall Road, Chorlton-cum-Hardy M21 2JJ (061-881 3139). *Location:* near junction of A5145 and A5103 (M63 Junction 9). Meadowland. 18 holes, 6003 yards. S.S.S. 69. *Green Fees:* weekdays £14.00, weekends and Bank Holidays £17.00. *Eating facilities:* meals by arrangement with Steward, snacks and sandwiches always available, sandwiches only on Mondays. *Visitors:* welcome without reservation, except on Competition days. *Society Meetings:* catered for by arrangement. Professional: David Screeton (061-881 9911). Secretary: F.E. Collis ((061-881 5830).

MANCHESTER. Davyhulme Park Golf Club, The Clubhouse, Gleneagles Road, Davyhulme, Urmston, Manchester M31 2SA (061-748 2260). *Location:* one mile from M63/M62. Wooded parkland course. 18 holes, 6237 yards. S.S.S. 70. *Green Fees:* information not provided. *Eating facilities:* lunches and dinners except Mondays. *Visitors:* welcome except competition days. *Society Meetings:* catered for by arrangement. Professional: H. Lewis. Secretary: E.W. Travis.

MANCHESTER. Didsbury Golf Club Ltd, Ford Lane, Northenden, Manchester M22 4NQ (061-998 2743). *Location:* Junction 3 on M56 to Palatine Road to

Church Road, to Ford Lane. Parkland. 18 holes, 6276 yards. S.S.S. 70. Good practice facilities. *Green Fees:* weekdays £13.00, weekends £15.00. *Eating facilities:* fully-equipped bar and restaurant. *Visitors:* Thursday/ Friday – Tuesday small societies. *Society Meetings:* catered for. Professional: P. Barber (061-998 2811). Manager: B. Hughes (061-998 9278).

MANCHESTER. Ellesmere Golf Club, Old Clough Lane, Worsley, Near Manchester M28 5HZ (061-790 2122). *Location:* off A580 East Lancs Road, adjacent to M62 northbound, (eastbound) access. Wooded parkland. 18 holes, 5954 yards. S.S.S. 69. *Green Fees:* weekdays: visitors £12.00, guests £4.00: weekends: visitors £16.00, guests £5.00. *Eating facilities:* bar; catering available, with or without reservation. *Visitors:* members of recognised golf clubs welcome, but not during club competitions or Bank Holidays; contact Professional for restrictions. *Society Meetings:* catered for by appointment. Professional: John Pennington (061-790 8591). Hon. Secretary: A.C. Kay (061-799 0554).

MANCHESTER. Fairfield Golf and Sailing Club, "Boothdale", Booth Road, Audenshaw, Manchester M34 5GA (061-370 1641). *Location:* off A635, five miles east of Manchester. Parkland bounded in part by reservoir. 18 holes, 4956 yards. S.S.S. 68. *Green Fees:* weekdays £9.50, weekends £12.50. *Eating facilities:* available. *Visitors:* welcome without reservation weekdays only. *Society Meetings:* catered for by prior arrangement mid-week. Professional: D. Butler (061-370 2292). Secretary: J. Humphries (061-336 3950).

MANCHESTER. Flixton Golf Club, Church Road, Flixton, Urmston (061-748 2116). *Location:* five miles from Manchester. 9 holes, 6410 yards. S.S.S. 71. *Green Fees:* £10.00 weekdays. £8.00 weekends, Bank Holidays and Christmas and New Year holiday period (playing with a member only). *Eating facilities:* daily except Tuesdays. *Visitors:* welcome with reservation. *Society Meetings:* catered for by arrangement. Professional: N. Rothe. Hon. Secretary: J.G. Frankland.

MANCHESTER. Heaton Park Golf Club, Heaton Park, Prestwich, Manchester (061-798 0295). *Location:* north Manchester, M62 to exit 19 M66 to A576, right to park entrance (200 yards). Undulating parkland. 18 holes, 5840 yards. S.S.S. 68. *Green Fees:* weekdays £4.00, weekends and Bank Holidays £6.00 per round. *Visitors:* welcome, book week in advance. Secretary: A.F. Roberts (061-681 1476).

MANCHESTER. Houldsworth Golf Club Ltd, Wingate House, Higher Levenshulme, Manchester M19 3JW (061-224 5055). *Location:* off A6 between Manchester and Stockport, Longford Road off Gorton Road, Reddish. Flat parkland with water hazards. 18 holes, 6078 yards, 5558 metres. S.S.S. 69. Practice area. *Green Fees:* weekdays £8.00, weekends £10.00. Reduced rates for parties. *Eating facilities:* bar snacks, or full restaurant service. *Visitors:* welcome. Ladies only on Tuesday afternoons; check club competitions at weekends. *Society Meetings:* catered for on application. Professional: David Naylor (061-224 4571). Secretary: J.B. Hogg (061-336 5044).

MANCHESTER. **Manchester Golf Club,** Hopwood Cottage, Middleton, Manchester M24 2QP (061-643 2718). *Location:* Exit 20 from M62, three minutes from motorway. Moorland/parkland. 18 holes, 6454 yards, 5895 metres. S.S.S. 72. Large practice ground. Driving range. *Green Fees:* weekdays, £18.00 per day, weekends £23.00 per day. *Eating facilities:* two bars and first class restaurant. *Visitors:* welcome weekdays. *Society Meetings:* parties up to 120 catered for by arrangement. Professional: B. Connor (061-643 2638). Secretary: K.G. Flett (061-643 3202).

MANCHESTER. **New North Manchester Golf Club Ltd,** Rhodes House, Manchester Old Road, Middleton, Manchester (061-643 2941). *Location:* A576, less than one mile from Junction 18 on M62/M66. Undulating and sometimes hilly terrain. 18 holes, 6527 yards, 5987 metres. S.S.S. 72. Large practice ground. *Green Fees:* £12.00 per round £14.00 per day weekdays. *Eating facilities:* catering every day except Tuesday. *Visitors:* welcome except weekends. *Society Meetings:* welcome. Professional: M. Vipond (061-643 7094). Secretary: J. Fallon (061-643 9033).

MANCHESTER. **Northenden Golf Club,** Palatine Road, Northenden, Manchester M22 4FR (061-998 4079). *Location:* 7 miles south of Manchester city centre, one mile north east of M56. 18 holes, 6469 yards, 5908 metres. S.S.S. 71. Practice net. *Green Fees:* £15.00 weekdays, £20.00 weekends. Reduced rates if playing with a member. *Eating facilities:* available, diningroom and bar snacks. *Visitors:* welcome most days preferably with reservation. *Society Meetings:* Tuesdays and Fridays only catered for. Professional: W. McColl (061-945 3386). Hon. Secretary: C.R. Rankin (061-998 4738). Clubhouse Manager: J.F. Fleet.

MANCHESTER. **Pikefold Golf Club,** Cooper Lane, Manchester M9 2QQ (061-740 1136). *Location:* four miles north of city centre off Rochdale Road A664, then A6104 Victoria Avenue. Undulating wooded course. 9 holes, 5789 yards. S.S.S. 68. *Green Fees:* weekdays £5.00 per round/day (£3.50 with member). Weekends and Bank Holidays £5.00, must play with member. *Eating facilities:* full catering and bar facilities. *Visitors:* welcome weekdays without reservation. *Society Meetings:* catered for by prior arrangement. Secretary: G.V.W. Kendell.

MANCHESTER. **Prestwich Golf Club,** Hilton Lane, Prestwich, Manchester (061-773 2544). *Location:* on A6044, one mile from junction with A56. 18 holes, 4757 yards. S.S.S. 63. *Green Fees:* information not provided. *Eating facilities:* by arrangement. *Visitors:* welcome without reservation. *Society Meetings:* catered for weekdays. Professional: Gary Coope.

MANCHESTER. **Stand Golf Club,** The Dales, Ashbourne Grove, Whitefield, Bury, Manchester M25 7NL (061-766 2388). *Location:* M62 Exit 17, A56/A665 one mile. Undulating parkland with sandy subsoil, playable all year round. 18 holes, 6426 yards. S.S.S. 71. *Green Fees:* weekdays £12.00, weekends £16.00. Reduced rates for parties over 16. *Eating facilities:* meals served daily and bar except Mondays, order in advance. *Visitors:* welcome Monday to Friday;

weekends by prior arrangement. *Society Meetings:* welcome Wednesday/Friday by prior arrangement. Professional: M. Dance (061-766 2214). Secretary: T.E. Thacker (061-766 3197).

MANCHESTER. **Swinton Park Golf Club,** East Lancashire Road, Swinton, Manchester M27 1LX (061-794 1785). *Location:* on the A580 Manchester to Liverpool road, five miles from Manchester centre. Parkland course. Three courses. Practice. *Green Fees:* on application. *Eating Facilities:* available. *Visitors:* welcome Tuesdays, Wednesdays and Fridays, Tee reservations 10am – noon, 2pm – 4pm. *Society Meetings:* catered for by prior arrangement. Professional: J. Wilson (061-793 8978). General Secretary: F. Slater (061-794 0861).

MANCHESTER. **Withington Golf Club,** 243 Palatine Road, West Didsbury, Manchester M20 8UD (061-445 3912). *Location:* three miles from Manchester city centre, adjacent M56 and M63. Flat parkland. 18 holes, 6410 yards. S.S.S. 71. *Green Fees:* weekdays £13.00, weekends £16.00. *Eating facilities:* lunches and evening meals to order. Snacks available at all times except Mondays. *Visitors:* ring Professional for times. *Society Meetings:* catered for by arrangement with the Secretary. Professional: R.J. Ling (061-445 4861). Secretary/Manager: A. Larsen (061-445 9544).

MARPLE. **Marple Golf Club,** Hawk Green, Marple SK6 7EL (061-427 2311). *Location:* off A6 at High Lane, then left at Hawk Green. 18 holes. *Green fees:* information not available. *Eating facilities:* full catering. *Society Meetings:* Special Golf and Catering packages available. Professional: Nick Wood. Secretary: M. Gilbert.

OLDHAM. **Crompton and Royton Golf Club Ltd,** High Barn, Royton, Oldham (061-624 2154). Heathland. 18 holes, 6187 yards. S.S.S. 70. *Green Fees:* weekends £15.00, weekdays £12.00. *Eating facilities:* lunches served at the club, except Mondays. *Visitors:* welcome without reservation, not at weekends. *Society Meetings:* catered for by arrangement with Secretary. Professional: D.A. Melling (061-624 2154). Secretary: T. Donovan (061-624 0986).

OLDHAM. **Oldham Golf Club,** Lees New Road, Oldham (061-624 4986). *Location:* B6194 between Ashton-under- Lyne and Oldham. Moorland course, no bunkers. 18 holes, 5045 yards. S.S.S. 65. *Green Fees:* information not available. *Eating facilities:* full catering. *Visitors:* welcome, telephone to check for competitions, especially weekends. *Society Meetings:* catered for by prior arrangement with Secretary. Professional: Andrew Laverty (061-626 8346). Secretary: B.C. Heginbotham (Saddleworth (04577) 6326).

OLDHAM. **Saddleworth Golf Club,** Mountain Ash, Ladcastle Road, Uppermill, Near Oldham (0457 872059). *Location:* five miles east of Oldham. Hillside/moorland course with superb views. 18 holes, 5976 yards. S.S.S. 69. Putting green and practice area. *Green Fees:* weekdays £12.50 (£4.50 per day with member), weekends and Bank Holidays £16.00 (£5.50 per day with member). *Eating facilities:* snacks and meals provided. *Visitors:* welcome without reservation except Saturdays and Sundays. *Society Meetings:* catered for except weekends (Package £19.50, Luxury £23.50). Professional: T. Shard (0457 873653). Secretary: H.A. Morgan (0457 873653).

OLDHAM. **Werneth Golf Club,** 124 Green Lane, Garden Suburb, Oldham (061-624 1190). 18 holes, 5275 yards. S.S.S. 66. Practice ground. *Green Fees:* £10.00 weekdays only. *Eating facilities:* full catering service available. *Visitors:* welcome, ring for details. *Society Meetings:* catered for, ring for details. Professional: Terence Morley. Secretary: J.H. Barlow.

ROCHDALE. **Lobden Golf Club,** Whitworth, Near Rochdale (Rochdale (0706) 343228). *Location:* Take A671 from Rochdale to Whitworth. 9 holes, 2885 yards. S.S.S. 68. *Green fees:* information not provided. *Visitors:* welcome all week except Saturday. *Society Meetings:* catered for except Saturday. Secretary: C. Buchanan.

ROCHDALE. **Rochdale Golf Club,** The Clubhouse, Edenfield Road, Bagslate, Rochdale OL11 5YR (Rochdale (0706) 46024). *Location:* M62 at Exit 20, three miles on A680. Parkland. 18 holes, 6002 yards. S.S.S. 69. *Green Fees:* £11.00 weekdays, £14.00 weekends. *Eating facilities:* meals available, order in advance. *Visitors:* welcome without reservation. *Society Meetings:* catered for by arrangement Wednesdays and Fridays. Professional: A. Laverty (0706 522104). Secretary: S. Cockroft (0706 43818).

ROCHDALE. **Springfield Park Golf Club,** Springfield Park, Marland, Rochdale (0706 56401). *Location:* A58 out of Rochdale, along Bolton Road on right. Parkland. 18 holes, 5209 yards. S.S.S. 66. *Green Fees:* £3.20 weekdays, £4.50 weekends. *Eating facilities:* none available. *Visitors:* welcome, no restrictions. Professional: D. Wills (0706 49801). Secretary: B. Wynn (0706 526064).

ROCHDALE. **Tunshill Golf Club,** Tunshill Lane, Milnrow, Rochdale OL16 3TS (Rochdale (0706) 342095). *Location:* alongside M62 at Milnrow. Moorland course. 9 holes, 5804 yards. S.S.S. 68. *Green Fees:* weekdays £7.00 (£2.50 if playing with member), weekends £8.00 (£3.00 if playing with member). *Eating facilities:* catering and bar by arrangement. *Visitors:* welcome weekdays, weekends by arrangement. *Society Meetings:* welcome by arrangement. Professional: Peter Lunt (0706 861982).Secretary: Derek Kennedy (0706 78842).

SALE. **Ashton on Mersey Golf Club,** Church Lane, Ashton on Mersey, Sale M33 5QQ (061-937 3220). *Location:* two miles from Sale Station. Parkland course. 9 holes, 6242 yards. S.S.S. 70. *Green Fees:* information not provided. *Eating facilities:* lunches available at club except Mondays. *Visitors:* welcome on weekdays, Saturdays, Sundays and Bank Holidays only with member. Professional: M.J. Williams. Secretary: A.H. Marsland.

SALE. **Sale Golf Club,** Sale Lodge, Golf Road, Sale M33 2LU (061-973 3404). *Location:* junction 8 M63, A6144. Parkland. 18 holes, 6346 yards. S.S.S. 71. *Green Fees:* £13.00 weekdays, £20.00 weekends. *Eating facilities:* dining room daily except Mondays.

Visitors: welcome weekdays, weekends and Bank Holidays with a member. *Society Meetings:* by arrangement. Professional: A.M. Lake (061-973 1730). Secretary: J. Blair (061-973 1638).

SALFORD. **Brackley Municipal Golf Course,** Bullows Road (off Captain Fold Road), Little Hulton, Salford (061-790 6076). *Location:* M61 to Junction 4 onto A6, left at roundabout onto A6 (Walkden), half a mile turn left at White Lion pub. Flat course with interesting doglegs. 9 holes, 3003 yards, 2747 metres. S.S.S. 69. *Green Fees:* £2.50 weekdays; £2.50 per 9 holes, £3.75 per 18 holes weekends. Senior Citizens £1.50, Juniors £2.00 weekdays. *Eating facilities:* none. *Visitors:* welcome anytime. Secretary: R. Heyes.

STOCKPORT. **Bramall Park Golf Club,** 20 Manor Road, Bramhall, Stockport (061-485 3119). *Location:* 10 miles south of Manchester, 3 miles south of Stockport, half a mile from Cheadle Hulme. Parkland. 18 holes, 6214 yards. S.S.S. 70. *Green Fees:* weekdays £15.00, weekends and Bank holidays £20.00. *Eating facilities:* full eating facilities except Fridays. *Visitors:* welcome apply to Professional. *Society Meetings:* catered for. Professional: M. Proffitt (061-485 2205). Secretary: J.C. O'Shea (061-485 3119).

STOCKPORT. **Disley Golf Club Ltd,** Stanley Hall Lane, Disley, Stockport SK12 2JX (Disley (0663) 62071). *Location:* six miles south-east of Stockport on A6. Moorland course with marvellous scenic views. 18 holes, 6015 yards. S.S.S. 69. *Green fees:* information not available. *Eating facilities:* full service except Mondays. *Visitors:* welcome most days except Mondays and Thursdays. *Society Meetings:* Tuesdays only. Professional: A.G. Esplin (0663 64001). Secretary: J.A. Lomas (0663 64001).

STOCKPORT. **Hazel Grove Golf Club,** Buxton Road, Hazel Grove, Stockport SK7 6LU (061-483 3217). *Location:* A6 to Buxton, three miles south of Stockport. Flat parkland with tree-lined fairways. 18 holes, 6300 yards. S.S.S. 70. *Green Fees:* weekdays £15.00, weekends £20.00. *Eating facilities:* available daily except Mondays. *Visitors:* welcome, ring Professional first to check availability. *Society Meetings:* catered for on Thursdays and Fridays. Professional: M.E. Hill (061-483 7272). Secretary: H.A.G. Carlisle (061-483 3978).

STOCKPORT. **Heaton Moor Golf Club,** Mauldeth Road, Heaton Mersey, Stockport SK4 3NX (061-432 2134). *Location:* A34 off M56. Flat parkland course. 18 holes, 5909 yards. S.S.S. 68. *Green Fees:* information not provided. *Eating facilities:* lunches and evening meals by arrangement. *Visitors:* welcome weekdays. *Society Meetings:* catered for. Professional: Clive Loydall (061-432 0846). Secretary: A.A. Gibbon.

STOCKPORT. **Mellor and Townscliffe Golf Club,** Gibb Lane, Tarden, Mellor, Stockport SK6 5NA (061-427 2208). *Location:* seven miles south east of Stockport off A626. Parkland with trees/moorland. 18 holes, 5925 yards. S.S.S. 69. *Green Fees:* weekdays £10.00 per round, £12.00 per day, Sundays and Bank Holidays £15.00. Playing with a member weekdays £3.00, Sunday £4.00. *Eating facilities:* available daily, Tuesdays by prior arrangement. *Visitors:* welcome weekdays, no visitors on Saturdays, and Sundays only by prior arrangement. *Society Meetings:* catered for, contact Secretary. Professional: Michael J. Williams (061-427 5759). Secretary: K. Bounds.

STOCKPORT. **Reddish Vale Golf Club,** Southcliffe Road, Reddish, Stockport SK5 7EE (061-480 2359). *Location:* one mile north east of Stockport. Varied undulating heathland course, designed by Dr A. MacKenzie. 18 holes, 6086 yards. S.S.S. 69. *Green Fees:* weekdays £15.00. *Eating facilities:* bar and catering. *Visitors:* welcome on weekdays (not 12.30 – 1.30pm). *Society Meetings:* catered for by arrangement. Professional: Richard Brown (061-480 3824). Secretary: J.L. Blakey.

STOCKPORT. **Romiley Golf Club Ltd,** Goosehouse Green, Romiley, Stockport SK6 4LJ (061-430 2392). *Location:* B6104 off A560, signposted from Romiley village. Parkland. 18 holes, 6335 yards. S.S.S. 70. *Green Fees:* weekdays £14.00 per round, £18.00 per day; weekends and Bank Holidays £20.00 per round, £25.00 per day. *Eating facilities:* full catering by arrangement except Mondays. *Visitors:* welcome. *Society Meetings:* catered for Tuesdays and Wednesdays by arrangement with Secretary. Reduced rates for groups of over 30 by arrangement £12.00 per round. Professional: Gary Butler (061-430 7122). Secretary: Frank Beard (061-430 7257).

STOCKPORT. **Stockport Golf Club Ltd,** Offerton Road, Stockport, Cheshire (061-427 2001). *Location:* one mile from lights at Hazel Grove, along Torkington Road. 18 holes, 6323 yards. S.S.S. 71. *Green Fees:* information not provided. *Eating facilities:* available, excellent. *Visitors:* welcome without reservation. *Society Meetings:* catered for. Professional: R.G. Tattersall. Hon. Secretary: H.E. Bagshaw.

TRAFFORD. **William Wroe Municipal Golf Course,** Pennybridge Lane, off Flixton Road, Flixton, Trafford (061- 748 8680). Course and shop managed by Trafford Borough Council, Acre Gate Golf Club play over the course. *Location:* M63 Exit 4, B5124 to Davyhulme Circle then one mile on B5158, left at Bird-in-Hand Hotel, Flixton. 18 holes, 3935 yards. *Green fees:* information not provided. *Visitors:* welcome anytime, but advisable to book the day before. Teaching Professional: Roland West. Secretary: Mrs P. Rowan. Golf course Manager: Mr B. Davies.

WESTHOUGHTON. **Westhoughton Golf Club,** Long Island, Westhoughton (Westhoughton (0942) 811085). *Location:* four miles south west of Bolton on A58. 9 holes, 5702 yards. S.S.S. 68. *Green Fees:*

information not provided. *Visitors:* welcome, preferably playing with a member. *Society Meetings:* catered for by special arrangement. Professional: Stephen Yates. Secretary: D.J. Kinsella.

WHITEFIELD. **Whitefield Golf Club,** Higher Lane, Whitefield, Manchester (061-766 2728 members). *Location:* Exit 17, off M62 then take road to Radcliffe for one mile. 18 holes, 6041 yards. S.S.S. 69. *Green Fees:* on application. *Eating facilities:* restaurant facilities every day. *Visitors:* welcome. *Society Meetings:* catered for. Professional: P. Reeves. Secretary: Mrs R. L. Vidler (061-766 2904).

WIGAN. **Gathurst Golf Club,** 62 Miles Lane, Shevington, Wigan WN6 8EW (Appley Bridge (02575) 2861). *Location:* one mile south of Junction 27 M6. Parkland. 9 holes, 6308 yards. S.S.S. 70. *Green Fees:* weekdays £10.00. *Eating facilities:* available bar hours, daily except Monday. *Visitors:* welcome Monday, Tuesday, Thursday and Friday with reservation. *Society Meetings:* catered for by appointment. Professional: D. Clarke (02575 4909). Secretary: J. Clarke (02575 2861).

WIGAN. **Haigh Hall Golf Club,** Haigh Country Park, Near Wigan WN2 1PE (Wigan (0942) 833337). *Location:* junction 27 M6 at Standish – country park at Haigh. Parkland. 18 holes, 6423 yards. S.S.S. 71. Practice area. *Green Fees:* weekdays £3.50, weekends £5.50. *Eating facilities:* cafeteria. *Visitors:* welcome, contact Professional. Professional: Ian Lee (0942 831107) Secretary: John McAllister (0257 422247).

WIGAN. **Hindley Hall Golf Club,** Hall Lane, Hindley, Wigan (Wigan (0942) 55131. *Location:* two miles east of Wigan, Junction 6 M61, or A58 to Ladies Lane/Hall Lane. 18 holes, 5841 yards. S.S.S. 68. *Green Fees:* informatioin not available. *Eating facilities:* not Mondays, book before playing. *Visitors:* welcome without reservation if members of a recognised golf club. *Society Meetings:* catered for by arrangement with the Secretary. Special rates for parties of 25 or more. Professional: S. Yates (0942 55991). Secretary: R. Bell.

WIGAN. **Wigan Golf Club,** Arley Hall, Haigh, near Wigan WN1 2UH (Standish (0257) 421360). *Location:* M6 at exit 27, 2 miles on B5329, left at traffic lights at canal bridge near the Crawford Arms Public House. 9 holes, 6058 yards. S.S.S. 69. *Green Fees:* £13.00 weekdays, £18.00 weekends. *Visitors:* welcome anytime except Tuesdays, Saturdays and Sundays. *Society Meetings:* catered for on written application. Secretary: J. Crompton (0942 41051).

Merseyside

BIRKENHEAD. **Arrowe Park Golf Course,** Arrowe Park, Birkenhead (051-677 1527). *Location:* Mersey Tunnel into Brough Road, then Woodchurch Road, head for Arrowe Park roundabout bear left approximately 400 yards turn right into Arrowe Park. Parkland. 18 holes, 5835 yards. S.S.S. 68. 9 hole pitch and putt, putting green. *Green fees:* information not available. *Eating facilities:* restaurant facilities available. *Visitors:* EVERYBODY WELCOME! Professional: Clive Scanlon. Secretary: K. Finlay.

BIRKENHEAD. **Prenton Golf Club,** Golf Links Road, Prenton, Birkenhead (051-608 1053). *Location:* off A552. Parkland course. 18 holes, 6411 yards. S.S.S. 71. *Green Fees:* £15.00 weekdays. *Eating facilities:* from 11.00am daily. *Visitors:* welcome, reservation advisable. *Society Meetings:* catered for Wednesdays. Professional: Robin Thompson. Secretary: P.E. Manley.

BIRKENHEAD. **The Wirral Ladies' Golf Club Ltd,** 93 Bidston Road, Oxton, Birkenhead (051-652 5797). *Location:* on boundary of town, Bidston Hill area. 18 holes, 4966 yards (Ladies), 5170 yards (Men). S.S.S. 70 (Ladies), S.S.S. 66 (Men). *Green Fees:* information not provided. *Eating facilities:* meals during day to order. *Visitors:* welcome with reservation. Introduction from Club Secretary. Professional: Mark Jones. Secretary: D.P. Cranston-Miller (051-652 1255).

BLUNDELLSANDS. **West Lancashire Golf Club,** Hall Road West, Blundellsands, Liverpool L23 8SZ (051-924 1076). *Location:* A565 Liverpool – Southport to Crosby, follow signposts for club or Waterloo Rugby Club. Links course. 6756 yards. S.S.S. 73. *Green Fees:* £20.00. *Eating facilities:* lunch, tea and dinner every day. *Visitors:* welcome on weekdays. *Society Meetings:* catered for by advance application. Professional: D.G. Lloyd. Secretary: D. E. Bell.

BOOTLE. **Bootle Golf Club,** Dunnings Bridge Road, Bootle L30 2PP (051-928 6196). *Location:* five miles north of Liverpool, one mile from M57 and M58. Flat.

18 holes, 6362 yards. S.S.S. 70. *Green Fees:* information not available. *Eating facilities:* full catering as required by arrangement. *Visitors:* unrestricted. *Society Meetings:* by appointment. Professional: Gary Brown (051-928 1371). Secretary: John F. Morgan (051-922 4792).

BROMBOROUGH. **Bromborough Golf Club,** Raby Hall Road, Bromborough, Wirral, Merseyside L63 0NN (051-334 2155). *Location:* Exit 4 Wirral Motorway M53. Parkland. 18 holes, 6650 yards, 6080 metres. S.S.S. 73. *Green Fees:* weekdays £18.000, weekends £27.00, reduced rates for Societies over 24. *Eating facilities:* bar and full catering facilities. *Visitors:* welcome without reservation weekdays, but essential to ring in advance for weekends and Bank Holidays. *Society Meetings:* catered for by prior arrangement. Professional: Paul Andrew (051-334 4499). Secretary: L.B. Silvester (051-334 2978).

EASTHAM. **Eastham Lodge Golf Club,** 117 Ferry Road, Eastham, Wirral, Merseyside L62 0AP (051-327 1483). *Location:* exit Junction 5 M53 into Eastham village from A41. 15 holes, 5826 yards (for 18). S.S.S. 68. *Green Fees:* weekdays £11.00 per round/day. *Eating facilities:* bar snacks, full restaurant (book in advance). *Visitors:* welcome weekdays, with member weekends. *Society Meetings:* Tuesdays only; £11.00 per day, £9.00 per round. Professional: Ivor Jones (051-327 3008). Secretary: C.S. Camden (051-327 3003).

FORMBY. **Formby Golf Club,** Golf Road, Formby, Liverpool L37 1LQ (Formby (07048) 72164). *Location:* one mile west of A565 by Freshfield Station. Seaside links, wooded. 18 holes, 6781 yards. S.S.S. 73. *Green Fees:* £30.00 weekdays only. *Eating facilities:* available. *Visitors:* welcome, except weekends and Bank Holidays. Accommodation available. *Society Meetings:* catered for. Professional: C.F. Harrison (07048 73090). Secretary: A. Thirlwell (07048 72164).

FORMBY. **Formby Ladies' Golf Club,** Golf Road, Formby, Liverpool L37 1YH (Formby (07048) 74127). Seaside links. 18 holes, 5374 yards, 4914 metres. S.S.S. 71. Practice area. *Green Fees:* weekdays £20.00, weekends £25.00. *Eating facilities:* light lunches, afternoon teas. *Visitors:* welcome with prior reservation, contact the Secretary. *Society Meetings:* catered for with prior reservation. Professional: C. Harrison (07048 73090). Secretary: Mrs V. Bailey (07048 73493).

HESWALL. **Heswall Golf Club,** Cottage Lane, Heswall, Wirral L60 8PB. *Location:* off A540, eight miles north west of Chester. Parkland on the banks of River Dee estuary overlooking Welsh coast and hills. 18 holes, 6472 yards, 5909 metres. S.S.S. 72. Large practice area. *Green Fees:* weekdays £20.00, weekends and Bank Holidays £25.00, Society Meetings £20.00. *Eating facilities:* bar snacks, full meals by arrangement. *Visitors:* welcome anytime subject to availability. Must have accredited Handicaps. *Society Meetings:* catered for fully on Wednesdays and Fridays only, minimum 24 players. Professional: Alan Thompson (051-342 7431). Secretary: C.P.R. Calvert (051-342 1237). Catering (051-342 2193).

HOYLAKE. **Royal Liverpool Golf Club,** Meols Drive, Hoylake, Wirral, Merseyside L47 4AL (051-632 3102). *Location:* 10 miles west of Liverpool on Wirral Peninsula. Approach from M6, M56 and M53. Championship links. 18 holes, 6804 yards. S.S.S. 74. Large practice area. *Green Fees:* weekdays £28.00, weekends £35.00. *Eating facilities:* hot and cold snacks daily, bars. *Visitors:* welcome weekdays, letter of introduction from home club required. *Society Meetings:* catered for Wednesday – Friday. Professional: John Heggarty (051-632 5868). Secretary: J.R. Davidson (051-632 3101).

HUYTON. **Bowring Golf Club,** Bowring Park, Roby Road, Huyton (051-489 1901). 9 holes, 5580 yards. S.S.S. 66. *Visitors:* unrestricted. Secretary: E. Hatton. Professional: Michael Sarsfield.

HUYTON. **Huyton and Prescot Golf Club Ltd,** Hurst Park, Huyton Lane, Huyton, Liverpool L36 1UA (051-489 3948 office), (051-489 1138 members). *Location:* M57 and M62. 18 holes, 5732 yards. S.S.S. 68. *Green Fees:* weekdays £14.00, weekends by special permission only. Golf Societies Package arrangement. *Eating facilities:* dining facilities from 11.00am to 5.00pm. *Visitors:* welcome weekdays only. Tee reserved for members between 12 and 2pm. *Society Meetings:* catered for mid-week only. Professional: Mr R. Pottage (051-489 2022). Secretary: Mrs E. Holmes (051-489 3948).

LIVERPOOL. **Allerton Park Golf Club,** Allerton Road, Liverpool 18 (051-427 8510). *Location:* Menlove Avenue. 18 holes, 5081 yards. S.S.S. 67. *Green Fees:* £2.90. *Eating facilities:* lunches at club. *Visitors:* welcome. Professional: Barry Large.

LIVERPOOL. **Dudley Golf Club,** Allerton Municipal Golf Course, Menlove Avenue, Allerton, Liverpool 18 (051-428 8510). *Location:* end of M62, then two miles on Allerton Road. Wooded parkland. 18 holes, 5459 metres. S.S.S. 67. 9 holes, 1685 metres. S.S.S. 34. *Green Fees:* information not provided. *Eating facilities:* hot meals available in clubhouse. *Visitors:* welcome at any time. *Society Meetings:* welcome. Professional: Barry Large (051-428 1046). Secretary: Terry Tollitt (051-427 6189).

LIVERPOOL. **Lee Park Golf Club,** Childwall Valley Road, Liverpool L27 3YA (051-487 3882). 18 holes, 6024 yards. Medal tees: 5569 yards. Front tees: S.S.S. 68. Ladies' tee: 5650 yards. S.S.S. 72. *Eating facilities:* dining room and bar snacks daily. *Visitors:* welcome with reservation. *Society Meetings:* catered for. Secretary: Mrs Doris Barr.

LIVERPOOL. **The Childwall Golf Club Ltd.,** Naylors Road, Gateacre, Liverpool L27 2YB (051-487 9982). *Location:* exit 6 M62 to Liverpool follow Huyton A5080 to second set of traffic lights turn left into Wheathill Road. Parkland, flat designed by James Braid. 18 holes, 6425 yards. S.S.S. 72. Practice area. *Green Fees:* £15.00 weekdays, £21.00 weekends. *Eating facilities:* bar, snacks and restaurant. *Visitors:* no visitors weekends and Tuesdays. *Society Meetings:* catered for on weekdays, contact the Secretary. Professional: Mr N.M. Parr (051-487 9871). Secretary: Mr L. Upton (051-487 0654).

LIVERPOOL. **The Kirkby Golf Club, Liverpool Municipal Golf Course,** Ingo Lane, Kirkby, Liverpool L23 4SS (051-546 5435). *Location:* M57, at B5192. Flat parkland. 18 holes, 6571 yards, 6019 metres. S.S.S. 71. Practice ground. *Green Fees:* £3.00 (£1.50 Senior Citizens and Juniors). *Eating facilities:* lunches available at weekends. *Visitors:* unrestricted. Public course played over by Kirkby Golf Club. Professional: D. Weston (051-546 3435). Asst Secretary: D.A. Stewart (051-480 6846 home).

LIVERPOOL. **West Derby Golf Club,** Yew Tree Lane, West Derby, Liverpool L12 9HQ. 18 holes, 6332 yards. S.S.S. 70. *Green Fees:* weekdays £15.00 per day, weekends £20.00. *Eating facilities:* soup and sandwiches, light meals available at lunch. Evening meals by prior arrangement (20 minimum). *Visitors:* welcome if members of a recognised golf club. *Society Meetings:* catered for only by arrangement with Secretary. Professional: Nick Brace (051-220 5478). Secretary/Manager: S. Young (051-254 1034).

LIVERPOOL. **Woolton Golf Club,** Doe Park, Speke Road, Woolton, Liverpool L25 7TZ (051-486 1601). *Location:* south Liverpool, one mile from Woolton Village. Parkland. 18 holes, 5706 yards. S.S.S. 68. *Green Fees:* weekdays £10.00, weekends £16.00. *Eating facilities:* bar snacks daily. *Visitors:* welcome without reservation. *Society Meetings:* catered for by arrangement. Professional Shop: (051-486 1298). Secretary: K.G. Jennions (051-486 2298).

MORETON. **Bidston Golf Club,** Scoresby Road, Leasowe, Moreton L46 1QQ (051-638 3412). *Location:* leave M53 (from Chester), Wallasey, Leasowe, one mile left Catholic Church, approximately one mile. 18 holes, 6204 yards. S.S.S. 70. Practice ground. *Green Fees:* weekdays £10.00, weekends £15.00. Reduced rates for Societies. *Eating facilities:* available.

Visitors: welcome weekdays with prior notification. *Society Meetings:* catered for, early application by letter required. Professional: Shaun Kerr (051-630 6650). Secretary/Manager: L.A. Kendrick (051-638 8685).

MORETON. Leasowe Golf Club, Leasowe Road, Moreton, Wirral, Merseyside L46 3RD (051-677 5852). *Location:* one mile west of Wallasey Village and one mile from M53. 18 holes, 6204 yards. S.S.S. 70. *Green Fees:* £10.00 weekdays, £14.00 weekends and Bank Holidays. *Eating facilities:* lunches served at club except Mondays. *Visitors:* welcome on weekdays, also weekends and Bank Holidays. *Society Meetings:* catered for weekdays. Secretary: R. Kerr.

NEWTON-LE-WILLOWS. Haydock Park Golf Club, Rob Lane, Newton-le-Willows (Newton-le-Willows (0925) 224389). Flat, wooded parkland course in beautiful setting. 18 holes, 6043 yards. S.S.S. 69. Large practice area. *Green Fees:* weekdays £18.00 (£5.00 playing with a member), weekends £18.00, only with a member. Small discount for visiting parties over 12. *Eating facilities:* restaurant and two bars. *Visitors:* welcome midweek as arranged through Secretary. *Society Meetings:* catered for by arrangement with Secretary. Professional: P. Kenwright (0925 226944). Secretary: G. Tait (0925 228525).

SOUTHPORT. Hesketh Golf Club, Cockle Dick's Lane, Cambridge Road, Southport PR9 9QQ (Southport (0704) 30226). *Location:* one mile north of town centre. Seaside links Championship course. 18 holes, 6478 yards. S.S.S. 72. Practice ground. *Green Fees:* weekdays £17.00 per round, £22.00 per day; weekends and Bank Holidays £25.00 per day. *Eating facilities:* bar snacks and dining room; three bars. *Visitors:* welcome by prior arrangement with Secretary. *Society Meetings:* catered for by arrangement with Secretary. Professional: John Donoghue (0704 30050). Secretary: Peter B. Seal (0704 36897).

SOUTHPORT. Hillside Golf Club, Hastings Road, Hillside, Southport PR8 2LU (0704 67169). *Location:* south of town, Hillside station one mile. 18 holes, 6850 yards. S.S.S. 74. *Green Fees:* contact Secretary. *Eating facilities:* dining room, except Friday. *Visitors:* welcome with reservation. *Society Meetings:* catered for except Fridays. Professional: Brian Seddon. Secretary: P.W. Ray.

SOUTHPORT. Park Golf Club, Park Road West, Southport (Southport (0704) 30133). Play over Southport Municipal Links. S.S.S. 69. Secretary: J.A.V. Turner. Professional: (0704) 35286).

SOUTHPORT. **Royal Birkdale Golf Club,** Waterloo Road, Birkdale, Southport PR8 2LX (0704 67920). *Location:* one mile south of Southport town centre. Classic Links on the Open Championship rota. 18 holes, 6703 yards. S.S.S. 73. *Green Fees:* contact the Secretary. *Visitors:* welcome by arrangement with Secretary, offical golf Handicap required. *Society Meetings:* catered for, package prices for 20 plus, diningroom facilities. Professional: Richard Bradbeer (0704 68857). Secretary: Norman Crewe (0704 67920).

SOUTHPORT. **Southport and Ainsdale Golf Club,** Bradshaw's Lane, Off Liverpool Road, Ainsdale, Southport PR8 3LG (Southport (0704) 78092). *Location:* three miles south of Southport on A565. Links course. 18 holes, 6615 yards. S.S.S. 73. *Green Fees:* weekdays £20.00 per round, £30.00 per day; weekends £35.00 per day. *Eating facilities:* full catering available. *Visitors:* advance booking recommended; no weekend visitors. *Society Meetings:* catered for by arrangement. Professional: M. Houghton (0704 77316). Secretary: I.F. Sproule (0704 78000).

SOUTHPORT. **Southport Municipal Golf Club,** Park Road West, Southport (Southport (0704) 55130). *Location;* Park Road West, north end of Promenade, near Marine Lake, Southport. Flat seaside links. 18 holes, 6139 yards. S.S.S. 70. *Green Fees:* information not available. *Eating Facilities:* licensed cafe. *Visitors;* booking system operates up to seven days in advance. (visitors unrestricted). *Society Meetings;* welcome, book in advance. Professional; William Fletcher (0704 35286).

SOUTHPORT. **Southport Old Links Golf Club,** Moss Lane, Churchtown, Southport (0704 28207). *Location:* end of Roe Lane, Churchtown. Links course. 9 holes, 6378 yards (x2). S.S.S. 71. *Green Fees:* weekdays £10.00 per day, weekends and Bank Holidays £15.00 per day. *Eating facilities:* available 11.30am onwards. *Visitors:* welcome except Wednesdays, Sundays and Bank Holidays or occasional Saturdays. *Society Meetings:* catered for by arrangement, not more than about 24. Secretary: W.A.D. Sims (0704 24294).

ST. HELENS. **Grange Park Golf Club,** Prescot Road, St. Helens, Merseyside WA10 3AD (St. Helens (0744) 22980). *Location:* on A58 road between St. Helens and Prescot. Parkland, fairly flat. 18 holes, 6209 yards. S.S.S. 71. Practice area. *Green . Fees:* weekdays £15.00, weekends £21.50. Mondays (except Bank Holidays) special tariff of £21.50 includes green fee and food. *Eating facilities:* dining room, two bars. *Visitors:* welcome weekdays, weekends with a member. *Society Meetings:* catered for. Professional: Paul Evans (0744 28785). Secretary: David A. Wood (0744 26318).

ST HELENS. **Sherdley Park Golf Club,** St. Helens (0744 813149). Clubhouse (0744 815518). *Location:* two miles east of town on A570. 18 holes, 5941 yards. S.S.S. 69. *Green Fees:* information not provided. *Visitors:* unrestricted. Professional: P.R. Parkinson. Secretary: B.M. Healiss.

WALLASEY. **Wallasey Golf Club,** Bayswater Road, Wallasey, Merseyside L45 8LA (051-639 3630). *Location:* via M53 through Wirral or 15 minutes from Liverpool centre via Wallasey Tunnel. Seaside links. 18 holes, 6607 yards, 6038 metres. S.S.S. 73. *Green Fees:* weekdays £18.00, weekends and Bank Holidays £22.00. *Eating facilities:* snacks and full catering facilities. *Visitors:* welcome with reservation. *Society Meetings:* catered for by arrangement. Professional: Mike Adams (051-638 3888). Secretary: D.F. Haslehurst (051-691 1024).

WALLASEY. **Warren Golf Club,** Grove Road, Wallasey. 9 holes, 5914 yards. S.S.S. 68. *Green Fees:* information not provided. Professional: Kenneth Lamb. Hon. Secretary: J. McKenzie.

WIRRAL. **Brackenwood Golf Club,** Bebington, Wirral. 18 holes. Professional: Colin Disbury.

WIRRAL. **Hoylake Golf Club,** Carr Lane, Hoylake (051-632 2956). *Location:* 10 miles from Liverpool. 18 holes, 6330 yards, re-measured. S.S.S. 70. *Green Fees:* £3.20 per round. *Eating facilities:* available all week. Phone Steward (M. Down) in advance (051-632 4883). *Visitors:* midweek unrestricted. Weekends

phone to book tee. Professional: R. Boobyer. Secretary: M.E. Down.

WIRRAL. The Caldy Golf Club Ltd, Links Hey Road, Caldy, Wirral L48 1NB (051 625 5660). *Location:* one mile south of West Kirby on the River Dee Estuary. Undulating parkland, links, open aspect with views across the Dee to the North Wales hills. 18 holes, 6675 yards, 6105 metres. S.S.S. 72. Practice ground and full clubhouse facilities. *Green Fees:* weekdays £20.00/£25.00; weekends with member only. *Eating facilities:* bars and restaurant throughout the day. *Visitors:* welcome, parties only by appointment. *Society Meetings:* Thursdays by prior arrangement. Professional: Kevin Jones (051-625 1818). Secretary: J.K. Mayberry (051-625 5660).

Norfolk

BAWBURGH. **Bawburgh Golf Club,** Long Lane, Bawburgh, Norwich NR9 3LX (0603 746390). *Location:* three miles west of Norwich off A47, at rear of Norfolk Showground. Undulating open parkland. 9 holes, 5278 yards. S.S.S. 66. Adjacent Norwich Golf Centre driving range. *Green Fees:* information not provided. *Eating facilities:* bar and snacks only. *Visitors:* restricted at weekends and Bank Holidays. *Society Meetings:* bookable at 12 months notice only. Professional: R. Waugh (0603 746390). Secretary: R.J. Mapes (0953 606776).

CROMER. **Links Country Park Golf Club,** Sandy Lane, West Runton, Cromer NR27 9QH. *Location:* midway between Cromer and Sheringham on the A149, turn left opposite the village inn. Undulating parkland with narrow fairways and tricky greens. 9 holes, 4814 yards, S.S.S. 64. Par 66. *Green Fees:* £12.00 weekdays, £14.00 weekends. *Eating facilities:* grill room, snacks, main restaurant table d'hôte and à la carte. *Visitors:* welcome anytime. *Society Meetings:* welcome anytime. Professional: Mike Jubb (026375 8215). Hon. Secretary: S. Mansfield.

CROMER. **Royal Cromer Golf Club,** 145 Overstrand Road, Cromer NR27 0JH (Cromer (0263) 512219). *Location:* one mile east of town centre on coast road. Undulating seaside course. 18 holes, 6508 yards. S.S.S. 71. Large practice ground. *Green Fees:* £18.00 weekdays, £22.00 weekends. *Eating facilities:* full catering and bar snacks. *Visitors:* welcome, booking essential from 1st April to 31st October, Handicap Certificates required. *Society Meetings:* welcome except weekends. Professional: Robin J. Page (0263 512267). Secretary: E. Robertson (0263 512884).

DEREHAM. **Dereham Golf Club,** Quebec Road, Dereham NR19 2DS (Dereham (0362) 693122). *Location:* three-quarters-of-a-mile from town centre on B1110. Wooded parkland. 9 holes, 6225 yards, 5693 metres. S.S.S. 70. *Green Fees:* weekdays £12.50, weekends £12.00 with member only. Players must produce proof of handicap and club of which a member. *Eating facilities:* lunches and sandwiches, booking necessary. *Visitors:* welcome with handicap, weekends with member only. *Society Meetings:* catered for with advance booking. Professional: Steven Fox (0362 695631). Secretary: Noel Dodds (0362 695900).

DISS. **Diss Golf Club,** Stuston, Diss. The course is in Suffolk but Postal Address is Diss, Norfolk. (Diss (0379) 2847). *Location:* B1077 off A140, half-a-mile from Diss railway station, one mile from town centre. 9 holes, 5824 yards. S.S.S. 68. *Green Fees:* information not available. *Eating facilities:* lunches, teas, evening meals. *Visitors:* welcome without reservation. *Society Meetings:* catered for. Professional: N. Taylor. Secretary: J.A. Bell.

DOWNHAM MARKET. **Ryston Park Golf Club,** Ely Road, Denver PE38 0HH (Downham (0366) 382133). *Location:* one mile south Downham Market on A10. 36 miles north Cambridge. 9 holes, 6292 yards. S.S.S. 70. *Green Fees:* information not provided. *Eating facilities:* meals served at club to order. *Visitors:* welcome weekdays only. *Society Meetings:* catered for midweek by arrangement. Secretary: Arthur Wilson.

FAKENHAM. Fakenham Golf Club, Gallow Sports Centre, Hempton Road, Fakenham (Fakenham (0328) 862867). *Location:* half-a-mile town centre on Swaffham Road. Parkland. 9 holes, 5992 yards. S.S.S. 69. Large practice area. *Green Fees:* weekdays £12.00, weekends and Bank Holidays £16.00 after 3pm. 10 per cent reduction for Societies. *Eating facilities:* available in Sports Centre. *Visitors:* welcome by appointment. *Society Meetings:* welcome, reduced rates. Professional: J. Westwood (0328 863534). Secretary: G.G. Cocker (0328 855665).

GREAT YARMOUTH. Gorleston Golf Club, Warren Road, Gorleston, Great Yarmouth NR31 6JT (Great Yarmouth (0493) 661082). *Location:* off A12, three miles south of Great Yarmouth, seven miles north of Lowestoft. Parkland overlooking North Sea. 18 holes, 6404 yards, 5854 metres. S.S.S. 71. *Green Fees:* weekdays £12.00, weekends and Public Holidays £14.00, weekly £35.00. Reductions if playing with member. *Eating facilities:* available except Mondays; bar. *Visitors:* welcome with reservation, must produce membership of recognised club. *Society Meetings:* catered for by prior arrangement (membership of recognised club required). Professional: R.L. Moffitt (0493 662103). Secretary: P.G. Rudd (0493 661911).

GREAT YARMOUTH. Great Yarmouth and Caister Golf Club, Beach House, Caister-on-Sea, Great Yarmouth NR30 5TD (Great Yarmouth (0493) 720214). *Location:* A149 coast road, two miles north of Great Yarmouth. Links. 18 holes, 6235 yards. S.S.S. 70. Practice ground. *Green Fees:* £17.00, £11.00 after 3.30pm. Member's guests 50%. *Eating facilities:* full range of catering; bar. *Visitors:* welcome, not before 10.30am Saturdays and not before 11.30am Sundays. *Society Meetings:* catered for. Professional: Nick Catchpole (0493 720421). Secretary: Mrs H.M. Marsh (0493 728699).

HELLESDON. Royal Norwich Golf Club, Drayton Road, Hellesdon, Norwich (Norwich (0603) 429928).

Location: centre of city and thence by A1067 Fakeham or via Ring Road, then 500 yards along A1067. 18 holes, 6603 yards. S.S.S. 72. *Green Fees:* £22.00 per round or day. *Eating facilities:* lunches and teas served at club. *Visitors:* welcome during week only, but must have membership card of a recognised golf club and a bona fide handicap. Professional: Barry Lockwood.

HUNSTANTON. **Hunstanton Golf Club,** Golf Course Road, Hunstanton PE36 6JQ (Hunstanton (04853) 2811). *Location:* adjoins old Hunstanton village, approximately half a mile north east of Hunstanton. Seaside links. 18 holes, 6670 yards. S.S.S. 72. Practice ground. *Green Fees:* weekdays £22.00, weekends £27.00. *Eating facilities:* available except Mondays (soup and sandwiches only). *Visitors:* welcome, but please contact Secretary. *Society Meetings:* catered for, contact Secretary. Professional: J. Carter (04853 2751). Secretary: R.H. Cotton (04853 2811).

KING'S LYNN. **King's Lynn Golf Club,** Castle Rising, King's Lynn PE31 6BD (Castle Rising (055-387) 656/227). *Location:* four miles north-east of King's Lynn. Undulating wooded course. 18 holes, 6646 yards. S.S.S. 72. Practice areas. *Green Fees:* weekdays £22.00, weekends £30.00. *Eating facilities:* snacks, lunches, teas available; other meals by prior arrangement, two bars. *Visitors:* welcome on production of Handicap Certificate. *Society Meetings:* catered for by prior arrangement Wednesdays to Fridays. Professional: C. Hanlon (055-387 655). Secretary: G.J. Higgins (055-387 654).

KING'S LYNN. **Royal West Norfolk Golf Club,** Brancaster, Near King's Lynn PE31 8AX (Brancaster (0485) 210223). *Location:* one mile off A149, Beach Road junction, seven miles east of Hunstanton. Seaside links. 18 holes, 6428 yards. S.S.S. 71. *Green Fees:* weekdays £22.00 per day, weekends £27.00 per day. *Eating facilities:* available. *Visitors:* all visitors to be members of a recognised Golf Club, hold an official Handicap and must make prior arrangements with the

Secretary to play. No visitors prior to 10.00am Sundays and no visitors during last week in July and until first week in September. *Society Meetings:* catered for by previous arrangement with the Secretary. Professional: R.E. Kimber (0485 210616). Secretary: Major N.A. Carrington Smith (0485 210087).

NORWICH. **Barnham Broom Hotel, Golf and Country Club,** Barnham Broom, Norwich NR9 4DD (Barnham Broom (060-545) 393). *Location:* eight miles south-west of Norwich between A11 and A47. River valley parkland and hill course. 18 holes, 6603 yards. S.S.S. 72. Full practice facilities. *Green Fees:* weekdays £20.00 per round, £25.00 per day; weekends on application. *Eating facilities:* snack bar and full restaurant. *Visitors:* casual and residential with prior notice. 52 bedroomed hotel. *Society Meetings:* welcome. Professional: Steve Beckham (060-545 393 ext. 132). Director of Golf: Peter Ballingall (060-545 393 ext. 138).

NORWICH. **Costessey Park Golf Course,** Old Costessey, Norwich NR8 5AL (Norwich (0603) 746333). *Location:* off the A47 Norwich to King's Lynn road, in the village of Old Costessey (adjacent to Norwich). Set in river valley with some parkland. 18 holes, 5853 yards. S.S.S. 68. Practice area. *Green Fees:* weekdays £10.00, weekends £15.00. *Eating facilities:* bar and bar snacks; carvery and set meals

available. *Visitors:* welcome anytime except weekends when visitors allowed only after 11.30am. Golf cart available for hire by physically handicapped golfers. *Society Meetings:* catered for by arrangement. Professional: D. Johnson (0603 747085). Secretary: B.A. Howson.

NORWICH. **Eaton (Norwich) Golf Club,** Newmarket Road, Norwich NR4 6SF (Norwich (0603) 52881). *Location:* A11 approximately one and a half miles from the city centre. Parkland course. 18 holes, 6135 yards. S.S.S. 69. Practice area available. *Green Fees:* £18.00 weekdays, £23.00 weekends and Bank Holidays. *Eating facilities:* snack lunches, dinners by arrangement. *Visitors:* welcome any time except Saturday and Sundays mornings. *Society Meetings:* limited numbers considered. Professional: Frank Hill (0603 52478). Secretary: (0603 57686).

NORWICH. **Mundesley Golf Club,** Links Road, Mundesley, Norwich NR11 8ES (Mundesley (0263) 720279). *Location:* one mile from village centre. 9 holes, 2682 yards. S.S.S. 66. *Green Fees:* information not provided. *Eating facilities:* meals to order except Tuesdays. *Visitors:* welcome except Wednesday 12.00 to 3.30pm and Sundays until 11.30am. *Society Meetings:* catered for (not weekends). Professional: T. G. Symmons. Secretary: B. D. Baxter (0263 720095).

SHERINGHAM. **Sheringham Golf Club,** Sheringham NR26 8HG (Sheringham (0263) 822038). *Location:* one mile west of town on Weybourne Road (A149). Cliff top course. 18 holes, 6464 yards. S.S.S. 71. Large practice area. *Green Fees:* weekdays £22.00, weekends and Bank Holidays £27.00. *Eating facilities:* full catering to order. *Visitors:* welcome with reservation for members of other clubs, Handicap Certificate required. *Society Meetings:* catered for by prior arrangement except weekends from 1st April to 31st October. Professional: M.T. Leeder (0263 822980). Secretary: M.J. Garrett (0263 823488).

SWAFFHAM. **Swaffham Golf Club,** Cley Road, Swaffham PE37 8AE (Swaffham (0761) 721611). *Location:* two miles south-west of Swaffham Market Place (signposted) on Cley Road. Heathland course. 9 holes, 6252 yards. S.S.S. 70. Practice ground. *Green Fees:* £12.00 weekdays. *Eating facilities:* full catering except Mondays and Tuesdays, bar snacks all week. *Visitors:* welcome without reservation weekdays, weekends only if playing with member. *Society Meetings:* catered for subject to prior notice being given. Professional: C. J. Norton. Secretary: R. Joslin.

THETFORD. **Thetford Golf Club,** Brandon Road, Thetford IP24 3ND (Thetford (0842) 752258). *Location:* half a mile from A11 – Thetford Norfolk. Wooded heathland course. 18 holes, 6879 yards. S.S.S. 73. *Green Fees:* £20.00 weekdays. *Eating facilities:* bar snacks, teas, meals available. *Visitors:* welcome weekdays. *Society Meetings:* catered for weekdays, if belong to golf clubs. Professional: N. Arthur. (0842 752662). Secretary: R.J. Ferguson (0842 752169).

Northamptonshire

CORBY. **Corby Public Golf Course Priors Hall Complex,** Corby (Corby (0536) 60756). *Location:* off A43 Kettering to Stamford Road one mile east of village of Weldon. 18 holes, 6677 yards. S.S.S. 72. *Green Fees:* weekdays £3.10, weekends and Bank Holidays £4.40. *Eating facilities:* available, also licensed bar. Professional: M. Summers.

DAVENTRY. **Daventry and District Golf Club,** Norton Road, Daventry (Daventry (0327) 702829). 9 holes, 5812 yards. S.S.S. 67. *Green Fees:* weekdays £6.00, weekends £8.00. *Visitors:* welcome weekdays and weekends. Summer all welcome except Sunday before 11.00am. Professional: Mike Higgins. Secretary: F. Higham.

DAVENTRY. **Staverton Park Hotel and Golf Club,** Daventry Road, Staverton, Near Daventry NN11 6JT (Daventry (0327) 705911). *Location:* one mile from Daventry on A425 to Leamington Spa. Easy access from M1 Junctions 16 or 18. Parkland. 18 holes, 6634 yards. S.S.S. 72. Driving range. *Green Fees:* weekdays £15.50 per round, £24.00 per day; weekends and Bank Holidays £20.00 per round, £30.00 per day. *Eating facilities:* full catering available at all times. *Visitors:* welcome by booking only. 50 bedroomed hotel with leisure facilities. Residential golf packages available. *Society Meetings:* catered for. Professional: Brian and Richard Mudge (0327 705506). Manager: Allan McLundie.

KETTERING. **Kettering Golf Club,** Headlands, Kettering (0536 512074). *Loaction:* course is at south end of Headlands which is continuation from High Street. 18 holes, 6035 yards, 5515 metres. S.S.S. 69. *Green Fees:* £18.00 day/round. *Eating facilities:* by prior arrangement. *Visitors:* welcome weekdays only, without reservation. *Society Meetings:* catered for Wednesdays only by arrangement. Professional: K. Theobald. Secretary: Mr J. Galt.

NORTHAMPTON. **Cold Ashby Golf Club,** Cold Ashby, Northampton NE6 7EP (Northampton (0604) 740548). *Location:* midway between Rugby, Leicester and Northampton, with easy access M1 Junction 18. Undulating parkland. 18 holes, 5898 yards. S.S.S. 69. *Green Fees:* midweek £10.00 per round, £15.00 per day; weekends £12.50 per round. *Eating facilities:* meals and bar snacks available daily. *Visitors:* welcome midweek anytime, weekends after 10.30am. *Society Meetings:* catered for weekdays. Professional: Tony Skingle (0604 740099). Secretary: David Croxton.

NORTHAMPTON. **Delapre Golf Complex,** Eagle Drive, Nene Valley Way, Northampton NN4 0DU (Northampton (0604) 764036). *Location:* two and a half miles from Junction 15 (M1), A45 to Wellingborough (exit at Swallow Hotel). Parkland. 18 holes, 6293 yards, S.S.S. 70. Additional 9 holes Par 33 to open 1991. Two 9 hole par 3 courses, pitch and putt course, floodlit covered driving range, 39 bays. *Green Fees:* weekdays £5.20, weekends and Bank Holidays £6.50. *Eating facilities:* meals available all day 9.00am

to 9.30pm, bar. *Visitors:* welcome without reservation, except all 18 hole course start times bookable; phone in advance. *Society Meetings:* catered for by appointment. Director and Professional: John Corby (0604 763957).

NORTHAMPTON. **Kingsthorpe Golf Club,** Kingsley Road, Northampton NN2 7BU (Northampton (0604) 711173). *Location:* off M1 and A43. Undulating parkland. 18 holes, 6006 yards. S.S.S. 69. *Green Fees:* (provisional) weekdays £16.00 per round/day, weekends £8.00 per round/day (must play with member). Reduced rates for Societies. *Eating facilities:* full catering except Mondays. *Visitors:* welcome weekdays, but must have a Certificate of Handicap. Weekends must be guest of member. *Society Meetings:* catered for by arrangement only, except Wednesdays and weekends. Professional: Paul Smith (0604 719602). Secretary: N.C. Liddington (0604 710610).

NORTHAMPTON. **Northampton Golf Club,** Kettering Road, Northampton NN3 1AA (Northampton (0604) 711054). *Location:* eastern outskirts of town on A43. 18 holes, 6002 yards. S.S.S. 69. *Green fees:* £12.00 per day/round weekdays only, weekends must play with a member. Reduced rates for Societies. *Eating facilities:* bar snacks available. *Visitors:* welcome weekdays but must have a Certificate of Handicap. *Society Meetings:* weekdays except Wednesdays (no catering Tuesdays). Professional: Mark Chamberlain (0604 714897). Secretary: T.C.A. Knight (0604 719453).

NORTHAMPTON. **Northamptonshire County Golf Club,** Sandy Lane, Church Brampton, Northampton NN6 8AZ (Northampton (0604) 842170). *Location:* four miles north of Northampton between A50 and A428. Heathland with woods and stream. 18 holes, 6503 yards. S.S.S. 71. Practice ground, indoor net. *Green Fees:* information not available. *Eating facilities:* restaurant and bar. *Visitors:* by arrangement (must have Club Handicap) unless with a member. *Society Meetings:* catered for Wednesdays, some Thursdays and Mondays. Professional: Stuart Brown (0604 842226). Secretary/Manager: G.G. Morley (0604 843025).

OUNDLE. **Oundle Golf Club,** Benefield Road, Oundle (Oundle (0832) 273267). *Location:* on A427 Oundle to Corby road. 18 holes, 5410 yards. S.S.S. 67. *Green Fees:* weekdays £12.00, weekends £25.00. *Eating facilities:* by prior arrangement. *Visitors:* welcome without reservation, not Saturday and Sunday mornings or Bank Holidays. *Society Meetings:* catered for. Secretary: R.K. Davis.

WELLINGBOROUGH. **Rushden Golf Club,** Kimbolton Road, Chelveston, Wellingborough NN9 6AN (Rushden (0933) 312581). *Location:* on A45 two miles east of Higham Ferrers. Undulating parkland. 9 holes, 6381 yards, 5860 metres. S.S.S. 70. Small practice area. *Green Fees:* weekdays £12.00, £5.00 with member; no visitors weekends. *Eating facilities:* bar and dining area. *Visitors:* welcome except Wednesday afternoons, weekends must play with member. *Society Meetings:* catered for weekdays. Secretary: R. Tomlin (0933 312197).

WELLINGBOROUGH. **Wellingborough Golf Club,** Great Harrowden Hall, Wellingborough NN9 5AD (Wellingborough (0933) 673022). *Location:* one mile out of Wellingborough on A509, turn right at crossroads by Great Harrowden Church. Undulating parkland. 18 holes, 6604 yards, 6039 metres. S.S.S. 72. Practice ground. *Green Fees:* £20.00 per round, £25.00 per day weekdays; weekends as members guest only. *Eating facilities:* bar with casual lunch or dinner menu, restuarant. *Visitors:* weekdays only by appointment and with Handicap Certificate. *Society Meetings:* welcome by appointment. Conference facilities available. Professional: David Clifford (0933 678752). Secretary: Major A. Furnival (0933 677234).

Please mention this guide when you write or phone to enquire about accommodation.

Northumberland

ALNMOUTH. **Alnmouth Golf Club Ltd,** Foxton Hall, Alnmouth NE66 3BE (Alnmouth (0665) 830231). Stewardess (0665 830687). 18 holes, 6414 yards, 5855 metres. S.S.S. 71. *Green Fees:* weekdays £15.00 per day, weekends £20.00 per day. *Eating facilities:* full service available on prior notice. *Visitors:* welcome with reservation. *Society Meetings:* catered for. Special Green Fees available on application to Secretary. Dormy House accommodation available, apply Secretary, also self catering flat available. Secretary: F.K. Marshall (0665 830368).

ALNMOUTH. **Alnmouth Village Golf Club,** Marine Road, Alnmouth (Alnmouth (0665) 830370). *Location:* five miles from Alnwick, leave A1 and join A1068. Undulating links course. 9 holes, 6200 yards. S.S.S. 70. *Green Fees:* weekdays £6.00 per day, weekends £10.00 per day. *Eating facilities:* bar, meals to order. *Visitors:* welcome, restrictions on club competition days. *Society Meetings:* book in advance. Secretary: W. Maclean (0665 602096).

ALNWICK. **Alnwick Golf Club,** Swansfield Park, Alnwick (Alnwick (0665) 602632). *Location:* southwest of town, top of Swansfield Park Road, off A1. Mature wooded parkland. 9 holes, 5387 yards. S.S.S. 66. *Green Fees:* weekdays £6.00 per round, £8.00 per day; weekends and Bank Holidays £8.00 per round, £10.00 per day. £5.00 with member at any time. *Eating facilities:* available on request; bar. *Visitors:* welcome without reservation, some restrictions on competition days. *Society Meetings:* welcome by prior arrangement. Secretary: L.E. Stewart (0665 602499).

ALNWICK. **Dunstanburgh Castle Golf Club,** Embleton, Alnwick NE66 3XQ (Embleton (066576)

562). *Location:* eight miles off A1, to the north-east of Alnwick. Seaside links course in area of outstanding natural beauty. 18 holes, 6298 yards. S.S.S. 70. *Green Fees:* weekdays £8.50 per day; weekends £10.50 per round, £12.75 per day. *Eating facilities:* snacks, lunches, high teas; bar. *Visitors:* welcome without reservation. Clubs for hire. *Society Meetings:* catered for. Secretary: P.F.C. Gilbert.

BAMBURGH. **Bamburgh Castle Golf Club,** Bamburgh NE69 7DE (Bamburgh (06684) 378). *Location:* north of Alnwick on A1, take B1341 or B1342 to Bamburgh. Links course with outstanding coastal views. 18 holes, 5465 yards, 4991 metres. S.S.S. 67. Practice area. *Green Fees:* weekdays £12.00 per day or round, weekends £12.00 per round, £16.00 per day. Weekly reductions. *Eating facilities:* full catering and bar. *Visitors:* welcome, except Bank Holidays and weekends. Buggy hire available. *Society Meetings:* catered for on application. Hon. Secretary: T.C. Osborne (06684 321).

BEDLINGTON. **Bedlingtonshire Golf Club,** Acorn Bank, Bedlington NG22 6AA (Bedlington (0670) 822457). *Location:* one mile south west of Bedlington on A1068. Parkland. 18 holes, 6546 metres. S.S.S. 73. Practice ground and putting green. *Green Fees:* weekdays £6.00 per round, £9.00 per day; weekends £9.00 per round, £12.00 per day (estimated). *Visitors:* welcome, but not before 10.30am, time restrictions at weekends. *Society Meetings:* catered for. Applications to Chief Leisure and Publicity Officer, Town Hall, Ashington. Professional: M. Webb (0670 822087). Secretary: R. Partis (0670 822457).

BERWICK-UPON-TWEED. **Berwick-upon-Tweed (Goswick) Golf Club,** Beal, Berwick-upon-Tweed TD15 2RW (0289 87256). *Location:* signposted off A1, eight miles south of Berwick-upon-Tweed. Links. 18 holes, 6425 yards, 5871 metres. S.S.S. 71. Practice ground. *Green Fees:* weekdays £13.00 per day, £10.00 per round; weekends £20.00 per day, £14.00 per round. *Eating facilities:* catering except Mondays, bar meals. *Visitors:* welcome anytime, parties by arrangement, after 9.30am weekdays, after 10am weekends. *Society Meetings:* catered for by arrangement. Professional: M. Leighton (0289 87380). Secretary: R.C. Oliver (0289 87256).

BERWICK-UPON-TWEED. **Magdalene Fields Golf Club,** Magdalene Fields, Berwick-upon-Tweed (0289 306384). *Location:* signposted from Marygate in town centre. Untypical seaside course with parkland-type fairways. 18 holes, 6551 yards, 6047 metres. S.S.S. 71. Practice area. *Green Fees:* information not available. *Eating facilities:* licensed clubhouse with catering. Two hotels within five minutes of the course. *Visitors:* welcome, reserve by telephone call to clubhouse. Tee closed Sundays 7.30am to 9.30am, Wednesday and Thursday 5.45pm to 6.30pm (matchdays). *Society Meetings:* book in writing through Secretary. Secretary: R. Patterson (0289 305758).

BLYTH. **Blyth Golf Club Ltd,** New Delaval and Newsham, Blyth NE24 9LB (Blyth (0670) 367728). *Location:* 12 miles north of Newcastle on the coast. Flat parkland, water hazzards. 18 holes, 6533 yards. S.S.S. 71. Large practice area. *Green Fees:* £10.00 per round, £12.00 per day weekdays; weekends only with a member. *Eating facilities:* bar and restaurant with full catering. *Visitors:* welcome weekdays but not after 3pm and only by arrangement with Secretary. *Society Meetings:* welcome weekdays only by prior arrangement. Professional: B. Rumney (0670 356514). Secretary: R. Mathewson (0670 540110).

CARLISLE. **Haltwhistle Golf Course,** Banktop, Greenhead, Via Carlisle (Gilsland (06972) 367). *Location:* off the A69 at the village of Greenhead, two and a half miles west of Haltwhistle. Undulating parkland course with wooded areas. 12 holes, 6154 yards over 18 holes. S.S.S. 69. Practice area. *Green Fees:* £5.00 per day, £12.00 weekly ticket for bona fide holidaymakers. *Eating facilities:* clubhouse bar, catering by prior arrangement. *Visitors:* welcome, no restrictions except on club competition days when course is closed until 4.00pm. *Society Meetings:* welcome by arrangement. Professional: Joe Metcalfe. Secretary: Bill Barnes (0434 320337).

GATESHEAD. **Ravensworth Golf Club Ltd,** Moss Heaps, Wrekenton, Gateshead NE9 7VU (091-4876014). *Location:* two miles south of Gateshead. 18 holes, 5900 yards. S.S.S. 69. *Green fees:* £8.00 weekdays, £12.00 weekends. *Eating facilities:* meals served with reasonable notice (not Mondays). *Visitors:* welcome without reservation. *Society Meetings:* catered for. Professional: Grant Noble. Secretary: L. Winter.

HEXHAM. **Allendale Golf Club,** Thornley Gate, Allendale, Hexham. *Location:* 10 miles south west of Hexham on B6305. Parkland course, hilly. 9 holes, 2244 yards. S.S.S. 63 (Ladies 65) *Green Fees:* weekdays £3.50, weekends and Bank Holidays £4.50. Special rates after 5.00pm and for visiting parties. *Eating facilities:* no catering apart from tea-making facilities, but several good hotels and pubs in Allendale. *Visitors:* welcome anytime except August Bank Holiday Monday; Sundays by prior booking. *Society Meetings:* catered for, special rates for 10 and over. Secretary: Jim Hall (091 2675875).

HEXHAM. **Bellingham Golf Club,** Bellingham, Hexham (Bellingham (0660) 20530). *Location:* four miles west of A68. 9 holes (18 tees), 5245 yards. S.S.S. 66. *Green Fees:* weekdays £6.00, weekends and Bank Holidays £7.00. Reduced rates after 5.00pm and in winter. *Eating facilities:* meals available. *Visitors:* welcome, no restrictions except during club competitions. No casual visitors on Sundays, only bookings. *Society Meetings:* catered for. Secretary: T.H. Thompson (0660 20281).

HEXHAM. **Hexham Golf Club,** Spital Park, Hexham NE46 3RZ (Hexham (0434) 602057). *Location:* 20 miles west of Newcastle upon Tyne, one mile west of Hexham town centre. 18 holes, 6272 yards. S.S.S. 70. *Green Fees:* weekdays £12.00 per round, weekends and Bank Holidays £16.00 per round. *Eating facilities:* lunch, high tea and dinner. *Visitors:* welcome without reservation. Preliminary booking advisable. *Society Meetings:* catered for Monday to Saturday by arrangement. Professional: Ian Waugh (0434 604904). Secretary: J.C. Oates (0434 603072).

HEXHAM. **Tynedale Golf Club,** Tynegreen, Hexham. *Location:* south side of River Tyne, half mile from Town Centre. 9 holes, 5640 yards. S.S.S. 67. *Green Fees:* information not available. *Visitors:* welcome without reservation except Sundays, when time must be booked. Secretary: Mr S. Plemper. Private Club, but course maintained by Tynedale District Council.

MORPETH. **Morpeth Golf Club,** The Common, Morpeth (Morpeth (0670) 512065.) *Location:* one mile south of Morpeth on A1. 18 holes, 6215 yards. S.S.S. 70. *Green Fees:* weekdays £10.00 per round, £15.00 per day; weekends £16.00 per round. *Eating facilities:* contact Stewardess, no meals Mondays. Sandwiches available. *Visitors:* must be members of a Golf Club and be in possession of a current Handicap Certificate. *Society Meetings:* catered for weekdays. Professional: M.R. Jackson. Secretary: T. Weddell.

MORPETH. **Newbiggin-by-the-Sea Golf Club,** Newbiggin-by-the-Sea NE64 6DW (Ashington (0670) 817344). *Location:* take signpost for Newbiggin off A189 (spine road from Tyne Tunnel). Clubhouse at most easterly point of village next to Church Point Caravan Park. Seaside links. 18 holes, 6444 yards. S.S.S. 71. Practice area. *Green Fees:* weekdays £5.50, weekends £7.50. *Eating facilities:* available by prior arrangement. *Visitors:* welcome, not before 10.00am. *Society Meetings:* catered for by arrangement with Secretary. Professional: D. Fletcher (0670 817833). Secretary: Derek Lyall (0670 815062 after 6.00pm).

MORPETH. **Warkworth Golf Club,** The Links, Warkworth, Morpeth (Alnwick (0665) 711596). *Location:* off A1 to B6345 at Felton, on to A1068 to Warkworth. Links course. 9 holes, 5817 yards. S.S.S. 68. *Green Fees:* weekdays £6.00 per day, weekends £10.00 per day. Weekly and fortnightly tickets can be arranged. *Eating facilities:* by arrangement only, bar open at nights. *Visitors:* welcome, avoid Tuesdays and Saturdays. *Society Meetings:* welcome. Secretary: J.W. Anderson (0665 75 608).

NEWCASTLE. **Arcot Hall Golf Club Ltd,** Arcot Hall, Dudley, Cramlington NE23 7QP (091 2362794). *Location:* seven miles north of Newcastle. Turn off A1 for Ashington and then signposted. 18 holes, 6389 yards, 5840 metres. S.S.S. 70. *Green Fees:* £14.00 (£18.00). *Eating facilities:* lunch and high tea daily except Monday. *Visitors:* welcome without reservation. Clubs for hire. *Society Meetings:* catered for on application to Secretary. Professional: Graham Cant (091 2362147). Secretary: A.G. Bell (091 2362794).

NEWCASTLE-UPON-TYNE. **Ponteland Golf Club,** Bell Villas, Ponteland, Newcastle-upon-Tyne NE20 9BD.*Location:* A696, one and a half miles north of Newcastle Airport. Parkland course. 18 holes, 6524 yards. S.S.S. 71. Large practice area. *Green Fees:* £15.00 weekdays (inclusive VAT). *Eating facilities:* full menu in restaurant and bar. *Visitors:* welcome weekdays only, must be members' guest at weekends. *Society Meetings:* Tuesdays or Thursdays, catered for with pre-booking agreed by Secretary. Professional: Alan Crosby (0661 22689). Secretary: G. Weetman (0661 22689). Steward: (0661 71872).

PRUDHOE. **Prudhoe Golf Club,** Eastwood Park, Prudhoe NE42 5DX (Prudhoe (0661) 9832466). *Loca-

tion:* 10 miles west of Newcastle upon Tyne, A695 to Hexham. 18 holes, 5814 yards, 5319 metres. S.S.S. 68. *Green Fees:* £10.00 per day weekdays only. Special rates for parties over 20. *Eating facilities:* bar snacks, lunches and evening meals by prior order. *Visitors:* welcome with reservation. *Society Meetings:* catered for weekdays by arrangement. Professional: John Crawford (0661 9836188). Secretary: G.B. Garratt.

ROTHBURY. **Rothbury Golf Club,** Old Race Course, Thorpton Road, Rothbury, Morpeth (0669 21271). *Location:* 15 miles north of Morpeth, take A697 turn off at Weldon Bridge for Rothbury. Flat course on Haugh alongside river. 9 holes, 5560 yards. S.S.S. 67. *Green Fees:* £3.50 weekdays, £6.00 weekends. *Eating facilities:* none available but there are plenty of good hotels in Rothbury, there is a bar open Wednesdays nights and weekends. *Visitors:* welcome during weekdays, but limited at weekends due to club competitions. *Society Meetings:* catered for weekdays by arrangement only. Hon. Secretary: W.T. Bathgate (0669 20718 or 20313).

SEAHOUSES. **Seahouses Golf Club,** Beadnell Road, Seahouses NE68 7XT (Alnwick (0665) 720794). *Location:* 15 miles north of Alnwick, turn off A1 for B1340. Flat seaside links. 18 holes, 5399 yards. S.S.S. 66. Practice net. *Green Fees:* weekdays £9.00 per day/round; weekends £10.00 per round, £11.50 per day. Weekly rates available; juniors under 16 half rates. *Eating facilities:* full catering and bar. *Visitors:* welcome with no restrictions, please telephone clubhouse on Sundays. *Society Meetings:* by arrangement. Secretary: Gordon Hogg (0665 720091).

STOCKSFIELD. **Stocksfield Golf Club,** New Ridley, Stocksfield NE43 7RE (Stocksfield (0661) 843041). *Location:* 15 miles west of Newcastle on A69, and three miles east of A68. Wooded parkland. 18 holes, 5594 yards. S.S.S. 68. Practice area. *Green Fees:* weekdays £10.00, weekends and Bank Holidays £15.00. Reductions for parties mid-week. *Eating facilities:* available, also bar. *Visitors:* welcome weekdays and after 4.30pm at weekends. *Society Meetings:* catered for. Professional: Ken Driver. Secretary: D.B. Moon.

TYNEMOUTH. **Tynemouth Golf Club Ltd,** Spital Dene, Tynemouth (North Shields (091) 2574578). *Location:* on A695. 18 holes, 6403 yards (forward tees). S.S.S. 71. *Green Fees:* weekdays £10.00, weekends and Bank Holidays £12.00. *Eating facilities:* lunches and high teas served at club. *Visitors:* welcome with reservation. *Society Meetings:* catered for. Professional: John McKenna. Secretary: W. Storey.

Nottinghamshire

BULWELL. **Bulwell Forest Golf Club,** Hucknall Road, Bulwell (0602 770576) *Location:* A610 3 miles north of Nottingham. 18 holes, 5746 yards. S.S.S. 67. *Green Fees:* £5.00. *Eating facilities:* meals served at all times. *Visitors:* welcome without reservation. *Society Meetings:* catered for. Professional: C. D. Hall. Secretary: D. Stubbs.

EAST LEAKE. **Rushcliffe Golf Club,** Stocking Lane, East Leake, Near Loughborough LE12 5RL (0509 852209). *Location:* on A60 signposted eight miles south of Nottingham. Wooded hills on edge of the Wolds. 18 holes, 6057 yards, 5539 metres. S.S.S. 69. Practice ground. *Green fees:* information not available. *Eating facilities:* full catering except Mondays when bar snacks only. *Visitors:* welcome with reservation, weekends with member only. *Society Meetings:* catered for Mondays, Wednesdays, Thursdays and Fridays strictly by prior booking. Professional: Tim Smart (0509 852701). Secretary: D.L. Robey (0509 852959).

EDWALTON. **Edwalton Municipal Golf and Social Club,** Wellin Lane, Edwalton NG12 4AS (0602 234713). *Location:* follow Nottingham ring road, course signposted from island on ring road. Gently sloping parkland, featured lakes. 9 holes, 3342 yards. S.S.S. 72. Also 9 hole par 3 course. Large practice ground. *Green Fees:* £3.00 for 9 holes. Students, pensioners, disabled and UB40's, £1.30 before 5 p.m., weekdays only. Par 3 course £1.90, special rate 70p. *Eating facilities:* first class catering, bar open all day. *Visitors:* welcome anytime, changing rooms (contact Professional for dates). Professional: J.A. Staples (0602 234775). Secretary: F. Shepperson (0949 37328).

KIRKBY IN ASHFIELD. **Notts Golf Club Ltd,** Hollinwell, Kirkby in Ashfield NG17 7QR (Mansfield (0623) 753225). *Location:* three miles from Exit 27 on M1, turn off M1 then left on A611. 18 holes, 7020 yards. S.S.S. 74. *Green Fees:* on application. *Visitors:* welcome on production of Handicap Certificate (weekends and Bank Holidays with member only). Advisable to book beforehand. *Society Meetings:* catered for Mondays and Tuesdays. Professional: Brian Waites. Secretary: J.R. Walker.

MANSFIELD. **Coxmoor Golf Club,** Coxmoor Road, Sutton in Ashfield, Mansfield NG17 5LF (Mansfield (0623) 559878). *Location:* on A611 Nottingham – Mansfield two miles south of Mansfield. Wooded

moorland. 18 holes, 6501 yards, 5944 metres. S.S.S. 72. Practice area and nets. *Green Fees:* weekdays £18.00, weekends £20.00. *Eating facilities:* restaurant. *Visitors:* welcome; pre-book through Professional. (Tuesday Ladies' Day). *Society Meetings:* catered for by prior application. Professional: D. Ridley (0623 559906). Secretary: Mr J.W. Tyler (0623 557359).

MANSFIELD. **Mansfield Woodhouse Golf Club,** Leeming Lane North, Mansfield Woodhouse MG19 9EU. *Location:* Junction 27 of M1, A60 Mansfield-Warsop. Flat parkland. 9 holes, 2800 yards. S.S.S. 64 (18 holes) 32 (9 holes). *Green Fees:* £2.00 for 9 holes, £3.00 for 18. *Eating facilities:* restaurant, snacks and bar. *Visitors:* welcome. *Society Meetings:* not catered for. Professional: L. Highfield Jnr. (0623 23521). Secretary: T. Mason.

MANSFIELD. **Sherwood Forest Golf Club,** Eakring Road, Mansfield NG18 3EW (Mansfield (0623) 23327). *Location:* leave M1 at Exit 27, take signs for Mansfield, proceed via Southwell Road and Oak Tree Lane. Traditional heathland course designed by James Braid (Championship standard). 18 holes, 6710 yards. S.S.S. 73. Two practice grounds. *Green Fees:* weekdays £20.00 per round, £25.00 per day; weekends and Bank Holidays £25.00 per round. *Eating facilities:* two dining rooms, gents' bar and mixed lounge. *Visitors:* welcome Mondays, Thursdays and Fridays, must be member of a golf club with a handicap. *Society Meetings:* catered for Mondays, Thursdays and Fridays. Professional: K. Hall (0623 27403). Secretary: K. Hall (0623 26689).

MANSFIELD. **Woodhouse Golf Club,** Mansfield. *Location:* two miles north of Mansfield. 9 holes. *Green Fees:* information not provided. *Visitors:* unrestricted. Secretary: W. F. Turner. Professional: Les Highfield.

MAPPERLEY. **Mapperley Golf Club,** Plains Road, Mapperley (Nottingham (0602) 265611). *Location:* off Woodborough Road, four miles north east of centre of Nottingham. 18 holes, 6224 yards. S.S.S. 70. *Green Fees:* information not available. *Eating facilities:* lunches at club except Wednesdays. *Visitors:* welcome. *Society Meetings:* catered for. Professional: R. Daibell. Secretary: S.J.D. Kinghan.

NEWARK. **Newark Golf Club,** Coddington, Newark NG24 2QX (0636 626241). *Location:* off the A17 Sleaford road four miles east of Newark. Parkland, wooded course. 18 holes, 6482 yards. S.S.S. 71.

Green Fees: £15.00 per round, £18.00 per day weekdays. *Eating facilities:* full catering. *Visitors:* welcome weekdays. *Society Meetings:* catered for weekdays by prior arrangement. Professional: H.A. Bennett (0636 626492). Secretary: A.W. Morgans (0636 626282).

NOTTINGHAM. **Beeston Fields Golf Club,** Beeston Fields, Nottingham NG9 3DD (Nottingham (0602) 257062). *Location:* Wollaton road off A52 Derby road, M1, Exit 25. Parkland. 18 holes, 6414 yards. S.S.S. 71. Practice net available. *Green Fees:* weekdays £15.00, weekends £17.00 (£5.00 if introduced by a member). Society Day £20.00. *Eating facilities:* available daily. *Visitors:* welcome with reservation. *Society Meetings:* catered for Wednesdays. Professional: Mike Pashley (0602 257503). Secretary: J.E.L. Grove (0602 257062).

NOTTINGHAM. **Chilwell Manor Golf Club,** Meadow Lane, Chilwell, Nottingham NG9 5AE (Nottingham (0602) 258958). *Location:* four miles from Nottingham on main Nottingham to Birmingham road. 18 holes, 6379 yards. S.S.S. 69. *Green Fees:* weekdays £12.00, no visitors weekends or Bank Holidays. *Eating facilities:* available. *Visitors:* welcome weekdays with reservation, restricted at certain busy times. *Society Meetings:* limited number catered for (early request preferred). Professional: E. McCausland. Hon. Secretary: G.A. Spindley.

NOTTINGHAM. **Nottingham City Golf Club,** Lawton Drive, Bulwell, Nottingham NG6 8BL (Nottingham (0602) 278021). *Location:* three miles north west of city centre, Exit 26 M1. Parkland. 18 holes, 6218 yards. S.S.S. 70. Practice area. *Green Fees:* £4.00 per round. *Eating facilities:* available. *Visitors:* welcome without reservation except weekends. *Society Meetings:* catered for. Professional: C.R. Jepson (0602 272767). Secretary: D.A. Griffiths (0602 278021).

NOTTINGHAM. **Ruddington Grange Golf Club,** Wilford Road, Ruddington, Nottingham NG11 6NB (0602 214139). *Location:* M1 junction 24 Nottingham road, A52 to Nottingham Knight island, right to Ruddington, half a mile outside Ruddington. Parkland. 18 holes, 6490 yards, 5935 metres. S.S.S. 71. *Green Fees:* weekdays £18.00/£20.00, weekends £22.00/£26.00. *Eating facilities:* full restaurant. *Visitors:* welcome all the times but at weekends members have priority. Swimming pool. *Society Meetings:* welcome. Professional: Robert Ellis (0602 211951). Secretary: J.A. Aston and D.J.T. Johnson (0602 846141).

NOTTINGHAM. **Wollaton Park Golf Club,** Wollaton Park, Nottingham (0602 77574). *Location:* turning off Ring Road Middleton Boulevard. 18 holes, 6545 yards. S.S.S. 71. *Green Fees:* weekdays £12.00 per round, weekends £14.50 per round. *Eating facilities:* available except Monday lunch. Bar snacks. *Visitors:* welcome without reservation. *Society Meetings:* catered for Tuesdays and Fridays. Professional: R. Hastings. Secretary: B. Morris, BSc, PhD.

RADCLIFFE-ON-TRENT. **Radcliffe-on-Trent Golf Club,** Cropwell Road, Radcliffe-on-Trent NG12 2JH (0602 333125). *Location:* six miles east of Nottingham, off A52. Flat, wooded parkland. 18 holes, 6423 yards.

S.S.S. 71. Practice area. *Green Fees:* weekdays £15.00 per day, weekends £20.00 per day (reductions for members' guests). *Eating facilities:* snacks, meals and bar. *Visitors:* members of golf clubs with handicaps only. *Society Meetings:* catered for on Wednesdays. Professional: P. Hinton (0602 333000). Secretary: P.J. Newton (0602 332500).

RETFORD. **Retford Golf Club Ltd,** Ordsall, Retford (0777 703733). *Location:* south off A620. 18 holes, 6301 yards. S.S.S. 71. *Green fees:* weekdays £15.00 per round (£8.00 with a member), £20.00 per day; weekends and Bank Holidays £8.00 (must be accompanied by a member). *Eating facilities:* meals at club. *Visitors:* welcome. Secretary/Manager: A. Harrison (0777 860682).

SOUTHWELL. **Oxton Golf Course Ltd,** Oaks Lane, Oxton, Southwell (Nottingham (0602) 653545). *Location:* adjoining A614 north of Nottingham. Attractive wooded estate courses. 18 holes, S.S.S. 72; also 9 hole course. 30-bay floodlit driving range. *Green fees:* information not provided. *Eating facilities:* bar and restaurant open to all golfers. *Visitors:* pay-as-you-play courses. Professional/Secretary: G.C. Norton.

STANTON-ON-THE-WOLDS. **Stanton-on-the-Wolds Golf Club,** Stanton-on-the-Wolds NG12 5BH (Plumtree (06077 2044). *Location:* seven miles south of Nottingham, one mile west of main Nottingham – Melton road. Agricultural land. 18 holes, 6437 yards, 5886 metres. S.S.S. 71. Practice ground. *Green Fees:* weekdays £16.00 per round, £18.00 per day, weekends with member only. *Eating facilities:* restaurant and bar. *Visitors:* welcome with prior arrangement with Secretary, weekends with member only. *Society Meetings:* catered for by arrangement with Secretary. Professional: Nick Hernon (06077 2390). Secretary: H.G. Gray, F.C.A. (0602 787291 or 0602 2006).

WORKSOP. **Kilton Forest Golf Club,** Worksop (0909 486563). *Location:* one mile north of Worksop on B6045. 18 holes, 6569 yards. S.S.S. 72. *Visitors:* unrestricted. Secretary: E.L. James. Professional: Peter Foster.

WORKSOP. **Lindrick Golf Club,** Lindrick, Worksop S81 8BH (Worksop (0909) 485802). *Location:* on A57 four miles west of Worksop. M1 junction 31 on to A57 Worksop. 18 holes, 6615 yards, 6048 metres. S.S.S. 72. *Green Fees:* on application. *Eating facilities:* by arrangement. *Visitors:* welcome weekdays, except Tuesday mornings. Prior booking required. *Society Meetings:* catered for weekdays. Professional: P. Cowen (0909 475820). Secretary: (0909 475282).

WORKSOP. **Worksop Golf Club,** Windmill Lane, Worksop S80 2SQ (Worksop (0909) 472696). *Location:* off A57 Worksop by-pass M1 Junction 30 seven miles, A1 (A57) three miles. Gently undulating, dry heathland with gorse and broom with wooded areas – oak and birch. 18 holes, 6651 yards. S.S.S. 72. *Green Fees:* £15.00 per round, £20.00 per day weekdays; £20.00 per round weekends. *Eating facilities:* full catering (closed some Mondays). *Visitors:* by arrangement with the Secretary. *Society Meetings:* also by arrangement with Secretary. Professional: J.R. King (0909 477732). Secretary: P.G. Jordan (0909 477731).

Oxfordshire

ABINGDON. **Frilford Heath Golf Club,** Abingdon OX13 5NW (Frilford Heath (0865) 390864). *Location:* on A338 Oxford/Wantage road seven miles south-west of Oxford, four miles west of Abingdon. Flat, wooded heathland. Red course: 18 holes, 6768 yards. S.S.S. 73; Green course: 18 holes, 5763 yards. S.S.S. 69. Two practice areas. *Green Fees:* £25.00 weekdays, £35.00 weekends and Bank Holidays. (After 5.00pm weekdays £15.00, weekends £20.00). *Eating facilities:* restaurant and two bars (one for members only). *Visitors:* welcome weekdays with Handicap Certificate, phone ahead; weekends and Bank Holidays accompanied by member only. *Society Meetings:* catered for Mondays, Wednesdays and Fridays only. Professional: D.C. Craik (0865 390887). Secretary: J. Kleynhans (0865 390864).

BANBURY. **Cherwell Edge Public Course,** Chacombe, Banbury (Banbury (0295) 711591). *Location:* A442, some four miles from Banbury. 18 holes, 5600 metres. Par 70. *Green Fees:* midweek £4.30 (18 holes), £5.50 (18 holes) weekends. Senior Citizens and Juniors weekdays £2.00 (18 holes). *Eating facilities:* bar and lounge. *Visitors:* open to the public. *Society Meetings:* contact the Golf Manager. Professional/ Manager: Richard Davies.

BANBURY. **Tadmarton Heath Golf Club,** Wiginton, Banbury OX15 5HL (0608 737649). *Location:* off B4035, off A41, five miles west of Banbury. Flat heathland. 18 holes, 5917 yards. S.S.S. 69. Practice area. *Green Fees:* by application. *Eating facilities:* full catering. *Visitors:* welcome weekdays (restrictions Thursdays); weekends with member only. *Society Meetings:* welcome weekdays except Thursdays. Professional: Les Bond (0608 730047). Secretary: R.E. Wackrill (0608 737278).

BICESTER. **Chesterton Golf Club,** Chesterton, Near Bicester OX6 8TE (Bicester (0869) 241204). *Location:* one mile off A421, Bicester/Oxford. Two miles south-west of Bicester. 18 holes, 6224 yards. S.S.S. 70. Practice ground and putting green. *Green Fees:* weekdays £12.00 per day, weekends and Bank Holidays £18.00 per day. *Eating facilities:* bars and lunchtime bar food, diningroom by arrangement. *Visitors:* welcome weekdays without reservation, weekends may book through Pro shop. Snooker room. *Society Meetings:* catered for except weekends. Professional: Jack Wilkshire (0869 242023). Secretary: Brian Carter (0869 241204).

BURFORD. **Burford Golf Club,** Burford OX8 4JG (Burford (099 382 2149). *Location:* A40 and A361 junction at Burford roundabout. Flat parkland. 18 holes, 6405 yards, 6083 metres. S.S.S. 71. *Green Fees:* £22.00 per day. No weekend visitors. *Eating facilities:* full catering. *Visitors:* welcome weekdays only. *Society Meetings:* catered for on application to Secretary. Professional: Norman Allen (099 382 2344). Secretary: Richard Cane (099 382 2583).

CHIPPING NORTON. **Chipping Norton Golf Club,** Southcombe, Chipping Norton OX7 5QH (Chipping Norton (0608 2383). *Location:* junction of A34 A44, 18 miles from Oxford. 20 miles from Stratford-on-Avon. Downland, with many planted trees. 18 holes, 6280 yards, 5743 metres. S.S.S. 70. Practice ground and putting green. *Green Fees:* weekdays £16.00, weekends only with a member, £8.00. *Eating facilities:* lunches and evening meals Mondays to Saturdays, bar open daily. *Visitors:* welcome Monday to Friday but not Bank Holidays. *Society Meetings;* Mondays, Tuesdays and Wednesdays. Professional: Robert Gould (0608 3356). Secretary: A.J.P. Norman.

HENLEY-ON-THAMES. **Badgemore Park Golf Club,** Henley-on-Thames RG9 4NR (0491 573667). *Location:* just west of Henley-on-Thames, on B290 Henley-Peppard road. Parkland with many trees. 18 holes, 6112 yards. S.S.S. 69. Practice ground. *Green Fees:* £18.00 per round/day. *Eating facilities:* full catering and bar facilities. *Visitors:* welcome weekdays by arrangement, must be regular golfers, preferably with handicaps. *Society Meetings:* complete Company and Society Golf Day packages a speciality. Professional: Mark Wright (0491 574175). Secretary: Leslie Booker (0491 572206).

HENLEY-ON-THAMES. **Henley Golf Club,** Harpsden, Henley-on-Thames RG9 4HG (Henley (0491) 573304). *Location:* from centre of Henley-Reading, one mile from Harpsden Way to clubhouse. Parkland with many trees. 18 holes, 6329 yards. S.S.S. 70. *Green Fees:* £24.00 per round/day. *Eating facilities:* bar snacks at all times, meals by arrangement. *Visitors:* welcome with reservation weekdays, not at weekends or Bank Holidays (Handicap Certificate holders only). Dormy house sleeping six. *Society Meetings:* catered for Wednesdays and Thursdays only. Professional: Mark Howell (0491 575710). Secretary: John Hex (0491 575742).

HENLEY-ON-THAMES. **Huntercombe Golf Club,** Nuffield, Henley-on-Thames RG9 5SL (0491 641207). *Location:* A432, six miles west of Henley-on-Thames. Downland wooded course. 18 holes, 6301 yards. S.S.S. 70. Practice ground. *Green Fees:* £23.00 weekdays, no weekend green fees. *Eating facilities:* catering and bar facilities. *Visitors:* welcome weekdays after 10.00am. *Society Meetings:* Tuesdays and Thursdays by arrangement. Professional: J.B. Draycott (0491 641241). Secretary: Lt Col T.J. Hutchinson.

OXFORD. **North Oxford Golf Club,** Banbury Road, Oxford (Oxford (0865) 54415). *Location:* just north of Oxford on the Banbury Road to Kidlington. 18 holes, 5805 yards, S.S.S. 67. *Green Fees:* £20.00 weekdays, £12.50 weekends and Bank Holidays with members only. *Eating facilities:* not available on Mondays. *Visitors and Societies:* welcome. Professional: Bob Harris (0865 53977). Secretary: W. Forster (0865 54924).

OXFORD. **Southfield Golf Club,** Hill Top Road, Oxford OX4 1PF. *Location:* one mile from Rover Works, Southfield Road, turn right and right at end of road. Hilly parkland. 18 holes, 6210 yards. S.S.S. 70. *Green Fees:* £20.00 per day weekdays. *Eating facilities:* bar and restaurant, full catering except Mondays. *Visitors:* welcome except weekends and Public Holidays. Handicap Certificates required. *Society Meetings:* welcome by arrangement (not weekends or Bank Holidays). Professional: Tony Rees (0865 244258). Secretary: A.G. Hopcraft (0865 242158).

SHRIVENHAM. **Shrivenham Park Golf Club,** Shrivenham (Swindon [0793] 782946). *Location:* Exit 15 M4. A420 Oxford – B400 Shrivenham. Through village, on left. 18 holes, 5134 yards. S.S.S. 67. *Green fees:* weekdays £12.50 per round, £17.50 per day. Weekends £15.00 per round, £20.00 per day. *Eating facilities:* full range of meals. Licensed bar. *Visitors:* welcome without reservation. *Society Meetings:* catered for. Professional: John Blanch (0793 783853). Secretary: D.J. Woodman (0793 783853).

WALLINGFORD near. **Royal Air Force Benson,** Near Wallingford OX10 6AA. *Location:* three and a half miles north-east of Wallingford, follow singposts to RAF Benson. Airfield course, through airfield installations. 9 holes, 4395 yards. S.S.S. 61. *Green Fees:* £3.00. *Visitors:* casual visitors not welcome, must be accommpanied by members. Secretary: Sqn Ldr M.F. Sanders (0491 38867).

THE GOLF FOUNDATION
57 London Road, Enfield, Middlesex EN2 6DU
Telephone: 081-367 4404

Established in 1952 The Golf Foundation has the specific aims of introducing more young people to the game of golf and of promoting and developing their skills and enjoyment of the game. The basis of the Foundation's work is the Coaching Scheme, whereby qualified members of the PGA give instruction to students at schools and universities. The Foundation also sponsors Open Coaching Centres during vacations, and implements a Coaching Award Scheme for teachers. A four-stage Merit Award Scheme operates successfully throughout the country, and Age Group Championships help raise the standard of junior golf by providing real competition at all levels of abillity.

A newsletter "Tee to Green" is published, as well as other coaching material, visual aids and films.

The Golf Foundation is a non-profit-making organisation and a Registered Charity, relying on support from organisations within the game, commerce and industry, and individual Golf Clubs and club members. As the national body responsible for junior golf it plays a vital role in the future development of the game.

PUBLISHER'S NOTE

One of the famous 'irons',
Ironbridge, Shropshire.

Shropshire

BRIDGNORTH. **Bridgnorth Golf Club,** Stanley Lane, Bridgnorth (Bridgnorth (0746) 763315). *Location:* one mile from town centre on Broseley road. Parkland, alongside River Severn. 18 holes, 6627 yards. S.S.S. 72. Practice ground. *Green Fees:* £15.00 weekdays, £20.00 weekends and Bank Holidays. *Eating facilities:* full catering available except Mondays. *Visitors:* welcome with Handicap Certificate or if bona fide club member. *Society Meetings:* catered for weekdays. Professional: Paul Hinton (0746 762045). Secretary: E.H. Thomas (0746 762400).

CHURCH STRETTON. **Church Stretton Golf Club,** Trevor Hill, Church Stretton (Church Stretton (0694) 722281). *Location:* one mile west of A49, adjacent to Carding Mill Valley. 18 holes, 5008 yards. S.S.S. 65. *Green Fees:* £8.00 weekdays, £12.00 weekends and Bank Holidays. *Eating facilities:* by prior arrangement. *Visitors:* welcome, no reservation required except Societies. *Society Meetings:* catered for by arrangement. Hon. Secretary: R. Broughton.

LUDLOW. **Ludlow Golf Club,** Bromfield, Ludlow SY8 2BT (Bromfield (058 477) 285). *Location:* A49 one mile north of Ludlow, turn right onto the Bridgnorth road. Well signposted. Parkland with hills to north east; two quarry holes. 18 holes, 6239 yards. S.S.S. 70. Practice ground. *Green Fees:* weekdays £12.00, weekends £16.00 (£6.00 with member). *Eating facilities:* full catering and bar service. *Visitors:* welcome weekdays with prior booking, weekends with member only. *Society Meetings:* catered for. Professional: G. Farr (058 477 366). Administrator: M. Cropper.

MARKET DRAYTON. **Market Drayton Golf Club,** Sutton, Market Drayton (Market Drayton (0630) 652266). *Location:* south of town leaving by Walkmill Road one mile past the swimming baths. Parkland with exceptional views. 18 holes, 6214 yards, 5702 metres. S.S.S. 70. *Green Fees:* weekdays £12.00, weekends only with member. Reduced fees if playing with member. *Eating facilities:* bar, high class catering by arrangement. *Visitors:* welcome weekdays only. Bungalow (sleeps 6) available for letting. *Society Meetings:* catered for weekdays by prior arrangement. Professional: R. Clewes. Secretary: J.J. Moseley (0630 3661).

NEWPORT. **Lilleshall Hall Golf Club,** Lilleshall, Near Newport (Telford (0952) 603840). *Location:* turn north off Abbey Road, which joins the A518 near Lilleshall. Wooded parkland. 18 holes, 5906 yards. S.S.S. 68. Practice ground. Lessons available. *Green Fees:* weekdays £12.50 (£5.00 with member), weekends £8.00 (only with member). Bank Holidays and following day plus Christmas holiday week £18.00. *Eating facilities:* meals served until 5.00pm, order in advance. *Visitors:* welcome on weekdays. *Society*

Meetings: catered for by prior arrangement. Professional: N.W. Bramall (0952 604104). Hon. Secretary: D.R. Higgs (0952 604776).

OSWESTRY. **Llanymynech Golf Club,** Pant, Near Oswestry SY10 8LB (Llanymynech (0691) 830542). *Location:* one mile west of A483 Welshpool to Oswestry, six miles south of Oswestry. Turn by Cross Guns Inn, Pant signposted to club. Upland course with extensive views. 18 holes, 6114 yards, 5899 metres. S.S.S. 69. Practice area. *Green Fees:* weekdays £15.00 per day, £11.00 per round; weekends £18.00 per day, £16.50 per round. Half price with member. Reductions for Juniors. *Eating facilities:* restaurant and bar (not Mondays). *Visitors:* welcome weekdays; some weekends by prior arrangement. *Society Meetings:* by arrangement with Secretary. Professional: A.P. Griffiths (0691 830879). Secretary: N. Clews (0691 830983).

OSWESTRY. **Oswestry Golf Club,** Aston Park, Oswestry SY11 4JJ (Queens Head (069188) 221). *Location:* four miles south-east of Oswestry on A5. Parkland course. 18 holes, 6038 yards. S.S.S. 69. *Green Fees:* weekdays £12.00, weekends £16.00. *Eating facilities:* full catering except Mondays by arrangement. *Visitors:* welcome; must be members of another club or playing with a member. *Society Meetings:* catered for Wednesday and Friday, by arrangement, application necessary. Professional: D. Skelton (069188 448). Secretary: Mrs P.M. Lindner (069188 535).

SHIFNAL. **Shifnal Golf Club,** Decker Hill, Shifnal TF11 8QL (Telford (0952) 460330). *Location:* one mile north east of Shifnal, one mile from A5, junction 4 M54. Parkland course. 18 holes, 6504 yards. S.S.S. 71. *Green Fees:* £14.00 per round, £18.00 per day; weekends with member only. *Eating facilities:* full catering service. *Visitors:* welcome, phone first, not weekends or Bank Holidays. *Society Meetings:* catered for by arrangement with Secretary. Professional: J. Flanagan (0952 460457). Secretary: J. Bell (0952 460330).

SHREWSBURY. **Hawkstone Park Hotel Ltd,** Weston-under-Redcastle, Shrewsbury SY4 5UY. Where Sandy Lyle, '85 Open Champion, learned his game. (Lee Brockhurst (093-924) 611). *Location:* 14 miles north of Shrewsbury on A49 Whitchurch road. Two golf courses, Hawkstone and Weston, both parkland courses with hills comprising antiquities. Hawkstone course 18 holes, Par 72, S.S.S. 71. Weston course 18 holes, Par 66, S.S.S. 66. *Green Fees:* £21.50 daily, weekends £26.50. *Eating facilities:* hotel restaurant and bar. *Visitors:* welcome but advisable to book tee times in advance. Residential bargain breaks available all year round with starting times reserved. *Society Meetings:* comprehensive super value packages available. Golf Professional: Keith Williams (093-924 209). Buggies available for hire through the Professional's Shop.

SHREWSBURY. **Shrewsbury Golf Club,** Condover, Shrewsbury (Bayston Hill (074372) 2976). *Location:* A49 south, west of Shrewsbury. Parkland. 18 holes, 6212 yards. S.S.S. 70. Large practice ground. *Green Fees:* £15.00 per day, £10.00 per round weekdays;

£20.00 per day, £16.00 per round weekends. *Eating facilities:* available. *Visitors:* welcome at all times. Professional: Peter Seal (074372 3751). Secretary: J.A. Morrison (074372 2977).

TELFORD. **Telford Hotel, Golf and Country Club,** Great Hay, Sutton Hill, Telford TF7 4DT (0952 585642). *Location:* turn off A442 between Bridgnorth and Telford, 2 miles to M54 junction 4. Rolling wooded parkland with lake features. 18 holes, 6766 yards, 6187 metres. S.S.S. 72. 9 hole par 3 course. All-weather driving range. *Green Fees:* £18.00 weekday, £22.00 weekends. *Eating facilities:* clubroom, coffee bar and restaurant, also private rooms for Societies. *Visitors:* welcome anytime but advance booking essential. Handicap Certificates or membership of bona fide golf club essential. Three star hotel, swimming, sauna, gym, squash, snooker etc. *Society Meetings:* by arrangement with Golf Co-ordinator extension 296. Professional: Mr Steve Marr (0952 586052). Secretary: Cdr John Brigham (0952 585642 ext. 274).

TELFORD. **Wrekin Golf Club,** Ercall Woods, Wellington, Telford (Telford (0952) 244032). *Location:* end of M54, turn back along Holyhead road to golf club sign. Undulating parkland. 18 holes, 5699 yards. S.S.S. 67. Small practice ground. *Green Fees:* £12.00 weekdays, £20.00 weekends. Numbers not to exceed 12. *Eating facilities:* by arrangement with Stewardess. *Visitors:* welcome except weekends. Parties by prior arrangement. *Society Meetings:* by arrangement. Professional: K. Housden (0952 223101). Secretary: S. Leys (0952 255586).

WHITCHURCH. **Hill Valley Golf and Country Club,** Terrick Road, Whitchurch SY13 4JZ (0948 3584). *Location:* fully signposted on A41/A49 trunk road in Whitchurch. Undulating course. 18 holes, 6050 yards. S.S.S. 69. 9 holes, 5106 yards. S.S.S. 66. *Green Fees:* weekdays £14.00, weekends and Bank Holidays £18.00. *Eating facilities:* full restaurant and bar facilities 8am–11pm. *Visitors:* welcome without reservation. *Society Meetings:* fully catered for every day. Squash, Tennis, Snooker Room and Saunas. Specialised golf lessons available through John Garner's (ex Ryder Cup) school of golf. Motel accommodation available. Professional: Tony Minshall (0948 3032). Secretary: R.B. Walker (0948 3584).

WOLVERHAMPTON. **Patshull Park Hotel, Golf and Country Club,** The Patshull Park Estate, Pattingham, Near Wolverhampton WV6 7HR (0902 700100). *Location:* take Junction 3 off M54 turn, left on A41 back towards Wolverhampton. Pass RAF Cosford on right and then fork right into village of Shifnal and then left to PPH through Burnhill Green/Albrighton, right in Albrighton. Set in glorious parkland landscaped by Capability Brown; Hon Jacobs designed course. 18 holes, 6412 yards. S.S.S. 72. Excellent practice area. *Green Fees:* weekdays £17.00 per round, £25.00 per day; weekends £20.00 per round, £30.00 per day. *Eating facilities:* available, two restaurants and three bars. *Visitors:* welcome on application. 48 bedroomed hotel, leisure club and swimming pool, fishing lakes (80 acres). *Society Meetings:* welcome and catered for, special group rates and facilities. Professional: Duncan J. McDowall (0902 700342).

Somerset

BRIDGWATER. **Enmore Park Golf Club,** Enmore, Bridgwater (Spaxton (0278) 67244). *Location:* M5 Exit 23, left at lights in town for one mile, course signposted two miles on left. Wooded parkland course on Quantock foothills. 18 holes, 6443 yards, 5891 metres. S.S.S. 71. Practice area. *Green Fees:* £14.00 weekdays, £18.00 weekends. *Eating facilities:* lunch and evening meal available. *Visitors:* welcome weekdays, weekends if no competitions. *Society Meetings:* welcome, but no catering Mondays. Professional: Nigel Wixon (0278 67519). Secretary/Manager: D.H. Smith (0278 67481).

BURNHAM-ON-SEA. **Brean Golf Club,** Coast Road, Brean, Burnham-on-Sea TA8 2RF (027 875 570 or 027 875 374). *Location:* leave M5 at Junction 22, follow Brean signs for five miles; three miles north of Burnham-on-Sea. Flat moorland. 18 holes, 5566 yards. S.S.S. 67. *Green Fees:* weekdays £8.00, weekends £12.00. *Eating facilities:* bar snacks at Clubhouse; meals at adjoining Leisure Centre on request. *Visitors:* welcome without reservation, except Sunday a.m. and Open Days. *Society Meetings:* welcome with prior notice. Secretary: W.S. Martin. Manager: Albert Clarke.

BURNHAM-ON-SEA. **Burnham and Berrow Golf Club,** St. Christopher's Way, Burnham-on-Sea TA8 2PE (Burnham-on-Sea (0278) 783137). *Location:* one mile north of Burnham-on-Sea. Leave M5 at Exit 22. Seaside links. 18 holes, 6327 yards. S.S.S. 72. *Green Fees:* £20.00 weekdays, £28.00 weekends and Bank Holidays. *Eating facilities:* catering available daily 11.00am to 6.00pm (other meals by arrangement). *Visitors:* welcome with reservation if members of a recognised golf club and with Handicap Certificate. *Society Meetings:* catered for. Professional: N.P. Blake (0278 784545). Secretary: Mrs E.L. Sloman (0278 785760).

CHARD. **Windwhistle Golf, Squash and Country Club Ltd,** Cricket St. Thomas, Chard TA20 4DG (Winsham (0460) 30231). *Location:* on A30 between Chard and Crewkerne, 12 miles from M5 and from Lyme Bay. Opposite Manor Born Wildlife Park. Flat parkland with scenic views. 11 holes, 6055 yards, S.S.S. 69. Chipping and putting greens. *Green Fees:* weekdays £8.00, weekends and Bank Holidays £12.00. *Eating facilities:* bar and catering facilities. *Visitors:* welcome without reservation but advise telephone in advance. Booked times at weekends and on Thursdays. *Society Meetings:* golf and squash catered for by appointment. Professional: Neil Morris. Squash

Professional: Phil Thompson. Secretary/Greenmaster: Ian Dodd.

MINEHEAD. **Minehead and West Somerset Golf Club,** The Warren, Minehead TA24 5SJ (Minehead (0643) 702057). *Location:* beside the beach at eastern end of the town, three quarters of a mile from town centre. Flat seaside links. 18 holes, 6137 yards. S.S.S. 70. *Green Fees:* weekdays £12.00, weekends and Bank Holidays £15.00. *Eating facilities:* available at clubhouse except on Tuesdays, bar open every day. *Visitors:* welcome without reservation but advisable to check with Professional. *Society Meetings:* catered for, subject to prior arrangement with the Secretary. Society groups numbering 15 or more qualify for 10 per cent discount. Wide wheel trolleys only. Professional: Ian Read (0643 704378). Secretary: A.R. Pettit (0643 702057).

SHEPTON MALLET. **Mendip Golf Club Ltd,** Gurney Slade, Shepton Mallet, Near Bath BA3 4UT (Oakhill (0749) 840570). *Location:* three miles north of Shepton Mallet (A37). Downland with extensive views. 18 holes, 5958 yards. S.S.S. 69 (Par 69). Practice ground and indoor net. *Green Fees:* weekdays £12.00 (£6.00 with member), weekends and Bank Holidays £20.00 (£8.00 with member). *Eating facilities:* meals and bar

snacks to order available daily. *Visitors:* welcome Monday to Friday, at weekends must be members of affiliated club unless playing with a member. *Society Meetings:* catered for Tuesdays to Fridays. Professional: R.F. Lee (0749 840793). Secretary: John Lee (0749 840570).

STREET. **Kingweston Golf Club,** (Millfield School), 24 Bramley Road, Street BA16 0QE (0458 43921). *Location:* one mile south of Butleigh Village, near Street, Somerset. Flat course – trees. 9 holes, 2378 yards. S.S.S. 62. Practice area. *Green Fees:* £2.00. *Eating facilities:* pub half a mile. *Visitors:* welcome only with a member. Secretary: J.G. Willetts (0458 43921).

TAUNTON. **Taunton and Pickeridge Golf Club,** Corfe, Taunton (Blagdon Hill 082-342 240). *Location:* B3170 four miles south of Taunton, first left. 18 holes, 5906 yards. S.S.S. 68. *Green Fees:* £15.00 weekdays, £18.00 weekends. *Eating facilities:* lunches served at club, advance notice necessary. *Society Meetings:* catered for. Professional: Graham Glew. Secretary: G.W. Sayers.

TAUNTON. **Taunton Golf Club,** Vivary Park, Taunton (Taunton (0823) 81946). 18 holes, 4280 yards. S.S.S. 62. *Green Fees:* information not provided.

TAUNTON. **Vivary Park Public Golf Course,** Vivary Park, Fons George, Taunton TA1 3JW. *Location:* one mile from town centre off main Wellington road. Access to course is through Vivary Park in central Taunton. Pleasant parkland course with spectacular water

hazards. 18 holes, 4620 yards. S.S.S. 63. Practice ground. *Green Fees:* £5.75. *Eating facilities:* restaurant and bar available. *Visitors:* always welcome but will need to book on the day of play. *Society Meetings:* catered for by prior arrangement. Professional: Jeremy Wright (0823 33875).

WELLS. **Wells (Somerset) Golf Club Ltd.** East Horrington Road, Wells BA5 3DS (Wells (0749) 72868). *Location:* one mile east of city centre opposite Mendip Hospital. Undulating wooded course with superb views. 18 holes, 5354 yards, 4950 metres. S.S.S. 66. Practice area. *Green Fees:* weekdays £12.00, weekends and Bank Holidays £15.00. *Eating facilities:* meals and snacks during bar hours. *Visitors:* welcome, Handicaps required weekends and no play before 9.30am weekends and Public Holidays. Caravan park adjacent. *Society Meetings:* catered for weekdays. Professional: Andrew England (0749 79059). Secretary: Mike Davis (0749 75005).

YEOVIL. **Yeovil Golf Club,** Sherborne Road, Yeovil BA21 5BW (Yeovil (0935) 75949). *Location:* on A30 towards Sherborne on right before Babylon Hill. Parkland. 18 holes, 6144 yards. S.S.S. 69. Practice ground and putting green. *Green Fees:* weekdays £14.00, weekends and Bank Holidays £16.00. *Eating facilities:* bars and dining room. *Visitors:* midweek unrestricted subject to Society bookings; weekends players with current handicaps only. Telephone for starting time. *Society Meetings:* welcome weekdays. Professional: G. Kite (0935 73763). Secretary/Manager: J. Riley (0935 22965).

Staffordshire

BARLASTON. **Barlaston Golf Club,** Meaford Road, Barlaston (Barlaston (078 139) 2795). *Location:* one mile south of Barlaston off A34. 18 holes, 5800 yards. S.S.S. 68. *Green Fees:* weekdays £12.00, £16.00 weekends. *Visitors:* welcome, but not before 10am at weekends. Secretary: M.J. Degg.

BURTON-ON-TRENT. **Branston Golf Club,** Burton Road, Branston, Burton-on-Trent DE14 3DP (Burton-on-Trent (0283) 43207). *Location:* A38 Burton-on-Trent. Parkland. 18 holes, 6480 yards, 5925 metres. S.S.S. 71. Practice area. *Green Fees:* weekdays £12.00, weekends £15.00. *Eating facilities:* dining room and bar. *Visitors:* welcome, weekend restrictions only. *Society Meetings:* welcome, special rates. Pro-

fessional: S.D. Warner (0283 43207). Secretary: K.L. George (0283 66984).

BURTON-ON-TRENT. **Burton-on-Trent Golf Club,** 43 Ashby Road East, Burton-on-Trent (Burton-on-Trent (0283) 44551). *Location:* on A50, Burton to Ashby Road, 3 miles from Burton centre. 18 holes, 6555 yards. S.S.S. 71. *Green Fees:* weekdays £12.00 per round, £16.00 per day, Sundays and Bank Holidays £16.00 per round, £20.00 per day. *Eating facilities:* full eating facilities at club except Mondays. *Visitors:* welcome, reservation advisable, letters of introduction. Bona fide Handicaps. *Society Meetings:* catered for. Professional: John M. Lower. Hon. Secretary: A. Maddock.

BURTON-ON-TRENT. **Craythorne Golf Centre,** Craythorne Road, Stretton, Burton-on-Trent DE13 0AZ (Burton-on-Trent (0283) 64329). *Location:* A38 (Burton North) A5121 signposted Stretton. Parkland. 18 holes, 5230 yards. S.S.S. 66. Floodlit driving range. *Green Fees:* £7.00 weekdays, £12.00 weekends and Bank Holidays. *Eating facilities:* bars and restaurant open daily. *Visitors:* welcome every day, booking necessary at weekends. 9 hole pitch and putt, golf hotel. *Society Meetings:* welcome. Professional: Steve Hadfield (0283 33745). Secretary/General Manager: John Bissell (0283 64329).

CANNOCK. **Beau Desert Golf Club,** Hazel Slade, Hednesford, Cannock WS12 5PJ (Hednesford (05438) 2773). *Location:* A460 Hednesford, signposted. Wooded course. 18 holes, 6300 yards. S.S.S. 70. Practice ground. *Green Fees:* £22.00 weekdays. *Eating facilities:* full catering and bar. *Visitors:* welcome except weekends and Bank Holidays. *Society Meetings:* catered for. Professional: Barrie Stevens (05438 2492). Secretary: I.E. Williams (05438 2626).

CANNOCK. **Cannock Park Golf Club,** Stafford Road, Cannock WS11 2AL. *Location:* half a mile off A5, side of Cannock Leisure Centre. Parkland course, playing alongside Cannock Chase. 18 holes, 5151 yards. S.S.S. 65. *Green Fees:* £3.50 weekdays, £5.00 weekends. Day and Junior tickets available. *Eating facilities:* available. *Visitors:* welcome every day. *Society Meetings:* welcome weekdays. Professional/Secretary: David Dunk (0543 578850).

LEEK. **Leek Golf Club,** Birchall, Cheddleton Road, Leek (Leek (0538) 385889). *Location:* one mile south of Leek on A520. Undulating semi-moorland. 18 holes, 6240 yards. S.S.S. 70. *Green Fees:* weekdays £18.00, weekends £25.00. *Eating facilities:* full bar facilities 12 noon-2 pm and 4-11 pm. Bar snacks or full menu at those times. *Visitors:* welcome most times by prior arrangement. *Society Meetings:* catered for by arrangement Wednesday only. Professional: P.A. Stubbs (0538 384767). Secretary: Frank Cutts B.E.M. (0538 384779).

LEEK. **Westwood Golf Club,** Newcastle Road, Leek ST13 7AA (Leek (0538) 383060). *Location:* A53 south of Leek. Moorland. 9 holes, 5480 yards. S.S.S. 67. Plus four extra holes. *Green fees:* information not available.

Eating facilities: by arrangement. *Visitors:* welcome weekdays. Saturdays one visitor per member, no visitors without member. No visitors Sundays. *Society Meetings:* by arrangement with Secretary. Secretary: A.J. Lawton (0782 503780).

LICHFIELD. **Whittington Barracks Golf Club,** Tamworth Road, Lichfield WS14 9PW (0543 432212). *Location:* on A51 Tamworth-Lichfield. Heathland. 18 holes, 6457 yards. S.S.S. 71. *Green Fees:* weekdays £20.00. *Eating facilities:* lunches served at club. *Visitors:* welcome with prior notification and Handicap Certificate or letter of introduction. *Society Meetings:* catered for Wednesdays and Thursdays by arrangement. Professional: Adrian Sadler (0543 432261). Secretary: M. Scargill (0543 432317).

NEWCASTLE-UNDER-LYME. **Newcastle-under-Lyme Golf Club,** Whitmore Road, Newcastle-under-Lyme (0782 616583). *Location:* one mile from Newcastle on A53, Shrewsbury Road. Parkland. 18 holes, 6450 yards. S.S.S. 71. *Green Fees:* weekdays £15.00, Societies £15.00. *Eating facilities:* dining room. *Visitors:* welcome weekdays. *Society Meetings:* catered for Mondays and Wednesdays. Professional: Paul Symonds (0782 618526). Secretary: R.B. Irving (0782 617006).

RUGELEY. **Lakeside Golf Club,** Rugeley Power Station, Armitage Road, Rugeley WS15 2QL (0889 583181 extension 2530). *Location:* nearest town Rugeley (between Lichfield and Stafford), course over power station grounds. Parkland, very tight fairways. 9 holes, 4768 yards, 4360 metres. S.S.S. 63. Limited practice area. *Green Fees:* information not provided. *Eating facilities:* none – local public houses. *Visitors:* must be accompanied by member. *Society Meetings:* considered. Secretary: Mr E.G. Jones (0889 583181 extension 2739).

STAFFORD. **Brocton Hall Golf Club,** Brocton, Stafford ST17 0TH (Stafford (0785) 662627). *Location:* four miles south east of Stafford on A34. Undulating parkland. 18 holes, 6095 yards. S.S.S. 69. *Green Fees:* weekdays £18.00, weekends and Bank Holidays £20.00. *Eating facilities:* diningroom. *Visitors:* by arrangement. *Society Meetings:* by arrangement Tuesdays and Thursdays. Professional: Bob Johnson (0785 661485).Secretary: W.R. Lanyon (0785 661901).

STAFFORD. **Ingestre Park Golf Club,** Ingestre, Near Stafford (Weston (0889) 270061). *Location:* six miles east of Stafford. 18 holes, 6334 yards. S.S.S. 70. *Green Fees:* on application. *Eating facilities:* menu and supper licence. *Visitors:* welcome with reservation. *Society Meetings:* catered for. Professional: Daniel Scullion (0889 270304). Manager: (0889 270845).

STAFFORD. **Stafford Castle Golf Club,** Newport Road, Stafford ST16 1BP (Stafford (0785) 223821). *Location:* M6 junction 13 or 14, 2 miles from club. Parkland course. 9 holes, 6073 yards. S.S.S. 60, Par 71. *Green Fees:* £10.00 weekdays, £14.00 weekends. *Eating facilities:* snacks and full catering available except Mondays. *Visitors:* welcome except Sunday mornings. *Society Meetings:* catered for by arrangement. Hon. Secretary: M.H. Fisher.

STOKE-ON-TRENT. **Alsager Golf and Country Club,** Audley Road, Alsager, Stoke-on-Trent (0270 875700). *Location:* take Junction 16 M6 to A500 turn-off, Alsager left, two and a half miles on right. Parkland. 18 holes, 6192 yards. S.S.S. 70. *Green Fees:* weekdays £12.00, weekends £16.00. *Eating facilities:* restaurant and bar snacks. *Visitors:* welcome weekdays without reservation. Disco, conference facilities. *Society Meetings:* welcome. Professional: Nick Rothe (0270 877432) Secretary: John Maxwell (0270 875700).

STOKE-ON-TRENT. **Burslem Golf Club Ltd,** Wood Farm, High Lane, Tunstall, Stoke-on-Trent ST6 7ST (Stoke-on-Trent (0782) 837006). *Location:* leave Burslem centre by Hamil Road, turn left at High Lane junction, two miles on right. 9 holes, 5800 yards. S.S.S. 68. *Green Fees:* information not provided. *Eating facilities:* meals and refreshments by arrangement except Wednesday and Sunday. *Visitors:* welcome weekdays with reservation. Bona fide golf club members only. *Society Meetings:* catered for. Secretary: R.J. Sutton.

STOKE-ON-TRENT. **Greenway Hall Golf Club,** Greenway Hall, Stockton Brook, Stoke-on-Trent (Stoke-on-Trent (0782) 50318). 18 holes, 5803 yards. *Green Fees:* information not provided. *Visitors:* only with member during week. not weekends.

STOKE-ON-TRENT. **Trentham Golf Club,** 14 Barlaston Old Road, Trentham, Stoke-on-Trent ST4 8HB (Stoke-on-Trent (0782) 642347). *Location:* off A34 south of Newcastle (Staffs.). Parkland. Two courses. 18 holes, 6644 yards. S.S.S. 72. 18 holes, 6206 yards. S.S.S. 70. Practice ground. *Green Fees:* £17.00 weekdays, £20.00 weekends. Playing with member £5.00 per day. *Eating facilities:* lunches and dinners available. *Visitors:* welcome, on written application. *Society Meetings:* catered for, limited numbers. Professional: Donald McDonald (0782 657309). Secretary: Lt Cdr J.R. Smith RN (Rtd) (0782 658109).

STOKE-ON-TRENT. **Trentham Park Golf Club,** Trentham Park, Trentham, Stoke-on-Trent ST4 8AE. *Location:* off A34 adjoining Trentham Gardens near Junction 15 on M6. 18 holes, 6403 yards. S.S.S. 71.

Green Fees: £15.00 weekdays, £20.00 weekends. *Eating facilities:* available at clubhouse except Mondays. *Visitors:* welcome weekdays with reservation. *Society Meetings:* catered for Wednesdays and Fridays only. Professional: R. Clarke. Secretary: C.H. Lindop (0782 658800).

STONE. **Stone Golf Club,** Filleybrooks, Stone ST15 0NB (Stone (0785) 813103). *Location:* one mile north of Stone on the A34 adjacent to the Wayfarer Hotel. Parkland. 9 holes, 6272 yards. S.S.S. 70. *Green Fees:* weekdays £10.00, Societies £7.00. *Eating facilities:* snacks and full meals if ordered. *Visitors:* welcome weekdays; weekends and Bank Holidays only with member. *Society Meetings:* catered for by arrangement. Secretary: M.G. Pharaoh (08897 224).

STOURBRIDGE. **Enville Golf Club Ltd,** Highgate Common, Enville, Stourbridge DY7 5BN (Kinver (0384) 872551). *Location:* leave A449 at Stewpony Hotel taking Bridgnorth Road A458, fork right after Fox Inn following signs for Halfpenny Green Airport. Two flat wooded parkland courses. 36 holes, 6541 and 6207 yards. S.S.S. 72 and 70. *Green Fees:* £16.00 per round, £22.00 per day. *Eating facilities:* meals available except Mondays. *Visitors:* welcome with Handicap Certificate, advisable to phone prior to visit. Ladies' day, Thursday. *Society Meetings:* welcome except Thursdays and weekends. Professional: S. Power (0384 872585). Secretary/Manager: R.J. Bannister (0384 872074).

STREETLY. **Little Aston Golf Club,** Streetly (021-353 2066). *Location:* off A454. Parkland course. 18 holes, 6724 yards. S.S.S. 73. *Green Fees:* information not provided. *Eating facilities:* lunches served at club except Mondays. *Visitors:* welcome on weekdays by prior arrangement, weekends with a member. *Society Meetings:* catered for on weekdays only. Professional: John Anderson.

TAMWORTH. **Drayton Park Golf Club,** Drayton Park, Tamworth B78 3TN (Tamworth (0827) 251139). *Location:* two miles south of Tamworth on A4091, next to Drayton Manor Leisure Park. Parkland with wooded areas. 18 holes, 6214 yards. S.S.S. 70. Practice area. *Green Fees:* weekdays £18.00 per round/day. Special rates for Societies over 12. *Eating facilities:* full catering facilities. *Visitors:* welcome weekdays, weekends with member only. *Society Meetings:* catered for Tuesdays and Thursdays, booked through Secretary. Professional: M.W. Passmore (0827 251478). Secretary: A.O. Rammell (0827 251139).

TAMWORTH. **Tamworth Municipal Golf Club,** Eagle Drive, Amington, Tamworth B77 4EG (Tamworth (0827) 53858). *Location:* off M42 Tamworth Junction - then signposted off B5000 Tamworth to Polesworth Road. Moorland course. 18 holes, 6083 yards. S.S.S. 72. Practice area. *Green Fees:* £2.75 9 holes, £4.25 18 holes. *Eating facilities:* bar and catering all week. *Visitors:* welcome without reservation. *Society Meetings:* advance bookings. Professional: Barry Jones (0827 53850). Secretary: Miss Kerry Udall (0827 57905).

UTTOXETER. **Uttoxeter Golf Club,** Wood Lane, Uttoxeter ST14 (Uttoxeter (0889) 564884). *Location:* approximately half a mile from Uttoxeter Racecourse. Undulating course with scenic views. 18 holes, 5700 yards, 5215 metres. S.S.S. 67. Practice net and putting area. *Green Fees:* £10.00 per day weekdays, £15.00 per day weekends and Bank Holidays. *Eating facilities:* by arrangement (not Mondays). *Visitors:* welcome, restrictions on major competition days. *Society Meetings:* welcome. Secretary: Mrs G. Davies (0889 565108/564352).

WOLSTANTON. **Wolstanton Golf Club,** Dimsdale Old Hall, Hassam Parade, Wolstanton, Newcastle (Newcastle (0782) 616995). *Location:* one mile north west of Newcastle, turn right (Dimsdale Parade), first right (Hassam Parade) then right again 75 yards. 18 holes, 5807 yards. S.S.S. 68. *Green Fees:* £14.00 per round/per day. *Eating facilities:* full catering service and bar. *Visitors:* welcome, must have golf passport. *Society Meetings:* catered for by arrangement. Secretary: D. Shelley.

Suffolk

ALDEBURGH. **Aldeburgh Golf Club,** Aldeburgh (Aldeburgh (0728) 452890). *Location:* one mile from town centre on A1094. Heathland course. 18 holes, 6366 yards. S.S.S. 71; also 9 holes. *Eating facilities:* lunches served daily at club. *Visitors:* welcome all year round with introduction from own club secretary. *Society Meetings:* by special arrangement. Professional: K.R. Preston. Secretary: R.C. Van de Velde.

BECCLES. **Wood Valley Beccles Golf Club,** The Common, Beccles (Beccles (0502) 712244). *Location:* on A146. Norwich 18 miles, Lowestoft 10 miles, Gt. Yarmouth 18 miles. Flat course. 9 holes, 5562 yards. S.S.S. 67. *Green Fees:* weekdays £7.00 (with member £6.00); weekends £8.00 (with member £7.00). Must play with member Sundays and Bank Holidays. *Eating facilities:* light refreshments and bar; other meals if ordered previous day. *Visitors:* welcome, must play with member on Sundays and Bank Holidays. *Society Meetings:* catered for (not Sundays or Bank Holidays). Professional: K. Allen (0502 712244). Secretary: Mrs L.W. Allen (0502 712479).

BUNGAY. **Bungay and Waveney Valley Golf Club,** Outney Common, Bungay NR35 1DS (Bungay (0986) 2337). *Location:* a quarter mile from town centre and A143. Flat, links-type course. 18 holes, 5950 yards. S.S.S. 68. *Green Fees:* £15.00 per day. *Eating facilities:* available. *Visitors:* welcome weekdays, weekends with member only. *Society Meetings:* by arrangement with Secretary. Professional: N. Whyte (0986 2337). Secretary: W.J. Stevens (0986 2329).

BURY ST. EDMUNDS. **Bury St. Edmunds Golf Club,** Tuthill, Fornham All Saints, Bury St. Edmunds IP28 6LG (0284 755977). *Location:* two miles from Bury St. Edmunds on A45 towards Newmarket, leave A45 at roundabout following A1106, 400 yards. 18 holes, 6615 yards. S.S.S. 72. *Green Fees:* £15.00 weekdays, weekends only with member. *Eating facilities:* lunches and snacks (dinner by arrangement). *Visitors:* welcome, except weekends. *Society Meetings:* catered for. Professional: Mark Jillings (0284 755978). Secretary: C. Preece (0284 755979).

BURY ST. EDMUNDS. **Flempton Golf Club,** Flempton, Bury St. Edmunds IP28 6EQ (Culford (028484) 291). *Location:* follow A1101 from Bury St. Edmunds towards Mildenhall for about four miles, course on right. 9 holes, 6056 yards. S.S.S. 69. *Green Fees:* weekdays £15.00 per round of 18 holes, £20.00 per day, weekends only with member. *Eating facilities:* by arrangement. *Visitors:* not weekends or Bank Holidays. Must produce Handicap Certificate. Professional: A. Currie (028484 8817). Secretary: P.H. Nunn.

BURY ST. EDMUNDS. **Fornham Park Golf Club,** St. John's Hill Plantation, Fornham St Genevieve, Bury St. Edmunds (0284 706777). *Location:* two miles from Bury St. Edmunds, A1101 to Mildenhall through village of Fornham St. Genevieve. Flat parkland, interesting water hazards. 18 holes, 6058 yards. Par 71. S.S.S. 70. Ample sized practice ground. *Green Fees:* £15.00 weekdays, £20.00 weekends and Bank Holidays. Reduction weekday if playing with a member. *Eating facilities:* restaurant and bars. *Visitors:* welcome during the week; after 10.30am; weekends welcome with a reservation. *Society Meetings:* welcome by prior arrangement. Professional: Sean Clark (0284 706777). Manager: Mrs Janet Matthews.

BURY ST. EDMUNDS. **Royal Worlington and New-market Golf Clubs,** Worlington, Bury St. Edmunds (Mildenhall (0638) 712216). *Green Fees:* information not provided. *Eating facilities:* lunch and tea available if ordered. *Visitors:* welcome except weekends. *Society Meetings:* catered for. Secretary: W.N. White. Professional: M. Hawkins.

FELIXSTOWE. **Felixstowe Ferry Golf Club,** Ferry Road, Felixstowe (0394 283060). *Location:* near Felixstowe Ferry, one mile north of Felixstowe. Links course. 18 holes, 6308 yards. S.S.S. 70. Practice area. *Green Fees:* £15.00 per day, weekends and Bank Holidays £18.00. *Eating facilities:* full lunchtime service daily, other meals by arrangement. *Visitors:* welcome, but advisable to check first. Two holiday flats available; each accommodates four to six persons, self catering, free golf included in charges. *Society Meetings:* catered for weekdays. Professional: Ian MacPherson (0394 283975). Secretary: Ian H. Kimber (0394 286834).

FRAMLINGHAM. Cretingham Golf Club, Grove Farm, Cretingham, Woodbridge IP13 7BA (Earl Soham (072882) 275). *Location:* turn off A1120 at Earl Soham, nearest town Framlingham. Parkland. 9 holes, 1955 yards. S.S.S. 30. *Green Fees:* weekdays £5.00, weekends £7.00 (for 18 holes). *Eating facilities:* hot drinks and snacks available. *Visitors:* welcome, no restrictions. Other sports facilities available. *Society Meetings:* welcome. Secretary: J. Austin.

HAVERHILL. Haverhill Golf Club Ltd, Coupals Road, Haverhill CB9 7UW (Haverhill (0440) 61951). *Location:* A604 Sturmer road turn into Chalkestone Way, near railway viaduct, right into Coupals Road. Club is one mile on right. Undulating parkland with river features. 9 holes, 5707 yards. S.S.S. 68. Practice ground. *Green Fees:* weekdays £12.00, weekends and Bank Holidays £17.00. *Eating facilities:* bar. *Visitors:* welcome at all times except when first tee booked for matches and societies. *Society Meetings:* by arrangement with Secretary. Professional: Mr S.P. Mayfield (0440 712628). Secretary: Mrs J. Webster (0440 61951).

IPSWICH. Ipswich Golf Club, Purdis Heath, Bucklesham Road, Ipswich IP3 8UQ (Ipswich (0473) 728941). *Location:* three miles east of Ipswich on Bucklesham Road, A12 and A45. Heathland. 18 holes, 6405 yards. S.S.S. 71. 9 holes, 1930 yards. S.S.S. 59. *Green Fees:* 18 hole course £20.00 weekdays, £25.00 weekends per day. 9 hole course £6.50 per day, £8.00 weekends and Bank Holidays. *Eating facilities:* full catering facilities available for visitors to 18 hole course only. *Visitors:* by prior arrangement for 18 hole course, and must produce Handicap Certificate or letter of introduction. No restriction for 9 hole course. *Society Meetings:* by special reservation only and on Society terms. Professional: S.J. Whymark (0473 724017). Secretary: A.E. Howell (0473 728941)

IPSWICH. Rushmere Golf Club, Rushmere Heath, Woodbridge Road, Ipswich IP4 5QQ (Ipswich (0473) 727109). *Location:* off A12 north from Ipswich, 300 yards signposted. Heathland course. 18 holes, 6287 yards. S.S.S. 70. Practice facilities. *Green Fees:* weekdays round £10.00, day £15.00; weekends £15.00. *Eating facilities:* full catering available. *Visitors:*

welcome except 4.30 – 5.30pm, weekends after 2.30pm. *Society Meetings:* welcome. Professional: N.T.J. McNeill (0473 728076). Secretary: R.W. Whiting (0473 725648).

LOWESTOFT. Rookery Park Golf Club, Beccles Road, Carlton Colville, Lowestoft (Lowestoft (0502) 574009). *Location:* west of Lowestoft on A146. Flat parkland. 18 holes, 6898 yards, S.S.S. 72. 9 holes par 3 course. Practice ground. *Green Fees:* weekdays £9.00, £6.00 with member; weekends £12.00, £7.00 with member. *Eating facilities:* full catering facilities 11.00am to 11.00pm except Mondays, two bars. *Visitors:* welcome if members of recognised golf club; not before 11.00am Sundays or Bank Holidays. *Society Meetings:* welcome. Professional: M. Elsworthy (0502 515103). Secretary: J. Almond (0502 560380).

NEWMARKET. Links Golf Club, Cambridge Road, Newmarket CB8 0TE (Newmarket (0638) 662708). *Location:* one and a half miles south of Newmarket High Street, opposite racecourse. Relatively flat parkland. 18 holes, 6378 yards. S.S.S. 71. Two practice grounds. *Green Fees:* £17.50 weekdays, £24.00 weekends and Bank Holidays. *Eating facilities:* full service available daily. *Visitors:* Current Handicap Certificate required, weekdays/weekends except for members of organised golf societies. Not before 11.30am Sunday unless member's guest. *Society Meetings:* mid-week only by arrangement. Professional: D. Thomson (0638 662395). Secretary: Mrs T. MacGregor (0638 663000).

SOUTHWOLD. Southwold Golf Club, The Common, Southwold (Southwold (0502) 723234). *Location:* from A12 Blythburgh turn off on A1095 to Southwold. Flat common land with sea views. 9 holes, 6001 yards. S.S.S. 69. *Green Fees:* £10.00 weekdays, £15.00 weekends. *Eating facilities:* bar and dining-room. *Visitors:* welcome, phone for availability. *Society Meetings:* welcome, subject to availability. Professional: B.G. Allen (0502 723790). Secretary: Ivan G. Guy (0502 723248).

STOWMARKET. Stowmarket Golf Club Ltd, Lower Road, Onehouse, Stowmarket IP14 3DA (Rattlesden (04493) 473). *Location:* on B1508 from Stowmarket to Onehouse. Parkland. 18 holes, 6101 yards. S.S.S. 69. *Green Fees:* weekdays £12.00 per round, £15.00 per day; weekends £18.00 per round, £25.00 per day.

Eating facilities: lunches except Monday and Tuesday, snacks all week. *Visitors:* welcome, avoid Wednesdays. Handicap Certificate required at weekends. *Society Meetings:* not Monday or Tuesday. Professional: C. S. Aldred (04493 392). Secretary: P.W. Rumball (04493 473).

SUDBURY. **Newton Green Golf Club,** Newton Green, Sudbury (Sudbury (0787) 77501). *Location:* on A134 east of Sudbury. 9 holes, 5488 yards, 5022 metres. S.S.S. 67. *Green Fees:* £10.00 weekdays, weekends only with member. *Eating facilities:* available. *Visitors:* welcome Monday to Friday (except Tuesday). *Society Meetings:* not more than 12 persons. Professional: K. Lovelock (0787 210910). Secretary: G. Bright (0787 71119).

THORPENESS. **Thorpeness Golf Club Hotel,** Thorpeness (Aldeburgh (0728-45) 2176). *Location:* leave A12 at Saxmundham, on to B119 then B1353. 18 holes, 6208 yards. S.S.S. 70. *Green Fees:* on application. *Visitors:* welcome without reservation. Accommodation available – 22 double bedrooms. *Society Meetings:* catered for. Professional: T. Pennock. Secretary: N. Griffin.

WOODBRIDGE. **Waldringham Heath Golf Club,** Newbourne Road, Waldringham, Woodbridge IP12 4PT (0473 36 768). *Location:* three miles north east of Ipswich off old A12. Heathland course – easy walking. 18 holes, 5873 yards. S.S.S. 68. Limited practice area. *Green Fees:* £9.00 per round, £13.00 per day weekdays; £11.00 per round, £14.00 per day weekends. Special rates available by arrangement. *Eating facilities:* full service. *Visitors:* welcome weekdays, weekends after 10.30am. *Society Meetings:* welcome weekdays by arrangement. Professional: A. Dobson. Secretary: L.J. McWade.

WOODBRIDGE. **Woodbridge Golf Club,** Bromeswell Heath, Woodbridge IP12 2PF (Woodbridge (03943) 3212). *Location:* leave A12 at Melton Roundabout. After traffic lights, follow A1152 over level crossing, fork left at roundabout. Club is 400 yards on right. Heathland. 18 or 9 holes. Large practice ground. *Green Fees:* £18.00 per round and £25.00 per day weekdays. *Eating facilities:* main bar, casual bar and restuarant. *Visitors:* not before 9.30am, not at weekends. No 4 balls. Handicap Certificates mandatory. Telephone call advisable. *Society Meetings:* by prior arrangement, maximum number 36. Professional: L.A. Jones (03943 3213). Secretary: Capt L.A. Harpum RN (03943 2038).

Surrey

BAGSHOT. **Pennyhill Park Country Club,** London Road, Bagshot GU19 5ET (0276 71774). *Location:* south west. Exit 3 of M3, about 27 miles from London, 13 miles from Heathrow. Parkland course. 9 holes, 2000 yards. *Green Fees:* £20.00. *Eating facilities:* available on hotel premises. *Visitors:* welcome with members/hotel guests and at the discretion of the management. A 120 acre estate with parkland and lake. 54 bedroom hotel, facilities include swimming pool, tennis courts, clay shooting, fishing, sauna and solarium. Green fees included in accommodation rates. *Society Meetings:* on application to the Sales Office. Secretary/Manager: Mr Graham Vallence.

BANSTEAD. **Cuddington (Banstead) Golf Club Ltd,** Banstead Road, Banstead SM7 1RD (01-393 0952). *Location:* 200 yards from Banstead Railway Station. 18 holes, 6282 yards, 5741 metres. S.S.S. 70. *Green Fees:* Information not provided. *Eating facilities:* lunches by prior arrangment. *Visitors:* welcome with reservation. *Society Meetings:* catered for on Thursdays. Professional: R. Gardner D.C.M. Secretary: D. M. Scott.

BROOKWOOD. **West Hill Golf Club,** Brookwood GU24 0BH (Brookwood (04867) 2110). *Location:* M3, Junction 3, A332 entrance adjacent railway bridge Brookwood. Heathland. 18 holes, 6368 yards. S.S.S. 70. Practice range and net. *Green Fees:* weekdays £25.00 per round, £35.00 per day, weekends £9.00 with member only. *Eating facilities:* bar snacks available, meals including dinner by prior arrangement. *Visitors:* by arrangement through the Professional. *Society Meetings:* catered for by arrangement. Professional: John Clements (04867 3172). Secretary: W.D. Leighton (04867 4365).

CAMBERLEY. **Camberley Heath Golf Club,** Golf Drive, Portsmouth Road, Camberley GU15 1JG (0276 23258). *Location:* adjacent to Ravenswood roundabout on the A325. Heathland and pine, designed by Harry Colt – his best. 18 holes, 6402 yards, 5888 metres. S.S.S. 71. Practice ground. *Green Fees:* weekdays £17.00 per round, Saturdays accompanied by a member, £22.00 per round. *Eating facilities:* two restaurants and three bars. *Visitors:* no visitors, guests of members and Societies only. *Society Meetings:* welcome by prior arrangement. Professional: Gary Smith (0276 27905). General Manager: S. Heron (0276 23258).

CARSHALTON. **Oaks Sports Centre Ltd,** Woodmansterne Road, Carshalton SM5 4AN (081-643 8363). *Location:* on the B2032 past Carshalton Beeches Station, Oaks Sports Centre signposted north of A2022, half way between A217 and A237. Meadowland course. 18 holes, 5975 yards. S.S.S 69. 9 holes, 1590 yards. Par 29. 18 bay golf range. *Green Fees:*

£6.00 18 hole, £3.00 9 hole weekdays; £8.50 18 hole, £4.00 9 hole weekends. *Eating facilities:* licensed bars, hot food and sandwiches throughout the day. *Visitors:* public course – everybody welcome. *Society Meetings:* by arrangement. Professional: Mr G.D. Horley. Secretary: Mr J. Bremer.

CHERTSEY. **Barrow Hill Golf Club,** Longcross, Chertsey. *Location:* four miles west of Chertsey. 18 holes, 3090 yards. S.S.S. 53. *Visitors:* with a member. Secretary: R.W. Routley.

CHERTSEY. **Laleham Golf Club,** Laleham Reach, Mixnams Lane, Chertsey KT16 8RP (Chertsey (0932) 564211). *Location:* M25 take directions to Thorpe Park, entrance opposite through Penton Park. Parkland course. 18 holes, 6203 yards. S.S.S. 70. *Green Fees:* weekdays £20.00 per round or day; weekends with member only. *Eating facilities:* lunches and snacks available. *Visitors:* welcome weekdays only. *Society Meetings:* catered for Mondays to Wednesdays. Professional: T. Whitton (0932 562877). Secretary: M.A. Ford (0932 564211).

CHESSINGTON. **Chessington Golf Club,** Garrison Lane, Chessington KT9 2LW (081-391 0948). *Location:* off A243, 500 yards from Chessington World of Adventure. Opposite Chessington South Station, Junction 9 M25. Flat course. 9 holes, 1530 yards, 1401 metres. S.S.S. 28. Covered floodlit driving range. Green fees: weekdays £2.75, weekends and Bank Holidays £3.30 (for 9 holes). Reductions for Juniors and Senior Citizens. *Eating facilities:* public bar and food available. *Visitors:* welcome, must book for weekend mornings. Facilities open to public 8 am until 10 pm seven days a week. *Society Meetings:* welcome. Professional: Bruce Cuff (081-331 0948). Secretary: Tony Maxted (081-974 1705).

CHESSINGTON. **Surbiton Golf Club,** Woodstock Lane, Chessington KT9 1UG (081-398 3101). *Location:* two miles east of Esher, off A3 at Ace of Spades roundabout. 18 holes, 6211 yards. S.S.S. 70. *Green Fees:* £24.00 per round, £36.00 per day. *Eating facilities:* snacks and lunches to order daily. *Visitors:* welcome with reservation. *Society Meetings:* catered for. Professional: Paul Milton. Secretary: G. Keith MBE.

CHIDDINGFOLD. **Shillinglee Park Golf Club,** Chiddingfold, Godalming GU8 4TA (Haslemere (0428) 53237). FAX: 0428 4391. *Location:* leave A3 at Milford, A283 to Chiddingfold, turn left at the Green, continue for two miles, turn right. Parkland. 9 holes, 2500 yards. S.S.S. 63. 6 hole pitch and putt course, ideal for learners. Well equipped Pro Shop. *Green Fees:* weekdays £7.00 for 9 holes, £14.00 for 18; weekends £7.50 for 9 holes, £15.00 for 18 holes. Daily rate, plus Senior Citizens' and Junior rates. *Eating* *facilities:* excellent menu from snacks to à la carte. *Visitors:* welcome at all times, advisable to book. Instruction available. *Society Meetings:* always welcome. Professional: Roger Mace. Secretary: Trudy Mace.

CHIPSTEAD. **Chipstead Golf Club Ltd,** How Lane, Chipstead (Downland (0737) 555781). *Location:* by Chipstead Station (Tattenham Corner Line). 18 holes, 5454 yards, 4351 metres. S.S.S. 66. *Green Fees:* £20.00 before 2.00pm, £15.00 after 2.00pm. *Eating facilities:* by arrangement. *Visitors:* welcome with reservation, weekends with member. *Society Meetings:* catered for Thursdays. Professional: Gary Torbett. Secretary: S. Spencer-Skeen.

COBHAM. **Silvermere Golf and Leisure Complex.** Redhill Road, Cobham (Cobham (0932) 66007). Individual bookings (0932) 67275). Open for the public seven days a week. Administration enquiries for Society bookings and company days (Cobham (0932) 66007). *Location:* from junction 10, M25 take B366 to Byfleet, half a mile on right. From London take Cobham turn-off then A245 to Byfleet, half a mile on left into Redhill Road. London 25 minutes, Heathrow 15 minutes, Gatwick 25 minutes. Seven holes tight heathland, 10 holes open parkland, one hole (17th) completely over water. 18 holes, 6333 yards. S.S.S. 71. 34 bay floodlit (till 10.00pm) driving range. *Green Fees:* weekdays £10.00, weekends £14.00 bookable by telephone. Members only Saturday/Sunday mornings. Professional's Golf Superstore open seven days till 10.00pm. All top named brands stocked. Clubs may be tried on range prior to purchase. *Eating facilities:* full service from 7.00am – breakfast, lunch, snacks and dinner; bar facilities seven days a week. *Societies:* welcome; £34.50 for full day including dinner. All enquiries to Secretary. Professional: Doug McClelland PGA (0932 67275). Secretary: Mrs Pauline Devereux (0932 66007).

COULSDON. **Coulsdon Court Golf Course,** Coulsdon Road, Coulsdon (081-668 0414). *Location:* off A23 London to Brighton road. Parkland. 18 holes, 6030 yards. S.S.S. 68. *Green Fees:* information not available. *Eating facilities:* full catering and bar facilities. *Visitors:* welcome. *Society Meetings:* welcome, full banquet and conference facilities. Professional: Colin Staff (081-660 6083). General Manager: Mr Thresh.

COULSDON. **Woodcote Park Golf Club Ltd,** Bridle Way, Meadow Hill (off Smithambottom Lane), Coulsdon (081-660 0176). *Location:* south of Croydon, on B2030. 18 holes, 6624 yards. S.S.S. 71. *Green Fees:* information not available. *Eating facilities:* meals by arrangement, bar snacks. *Visitors:* welcome with reservation. *Society Meetings:* up to 60 catered for, by arrangement. Professional: Ian Martin. Secretary: Philip Rothwell (081-668 2788).

CRANLEIGH. **Fernfell Golf and Country Club,** Barhatch Lane, Cranleigh GU6 7NG (Guildford (0483) 276626). *Location:* Guildford A281 Horsham take Cranleigh turn-off. Part wooded parkland course. 18 holes, 5236 yards. S.S.S. 66. *Green Fees:* £12.00 per round, £15.00 per day weekdays. *Eating facilities:* bar, coffee shop. Banqueting facilities available. *Visitors:* welcome weekdays only. Other sports facilities available (tennis). *Society Meetings:* welcome weekdays. Professional: Trevor Longmuir (0483 277188). Secretary: Gail Peterson (0483 276626).

CROYDON. **Addington Court Golf Courses,** Featherbed Lane, Addington, Croydon CR0 9AA (081-657 0271). *Location:* two miles east of Croydon. Leave B281 at Addington Village. Undulating. Four courses – Old Championship 5577 yards, S.S.S. 67, New Falconwood 5513 yards, S.S.S. 66. Lower 9 hole course 1812 yards, S.S.S. 62. 18 hole, Par 3 course. *Green Fees:* £4.50 – £7.90. *Eating facilities:* full range available. *Visitors:* golfers and non-golfers welcome. *Society Meetings:* catered for weekdays only. Professional/ Managing Director: G.A. Cotton.

CROYDON. **Addington Palace Golf Club,** Gravel Hill, Addington, Croydon CR0 5BB (081-654 3061). *Location:* 2 miles East Croydon Station. 18 holes, 6262 yards. S.S.S. 71. *Visitors:* weekdays £25.00, weekends and Bank Holidays with a member. Secretary: Mr J. Robinson. Professional: J. M. Pilkington.

CROYDON. **Croham Hurst Golf Club,** Croham Road, South Croydon CR2 7HJ (081-657 2075). *Location:* one mile from South Croydon Station, on road to Selsdon. 18 holes, 6274 yards. S.S.S. 70. *Green Fees:* weekdays £25.00 per round/day (subject to increase). Weekends and Bank Holidays as members' guests only. *Eating facilities:* lunches, teas, snacks. *Visitors:* welcome without reservation on weekdays. *Society Meetings:* catered for booked one year ahead. Professional: E. Stillwell (081-657 7705).

Golf

On a 200 acre country estate

Our 6,402 yard Championship golf course is just the beginning of the perfect, relaxing break from the daily routine.

The Selsdon Park Hotel offers guests enjoying a golfing holiday, or weekend, an unparalleled opportunity to play – even after the round is completed.

The Tropical Leisure Complex, for example, has a sauna, jacuzzi, gymnasium, steam room, solarium and swimming pool.

Selsdon Park also offers fine cuisine in the surroundings you'd expect of a 170 bedroom, four star hotel. Plus excellent facilities for tennis, squash, croquet, putting, boules, jogging and snooker.

All of which helps make Selsdon Park Hotel the perfect place to play golf. Reserve now.

Selsdon Park is 30 minutes from London and just 10 minutes from junction 6 of the M25.

SELSDON PARK HOTEL

Sanderstead, South Croydon, Surrey CR2 8YA Tel: 081-657 8811 Fax: 081-651 6171 Telex: 945003

CROYDON. **Selsdon Park Hotel Golf Course,** Sanderstead, South Croydon, Surrey CR2 8YA (081-657 8811). *Location:* three miles south of Croydon on A2022 Purley-West Wickham road. Parkland course, designed by J.H. Taylor. 18 holes, 6402 yards, 5854 metres. S.S.S. 71. Practice ground. *Green Fees:* weekdays £20.00 (18), £30.00 (36); Saturdays £25.00, Sundays and Bank Holidays £30.00. Reduced rates if starting after 4.00pm weekends, 2.00pm winter. Free to resident guests with certain restrictions. *Eating facilities:* hotel bars, restaurant and grill. *Visitors:* welcome all week with pre-bookable tee-off times, some times reserved for hotel guests. *Society Meetings:* welcome by prior arrangement with proprietor. P.G.A. Professionals: Iain Naylor, Tom O'Keefe (081-657 4129). Golf Reservations: (081-657 8811 extension 652).

CROYDON. **Shirley Park Golf Club Ltd,** 194 Addiscombe Road, Croydon CR0 7LB (081-654 3385). *Location:* on A232 one mile from East Croydon Station. Parkland. 18 holes, 6210 yards. S.S.S. 70. Practice area. *Green Fees:* £17.50 weekdays. *Eating facilities:* breakfast/snack lunch/dinner. *Visitors:* welcome Monday to Friday, not at weekends unless with a member. Snooker room. *Society Meetings:* catered for Mondays, Tuesdays, Thursdays and Fridays. Professional: Hogan Stott (081-654 8767). Secretary: Andrew Baird (081-654 1143).

DORKING. **Betchworth Park Golf Club (Dorking) Ltd,** Reigate Road, Dorking (Dorking (0306) 882052). *Location:* on A25 one mile east of Dorking on Reigate Road. Parkland course. 18 holes, 6266 yards. S.S.S. 70. *Green Fees:* information not provided. *Eating facilities:* lunches to order. *Visitors:* welcome with reservation, Handicap Certificate required. *Society Meetings:* Monday, Thursday, catered for lunch or dinner. Professional: Alex King. Secretary: D. A. S. Bradney.

DORKING. **Dorking Golf Club,** Chart Park, Dorking (Dorking (0306) 886917). *Location:* on A24 half-a-mile south of junction with A25. Parkland/downland. 9 holes, alternative tees second 9, 5106 yards. S.S.S. 65. *Green Fees:* £14.00 per round. *Eating facilities:* full catering except Mondays. *Visitors:* weekdays only without reservation. *Society Meetings:* catered for up to 24, over this number by arrangement. Professional: P. Napier. Secretary: R. Payne.

DORKING. **Gatton Manor Hotel and Golf Club,** Ockley, Near Dorking RH5 5PQ (Oakwood Hill (030-679 555/6). *Location:* one-and-a-half miles off A29 at Ockley, nine miles south of Dorking, midway between London and the coast. Undulating, wooded course with scenic water holes. 18 holes, 6903 yards. S.S.S. 72. Practice facilities. *Green Fees:* weekdays: £20.00 per day, £12.00 per round (after 4.00pm £7.00). Weekends: £34.00 per day, £17.00 per round (after 4.00pm £9.00). *Eating facilities:* bar and snacks. *Visitors:* welcome every day except Sunday until after 12 noon. Conference and Hotel facilities available. *Society Meetings:* catered for Monday to Friday. Professional: R. Sargent (030-679 557). Managing Director: D.G. Heath.

EAST HORSLEY. **Drift Golf Club,** The Drift, Off Forest Road, East Horsley (East Horsley (04865) 4641). *Location:* the club is located just off the Drift Road which runs between Ockham Road and Forest Road, East Horsley. 18 holes, 6414 yards. S.S.S. 71. *Green Fees:* information not provided. *Eating facilities:* restaurant/buffet service. *Visitors:* welcome Monday to Friday. *Society Meetings:* catered for. Professional: Joe Hagan. Secretary: Charles Rose.

EFFINGHAM. **Effingham Golf Club,** Guildford Road, Effingham KT24 5PZ (0372 52203). *Location:* A246 between Guildford and Leatherhead. Downland course with magnificent views towards London. 18 holes, 6488 yards. S.S.S. 71. Large practice ground. *Green Fees:* on application. *Eating facilities:* full bar and restaurant service all week. *Visitors:* welcome with reservation Monday-Friday. *Society Meetings:* Wednesdays, Thursdays, Fridays catered for. Professional: S. Hoatson (0372 52606). Secretary: Lt Col (Rtd) S.C. Manning OBE (0372 52204).

EPSOM. **Epsom Golf Club,** Longdown Lane South, Epsom KT17 4JR (Epsom (0372) 723363). *Location:* off A240 into B288, 200 yards north of Epsom Downs Station. Downland. 18 holes, 5118 yards. S.S.S. 65. Practice ground and practice putting green. *Green Fees:* £10.00 weekdays, £12.50 weekends. *Eating facilities:* bar snacks/meals. *Visitors:* welcome, but after 12 noon on Tuesdays, and from 12 noon weekends and Bank Holidays. Advisable to phone in advance at all times. *Society Meetings:* Wednesdays or Fridays, by prior arrangement only. Professional: R. Wynn (0372 741867). Secretary: K.H. Watson (0372 721666).

EPSOM. **R.A.C. Country Club,** Wilmerhatch Lane, Woodcote Park, Epsom KT18 7EW (0372 276311, Fax 0372 276117). *Location:* one mile from Epsom Station. 2 courses by 18 holes. S.S.S. Old course 72. Coronation course 67. *Green Fees:* information not provided. *Eating facilities:* full catering. *Visitors:* welcome with members only. *Society Meetings:* catered for by arrangement if sponsored by a member. Professional: Peter Butler (0372 276311 extension 248). Estate and Sports Manager: Keith Symons (0372 273091).

ESHER. **Moore Place Golf Club,** Portsmouth Road, Esher KT10 9LN (0372 63533). *Location:* Portsmouth Road through Cobham to A3 and M25. Parkland course with featured trees. 9 holes, 3512 yards. S.S.S. 58. Practice ground. *Green Fees:* weekdays £7.00, weekends £9.00 (18 holes). *Eating facilities:* two restaurants and bar. *Visitors:* unrestricted. Professional: David Allen (0372 63533). Secretary: J. Darby (0932 220575).

ESHER. **Sandown Park Golf Club,** More Lane, Esher KT10 8AN (Esher (0372) 63340). 9 holes, 5658 yards. S.S.S. 67. Par 70 (18 holes). 9-hole par 3; 9-hole Pitch and putt. Floodlit 33-bay driving range, open until 10.30 p.m. *Eating facilities:* lunches served daily, bar snacks available evenings. Bar open normal bar hours. *Visitors:* unrestricted (public course). *Green Fees:* New Course: non-members £3.00 weekdays, £4.50 weekends and Bank Holidays. Members £2.40

165

weekdays, £3.50 weekends and Bank Holidays. Par 3 £2.40 weekdays, £3.00 weekends and Bank Holidays. Pitch and putt £1.50. Membership per year £55.00 plus joining fee of £5.00; Senior Citizens and Juniors £27.50 plus £5.00 joining fee. Lessons £12 per half hour, book of six half hour lessons £60. Operations Manager: P. Barrieball. Professional: Neil Bedward.

ESHER. **Thames Ditton and Esher Golf Club,** Marquis of Granby, Portsmouth Road, Esher (081-398 1551). 9 holes played twice from different tees. 5190 yards. S.S.S. 65. *Green Fees:* £8.00 weekdays, £10.00 weekends. *Eating facilities:* Breakfast-lunches, evening meals served on advance bookings by arrangement. *Society Meetings:* welcome except mornings on Sundays. Professional: R. Hutton. Secretary: B.A.J. Chandler.

FARNHAM. **Farnham Golf Club Ltd,** The Sands, Farnham GU10 1PX (Runfold (02518) 3163). *Location:* off A31 Crooksbury Road, Near "Jolly Farmer", signposted. Mixture of wooded parkland and heathland. 18 holes, 6313 yards. S.S.S. 70. Putting green and practice ground. *Green Fees:* £20.00 round, £23.50 day. Playing with member £6.50 per day. *Eating facilities:* three bars and diningroom, full high standard catering. *Visitors:* welcome if introduced by member and must have a Handicap Certificate. *Society Meetings:* groups up to 60 catered for, Wednesdays and Thursdays preferred. Must have Handicap Certificate. Professional: Grahame Cowlishaw (02518 2198). Secretary: James Pevalin (02518 2109).

FARNHAM. **Hankley Common Golf Club,** Tilford Road, Tilford, Farnham GU10 2DD (Frensham (025 125) 3145). *Location:* off A3, right at lights at Hindhead. Off A31 (Farnham by-pass) left at lights, three miles beyond level crossing on A287. Heathland, dry and sandy links-type course. 18 holes, 6418 yards. S.S.S. 71. Practice ground. *Green Fees:* weekdays £20.00 per round, £27.50 per day; weekends £27.50 after 2pm. *Eating facilities:* full range available, restaurant and two bars. *Visitors:* Mondays to Fridays, weekends after 2pm only. Handicap Certificate required. *Society Meetings:* catered for on Tuesdays and Wednesdays. Professional: Will Brogden (025125 3761). Secretary: Mr J.K.A. O'Brien (025125 2493).

GODALMING. **West Surrey Golf Club,** Enton Green, Godalming GU8 5AF (Godalming (04868) 21275). *Location:* off the A3 half mile past Milford Station/crossing. Wooded parkland. 18 holes, 6247 yards, 5711 metres. S.S.S. 70. *Green Fees:* £20.00 weekdays, £35.00 weekends. *Eating facilities:* bar, diningroom. *Visitors:* welcome, must be members of recognised golf clubs and have current Handicaps. *Society Meetings:* catered for by prior arrangement. Professional: J. Hoskison (04868 7278). Secretary: R.S. Fanshawe (04868 21275).

GUILDFORD. **Bramley Golf Club,** Bramley, Near Guildford GU5 0AL. *Location:* three miles south of Guildford on the Horsham road, A281. Parkland. 18 holes, 5966 yards. S.S.S. 68. Practice area, golf range. *Green Fees:* round £17.50, day £22.00; weekends with member only, £7.50. *Eating facilities:* lunches, snacks, evening meals. *Visitors:* welcome Monday to Friday. *Society Meetings:* by prior arrangement with Secretary.

Professional: Gary Peddie (0483 893685). Secretary: Mrs M. Lambert (0483 892696).

GUILDFORD. **Guildford Golf Club,** High Path Road, Merrow, Guildford (Guildford (0483) 63941). Steward: (0483 31842). *Location:* from Guildford take Epsom Road (A246) turn right at the third set of traffic lights. 18 holes, 6080 yards. S.S.S. 70. *Green Fees:* Information not provided. *Eating facilities:* snacks and restaurant service. *Visitors:* welcome weekdays, with member weekends. *Society Meetings:* catered for Monday to Friday. Professional: P. G. Hollington (0483 66765). Secretary: Harry Warburton (0483 63941).

GUILDFORD. **Puttenham Golf Club,** Guildford GU3 1AP (Guildford (0483) 810498). *Location:* half-way between Farnham and Guildford, 600 yards south of Hog's Back (A31). Wooded/heathland course. 18 holes, 6220 yards. S.S.S. 70. *Green Fees:* on application. *Visitors:* welcome weekdays only by prior arrangement. (weekends playing with a member). Handicap Certificate required. *Society Meetings:* catered for Wednesdays and Thursdays. Secretary and Professional: Gary Simmons.

HINDHEAD. **Hindhead Golf Club,** Churt Road, Hindhead GU26 6HX (Hindhead (0428) 604614). *Location:* one and a half miles north of Hindhead on A287 to Farnham. Heathland, wooded and fairly hilly course. 18 holes, 6349 yards, 5806 metres. S.S.S. 70. *Green Fees:* £34.00 weekends and Bank Holidays, £30.00 weekdays. *Eating facilities:* restaurant, snack bar, summer bar and members bar. *Visitors:* welcome with Handicap Certificate, weekends by appointment. *Society Meetings:* Wednesdays and Thursdays only. Professional: Neil Ogilvy (0428 604458). Manager: M.L. Brown.

KINGSTON-UPON-THAMES. **Coombe Hill Golf Club,** Golf Club Drive, Kingston Hill, Kingston-upon-Thames (081-942 2284/5). *Location:* leave A3 on Coombe Lane west A238 towards Kingston. Club one mile on right. 18 holes, 6286 yards. S.S.S. 71. *Green Fees:* weekdays only £45.00. *Eating facilities:* lunches daily. *Society Meetings:* limited. Professional: Craig De Foy. Secretary: A.L. Foster.

KINGSTON-UPON-THAMES. **Coombe Wood Golf Club,** George Road, Kingston KT2 7NS (081-942 3828). *Location:* on A307. Wooded course. 18 holes, 5210 yards, 4764 metres. S.S.S. 66. *Green Fees:* weekdays £25.00, weekends with member only. *Eating facilities:* catering except Mondays and Tuesdays. *Visitors:* welcome Wednesdays to Fridays. *Society Meetings:* by arrangement Wednesday to Friday. Professional: D. Butler (081-942 6764). Secretary: T. Duncan (081-942 0388).

KINGSWOOD. **Kingswood Golf Club,** Sandy Lane, Kingswood KT20 6NE (Mogador (0737) 832188). *Location:* five miles south of Sutton just off A217. 18 holes, 6855 yards. S.S.S. 73. Large practice area. *Green Fees:* weekdays £25.00, weekends £30.00. *Eating facilities:* full range available. *Visitors:* welcome, not before 12 noon weekends. *Society Meetings:* catered for. Professional: R. Blackie (0737 832334). Administrator: M.A. Fletcher (0737 832188).

LEATHERHEAD. Leatherhead Golf Club, Kingston Road, Leatherhead (Oxshott (037 284) 3966). *Location:* off Leatherhead section (Junction 9) of M25, onto A243 to Kingston. Parkland. 18 holes, 6060 yards. S.S.S. 69. *Green Fees:* weekdays £27.50 one round, £32.50 two rounds; weekends £37.50 one round, £42.50 two rounds. *Eating facilities:* a la carte restaurant and full snack service available. *Visitors:* welcomed. *Society Meetings:* from 16 to 100 by reservation. Secretary: W.G. Betts.

LEATHERHEAD. Tyrrells Wood Golf Club Ltd, Leatherhead KT22 8QP (Leatherhead (0372) 376025). *Location:* south-east on A24 Leatherhead by-pass after A.A. caravan, one mile left to Headley, then 200 yards right into Tyrrells Wood Estate, one mile off Junction 9 on M25. Very hilly wooded course. 18 holes, 6219 yards. S.S.S. 70. Small practice ground. *Green Fees:* weekdays £25.00, weekends £34.00. *Eating facilities:* full catering and bar. *Visitors:* Handicap Certificates or proof of membership of a club required. No visitors Saturdays or Sunday mornings. *Society Meetings:* catered for by arrangement with Manager. Professional: Philip Taylor (0372 375200). Secretary: Mrs P. Humphries (0372 376025).

LINGFIELD. Lingfield Park Golf Club, Racecourse Road, Lingfield Park, Lingfield RH7 6PQ (0342 834602). *Location:* A22 turn off at Blindley Heath, six miles from M25 Junction 6. Parkland/wooded. 18 holes, 6500 yards. S.S.S. 72. Driving range. *Green Fees:* weekdays £18.00 per round £25.00 per day; weekends £30.00. *Eating facilities:* available. *Visitors:* welcome weekdays only. Horse racing. *Society Meetings:* catered for all week. Professional: Trevor Collingwood (0342 832659). Secretary: Colin Manktelow (0342 834602).

MITCHAM. Mitcham Golf Club, Carshalton Road, Mitcham Junction, Mitcham (081-648 1508). *Location:* off A217, off A23. Flat course. 18 holes, 5895 yards. S.S.S. 68. *Green Fees:* £7.00. *Eating facilities:* meals and snacks daily. *Visitors:* welcome with restriction at weekends, book via Professional. *Society Meetings:* catered for, book through Secretary. Professional: J.A. Godfrey (081-640 4280). Secretary: C.A. McGahan (081-640 4197).

NEW MALDEN. Malden Golf Club, Traps Lane, New Malden KY3 4RS (081-942 0654). *Location:* off Kingston by-pass (A3) at underpass through town, one mile beyond station. Parkland. 18 holes, 6201 yards, 5670 metres. S.S.S. 70. *Green Fees:* weekdays £21.00, weekends £35.00. *Eating facilities:* lunches served if ordered by 10.00am. *Visitors:* welcome without reservation weekdays. *Society Meetings:* catered for except Mondays and Tuesdays. Professional: George Howard (081-942 6009). Secretary: Mrs C.W. Penhale.

OTTERSHAW. Foxhills Country Club, Stonehill Road, Ottershaw KT16 0EL (Ottershaw (093 287) 2050). *Location:* 20 miles London, 10 miles London Heathrow off A320 Chertsey/Woking road behind St. Peter's church. 36 holes, two 18 hole courses. Chertsey 6880 yards, S.S.S. 73. Longcross 6747 yards, S.S.S. 72. Par 3 course. *Green Fees:* weekdays £35.00/ £45.00. *Eating facilities:* three restaurants, service 7 days a week. *Visitors:* welcome on weekdays only. Bedroom suites, tennis, squash, two pools and health club available. *Society Meetings:* catered for by arrangement. Professionals: Bernard Hunt and Malcolm Henbery. Golf Executive: Arthur Dupuy.

OXTED. Limpsfield Chart Golf Club, Westerham Road, Limpsfield, Oxted RH8 0SL (0883 713097). *Location:* on A25 between Westerham and Oxted. Heathland, fairly flat course. 9 holes – alternate tees for 18 holes, 5718 yards. S.S.S. 68 mens, 70 ladies. *Green Fees:* weekdays £15.00, weekends £18.00 with a member only. *Eating facilities:* by prior arrangement. *Visitors:* welcome weekdays except Thursday (Ladies Day) when only after 3.30pm. *Society Meetings:* catered for by prior arrangement. Secretary: W.G. Bannochie.

OXTED. Tandridge Golf Club, Oxted (Oxted (0833) 2273). *Location:* A25 between Godstone and Sevenoaks. 18 holes, 6260 yards. S.S.S. 70. *Green Fees:* information not provided. *Eating facilities:* lunch and tea every day. *Visitors:* welcome with reservation by letter or phone; must be organised into a society. *Society Meetings:* catered for booking two years ahead. Professional: A. Farquhar. Secretary: I.D. Wheater.

PIRBRIGHT. Goal Farm Golf Course, Golf Road, Pirbright GU24 0PZ (04867 3183). *Location:* between Woking and Guildford, off A322. Challenging, picturesque course. 9 holes, 1273 yards. S.S.S. 50. Practice net, putting green. *Green Fees:* weekdays £2.00, weekends £2.20. *Eating facilities:* restaurant and bar. *Visitors:* welcome, booking not required. Tees reserved for members Saturdays and Thursday mornings. *Society Meetings:* welcome by arrangement. Secretary: Bruce Tapsfield (09323 43868).

PURLEY. Purley Downs Golf Club, 106 Purley Downs Road, Purley CR2 0RB (01-657 8347). *Location:* three miles south of Croydon, turn east by Royal Oak Centre, first left Purley Downs Road. 18 holes, 6237 yards. S.S.S. 70. *Green Fees:* weekdays £20.00, Fridays £23.00; weekends £35.00. Visitors are not allowed to play at weekends unless with a Full Member of the club. *Eating facilities:* lunch and snacks daily. *Visitors:* no visitors Sunday mornings, must be accompanied by a full member of the club at weekends. Handicap Certificate required. *Society Meetings:* caterd for Mondays, Thursdays and Fridays. Professional: G. Wilson (01-651 0819). Secretary: Miss K.N.R. Pudner.

REDHILL. Redhill and Reigate Golf Club, Clarence Lodge, Pendleton Road, Redhill (Reigate (0737) 244626). *Location:* one mile south of Reigate between A23 and A25. Well wooded course. 18 holes, 5261 yards. S.S.S. 66. Small practice area. *Green Fees:* weekdays £10.00 per round, weekends £14.00 per round. No green fees before 11.00am at weekends. No play after 2.00pm Sundays June to September. *Eating facilities:* available but very limited on Mondays. *Visitors:* welcome without reservation most days. Telephone enquiry advised weekends. *Society Meetings:* catered for by arrangement with Professional. Professional: Barry Davies (0737 244433). Secretary: Frank R. Cole (0737 240777 or 246409).

REIGATE. **Reigate Heath Golf Club,** The Clubhouse, Reigate Heath, Reigate RH2 8QR (Reigate (0737) 242610). *Location:* south of A25 on western boundary of Reigate. Heathland. 9 holes, 5554 yards. S.S.S. 67. *Green Fees:* weekdays £12.00 per round, £17.00 per day; Saturdays £14.00 per round, £19.00 per day. *Eating facilities:* meals by arrangement with Steward. Light lunches and snacks available except Mondays. *Visitors:* welcome weekdays, advisable to telephone before coming. *Society Meetings:* catered for Wednesdays or Thursdays. Professional: W. H. Carter. Secretary: Mrs D.M. Howard (0737 245530).

RICHMOND. **Richmond Golf Club,** Sudbrook Park, Petersham, Richmond TW10 7AS (081-940 1463). *Location:* off A307 two miles south of Richmond, end of Sudbrook Lane. Parkland. 18 holes, 6040 yards, 6602 metres. S.S.S. 69. *Green Fees:* weekdays £20.00. *Eating facilities:* lunches available Monday to Saturday; teas daily. *Visitors:* welcome weekdays without reservation. *Society Meetings:* welcome Tuesdays, Thursdays and Fridays by arrangement with Secretary. Professional: Nicholas Job (081-940 7792). Secretary: John F. Stocker (081-940 4351).

RICHMOND. **Royal Mid-Surrey Golf Club,** Old Deer Park, Richmond TW9 2SB (081 940 4847). *Location:* in Old Deer Park off A316 at Richmond. Parkland course. Two 18 holes courses, Inner – 5544 yards, S.S.S. 67 men, 5446 yards, S.S.S. 71 ladies; Outer – 6337 yards, S.S.S. 70 men, 5755 yards, S.S.S. 73 ladies. Practice ground, practice shed and chipping area. *Green Fees:* £30.00 weekdays. *Eating facilities:* the Buttery daily, the diningroom daily except Mondays, the bar daily. *Visitors:* welcome weekdays only, accompanied by introduction from own club. *Society Meetings:* welcome by prior arrangement. Professional: D. Talbot (081 940 0459). Secretary: M.S.R. Lunt (081 940 1894).

SUNNINGDALE. **Sunningdale Golf Club,** Sunningdale SL5 9RR (Ascot (0990) 21681). *Location:* Ridgemount Road, 350 yards west of station, off A30, 25 miles from London. Heathland, 36 holes, 2 courses. *Green Fees:* weekdays £58.00. *Eating facilities:* diningroom and three bars. *Visitors:* require introduction from Secretary of own club on weekdays. At weekends with member only. *Society Meetings:* accepted Tuesday, Wednesday, Thursday only, by arrangement. Secretary: Keith Almond. Professional: Keith Maxwell

(0990 20128). Caddiemaster for bookings (0990 26064).

SUTTON. **Banstead Downs Golf Club,** Burdon Lane, Belmont, Sutton (081-642 2284: Lady Members 081-642 8131). *Location:* A217 (10 minutes from Belmont Station). 18 holes, 6190 yards. S.S.S. 69. *Green Fees:* weekdays £20.00 mornings, £15.00 afternoons. *Eating facilities:* lunches served at Club except on Mondays. *Visitors:* welcome on weekdays with letter of introduction, at weekends with member. *Society Meetings:* catered for. Professional: Ian Marr. Secretary/Manager: A.W. Schooling.

TADWORTH. **Walton Heath Golf Club,** Deans Lane, Tadworth KT20 7TP (Tadworth (0737) 812060). *Location:* Junction 8 M25, A217 towards London, B2032 towards Dorking, turning right hand side Deans Lane. Two 18 hole courses. Old 6813 yards, S.S.S. 73. New 6659 yards. S.S.S. 72. Practice ground and shed. *Green Fees:* £45.00 weekdays, after 11.30am £40.00. *Eating facilities:* restaurant and two bars. *Visitors:* welcome by previous arrangement, Handicap Certificate or letter of introduction required. *Society Meetings:* catered for. Professional: Ken MacPherson (0737 812152). Secretary: Norman G. Dampney (0737 812380).

VIRGINIA WATER. **Wentworth Club,** Wentworth Drive, Virginia Water GU25 4LS (Wentworth (09904) 2201/2/3). *Location:* 21 miles south-west of London, just off the A30 at junction with A329 to Ascot. M25 and M3 three miles. Wooded heathland. West course – 6945 yards, S.S.S. 72; East course – 6500 yards, S.S.S. 70; South course – 6979 yards, S.S.S. 72; Executive course – 9 holes. *Green Fees:* weekdays from £55.00 including VAT. *Eating facilities:* full a la carte restaurant and bars, snack bar; banqueting facilities for up to 200. *Visitors:* welcome weekdays only with prior booking and Handicap Certificate. Accommodation available. *Society Meetings:* maximum 50, Tuesdays, Wednesdays and Thursdays. Professional: Bernard Gallacher (09904 3353). Managing Director: Richard Doyle-Davidson (09904 2201).

WALTON-ON-THAMES. **Burhill Golf Club,** Walton-on-Thames KT12 4BL (Walton (0932) 227345). *Location:* off A3 to A245, right into Seven Hills Road and again into Burwood Road or from Walton Railway Bridge through Burwood Park. 18 holes, 6224 yards.

S.S.S. 70. *Green Fees:* information not provided. Professional: Lee Johnson. Secretary: A.J. Acres.

WEST BYFLEET. **West Byfleet Golf Club,** Sheerwater Road, West Byfleet KT14 6AA (Byfleet (0932) 345230). *Location:* Junction 10 M25 onto A245 – half a mile west of West Byfleet. Flat, wooded course. 18 holes, 6211 yards. S.S.S. 70. *Green Fees:* weekdays £25.00 per round, £30.00 per day. *Eating facilities:* lunches, bar snacks, teas and evening meals available. *Visitors:* welcome weekdays with reservation, weekends with member only. *Society Meetings:* catered for, advance bookings, minimum group size 25. Professional: David Regan (0932 346584). Secretary: D.G. Smith (0932 343433).

WEYBRIDGE. **New Zealand Golf Club,** Woodham Lane, Woodham, Weybridge KT15 3QD (Byfleet (0932) 345049). *Location:* junction Woodham Lane and Sheerwater Road on A245. 18 holes, 6012 yards. S.S.S. 69. *Green fees:* information not provided. *Eating facilities:* lunch available Tuesdays to Fridays. *Visitors:* welcome Monday to Friday with reservation. *Society Meetings:* catered for Tuesday, Wednesday, Thursday and Friday. Professional: V. R. Elvidge. Secretary: M. J. Wood.

WEYBRIDGE. **St. George's Hill Golf Club,** St. George's Hill, Weybridge KT13 0NL (0932 842406). *Location:* M25, Junction 10 take A3 off toward London, turn left is Byfleet, Outer estate at S.P's St. George's Hill. Hilly, Surrey heathland – well wooded with plentiful heather and rhododendron. 18 holes, 6492 yards. S.S.S. 71. 9 holes, 4562 yards. S.S.S. 62. *Green Fees:* £35.00 weekdays, £24.00 after 1.45pm. *Eating facilities:* luncheons only, two bars. *Visitors:* Wednesday/Thursdays and Fridays. *Society Meetings:* catered for by prior arrangement. Professional: A.C. Rattue (0932 843523). Secretary: M.R. Tapsell (0932 847758).

WOKING. **Hoebridge Golf Centre,** Old Woking Road, Old Woking, Near Woking (0483 722611). Parkland with some trees. 18 holes, 6587 yards. S.S.S. 71. Par 3 course. (9 hole intermediate course). Covered driving range. *Green Fees:* £8.50 per round. *Eating*

facilities: large dining room and bar. *Visitors:* welcome. *Society Meetings:* welcome weekdays. Professional/Secretary: Tim Powell.

WOKING. **Windlemere Golf Club,** Windlesham Road, West End, Near Woking (0276 858727). *Location:* off A322. Well designed parkland course. 9 holes, 2673 yards. S.S.S. 33. Floodlit 12-bay driving range. *Green Fees:* weekdays £5.00, weekends £6.00. Reduced rates for Senior Citizens and Juniors. *Eating facilities:* bar with light menu, normal clubhouse facilities. *Visitors:* always welcome, may book up to one week in advance. Snooker, pool facilities. *Society Meetings:* welcome to book. Professionals: Dave Thomas and Alistair Kelso. Secretary: Mike Walsh.

WOKING. **Woking Golf Club,** Pond Road, Hook Heath, Woking (Woking (04862) 60053). *Location:* via Hollybank Road, just south of first road bridge, over Woking/Brookwood railway. 18 holes, 6365 yards. S.S.S. 70. *Green Fees:* on application. *Eating facilities:* lunches and snacks available. *Visitors:* welcome with reservation, please telephone. *Society Meetings:* catered for. Professional: J. Thorne. Secretary: A.W. Riley.

WOKING. **Worplesdon Golf Club,** Woking (Brookwood (04867 89876). *Location:* off A322 Guildford, Bagshot Road, Heath House Lane, first left south of West Hill G.C. Heather parkland course. 18 holes, 6440 yards. S.S.S. 71. *Green Fees:* weekdays £40.00 per day. *Eating facilities:* lunches served at club. *Visitors:* welcome weekdays. *Society Meetings:* catered for by arrangement. Professional: Jim Christine (04867 3287). Secretary: Major R.E.E. Jones (04867 2277).

WOLDINGHAM. **North Downs Golf Club,** North Down Road, Woldingham CR3 7AA (Woldingham (088 385) 3298). *Location:* Eastbourne Road roundabout at Caterham. 2 miles Woldingham road. 18 holes, 5787 yards, S.S.S. 68. *Green Fees:* enquire from Professional. *Eating facilities:* snacks available. *Visitors:* welcome. *Society Meetings:* catered for. Professional: P. Ellis (088 385 3004). Secretary: J.A.L. Smith (088 385 2057).

East Sussex

BEXHILL-ON-SEA. **Cooden Beach Golf Club,** Cooden Beach, Bexhill-on-Sea TN39 4TR (Cooden (04243) 3936). *Location:* A259 Eastbourne to Hastings road, follow 'Cooden Beach' sign at Little Common roundabout (one mile). Seaside course, slightly undulating, easy walking. 18 holes, 6450 yards. S.S.S. 71. Practice facilities. *Green Fees:* £17.00 weekdays,

weekends and Bank Holidays £20.00, per round or day. *Eating facilities:* catering and bar every day. *Visitors:* welcome preferably by prior arrangement. *Society Meetings:* catered for by arrangement. Professional: Keith Robson (04243 3938). Secretary: R.L. Wilkins (04243 2040).

BEXHILL-ON-SEA. **Highwoods Golf Club,** Ellerslie Lane, Bexhill-on-Sea TN39 4LJ (Bexhill (0424) 219600). *Location:* off A259 north west of town. Parkland course. 18 holes, 6218 yards. S.S.S. 70. *Green Fees:* information not provided. *Eating facilities:* snacks always available, lunch by prior arrangement. *Visitors:* Handicap Certificate required. Sunday mornings with member only. *Society Meetings:* welcome Wednesdays and Thursdays by arrangement. Professional: M. Andrews (0424 212770). Secretary: P. Robins (0424 212625).

BRIGHTON. **Brighton and Hove Golf Club,** Dyke Road, Brighton BN1 8YJ (Brighton (0273) 507861). *Location:* south from A23 at Patcham traffic lights turn right and right again at mini roundabout to Devils Dyke. Downland course. 9 holes, 5722 yards. S.S.S. 68. *Green Fees:* £6.00 9 holes, £12.00 18 holes weekdays, £18.00 weekends and Bank holidays. *Eating facilities:* every day except Mondays and Tuesdays. *Visitors:* welcome without reservation. *Society Meetings:* catered for. Secretary: C. S. Cawkwell (0273 556482).

BRIGHTON. **Dyke Golf Club,** Dyke Road, Brighton BN1 8YJ (Poynings (079 156) 260). *Location:* off A23 on to A2038 on entering Brighton. Downland course. 18 holes, 6577 yards, 6014 metres. S.S.S. 71. Practice fairway. *Green Fees:* weekdays £16.00 per round, £18.00 per day; weekends and Bank Holidays £25.00 per round. *Eating facilities:* full restaurant and bar available. *Visitors:* welcome with reservation, not Sunday mornings. *Society Meetings:* catered for by appointment, £32.00 for full day inclusive of lunch and dinner. Professional: P. Longmore (079 156 230). Secretary: B. Gazzard (079 156 296).

BRIGHTON. **East Brighton Golf Club,** Roedean Road, Brighton BN2 5RA (Brighton (0273) 603989). *Location:* east end of Brighton just off A259, behind the Marina. Undulating downland course. 18 holes, 6337 yards. S.S.S. 70. *Green Fees:* weekdays £17.00, weekends and Bank Holidays £25.00. *Eating facilities:* diningroom and bars, lunches and teas served except Mondays. *Visitors:* welcome from 9am weekdays, after 11am weekends. *Society Meetings:* catered for weekdays on application. Professional: W. Street (0273 603989). Secretary: K.R. Head (0273 604838).

BRIGHTON. **Hollingbury Park Golf Club,** Ditchling Road, Brighton (0273 552010). *Location:* between A23 and A27. 18 holes, 6502 yards. S.S.S. 71. *Green Fees:* weekdays £9.00 per round, £14.00 per day; weekends £11.50 per round. *Eating facilities:* full catering service seven days. *Visitors:* welcome without reservation. *Society Meetings:* catered for weekdays only. Professional: Peter Brown (0273 500086). Secretary: J. Walling.

BRIGHTON. **Pyecombe Golf Club,** Clayton Hill, Pyecombe, Brighton BN4 7FF (Hassocks (07918) 4176). *Location:* four miles north of Brighton on A273 Burgess Hill Road. Downland. 18 holes, 6234 yards. S.S.S. 70. Two practice areas. *Green Fees:* weekdays £16.00, weekends and Bank Holidays £25.00. *Eating facilities:* club diningroom and bar. *Visitors:* welcome, some time restrictions. *Society Meetings:* catered for on

application. Professional: C.R. White (07918 5398). Secretary: W.M. Wise (07918 5372).

BRIGHTON. **Waterhall Golf Club,** Devils Dyke Road, Brighton BN1 8YN (Brighton (0273) 50865-8).*Location:* three miles north of Brighton. Downland course. 18 holes, 5773 yards, 5328 metres. S.S.S. 68. Practice area. *Green Fees:* weekdays £9.20 per round, weekends £11.50 per round. *Eating facilities:* catering available everyday except Tuesdays. *Visitors:* welcome except Saturday and Sunday mornings. *Society Meetings:* catered for, except Tuesdays, weekends or Bank Holidays, by prior arrangement with Secretary. Professional: Paul Charman-Mitchell. Secretary: David Birch.

CROWBURGH. **Crowborough Beacon Golf Club,** Beacon Road, Crowborough (Crowborough (0892) 661511). *Location:* six miles south of Tonbridge Wells on the A26. Heathland. 18 holes, 6279 yards. S.S.S. 70. Practice ground. *Green Fees:* £20.00 per round, £30.00 per day weekdays. *Eating facilities:* available. *Visitors:* welcome after 9.30am weekdays, not allowed at weekends. *Society Meetings:* catered for. Professional: D. Newnham (0892 653877). Secretary: M.C. Swatton (0892 661511).

EAST GRINSTEAD. **Ashdown Forest Hotel and Golf Course,** Chapel Lane, Forest Row (Forest Row (0342 82) 4866). *Location:* Approx. 25 miles from Brighton, approximately 35 miles from London, approx. 3 miles East Grinstead. 18 holes, 5549 yards. S.S.S. 67. Par 68. *Green fees:* £7.00 weekdays, £8.00 weekends and Bank holidays. Bar snacks, Restaurants and Banqueting Suite, accommodation, Golf Break packages. Superb Cuisine. *Visitors:* welcome, best to phone first. *Society Meetings:* catered for. Professional: M. Landsborough. Proprietors: Alan Riddick and Robin Pratt.

EAST GRINSTEAD. **Royal Ashdown Forest Golf Club (Old Course),** Forest Row, East Grinstead (Forest Row (034 282) 2018/3014). *Location:* four miles south of East Grinstead and one mile from Forest Row. From EG take A22 south to FR – a distance of four miles. Turn left on to B2110 Hartfield Road half a mile, turn right up Chapel Lane and bear left at the top of the hill. 18 holes, 6249 white, 6215 yellow. S.S.S. 71 (white), 70 (yellow). *Green Fees:* £25.00 weekdays, £27.50 weekends and Bank Holidays. *Eating facilities:* lunch and tea (prior arrangement).*Visitors:* welcome, advisable phone beforehand. *Society Meetings:* catered for, prior reservation essential. Professional: M. Landsborough. Secretary: K.P.A. Mathews.

EAST GRINSTEAD. **Royal Ashdown Forest (New Course),** Forest Row, East Grinstead (Forest Row (034 282) 4866). *Location:* directions as for Old Course except turn right at top of Chapel Lane. 18 holes, S.S.S. 67. Par 69. *Eating facilities:* full catering. *Visitors and Society Meetings:* welcome weekdays and weekends.

EASTBOURNE. **Eastbourne Downs Golf Club,** East Dean Road, Eastbourne BN20 8ES (Eastbourne (0323) 21844). *Location:* five minutes from town centre via Old Town on A259. Downland. 18 holes, 6635 yards. S.S.S. 72. Practice area. *Green Fees:* weekdays

£10.00, weekends £12.00. *Eating facilities:* food available except Monday and Tuesday, two bars. *Visitors:* welcome any time. *Society Meetings:* catered for by arrangement. Professional: Terry Marshall (0323 32264). Secretary: D.J. Eldrett (0323 20827).

EASTBOURNE. **Royal Eastbourne Golf Club,** Paradise Drive, Eastbourne BN20 8BP (0323 30412) (Steward and Members). *Location:* one mile from town centre via Meads Road and Compton Place Road. (a) 18 holes, 6109 yards. S.S.S. 69. (b) 9 holes, 2147 yards 2. S.S.S. 61. *Green Fees:* weekdays £15.00, weekends and Bank Holidays £20.00. *Eating facilities:* full catering except on Mondays. *Visitors:* welcome. Handicap Certificate required Long Course only. Cottage accommodation for four people. *Society Meetings:* catered for. Professional: Richard Wooller (0323 36986). Secretary: (0323 29738).

EASTBOURNE. **Willingdon Golf Club,** Southdown Road, Eastbourne BN20 9AA (Eastbourne (0323) 410983). *Location:* north of Eastbourne, one mile from station, just off A22 at traffic lights (signposted). Downland course of particular beauty. 18 holes, 6049 yards, 5530 metres. S.S.S. 69. Practice ground and nets. *Green Fees:* weekdays £18.00, Saturdays and Bank Holidays £24.00. *Eating facilities:* diningroom, lounge and casual bar. *Visitors:* welcome after 9.00am weekdays, Saturday check for tee bookings, not Sunday mornings, check for tee bookings. *Society Meetings:* welcome – book well in advance. Professional: (0323 410984). Secretary: Brian Kirby (0323 410981).

HASTINGS. **Beauport Park Golf Club** (Associated to Hastings Golf Course), Battle Road, St. Leonards on Sea (Hastings (0424) 52977). *Location:* A2100 3 miles north of Hastings and 3 miles south of Battle. 18 holes, 6248 yards. S.S.S. 70. *Green Fees:* Information on request. *Eating facilities:* cafe, snacks; book lunches in advance. *Visitors:* welcome without reservation. *Society Meetings:* catered for, not at weekends. Professional: M. Barton (0424 52981). Hon. Secretary: D.C. Funnell.

HEATHFIELD. **Horam Park Golf Course,** Chiddingly Road, Horam, Near Heathfield TN21 0JJ (04353 3477). Wooded course, with several lakes and ponds. 9 holes, 2844 yards. S.S.S. 68. Floodlit driving range. *Green Fees:* weekdays £7.00 for 9 holes, £14.00 for 18

holes; weekends £7.50 for 9 holes, £15.00 for 18 holes. *Eating facilities;* restaurant and bar; Golf Society catering a speciality. *Visitors:* welcome all week, advisable to book in advance. *Society Meetings:* catered for weekdays, we specialise in Company Days. Professional: Richard Foster (04353 3477). Secretary: Howard Fisher (04353 3477). Club Manager: M. Cousens.

HOVE. **West Hove Golf Club,** 369 Old Shoreham Road, Hove BN3 7GD (Brighton (0273) 413411). *Location:* on A27 traffice lights north of Portswade Station. Downland course. 18 holes, 6132 yards, 5605 metres. S.S.S. 69. Practice area. *Green Fees:* £12.00 weekdays, £20.00 weekends. *Eating facilities:* light catering daily, special catering by arrangement, bar. *Visitors:* welcome, book through Pro Shop. *Society Meetings:* catered for weekdays. Professional: Chris White (0273 413494). Secretary: R.W. Charman (0273 419738).

LEWES. **Lewes Golf Club,** Chapel Hill, Lewes (Lewes (0273)473245). *Location:* opposite Cliffie High Street at junction with Malling Street. 18 holes, 5951 yards. S.S.S. 69. *Green fees:* information not provided. *Eating facilities:* full catering. *Visitors:* welcome without reservation. *Society Meetings:* catered for as required. Professional: E. Goldring. Secretary: G.J. Cull.

NEWHAVEN. **Peacehaven Golf Club,** The Clubhouse, Brighton Road, Newhaven BN9 9UH (0273 514049). *Location:* one mile from Newhaven on the right hand side of the main South Coast road towards Brighton and on the left hand side just out of Peacehaven. 9 holes, 5235 yards. S.S.S. 66. *Green Fees:* Information not provided. *Eating facilities:* light meals unless previously ordered. *Visitors:* welcome without reservation. *Society Meetings:* catered for up to 20. Professional: G. Williams. Secretary: D. Jenkins.

RYE. **Rye Golf Course,** Camber, Rye (Rye (0797) 225241). *Location:* A259 from Rye, take Camber road to coast. Seaside links. 18 holes, 6310 yards. S.S.S. 71. 9 holes, 6141 yards. S.S.S. 71. *Green Fees:* information not provided. *Eating facilities:* lunch and tea only, but not Tuesdays. Bars. *Visitors:* welcome, only playing with a member or on introduction by a member. *Society Meetings:* very limited. Professional: Peter Marsh (0797 225218). Secretary: Commander J.M. Bradley (0797 225241).

SEAFORD. **Seaford Golf Club,** East Blatchington, Seaford BN25 2JD (Seaford (0323) 892597). *Location:* turn inland at War Memorial in Seaford, follow the road for one and a quarter miles. Downland course. 18 holes, 6233 yards, 5700 metres. S.S.S. 70. Practice ground. *Green Fees:* weekdays £20.00 (£15.00 after 12 noon, £10.00 after 3.00pm). *Eating facilities:* diningroom for all meals and bar snacks available in bar. *Visitors:* welcome weekdays other than Tuesdays. Telephone first. *Society Meetings:* catered for Wednesdays, Thursdays and Fridays if club members with Handicap Certificates. Residential accommodation for 18 guests. Professional: P. Stevens (0323 894160). Secretary: M.B. Hichisson (0323 892442).

SEAFORD. **Seaford Head Golf Club,** Southdown Road, Seaford (Seaford (0323) 890139. *Location:* midway between Eastbourne and Brighton on A259. 18 holes, 5812 yards. S.S.S. 68. *Green fees:* information not provided. *Eating facilities:* at Club by appointment. *Visitors:* welcome without reservation. *Society Meetings:* catered for by written appointment. Professional: A. J. Lowles. Secretary: A. T. Goodman.

UCKFIELD. **Piltdown Golf Club,** Piltdown, Uckfield TN22 3XB (Newick (082-572) 2033). *Location:* one mile west of Marefield off A272, signposted Isfield. Undulating gorse and heather. 18 holes, 5890 yards, 5385 metres. S.S.S. 69. Practice ground, putting green. *Green Fees:* any day round or day £25.00. *Eating facilities:* bar, full catering (phone (082-572 4112) first to book). *Visitors:* welcome but must bring Handicap Certificate or letter of introduction from own club Secretary. Some time restrictions. Jacket and tie obligatory in lounge and diningroom. Smart dress on course. *Society Meetings:* catered for by arrangement Mondays, Wednesdays and Fridays only. Professional: John Amos (082-572 2389). Secretary: J.C. Duncan (082572 2033).

WADHURST. **Dale Hill Golf Club,** Ticehurst, Wadhurst (0580 200112). *Location:* on B2087, one mile off A21, 50 miles south London, 16 miles north Hastings. Wooded/parkland course. 18 holes, men 6055 yards, S.S.S. 70, ladies 5246 yards, S.S.S. 73. Practice area planned for near future. *Green Fees:* weekdays £15.00, weekends £20.00. Reductions for SCGU members. *Eating facilities:* breakfast and dinner to order, lunches and snacks always available. *Visitors:* welcome with reservation, handicap players only at weekends. *Society Meetings:* catered for. Professional: (0580 201090). Secretary: A.G. Smith (0580 200112).

West Sussex

ANGMERING. **Ham Manor Golf Club Ltd,** Angmering BN16 4JE (0903 783288). *Location:* on A259 between Worthing and Littlehampton. 18 holes, 6216 yards. S.S.S. 70. *Green Fees:* on application. *Eating facilities:* lunches served at club except on Mondays. *Visitors:* welcome with reservation. Handicap Certificate required. *Society Meetings:* catered for weekdays only. Professional: Simon Buckley. Secretary: P.H. Saubergue.

BOGNOR REGIS. **Bognor Regis Golf Club,** Downview Road, Felpham, Bognor Regis (Bognor Regis (0243) 865867). *Location:* turn north at traffic lights on A259 at Felpham village. Flat parkland. 18 holes, 6238 yards. S.S.S. 70. Practice area. *Green Fees:* £16.00 weekdays, £20.00 weekends and Bank Holidays. *Eating facilities:* bar snacks available most days. *Visitors:* welcome weekdays, weekends only with a member. Handicap Certificate required. *Society Meetings:* catered for, minimum 20. Professional: R. Day (0243 865209). Secretary: B.D. Poston (0243 821929).

CHICHESTER. **Goodwood Golf Club,** Goodwood, Chichester PO18 0PN (Chichester (0243) 785012). *Location:* three and a half miles north east Chichester on Racecourse Road. Downland course, hilly with fine views to Isle of Wight. 18 holes, 6383 yards. S.S.S. 70. Limited practice only. *Green Fees:* weekdays £20.00, weekends and Bank Holidays £30.00 *Eating facilities:* bar meals at all times, others by prior arrangement. *Visitors:* welcome most days except during competitions, advisable to phone prior to play. Handicap Certificates required at all times. *Society Meetings:* limited to Wednesdays and Thursdays only. Professional: Keith MacDonald (0243 774994). Managing Secretary: Michael Hughes-Narborough (0243 774968).

CHICHESTER. **Selsey Golf Club,** Golf Links Lane, Selsey, Chichester (0243 602203/602165). *Location:* B2145, seven miles south of Chichester. Flat course. 9 holes playing 18, 5932 yards. S.S.S. 68. *Green Fees:* weekdays £10.00 per round, weekends and Bank Holidays £15.00 per round. *Eating facilities:* lunches served at club. *Visitors:* welcome weekends and Bank Holidays only if holding a bona fide Handicap Certificate or playing with a member. *Society Meetings:* catered for weekdays only. Professional: P. Grindley. Secretary: E.C. Rackstraw (0243 602029).

CRAWLEY. **Copthorne Golf Club,** Borers Arms Road, Copthorne, Crawley RH10 3LL (Copthorne (0342) 712033). *Location:* off Exit 10 M23, one mile on A264 towards East Grinstead. Flat wooded course. 18 holes, 6505 yards. S.S.S. 71. Practice area. *Green Fees:* weekdays £20.00 per round, £30.00 per day; weekends £35.00. Half fees if playing with member. *Eating facilities:* catering all day, bar. *Visitors:* welcome weekdays without reservation, after 1pm weekends. *Society Meetings:* catered for Thursdays and Fridays. Professional: Joe Burrell (0342 712405). Secretary: J. Appleton (0342 712508).

CRAWLEY. **Cottesmore Golf Club,** Buchan Hill, Pease Pottage, Crawley (Crawley (0293) 28256). *Location:* one mile out of Pease Pottage, last exit south M23, on Horsham Road, righthand side. Undulating Sussex countryside. 36 holes, Old Course – 6100 yards. S.S.S. 70. New Course – 5700 yards. S.S.S. 68. *Green Fees:* £18.00 Old Course, £14.00 New Course weekdays, £22.00 Old Course, £16.00 New Course weekends. *Eating facilities:* spikes cafe, club bar and diningroom. *Visitors:* welcome except before 1pm weekends, no non-handicap players. *Society Meetings:* catered for weekdays. Professional: Paul Webster (0293 35399). Secretary: M. F. Rogerson (0293 29196).

CRAWLEY. **Ifield Golf and Country Club,** Rusper Road, Ifield, Crawley RH11 0LN (Crawley (0293) 573627). *Location:* outskirts of Crawley near A23 to Glossops Green. Parkland. 18 holes, 6200 yards. S.S.S. 70. Practice area. *Green Fees:* £20.00 per round or day, £15.00 per 1pm. *Eating facilities:* all day bar and catering. *Visitors:* welcome Monday, Tuesday and Wednesday afternoons, Thursday, Friday till 3.30pm.

Society Meetings: cartered for. Professional: C. Stratheam (0293 23088). Secretary: (0293 20222).

CRAWLEY. **Tilgate Forest Golf Club,** Titmus Drive, Tilgate, Crawley RH10 5EU (0293 30103). *Location:* last turn-off on M23 at Pease Pottage, then to Crawley. Parkland with interesting 17th hole. 18 holes, 6300 yards. S.S.S. 71. *Green Fees:* weekdays £7.20 per round, weekends £10.20. Weekday reductions for Juniors £4.00. *Eating facilities:* full catering facilities and bar. *Visitors:* must book at weekends. *Society Meetings:* weekdays by arrangement with Professional. Professional: H. Spencer.

EFFINGHAM. **Effingham Park Golf Club,** Copthorne Effingham Park Hotel, Copthorne (0342 716528). *Location:* Junction 10 M23, two miles east on A264. Wooded parkland around lake. 9 holes, 1750 yards. S.S.S. 57. *Green Fees:* weekdays £10.00 for 18 holes (two rounds), weekends £12.00 for 18 holes. *Eating facilities:* Wellingtonia Restuarant, McLaren Restaurant and Charlies bar. *Visitors:* not before 1pm at weekends or on a Tuesday evening. Four star Hotel on site and leisure club. *Society Meetings:* catered for on request. Professional: I. Dryden. Secretary: Mrs C. Mann.

HAYWARDS HEATH. **Haywards Heath Golf Club,** High Beech Lane, Haywards Heath RH16 1SL (Haywards Heath (0444) 414310). *Location:* two miles north of Haywards Heath. Parkland. 18 holes, 6034 yards. S.S.S. 70. Practice area. *Green Fees:* weekdays £15.00 per round £20.00 two rounds, weekends and Bank Holidays £25.00 per round, £30.00 two rounds.. *Eating facilities:* bar and catering both available. *Visitors:* by arrangement, phone Professional. *Society Meetings:* catered for Wednesdays and Thursdays only, numbers over 20. Professional: M. Henning (0444 414866). Secretary: John Duncan (0444 414457).

HORSHAM. **Mannings Heath Golf Club,** Goldings Lane, Mannings Heath, Near Horsham RH13 6JU (Horsham (0403) 210168). *Location:* three miles southeast of Horsham off A281, seven miles west of M23. Undulating wooded course with featured streams. 18 holes, 6402 yards. S.S.S. 71. Restricted practice area. *Green Fees:* weekdays £17.00 per round, £25.00 per day; weekends £25.00 afternoons only. *Eating facilities:* bar and diningroom (not Mondays). *Visitors:*

welcome weekdays preferably by prior arrangement, Handicap Certificate essential; weekends after 2.30pm. *Society Meetings:* catered for by arrangement Tuesdays, Wednesdays and Fridays. Professional: Mike Denny (0403 210332). Secretary: J.D. Coutts (0403 210228).

LITTLEHAMPTON. **Littlehampton Golf Club,** 170 Rope Walk, Riverside West, Littlehampton BN17 5DL (Littlehampton (0903) 717170). *Location:* leave A259 one mile west of Littlehampton at sign. Seaside links. 18 holes, 6244 yards. S.S.S. 70. *Green Fees:* £20.00 weekdays, £30.00 weekends. *Eating facilities:* restaurant and two bars. *Visitors:* welcome weekdays, weekends after midday, but phone prior to arrival. *Society Meetings:* recognised societies only. Professional: Clive A. Burgess (0903 716369). Secretary: Keith Palmer.

MIDHURST. **Cowdray Park Golf Club,** Midhurst GU29 0BB (0730) 812088). *Location:* one mile east of Midhurst on A272. Undulating parkland. 18 holes, 6212 yards. S.S.S. 70. Two practice grounds. *Green Fees:* £20.00 weekdays, £30.00 weekends. Reduction when playing with member. *Eating facilities:* available. *Visitors:* welcome weekends only after 11.00am. *Society Meetings:* catered for except Tuesdays, Fridays, weekends and Bank Holidays. Professional: Stephen Hall (0730) 812091). Secretary: Mrs J.D. Huggett (0730) 813599).

PULBOROUGH. **West Sussex Golf Club,** Hurston Warren, Pulborough RH20 2EN (Pulborough (07982) 2563). *Location:* between Storrington and Pulborough on the A283. Heathland. 18 holes, 6221 yards. S.S.S. 70. Large practice ground. *Green Fees:* on application. *Eating facilities:* lunch and tea daily, bars. *Visitors:* welcome by prior arrangement (not Tuesdays). No three or four balls. *Society Meetings:* catered for Wednesdays and Thursdays. Professional: T. Packham (07982 2426). Secretary: G.R. Martindale (07982 2563).

WEST CHILTINGTON. **West Chiltington Golf Club,** Broadford Bridge Road, West Chiltington RH10 2YA (0798 813574). *Location:* near Pulborough. Gently undulating with spectacular views. 18 holes, 6000 yards. S.S.S. 69. 9 holes Par 3 course. 18 bay driving range (eight covered). *Green Fees:* weekdays

£8.00, weekends £12.00. *Eating facilities:* Cordon Bleu chef, comfortable bar. *Visitors:* always welcome, smart dress. *Society Meetings:* welcome. Professional: Brian Barnes (07983 2115). Secretary: S.G. Coulson.

WORTHING. **Hill Barn Golf Course,** Hill Barn Lane, Worthing BN14 9QE (Worthing (0903) 33918). *Location:* signposted on the roundabout outside of Worthing on the A27. Downland/parkland course with a few trees but generally fairly open. 18 holes, 6224 yards. S.S.S. 70. Putting green and practice area (balls not provided). *Green Fees:* weekdays £8.00, weekends £9.50. *Eating facilities:* bar and restaurant. *Visitors:* welcome at all times. *Society Meetings:* catered for except at weekends. Restricted to 30 per year. Pro-

fessionals: P. and A.P. Higgins (0903 37301). Secretary: M. Petite (0903 37301).

WORTHING. **Worthing Golf Club,** Links Road, Worthing BN14 9QZ (Worthing (0903) 60801). *Location:* on A27 near junction with A24 (Offington Roundabout). Two downland courses. Lower course: 18 holes, 6519 yards. S.S.S. 72. Upper course: 5243 yards. S.S.S. 66. *Green Fees:* weekdays £22.00 per day, weekends and Bank Holidays £26.00 per day. *Eating facilities:* first class restaurant facilities. *Visitors:* welcome, check in advance with Secretary. *Society Meetings:* catered for by arrangement. Professional: Stephen Rolley. Secretary: R.B. Carroll.

Tyne & Wear

BIRTLEY. **Birtley (Portobello) Golf Club,** Birtley Lane, Birtley (Tyneside (091-4102207)). *Location:* off A1 (M) Chester-le-Street, A647 to Birtley. 9 holes, 5660 yards. S.S.S. 67. *Green Fees:* £8.00 (£4.00 with member) weekdays, £8.00 weekends if accompanied by a member. *Visitors:* not allowed after 2pm on Fridays or at weekends unless accompanied by a member. *Society Meetings:* only by special arrangement. Secretary: B. Richardson.

CHOPWELL. **Garesfield Golf Club,** Chopwell NE17 7AP (Ebchester (0207) 561278). *Location:* leave A694 at Rowlands Gill, follow signposts for Chopwell, approximately three miles. Undulating wooded parkland. 18 holes, 6203 yards. S.S.S. 70. Practice nets and area. *Green fees:* £7.00 weekdays and after 4.30pm only, weekends and Bank Holidays. Weekly tickets available and reduced fees for parties of 16 or over. *Eating facilities:* full catering and bar service. *Visitors:* welcome without reservation weekdays. *Society Meetings:* catered for with prior reservation, except Sundays. Reduced rates for groups of 20 or more. Secretary: J.R. Peart (0207 561309).

EAST BOLDON. **Boldon Golf Club Ltd,** Dipe Lane, East Boldon (Wearside (091) 5364182). *Location:* near Sunderland approximately one mile from roundabout at junction of A19 and A1 highways. Fairly flat parkland. 18 holes, 6348 yards. S.S.S. 70. *Green Fees:* £12.00 weekdays, £15.00 weekends. Reduced rates for parties of over 20. *Eating facilities:* bar snacks and restaurant. *Visitors:* welcome, not between 9am and 10am, 12.30pm and 1.30pm and 4.30pm and 6.00pm. Not before 3.30pm at weekends. *Society Meetings:* catered for. Professional: Phipps Golf (091-5365835). Hon Secretary: R.E. Jobes (091-5365360).

GATESHEAD. **Heworth Golf Club,** Gingling Gate, Heworth, Gateshead (091 4692137). *Location:* A1 (M) south east boundary of Gateshead. Flat wooded course. 18 holes, 6437 yards. S.S.S. 71. *Green Fees:* £10.00 weekdays, £12.00 weekends. *Eating facilities:* bar and lounge. *Visitors:* weekdays up to 4pm, no visitors Saturdays; after 10am on Sundays. *Society Meetings:* mid-week only. Secretary: G. Holbrow (091 4699832).

HEDDON-ON-THE-WALL. **Close House Golf Club,** Heddon-on-the-Wall, Newcastle-upon-Tyne NE15 0HT (0661 852953). *Location:* nine miles west of city on A69. 18 holes, 5506 yards, 5033 metres. S.S.S. 67. *Green Fees:* private golf club. *Eating facilities:* by arrangement with steward (Mr R. Nairn). *Visitors:* with member only. *Society Meetings:* weekdays only by arrangement with Secretary. Secretary: Mrs L. Steel (0661 852303).

HOUGHTON-LE-SPRING. **Houghton-le-Spring Golf Club,** Copt Hill, Houghton-le-Spring (Tyneside (091) 5841198). *Location:* off A690 Durham Road, take Houghton to Seaham road, course is situated at the top of Copt Hill bank. Testing hillside course. 18 holes, 6416 yards, 5867 metres. S.S.S. 71. *Green Fees:* weekdays £8.00, weekends £12.00. *Eating facilities:* available most days, bar open every day. *Visitors:* welcome most days but not on competition days (Sundays). *Society Meetings:* catered for by arrangement. Professional: S.J. Bradbury (091 584 7421). Secretary: N. Wales (091 528 6716).

NEWCASTLE UPON TYNE. **City of Newcastle Golf Club,** Three Mile Bridge, Gosforth, Newcastle upon Tyne NE3 2DR (Tyneside (091-2851775). *Location:* on A1 three miles north of city. Flat parkland. 18 holes, 6510 yards. S.S.S. 71. *Green Fees:* weekdays £11.00, weekends and Bank Holidays £15.00. *Eating facilities:* bar, meals (not Mondays). *Visitors:* welcome without reservation, restricted times Fridays. *Society Meetings:* very welcome. Professional/Secretary: A.J. Matthew (091-2855481).

NEWCASTLE UPON TYNE. **Gosforth Golf Club,** Broadway East, Gosforth, Newcastle upon Tyne NE3 5ER (Tyneside (091-2853495). *Location:* three miles north of Newcastle city centre, on A6127. 18 holes, 6030 yards. S.S.S. 69. *Green Fees:* weekdays £10.00, £5.00 with member; weekends and Bank Holidays £15.00, £5.00 with member. *Eating facilities:* full catering, order in advance. *Visitors:* welcome with reservation, arrange with Secretary. *Society Meetings:* catered for. Professional: D. Race. Secretary: H.V. Smith.

NEWCASTLE UPON TYNE. **Hobson Municipal Golf Club,** Hobson, Burnopfield, Newcastle upon Tyne (0207 70941). *Location:* on main Newcastle to Consett road. Fairly flat, well designed course. 18 holes, 6582 yards, 6018 metres. S.S.S. 71. Practice area. *Green Fees:* on request. *Eating facilities:* bar, lounge and restaurant. *Visitors:* no restrictions except short periods Saturdays for Club Competitions. *Society Meetings:* by prior arrangement with Professional (all bookings). Professional: J.W. Ord (0207 71605). Secretary: G. Allan (0207 236980).

NEWCASTLE UPON TYNE. **Newcastle United Golf Club,** 60 Ponteland Road, Cowgate, Newcastle upon Tyne NE5 3JW (Tyneside (091-2864693). *Location:* two miles west of city centre in direction of airport. Moorland. 18 holes, 6498 yards, 5942 metres. S.S.S. 71. Practice area. *Green Fees:* weekdays £7.50 (£5.00 with member), weekends £10.00 (£6.25 with member). Ladies and juniors £5.00 weekdays. *Eating facilities:* bar meals available. *Visitors:* no restrictions midweek, weekends must play with member. *Society Meetings:* welcome, book through Secretary. Shop: (091-2869998). Secretary: J. Simpson.

NEWCASTLE UPON TYNE. **Northumberland Golf Club Ltd,** High Gosforth Park, Newcastle upon Tyne NE3 5HT (Tyneside (091-2362009). *Location:* off A1. 18 holes, 6629 yards. S.S.S. 72. *Green Fees:* £20.00. *Visitors:* welcome with prior reservation or introduction. *Society Meetings:* catered for except on Mondays, Wednesdays and weekends. Secretary: D. Lamb (091-2362498).

NEWCASTLE UPON TYNE. **Tyneside Golf Club Ltd,** Westfield Lane, Ryton NE40 3QE (Tyneside (091) 413 2177). *Location:* seven miles west of Newcastle upon Tyne, off A695 in Ryton Village. Parkland, hilly with water hazards. 18 holes, 6042 yards, 5522 metres. S.S.S. 69. Practice field. *Green Fees:* weekdays £12.00, weekends £16.00. *Eating facilities:* full catering. *Visitors:* bona fide golfers welcome. *Society Meetings:* by arrangement with Secretary, weekdays only. Professional: M. Gunn (091-413 2177). Secretary: J.R. Watkin (091-413 2742).

NEWCASTLE UPON TYNE. **Westerhope Golf Club,** Whorlton Grange, Westerhope, Newcastle-upon-Tyne NE5 1PP (Tyneside (091-2869125). *Location:* A69, Jingling Gate Public House. Parkland/wooded. 18 holes, 6468 yards, 5912 metres. S.S.S. 71. Two practice areas. *Green Fees:* weekdays £10.00 per round, £15.00 per day (with a member £8.00 per round, £12.00 per day); weekends £10.00 with member only. *Eating facilities:* lunches and high teas. *Visitors:* visitors welcome weekdays, weekends and Bank Holidays with a member only. *Society Meetings:* by appointment. Professional: N. Brown (091-2860594). Secretary: G.S. Bazley (091-2867636).

NEWCASTLE-UPON-TYNE. **Parklands Golf Club,** High Gosforth Park, Newcastle-upon-Tyne (091 2364867). *Location:* just off A1 north of Newcastle, follow signs for Gosforth Park. Parkland. 18 holes, 6180 yards. S.S.S. 71. 9 holes pitch and putt, 30 bay floodlit driving range. *Green Fees:* weekdays £7.50, weekends £9.00. *Eating facilities:* restaurant and bar.

Visitors: welcome, no restrictions. *Society Meetings:* catered for. Professional: Grahame Garland (091 2364480). Secretary: Brian Woof.

NEWCASTLE-UPON-TYNE. **Whickham Golf Club,** Hollinside Park, Whickham, Newcastle-upon-Tyne NE16 5BA (Tyneside (091) 4887309). *Location:* five miles south west of Newcastle. Parkland. 18 holes, 6179 yards. S.S.S. 69. *Green Fees:* weekdays £10.00 per round, £12.00 per day; weekends £15.00 per day. *Eating facilities:* lunches, teas, evening meals available by prior order. *Visitors:* welcome without reservation. *Society Meetings:* catered for by arrangement. Professional: Greg Towne (091-4888591). Secretary: N. Weightman (091-4881576).

RYTON. **Ryton Golf Club,** Dr. Stanners, Clara Vale, Ryton (Tyneside (091-4133737). *Location:* off A695 at Crawcrook to Clara Vale. Flat parkland. 18 holes, 6034 yards. S.S.S. 69. *Green Fees:* £8.00 weekdays, weekends with a member. *Eating facilities:* available. *Visitors:* welcome on weekdays, weekends with a member only. *Society Meetings:* catered for by arrangement. Secretary: T.V. Wakeford (091 2679720).

SHIREMOOR. **Backworth Golf Club,** The Hall, Backworth, Shiremoor (Tyneside (091) 2681048). *Location:* from Newcastle to Shiremoor Crossroads then left for mile. 9 holes, 5930 yards. S.S.S. 69. *Green Fees:* information not provided. *Visitors:* welcome by arrangement.

SOUTH SHIELDS. **South Shields Golf Club Ltd,** Cleadon Hills, South Shields NE34 8EG (Tyneside (091-4560475). *Location:* near A19 and A1 M, Cleadon Chimney prominent landmark. 18 holes, 6264 yards, 5729 metres. S.S.S. 70. *Green Fees:* weekdays £11.00, weekends and Bank Holidays £15.00. *Eating facilities:* meals available at all times, bar. *Visitors:* welcome at all times without reservation. *Society Meetings:* catered for. Professional: Gary Parsons (091-4560110). Secretary: W.H. Loades (091-4568942).

SOUTH SHIELDS. **Whitburn Golf Club,** Lizard Lane, South Shields (Wearside (091) 5292144). *Location:* between Sunderland and South Shields adjoining Coast Road. 18 holes, 6046 yards. S.S.S. 69. *Green Fees:* weekdays £10.00, introduced by and playing with member £5.00. Saturdays, Sundays and Bank Holidays £15.00, introduced by and playing with a member £8.00. *Eating facilities:* available. *Visitors:* welcome except on Saturday or Sunday when competition being held. *Society Meetings:* catered for on weekdays by prior reservations. Professional: D. Stephenson. Secretary: Mr W. Anderson.

SUNDERLAND. **Wearside Golf Club,** Cox Green, Sunderland SR4 9JT (091-534 2518). *Location:* on south bank of River Wear, one mile west of A19. From A19 exit for A183, direction Chester-le-Street, at 200 yards turn right, signposted Offerton/Cox Green, then left at T junction, down hill over humped bridge. Parkland, bordered on north by River Wear, deep wooded gully traverses course. 18 holes, 6323 yards. S.S.S. 70. 4 holes par 3 field and separate practice tees. *Green Fees:* weekdays £12.00, weekends and Bank

Holidays £18.00. *Eating facilities:* full catering and bar service. *Visitors:* welcome most times, telephone Professional for information. *Society Meetings:* by advance application. Professional: Mr Steven Wynn (091-534 4269). Secretary: K.D. Wheldon (091-534 1193).

WALLSEND. **Wallsend Golf Club,** Bigges Main, Wallsend. *Location:* western boundary. Parkland. 18 holes, 6608 yards, 6043 metres. S.S.S. 72. *Green Fees:* weekdays £6.50, weekends £7.50. *Eating facilities:* meals available on request. *Visitors:* restricted weekends – not before 12.30pm April to October. *Society Meetings:* weekdays only. Professional: (091-262 2431). Secretary: L. Rowe (091-262 1973).

WASHINGTON. **Washington Moat House Golf Club,** Stonecellar Road, Washington NE33 1PH (091 4172626). *Location:* half a mile from A1 M junction A184. Parkland. 18 holes, 6604 yards, 6038 metres.

S.S.S. 72. *Green Fees:* weekdays £8.50, weekends £12.50. *Eating facilities:* fully licensed hotel on site. *Visitors:* by arrangement. Special rates for visiting parties of over 15 mid-week. Hotel with 150 plus bedrooms. *Society Meetings:* by arrangement. Professional: David Howdon (091-4178346). Secretary: D.W. Duffy (091 4162609).

WHITLEY BAY. **Whitley Bay Golf Club,** Claremont Road, Whitley Bay NE26 3UF (Tyneside (091-2520180). *Location:* north side of town. Undulating parkland. 18 holes, 6617 yards. S.S.S. 72. *Green Fees:* information not provided. *Eating facilities:* available except Mondays. *Visitors:* welcome with reservation weekdays, weekends only with member. *Society Meetings:* catered for by arrangement with Secretary. Professional: W.J. Light (091-2525688). Secretary: B. Dockar (091-2520180).

Warwickshire

ATHERSTONE. **Atherstone Golf Club,** The Outwoods, Atherstone CV9 2RL (Atherstone (0827) 713110). *Location:* five miles north of Nuneaton and seven miles south of Tamworth. Undulating parkland. 11 holes, 6239 yards. S.S.S. 70. Practice ground. *Green Fees:* £10.00 weekdays, Saturdays £6.00 with member only. *Eating facilities:* bar and dining room. *Visitors:* welcome weekdays (except Tuesdays) without reservation, Saturdays with member only. *Society Meetings:* by prior appointment. Professional: Ken Williams (0827 713110). Secretary: A.G. Sarson (0827 714579).

KENILWORTH. **Kenilworth Golf Club Ltd,** Crew Lane, Kenilworth (Kenilworth (0926) 54296). *Location:* A429 Coventry to Kenilworth adjacent to A46 Coventry to Warwick Road. Parkland and wooded course. 18 holes, 6410 yards. S.S.S. 71. Practice ground and 9 hole Par 3 course. *Green Fees:* £17.00 weekdays, £25.00 weekends. *Eating facilities:* diningroom, bar snacks, two bars. *Visitors:* must be members of another club with official Handicap Certificate. *Society Meetings:* Wednesdays only, Handicap Certificates required. Professional: S. Mouland (0926 512732). Secretary: B.V. Edwards (0926 58517).

LEAMINGTON SPA. **Leamington and County Golf Club,** Golf Lane, Whitnash, Leamington Spa (Leamington Spa (0926) 425961). *Location:* two miles south of town centre of Royal Leamington Spa. 18 holes, 6430 yards, 5878 metres. S.S.S. 71. *Green Fees:* Information not provided. *Eating facilities:* luncheons, teas, evening meals and snacks (except Mondays). *Visitors:* welcome without reservation. *Society Meetings:* catered for. Professional: I. Grant. Secretary: S.M. Cooknell.

LEAMINGTON SPA. **Newbold Comyn Golf Club,** Newbold Terrace East, Leamington Spa (0926

421157). *Location:* central, off Willes Road B4099. Parkland, front 9 hilly, back 9 flat. 18 holes, 6259 yards, 5719 metres. S.S.S. 70. Pitch and putt course 9 holes. *Green fees:* weekdays £4.60, weekends £5.60. *Eating facilities:* restaurant and bar. *Visitors:* welcome, unrestricted. *Society Meetings:* catered for, book through Professional. Professional: D.R. Knight (0926 421157). Secretary: A.A. Pierce (0926 422660).

NUNEATON. **Nuneaton Golf Club,** Golf Drive, Whitestone, Nuneaton CV11 6QF (Nuneaton (0203 383281). *Location:* two miles south of Nuneaton. Wooded course. 18 holes, 6429 yards. S.S.S. 71. *Green Fees:* weekdays £14.00 per day/round, weekends £14.00 with member only. *Visitors:* welcome weekdays. *Society Meetings:* Wednesdays and Fridays only. Professional: N. Gilks (0203 340201). Secretary/Manager: G. Pinder (0203 347810).

NUNEATON. **Purley Chase Golf and Country Club,** Ridge Lane, Near Nuneaton CV10 0RB (Chapel End (0203) 397468). *Location:* one and a half miles south Mancetter Island A5, half a mile north east of A47 (Pipers Lane), tourist signs at all approaches. Flattish parkland, eight holes water in play, highest point in area (4th par 3) 160ft drop. 18 holes, 6734 yards, 6014 metres. S.S.S. 71. Floodlit driving range. *Green Fees:* weekdays £10.00, weekends £15.00. Reductions if member's guest. *Eating facilities:* full catering service. *Visitors:* welcome at all times weekdays. *Society Meetings:* welcome weekdays only. Professional: (Tour) David Llewelyn (0203 395348). General Manager/Secretary: Reg Place (0203 393118).

RUGBY. **Rugby Golf Club,** Clifton Road, Rugby (0788 2306). 18 holes, 5457 yards. S.S.S. 67. *Green fees:* information not available. *Visitors:* welcome. Professional: D. Sutherland (0788 75134). Secretary: H.L. Barker (0788 810933).

WELCOMBE
Hotel & Golf Course
WARWICK ROAD
STRATFORD UPON AVON CV37 0NR
Tel: 0789 295252 Fax: 0789 414666
Telex: 31347

Olde Worlde charm and every modern luxury at this leading Heart of England hotel. Own 18-hole golf course with well-equipped club house, ample parking, pro-shop and changing facilities.

ALSO SEE COLOUR ADVERTISEMENT ON PAGE 26.

STRATFORD-UPON-AVON. **Stratford-upon-Avon Golf Club,** Tiddington Road, Stratford (0789 5749). *Green Fees:* information not provided. Professional: Pip Elson.

STRATFORD-UPON-AVON. **Welcombe Hotel Golf Course,** Warwick Road, Stratford-upon-Avon CV37 0NR (0789 295252). *Location:* one and a half miles from Stratford on A439 to Warwick. Wooded parkland. 18 holes, 6202 yards. S.S.S. 70. Practice area. *Green Fees:* weekdays £20.00, weekends and Bank Holidays £22.50. *Visitors:* welcome, except weekends before 2pm. Hotel on site, 4 star facilities. *Society Meetings:*

weekdays by prior arrangement. Golf Manager: P.J. Day (0789 299012).

WARWICK. **Warwick Golf Club,** Warwick Golf Centre, Racecourse, Warwick (Warwick (0926) 494316). *Location:* from A41/A46 junction, travel half a mile towards Warwick, turn right into racecourse. Flat parkland. 9 holes, 2682 yards. S.S.S. 66. Driving range (floodlit). *Green Fees:* weekdays £2.20 per 9 holes, weekends £3.00 per 9 holes. *Visitors:* welcome any time except Sunday mornings. Professional: P. Sharp (0926 491284). Secretary: R. Dunkley.

West Midlands

BIRMINGHAM. **Brand Hall Golf Club,** Heron Road, Oldbury, Warley B68 8AQ (021 552 7475). *Location:* Junction 2 M5, A4123, right at traffice lights signposted from there. Wooded course. 18 holes, 5855 yards. S.S.S. 68. Practice area. *Green Fees:* £3.00. *Eating facilities;* cafe and bar. *Visitors:* welcome, no restriction except weekends. Tee reserved for club members only Saturdays 8-10.00am and Sundays 8-10.30am. *Society Meetings:* phone Pro Shop (021-552 2195) to book times. Secretary: W.H. Rushton (021-544 6184).

BIRMINGHAM. **Cocks Moors Woods Golf Club,** Alcester Road, Kings Heath, Birmingham B14 4ER (021-444 3584). *Location:* A535 near city boundary. Wooded course. 18 holes, 5820 yards. S.S.S. 69. *Green fees:* information not available. *Eating facilities:* full catering and bars. *Visitors:* welcome at all times. Full range of leisure facilities within complex. *Society Meetings:* catered for, by arrangement with Professional. Professional: Steve Ellis. Secretary: Mr Glyn Spencer.

BIRMINGHAM. **Edgbaston Golf Club,** Church Road, Edgbaston, Birmingham B15 3TB (021-454 1736). *Location:* from centre of city take A38 (Bristol Road). After one mile and at second traffic lights turn right into Priory Road, at end turn left into Church Road, club entrance 200 yards on left. Parkland course. 18 holes, 6172 yards. S.S.S. 69. *Green Fees:* weekdays £22.00, with member £5.00; weekends and Bank Holidays £28.00. *Eating facilities:* lunches and teas daily except Sundays, other meals by arrangement. *Visitors:* welcome. *Society Meetings:* catered for by arrangement with Secretary. Professional: A.H. Bownes. Secretary: T. Ascough-Patterson.

BIRMINGHAM. **Gay Hill Golf Club,** Hollywood Lane, Hollywood, Birmingham B47 5PP (021-430

6523). *Location:* M42 Junction 3, three miles. Flat course. 18 holes, 6532 yards. S.S.S. 71. Practice area. *Green Fees:* £20.00 weekdays. *Eating facilities:* available. *Visitors:* welcome all week; weekends by invitation only. *Society Meetings:* catered for by arrangement Thursdays. Professional: Andrew Hill (021-474 6001). Secretary: Mrs E.K. Devitt (021-430 8544).

BIRMINGHAM. **Great Barr Golf Club,** Chapel Lane, Great Barr, Birmingham B43 7BA (021-357 1232). *Location:* six miles north-west of Birmingham M6 Junction 7. 18 holes, 6545 yards. S.S.S. 72. *Green Fees:* £15.00 weekdays, £20.00 weekends. *Eating facilities:* meals served, order in advance. *Visitors:* welcome weekdays, restricted at weekends. Weekends maximum handicap 18. Handicap Certificate required. *Society Meetings:* small groups catered for. Professional: S.M. Doe (021-357 5270). Secretary: K.J. Pembridge (021-358 4376).

BIRMINGHAM. **Handsworth Golf Club,** 11 Sunningdale Close, Handsworth, Birmingham B20 1NP (021-554 0599). *Location:* Junction 7 M6, then via A34 Birmingham Road, Old Walsall Road, Vernon Avenue, Westover Road, Craythorn Avenue. Parkland course. 18 holes, 6290 yards. S.S.S. 70. Practice area and large putting green. *Green Fees:* weekdays £20.00 per day, £5.00 with a member; weekends with member only. *Eating facilities:* snacks and restaurant Tuesdays – Sundays. *Visitors:* welcome weekdays. *Society Meetings:* catered for Mondays to Fridays. Professional: M. Hicks (021 523 3594). Hon. Secretary: Mr R.L. Neale (021-554 3387).

BIRMINGHAM. **Harborne (Church Farm) Golf Club,** Vicarage Road, Harborne, Birmingham B17 0SN (021-427 1204). *Location:* signposted from Harborne Centre. Parkland. 9 holes, 4062 yards. S.S.S. 63.

Green Fees: on application. *Eating facilities:* lunches and sandwiches available anytime. *Visitors:* welcome anytime. *Society Meetings:* by arrangement with the Professional. Professional: Mark Hampton. Secretary: Keith Williams (021-427 7889).

BIRMINGHAM. **Harborne Golf Club,** 40 Tennal Road, Birmingham B32 2JE (021-427 1728). *Location:* A4123, A456, B4124 three miles west Birmingham city centre. Undulating parkland/moorland. 18 holes, 6240 yards, 5703 metres. S.S.S. 70. *Green Fees:* weekdays £17.00, weekends and Bank Holidays £7.00 (must play with member). *Eating facilities:* bar and dining area, daily except Mondays. *Visitors:* must be members of golf club with Handicap Certificate. *Society Meetings:* Wednesday – Friday. Professional: A. Quarterman (021-427 3512). Secretary: E.J. Humphreys (021-427 3058).

BIRMINGHAM. **Harborne Municipal Golf Club,** Vicarage Road, Harborne, Birmingham B17 0SN (021-427 1204). *Location:* A456 to Harborne Village then course is signposted. Parkland course, beware of brooks! 9 holes, 2366 yards. S.S.S. 63. *Green Fees:* £3.50 weekdays, unemployed and Senior Citizens £1.90; £4.00 weekends, £2.20 unemployed and Senior Citizens. *Eating facilities:* restaurant. *Visitors:* welcome anytime. Free car parking. *Society Meetings:* welcome weekdays only. Professional: M.J. Hampton (021-427 1204). Secretary: K. Williams (021-427 1204).

BIRMINGHAM. **Hatchford Brook Golf Club,** Coventry Road, Sheldon, Birmingham B26 3PY (021-743 9821). *Location:* A45 next to Birmingham Airport, M6 Exit 4. Parkland. 18 holes, 6157 yards. S.S.S. 69. *Green Fees:* £4.65 per round. *Eating facilities:* restaurant at club. *Visitors:* welcome without reservation. *Society Meetings:* not catered for. Professional: P. Smith. Secretary: D. Williams (0676 23383).

BIRMINGHAM. **Hilltop Golf Club,** Park Lane, Birmingham B21 8LJ (021-554 4463). *Location:* M5 exit West Bromwich, take Birmingham road first left past W.B.A. football ground. Parkland, gently sloping fairways, large greens. 18 holes, 6114 yards. S.S.S. 69. *Green fees:* information not available. *Eating facilities:* cafe serving drinks and hot meals. *Visitors:* welcome, Municipal course. Professional: Kevin Highfield. Secretary: Terry James.

BIRMINGHAM. **Kings Norton Golf Club Ltd,** Brockhill Lane, Weatheroak, Alvechurch, Birmingham B48 7ED (Wythall (0564) 822821). *Location:* M42 Junction 3, towards Birmingham. Sign on left to Weatheroak, follow for 2 miles, over first crossroads. Club on left hand side. Parkland, 27 holes, 7000 yards. S.S.S. 72. *Green Fees:* £20.00 per round/day. *Eating facilities:* available. *Visitors:* welcome weekdays only, weekends with member. *Society Meetings:* catered for weekdays only. Professional: C. Haycock (0564 822822). Secretary: L.N.W. Prince (0564 826789).

BIRMINGHAM. **Maxstoke Park Golf Club,** Castle Lane, Coleshill, Birmingham B46 2RD (Coleshill (0675) 62158). *Location:* three miles north east of Coleshill on A47, turn right for Maxstoke. Parkland with trees and lake. 18 holes, 6478 yards, 5925 metres.

S.S.S. 71. Two practice areas. *Green Fees:* £12.00 per round, £16.00 per day. *Eating facilities:* restaurant and bar. *Visitors:* welcome weekdays only, weekends with member. *Society Meetings:* catered for. Professional: R.A. Young (0675 64915). Secretary: J.C. Evans.

BIRMINGHAM. **Moseley Golf Club,** Springfield Road, Kings Heath, Birmingham B14 7DX (021-444 2115). *Location:* south Birmingham. 18 holes, 6227 yards. S.S.S. 70. *Green Fees:* £25.00. *Eating facilities:* in clubhouse. *Visitors:* welcome only by prior arrangement with Secretary. *Society Meetings:* catered for. Professional: G. Edge (021-444 2063). Secretary: P. Muddiman (021-444 4957 10.00am – 10.00pm).

BIRMINGHAM. **North Worcestershire Golf Club,** Frankley Beeches Road, Northfield, Birmingham B31 5LP (021-475 1026). *Location:* from city centre main Bristol road (A38) to Northfield, turning right into Frankley Beeches Road by Black Horse Public House. Parkland, established inland course. 18 holes, 5954 yards. S.S.S. 69. *Green Fees:* £15.00 weekdays. *Eating facilities:* full restaurant and bar, luncheon and dinners. *Visitors:* welcome weekdays without reservation. *Society Meetings:* catered for Tuesdays and Thursdays. Professional: K.E. Jones (021-475 5721). Secretary: K.S. Reading (021-475 1047).

COVENTRY. **Brandon Wood Golf Course,** Brandon Lane, Wolston, Near Coventry. *Location:* off A45 southbound. Parkland on banks of River Avon. 18 holes. 6530 yards. S.S.S. 71. Driving range. *Green Fees:* information not provided. *Eating facilities:* bar and restaurant. *Visitors:* public course, phone Professional to book (up to seven days in advance for weekends, on the day for weekdays). *Society Meetings:* phone for details. Professional/Secretary: Chris Gledhill (0203 543141).

COVENTRY. **City of Coventry Golf Club,** Brandon Lane, Coventry (Coventry [0203] 543141). *Location:* 6 miles south-east from City centre. 18 holes, 6530 yards. S.S.S. 71. *Green Fees:* information not provided. *Visitors:* unrestricted. Professional/Secretary: C. Gledhill.

COVENTRY. **Coventry Golf Club,** Finham Park, Coventry CV3 6PJ (Coventry (0203) 411123). *Location:* on A444 south of A45, one mile on left. Parkland, wooded. 18 holes, 6613 yards. S.S.S. 72. Practice ground. *Green Fees:* £20.00 weekdays. *Eating facilities:* available. *Visitors:* welcome weekdays only, without reservation. *Society Meetings:* catered for on Wednesdays and Thursdays by arrangement. Rates dependent on numbers. Professional: P. Weaver (0203 411298). Secretary: J.E. Jarman (0203 414152).

COVENTRY. **Coventry Hearsall Golf Club,** Beechwood Avenue, Coventry CV5 6DF (Coventry (0203) 675809). *Location;* off A46 south of Coventry, one mile south of city centre. 18 holes, 5958 yards. S.S.S. 69. *Green Fees:* Mondays to Fridays £14.00, Sundays £8.00. *Eating facilities:* full restaurant facilities. *Visitors:* welcome Mondays to Saturdays, Sundays after 9am as a member's guest. *Society Meetings;* limited. Professional: T. Rouse (0203 713156). Secretary: W.G. Doughty (0203 713470).

COVENTRY. **Forest of Arden Hotel, Golf and Country Club,** Maxstoke Lane, Meriden, Coventry CV7 6HR (0676 23721). *Location:* three miles from Junction 6 of M42, three miles from Junction 4 of M6. Parkland course. 18 holes, 6479 yards. S.S.S 71; second course 9 holes, 3035 yards. S.S.S. 35. *Green Fees:* £18.00 weekdays, £22.00 weekends. *Eating facilities:* bars and restaurant available. 152 bedroom four star hotel with extensive conference and leisure facilities. *Society Meetings:* enquiries welcome. Professional: M. Tarn (0676 22118).

COVENTRY. **Grange Golf Club,** Copeswood, Coventry (Coventry (0203) 451465). *Location:* three miles from centre of Coventry on A427/A428 road to Rugby, Lutterworth. 9 holes, 6002 yards. S.S.S. 69. *Green Fees:* weekdays £7.00 per round, Sundays £10.00 per round. *Visitors:* welcome except Saturdays, weekday evenings or Sunday mornings. Secretary: E. Soutar.

COVENTRY. **John Reay Golf Centre,** Sandpits Lane, Keresley, Coventry CV6 3FR (020333 6465). Coventry's leading Golf Centre, established 1973. *Location:* Coventry – A51 Coventry to Tamworth road. 250 yard 30-bay floodlit driving range. *Green Fees:* information not provided. Robert Hunter's Golf School and Alan Morgan for Club Repairs nearby. *Eating facilities:* Hogan's Bar Bistro – seats approximately 120. *Visitors:* open to the public. Professional: John Reay (020333 3920/3405).

COVENTRY. **North Warwickshire Golf Club Ltd,** Hampton Lane, Meriden, Coventry CV7 7LL (Meriden (0676) 22259). *Location:* on B4102, one mile from Stonebridge on A45, approximately midway between Birmingham and Coventry. 9 holes, 6352 yards. S.S.S. 70. *Green Fees:* £12.00 weekdays, weekends £16.00 with member. *Eating facilities:* full catering and bar. *Visitors:* welcome without reservation except Thursdays. *Society Meetings:* catered for by prior arrangement. Professional: Roy Young (0676 22259). Secretary: E.G. Barnes (0676 22915).

DUDLEY. **Dudley Golf Club Ltd,** Turners Hill Rowley Regis, Warley (Dudley (0384) 253719). *Location:* one mile south of Dudley town centre on Blackheath Road. 18 holes, 6000 yards. S.S.S. 68. *Green Fees:* £12.00 weekdays. *Eating facilities:* full catering facilities available. *Visitors:* welcome but only with a member at weekends. *Society Meetings:* by prior arrangement. Professional: L. Bashford (0384 254020). Secretary: R.P. Fortune (0385 233877).

DUDLEY. **Himley Hall Golf Centre,** Log Cabin, Himley Hall Park, Himley Road, Dudley DY3 4DF (0902 895207). *Location:* A449 Himley Road, Dudley. Parkland. 9 holes, 3090 yards. S.S.S. 35 for 9 holes. Practice area. *Green Fees:* weekdays £2.50 for 9 holes, £4.00 for 18 holes; weekends £3.00 for 9 holes, £4.50 for 18 holes. Juniors and Senior Citizens £1.60 for 9 holes, £2.50 for 18 holes weekdays, £2.50 for 9 holes, £3.50 for 18 holes weekends. *Eating facilities:* cafe. *Visitors:* welcome weekdays. *Society Meetings:* catered for weekdays.

DUDLEY near. **Swindon Golf Club,** Bridgnorth Road, Swindon, Near Dudley DY3 4PU (0902

896765). *Location:* B4176 Dudley/Bridgnorth Road, three miles from A449 at Himley. Woodland and parkland course with exceptional views. 27 holes, 9 – 1135 yards, 18 – 6042 yards. S.S.S. 18 – 69, 9 – Par 3. *Green Fees:* £12.00 per round, £18.00 per day weekdays; £18.00 per round weekends and Bank Holidays. *Eating facilities:* fully licensed bar and restaurant. *Visitors:* always welcome, booking not required. Buggies available. Fishing. *Society Meetings:* by arrangement weekdays only. Secretary: Mrs A. Wilkinson (0902 897031).

HALESOWEN. **Halesowen Golf Club,** The Leasowes, Leasowes Lane, Halesowen B62 8QF (021-550 1041). *Location:* exit Junction 3 M5, A456 (Kidderminster) two miles, Halesowen town one mile. Parkland course. 18 holes, 5754 yards. S.S.S. 68. *Green Fees:* weekdays £12.00 per round, £15.00 per day, weekends must play with a member. *Eating facilities:* no catering Mondays. *Visitors:* welcome weekdays. *Society Meetings:* by arrangement with Secretary. Professional: Mark Smith (021-503 0593). Secretary: Mrs M. Bateman (021-501 3606).

REDNAL. **Lickey Hills (Municipal) Golf Club,** Old Birmingham Road, Rednal, Near Birmingham (021-453 3159). *Location:* M5 Exit 4 on city boundary. 18 holes, 5721 yards. S.S.S. 67. *Green Fees:* information not provided. *Eating facilities:* restaurant at club. *Visitors:* welcome.

REDNAL. **Rose Hill Golf Club,** Rednal, near Birmingham (021-453 3159). *Location:* M5 Exit 4 Lydiate Ash, Lickey Hills one mile. 18 holes, 6010 yards. S.S.S. 69. *Green fees:* information not provided. *Eating facilities:* full catering. *Visitors:* welcome without reservation. *Society Meetings:* catered for. Professional: M. March. Secretary: A. Cushing.

SOLIHULL. **Copt Heath Golf Club,** 1220 Warwick Road, Knowle, Solihull B93 9LN (Knowle (0564) 772650). *Location:* on A41 half a mile south of junction 5 with M42. Flat parkland. 18 holes, 6504 yards. S.S.S. 71. Full practice facilities available. *Green Fees:* weekdays £27.50 per round or day. Weekends and Public Holidays must be introduced by a member. *Eating facilities:* lunch and evening meal available except Mondays. *Visitors:* no restrictions weekdays. *Society Meetings:* by arrangement with Secretary. Professioanl: Brian Barton. Secretary: W. Lenton.

SOLIHULL. **Ladbrook Park Golf Club Ltd,** Poolhead Lane, Tanworth-in-Arden, Solihull B94 5ED (Tanworth-in-Arden (05644) 2264). Parkland. 18 holes, 6407 yards. S.S.S. 71. *Green Fees:* weekdays £20.00 per day, £5.00 playing with a member; weekends £6.00 with a member. *Eating facilities:* catering daily except Mondays, bars. *Visitors:* welcome weekdays, weekends with member only. *Society Meetings:* catered for by prior arrangement with Secretary. Professional: Graham Taylor (05644 2581). Secretary: Mrs G.P. Taylor (05644 2264).

SOLIHULL. **Olton Golf Club Ltd,** Mirfield Road, Solihull B91 1JH (021-705 1083). *Location:* one mile from Solihull along Warwick Road towards Birmingham. 18 holes, 6153 yards. S.S.S. 71. *Green Fees:* information not provided. *Eating facilities:* by prior arrangement. *Visitors:* welcome with reservation, not at weekends or Bank Holidays. *Society Meetings:* limited, catered for by arrangement. Professional: David Playdon. Secretary: M.A. Perry.

SOLIHULL. **Robin Hood Golf Club,** St. Bernards Road, Solihull B92 7DJ. *Location:* eight miles south of Birmingham, off A40 Birmingham to Warwick road. Flat parkland. 18 holes, 6609 yards, 6043 metres. S.S.S. 72. *Green Fees:* £16.00 per round, £20.00 per day. *Eating facilities:* by prior arrangement with Steward (021-706 0159). *Visitors:* welcome weekdays only subject to limitations. Arrange with Professional. *Society Meetings:* catered for. Professional: F.E. Miller (021-706 0806). Secretary: P.T. Richardson (021-706 0061).

SOLIHULL. **Shirley Golf Club,** Stratford Road, Monkspath, Shirley, Solihull (021-744 7024). *Location:* eight miles from Birmingham on A34 to Stratford. 18 holes, 6411 yards. S.S.S. 71. *Green Fees:* £16.00 per round, £27.00 per day. *Eating facilities:* meals at club except Mondays. *Visitors:* welcome weekdays without reservation. *Society Meetings:* catered for weekdays. Professional: Chris Wicketts (021-745 4979). Secretary: A.J. Phillips (021-744 6001).

SOLIHULL. **Whitelakes Golf Club,** Tilehouse Lane, Tidbury Green, Solihull B90 1PT (0564 824414). *Location:* two miles from Shirley and three miles off the M42. To play over numerous ponds, lakes and the River Coal. 9 holes, 987 yards. S.S.S. 27. 15-bay golf range. *Green Fees:* 9 holes £2.25, 18 holes £3.25. *Eating facilities:* excellent bar and restaurant facilities. *Visitors:* welcome, no restrictions. Facilities for fishing, clay pigeon shooting, archery, swimming pool available. *Society Meetings:* catered for.

STOURBRIDGE. **Stourbridge Golf Club,** Worcester Lane, Pedmore, Stourbridge DY8 2RB (Stourbridge (0384) 393062). *Location:* one mile town from centre on Worcester road. Parkland. 18 holes, 6178 yards S.S.S. 69. *Green Fees:* £20.00. *Eating facilities:* available. *Visitors:* welcome weekdays, weekends with member. *Society Meetings:* catered for Tuesdays. Professional: W.H. Firkin (0384 393129). Secretary: F.R. McLachlan (0384 395566).

SUTTON COLDFIELD. **Boldmere Municipal Golf Club,** Monmouth Drive, Sutton Coldfield (021-354

3379). *Location:* A34, seven miles from centre of Birmingham. 18 holes, 4463 yards. S.S.S. 61. *Green Fees:* information not available. *Eating facilities:* meals daily. *Visitors:* welcome without reservation. *Society Meetings:* not catered for. Professional: T.J. Short. Secretary: D. Duffy.

SUTTON COLDFIELD. **Moor Hall Golf Club Ltd,** Moor Hall Drive, Sutton Coldfield B75 6LN (021-308 0103). *Location:* one mile east of Sutton Coldfield, A446. Parkland. 18 holes, 6249 yards. S.S.S. 70. Practice area. *Green Fees:* £17.00 per round, £23.00 day ticket. *Eating facilities:* available weekdays except for Mondays. *Visitors:* welcome weekdays only (not Thursday mornings). *Society Meetings:* catered for Tuesdays and Wednesdays only. Professional: Alan Partridge (021-308 5106). Hon. Secretary: W.C. Brodie (021-308 6130).

SUTTON COLDFIELD. **Pype Hayes Golf Club,** Eachelhurst Road, Sutton Coldfield B76 8EP (021-351 1014). *Location:* turn right, off A453 Sutton to Walmley. 18 holes, 5811 yards. S.S.S. 68. Practice net. *Green Fees:* weekdays £3.80, weekends £4.60. *Eating facilities:* full facilities available. *Visitors:* welcome without reservation. *Society Meetings:* welcome, much used course – weekdays. Professional: J.F. Bayliss. Secretary: William C. Marks (021-353 4594).

SUTTON COLDFIELD. **Sutton Coldfield Golf Club,** Thornhill Road, Streetly, Sutton Coldfield B74 3ER (021-353 2014). *Location:* situated in Sutton Park, one mile off A452, seven miles from centre of Birmingham. 18 holes, 6491 yards. S.S.S. 71. *Green Fees:* £18.00 inc. VAT (weekdays), £25.00 inc. VAT (weekends). *Eating facilities:* by arrangement with Steward. *Visitors:* welcome without reservation. Handicap Certificate required. *Society Meetings:* catered for by arrangement with Secretary. Professional: J.K. Hayes. Administrator: Mr M. McClean.

SUTTON COLDFIELD. **Walmley Golf Club (Wylde Green) Ltd,** Brooks Road, Sutton Coldfield B72 1HR (021-373 0029). *Location:* Birmingham/Sutton Coldfield main road, turn right at Greenhill Road. Flat parkland. 18 holes, 6537 yards. S.S.S. 72. Practice area. *Green Fees:* weekdays £18.00 18 holes, £25.00 18+ holes; weekends playing with member only. *Eating facilities:* lunch and evening meals available except Mondays. *Visitors:* welcome with member. *Society*

Meetings: catered for weekdays except Mondays. Secretary: J.P.G. Windsor. Professional: Mike Skerritt (021-373 7103).

WALSALL. **Bloxwich Golf Club,** Stafford Road, Bloxwich, Walsall WS3 3PQ (Bloxwich (0922) 405724). *Location:* off main Walsall-Cannock road (A34). Parkland. 18 holes, 6286 yards. S.S.S. 70. *Green Fees:* weekdays £17.00. *Eating facilities:* available. *Visitors:* welcome with or without reservation except weekends and Bank Holidays. *Society Meetings:* catered for preferably mid week, reduced rates for 20 or more. Professional: B. Janes (0922 476889). Secretary: A.D. Perry (0922 476593).

WALSALL. **Calderfields Golf Club Ltd,** Aldridge Road, Walsall WS4 2JS (0922 640540). *Location:* A454 Bilice Public Arms. Parkland, lake. 18 holes, 6700 yards, 6100 metres. S.S.S. 73. Practice area. *Green Fees:* weekdays £8.00, weekends £15.00. *Eating facilities:* restaurant and bar. *Visitors:* welcome always. *Society Meetings:* package deals most welcome. Professional: Roger Griffin (0922 32243). Secretary: Jim Wooster (0922 640540 or 23319).

WALSALL. **Druids Heath Golf Club,** Stonnall Road, Aldridge, Walsall WS9 8JZ (Aldridge (0922) 55595). *Location:* between Sutton Coldfield and Walsall, near A454. 18 holes, 6914 yards. S.S.S. 73. *Green Fees:* £15.00 weekdays, £20.00 weekends. *Eating facilities:* diningroom and bar snacks. *Visitors:* welcome without reservation weekdays, with member at weekends. Ladies' Day Thursdays. *Society Meetings:* catered for on weekdays. Professional: M.P. Daubney (0922 59523). Secretary: P.M. Halldron.

WALSALL. **Walsall Golf Club,** The Broadway, Walsall WS1 3EY (0922 20014 or 22710). *Location:* one and a half miles from M6/M5 junction. Wooded course. 18 holes, 6243 yards. S.S.S. 70. *Green Fees:* £20.00 per round, £25.00 per day. Reduced rates for organised societies, minimum 16. *Eating facilities:* all facilities available. *Visitors:* welcome weekdays only. *Society Meetings:* catered for. Professional: R. Lambert (0922 26766). Secretary: E. Murray (0922 613512).

WARLEY. **Warley Golf Club,** Lightwood Hill, Warley (021-429 2440). *Location:* five miles west of Birmingham centre, just off main Hawley Road West. 9 holes, 2606 yards. S.S.S. 64. *Green Fees:* £3.60 weekdays,

£4.20 weekends. *Eating facilities:* cafe. *Visitors:* welcome without reservation. *Society Meetings:* catered for, but not advised (Municipal Golf Course). Professional: David Owen. Secretary: C. Lowndes.

WEST BROMWICH. **Dartmouth Golf Club,** Vale Street, West Bromwich. *Location:* one mile centre at rear of Churchfields High School. 9 holes, 6060 yards. S.S.S. 69. *Green Fees:* information not provided. *Visitors:* welcome weekdays, weekends restricted. Records – Amateur – 68, P. Griffiths; Professional 70, P. Lester. Secretary: R.H. Smith (021-588 2131). Professional: J. Flanagan (021-588 2131).

WEST BROMWICH. **Sandwell Park Golf Club,** Birmingham Road, West Bromwich (021-553 4637). *Location:* on A41 to Birmingham close to Junction 1 M5. 18 holes, 6422 yards. S.S.S. 72. *Green Fees:* £25.00 per day. *Eating facilities:* lunches except Mondays. *Visitors:* welcome except weekends and Bank Holidays. *Society Meetings:* by prior arrangement. Professional: A.W. Mutton (021-553 4384).

WISHAW. **The Belfry,** Wishaw, North Warwickshire B76 9PR (Curdworth (0675) 470301). *Location:* junction of A446 Coventry-Lichfield road and A4091 Tamworth road off Junction 9 M42. Two challenging parkland courses. Brabazon (venue of 1985 and 1989 Ryder Cup matches): 18 holes, 6975 yards. S.S.S. 73 (must have handicap of 24 or better). Derby: 18 holes, 6077 yards. S.S.S. 69. Full practice facilities available. *Green Fees:* Brabazon £35.00 weekdays, £38.00 weekends. Derby: £12.00 weekdays, £15.00 weekends. *Eating facilities:* snacks and full meals available, two bars. *Visitors:* welcome at all times. The Belfry is a 4 Star Hotel with extensive leisure facilities. *Society Meetings:* welcome at all times. Professionals: Peter McGovern, Graham Laidlaw (0675 470301 extension 267).

WOLVERHAMPTON. **Oxley Park Golf Club Ltd,** Stafford Road, Bushbury, Wolverhampton WV10 6DE (0902 20506). *Location:* one and a half miles M54/A449 junction. One and a half miles Wolverhampton town centre. Undulating parkland. 18 holes, 6168 yards, 5639 metres. S.S.S. 69. *Green Fees:* weekdays £14.00, weekends £16.00. *Eating facilities:* each day except Monday. *Visitors:* welcome weekdays, weekends by arrangement with Professional. *Society Meetings:* catered for Wednesdays only. Secretary: Mrs

---

MOORS FARM AND COUNTRY RESTAURANT
Chillington Lane, Codsall, Near Wolverhampton Tel: (09074) 2330
Quiet superior Farmhouse accommodation. En suite rooms with tea/coffee facilities, colour TV.
Wonderful views. Quality home produced fresh farm food on menu. Special diets catered for.
8 well known Golf Courses within 12 mile radius.

Kathryn Mann (0902 25892). Professional: Leslie Burlison (0902 25445)

WOLVERHAMPTON. **Penn Golf Club,** Penn Common, Penn, Wolverhampton (Wolverhampton (0902) 341142). *Location:* two miles south west of Wolverhampton. 18 holes, 6449 yards. S.S.S. 71. *Green Fees:* £15.00. *Eating facilities:* available, excluding Sunday and Monday. *Visitors:* welcome weekdays, without advance booking. *Society Meetings:* catered for. Professional: A. Briscoe. Secretary: P.W. Thorrington.

WOLVERHAMPTON. **South Staffordshire Golf Club,** Danescourt Road, Tettenhall, Wolverhampton WV6 9BQ (Wolverhampton (0902) 756401). *Location:* two miles from Wolverhampton, on A41 to Telford. Parkland. 18 holes, 6621 yards. S.S.S. 72. Two practice grounds. *Green Fees:* weekdays £16.00 per round, £20.00 per day. *Eating facilities:* full catering and bar. *Visitors:* welcome weekdays. Weekends only with member. *Society Meetings:* catered for weekdays. Professional: J. Rhodes (0902 754816). Secretary: H. Williams (0902 751065).

Wiltshire

CHIPPENHAM. **Chippenham Golf Club,** Malmesbury Road, Chippenham SN15 5LT (Chippenham (0249) 652040). *Location:* A429 one mile from Chippenham, two miles from M4 (Junction 17). Flat parkland. 18 holes, 5540 yards. S.S.S. 67. *Green Fees:* weekdays £16.00, weekends £20.00. *Eating facilities:* snacks and evening à la carte (not Mondays). *Visitors:* welcome; current Handicap Certificate required. Prior arrangement necessary. *Society Meetings:* catered for weekdays only. Professional: Bill Creamer (0249 655519). Secretary: V.J. Carlisle (0249 652040).

CORSHAM. **Kingsdown Golf Club,** Corsham SN14 9BD (Box (0225) 742530). *Location:* five miles east of Bath. Heathland. 18 holes, 6445 yards, 5891 metres. S.S.S. 71. *Green Fees:* weekdays £15.00. *Eating facilities:* lounge bar and dining room. *Visitors:* welcome except at weekends and Bank Holidays and must have current Handicap Certificate. *Society Meetings:* catered for by arrangement. Professional: Richard Emery (0225 742634). Secretary: S.H. Phipps (0225 743472).

DEVIZES. **North Wilts Golf Club,** Bishop's Cannings, Devizes SN10 2LP (Cannings (038-086 257). *Location:* one mile from A4 at Quemerford, Calne. Four miles from Devizes. 18 holes, 6451 yards, 5898 metres. S.S.S. 71. *Green Fees:* information not available. *Eating facilities:* full catering service. *Visitors:* welcome without reservation. *Society Meetings:*

catered for by prior arrangement. Professionals: Graham Laing and Colin Harraway. Secretary: J. B. W. McKelvie (038-086 627).

MARLBOROUGH. **Marlborough Golf Club,** The Common, Marlborough SN8 1DU (Marlborough (0672) 512147). *Location:* about one mile from town centre on A345 travelling towards Swindon. Downland. 18 holes, 6241 yards. S.S.S. 70. Practice ground and putting green. *Green Fees:* weekdays only £15.00 per round, £20.00 per day; weekends £30.00 per round. *Eating facilities:* restaurant serving snacks and full meals open most of day. *Visitors:* welcome generally, but it is best to telephone in advance as course may be too busy to allow green fees; some weekends course is closed to green fees. *Society Meetings:* catered for with advance notice. Professional: Billy McAdams (0672 512493). Secretary/General Manager: Laurence Ross (0672 512147).

SALISBURY. **High Post Golf Club Ltd,** Great Durnford, Salisbury SP4 6AT (Middle Woodford (072 273) 231). *Location:* midway between Salisbury and Amesbury on A345. Downland and blackthorn. 18 holes, 6267 yards, 5730 metres. S.S.S. 70. Large practice ground. *Green Fees:* £18.00 weekdays, £22.00 weekends. *Eating facilities:* full catering and bars available. *Visitors:* welcome with valid Handicap Certificate. *Society Meetings:* catered for mid-week by arrangement. Professional: Tony Harman (072 273 219). Secretary: W. Goodwin (072 273 356).

SALISBURY. **Salisbury and South Wilts Golf Club,** Netherhampton, Salisbury SP2 8PR (Salisbury (0722) 742131). *Location:* on A3094, two miles Salisbury, two miles Wilton, opposite Netherhampton village. Parkland. 18 holes, 6130 yards. S.S.S. 70. Practice ground. *Green Fees:* weekdays £14.00 per day, weekends and Bank Holidays £22.00 per day. *Eating facilities:* full catering service and bar. *Visitors:* welcome without reservation at all times, but preliminary phone call advised. *Society Meetings:* catered for by prior arrangement. Professional: G. Emerson (0722 742929). Secretary: Wg. Cdr. A.W. Pawson (0722 742645).

SHRIVENHAM. **Shrivenham Park Golf Course,** Shrivenham, Swindon SN6 8EX (0793 782946). *Location:* M4 exit 15. Follow Oxford signs then Shrivenham. Just through village on left. Parkland with special features. 18 holes, 5622 yards. S.S.S 67. Practice area. *Green Fees:* £12.50 per round, £17.50 per day weekdays; £15.00 per round, £20.00 per day weekends. *Eating facilities:* lounge bar, bar meals, carvery. *Visitors:* welcome without restriction. *Society Meetings:* special rates for Company Days and Golf Societies. Professional: John Blanch (0793 783853). Secretary: David J. Woodman (0793 783583).

SWINDON. **Broome Manor Golf Complex,** Pipers Way, Swindon SN3 1RG (Swindon (0793) 495761). *Location:* two miles from Junction 15, M4 (follow signs for "Golf Complex". Wooded parkland. 18 holes, 6359 yards, 5815 metres. S.S.S. 71. 9 holes, 5610 yards, 5130 metres. S.S.S. 67. Floodlit covered driving range. *Green Fees:* weekdays £3.65 for 9 holes, £6.10 for 18 holes; weekends £3.35 for 9 holes, £5.60 for 18 holes. *Eating facilities:* full facilities. *Visitors:* welcome, no restrictions. Simulated clay pigeon shooting. *Society Meetings:* catered for Monday to Thursday. Pro-

fessional: Barry Sandry (0793 532403). Manager: Tom Watt (0793 495761). Catering: (0793 490939).

SWINDON. **Swindon Golf Club,** Ogbourne St. George, Marlborough SN8 1TB (Ogbourne St. George (067 284) 217). *Location:* on A345 between Swindon and Marlborough, four miles south of M4 (Junction 15). Downs course. 18 holes, 6226 yards. S.S.S. 70. Practice area. *Green Fees:* £15.00 per round, £20.00 per day. *Eating facilities:* full daily catering available. *Visitors:* welcome with reservation weekdays. Weekends and Bank Holidays with member only. *Society Meetings:* catered for weekdays only by prior arrangement with Secretary. Professional: Colin Harraway (067 284 287). Secretary: A. Grant (067 284 327).

UPAVON. **Royal Air Force Upavon Golf Club,** York Road, Upavon, Pewsey SN9 6BQ (0980 630787). *Location:* one mile south east of Upavon village on A342. Undulating course. 9 holes, 5116 yards. S.S.S. 67. *Green Fees:* £10.00 (payable at Guardroom). *Visitors and Societies:* welcome, but visitors must be accompanied by a member on Sunday mornings. Secretary: Sqn. Ldr. I.F. Davidson (0980 630351 extension 654).

WARMINSTER. **West Wilts Golf Club,** Elm Hill, Warminster (Warminster (0985) 212702). *Location:* on A350 half-a-mile out of Warminster on Westbury Road. Downland. 18 holes, 5701 yards. S.S.S. 68. *Green Fees:* weekdays £15.00, weekends £24.00. *Eating facilities:* full meals and snacks available at all times. *Visitors:* welcome, but must produce a Handicap Certificate. Afternoons only at weekends. *Society Meetings:* catered for Wednesday to Friday. Professional: Alan Harvey (0985 212110). Secretary: L.R. Weaver (0985 213133).

North Yorkshire

BEDALE. **Bedale Golf Club,** Leyburn Road, Bedale (Bedale (0677) 22568). *Location:* close to northern boundary of town. 18 holes, 5857 yards. S.S.S. 68. *Green Fees:* £12.00 weekdays, £18.00 weekends. *Eating facilities:* caterer employed. *Visitors:* welcome without reservation. *Society Meetings:* catered for on application. Professional: A.D. Johnson. Secretary: G.A. Shepherdson.

BENTHAM. **Bentham Golf Club,** Robin Lane, Bentham, Near Lancaster LA2 7AG (Bentham (05242) 61018). *Location:* B6480 north-west of Lancaster towards Settle. Parkland with magnificent views. 9 holes, 5752 yards. S.S.S. 69. *Green Fees:* weekdays £8.00, Juniors £3.75; weekends and holidays £10.00, Juniors £4.50. Weekly tickets £30.00, Juniors £10.00. *Eating facilities:* hot and cold snacks and meals available. *Visitors:* welcome all week without reservation. *Society Meetings:* welcome - contact Secretary. Secretary: J.M. Philipson (05242 62455).

CATTERICK. **Catterick Garrison Golf Club,** Leyburn Road, Catterick Garrison, Catterick DL9 3QE (Richmond (0748) 833268). *Location:* six miles south-west Scotch Corner, A1 turn off to Catterick Garrison. 18 holes, 6322 yards. S.S.S. 70. *Green Fees:* weekdays £12.00, weekends and Bank Holidays £16.00. *Eating facilities:* restaurant and snacks except Mondays. *Visitors:* welcome without reservation. *Society Meetings:* catered for on application. Professional: Stephen Bradley. Secretary: Major (retd) L. Layton.

EASINGWOLD. **Easingwold Golf Club,** Stillington Road, Easingwold, York YO6 3ET (Easingwold (0347) 21486). *Location:* 12 miles north of York, course half-a-mile along Stillington Road. Flat, wooded parkland. 18 holes, 5679 metres. S.S.S. 70. *Green Fees:* weekdays £14.00 (£7.00 with a member); weekends and Bank Holidays £18.00 (£7.00 with member). *Eating facilities:* catering except Mondays, order in advance. *Visitors:* welcome without reservation. *Society Meetings:* maximum 48, weekdays only, prior booking essential. Contact G.C. Young. Professional: John Hughes (0347 21964). Secretary: K.C. Hudson (0347 22474).

FILEY. **Filey Golf Club,** The Clubhouse, West Avenue, Filey YO14 9BQ (Scarborough (0723) 513116). *Location:* one mile from town centre. Seaside links. 18 holes, 6030 yards. S.S.S. 69. Large practice area. *Green Fees:* weekdays £11.00, weekends £14.00. *Eating facilities:* dining room April to September, full bar. *Visitors:* welcome if members of a golf club and holding current Handicap Certificate. *Society Meetings:* catered for. Professional: D. Currey (0723 513134). Secretary: T.M. Thompson (0723 513293).

HARROGATE. **Crimple Valley Golf Club,** Hookstone Wood Road, Harrogate HG2 8PN (Harrogate (0423) 883485). *Location:* one mile south from town centre. Turn off A61 at Appleyards Garage on to Hookstone Road, signposted to right. Gently sloping

fairways in rural setting. 9 holes, 2500 yards. S.S.S. 33. *Green fees:* information not provided. *Eating facilities:* licensed bar, lunches available weekdays, breakfasts weekends. *Visitors:* welcome at all times. Professional: R.A. Lumb. Secretary: A.M. Grange.

HARROGATE. **Harrogate Golf Club Ltd,** Forest Lane Head, Harrogate HG2 7TF (Harrogate (0423) 863158). *Location:* two miles from Harrogate on the A59 Harrogate/Knaresborough road. Parkland. 18 holes, 6241 yards. S.S.S. 70. *Green Fees:* weekdays £18.00, weekends £25.00. *Eating facilities:* 19th bar, lounge bar, diningroom, full catering. *Visitors:* welcome but enquiry advised. *Society Meetings:* catered for. Professional: P. Johnson (0423 862547). Secretary: J. McDougall (0423 862999).

HARROGATE. **Oakdale Golf Club,** Oakdale, off Kent Road, Harrogate HG1 2LN (Harrogate (0423) 502806). *Location:* three-quarters of a mile from town centre, leave Ripon road (A61 from Leeds) at Kent Road. Parkland, with featured stream. 18 holes, 6456 yards. S.S.S. 71. Practice ground. *Green Fees:* weekdays £16.00, weekends £21.00. *Eating facilities:* full dining facilities. *Visitors:* welcome, groups by prior arrangement. *Society Meetings:* welcome by arrangement. Professional: Richard Jessop (0423 560510). Secretary: Frank Hindmarsh (0423 567162).

HARROGATE. **Pannal Golf Club,** Follifoot Road, Pannal, Harrogate HG3 1ES (Harrogate (0423) 871641). *Location:* two miles south of Harrogate A61 (Leeds Road). 18 holes, 6659 yards. S.S.S. 72. Large practice ground. *Green Fees:* £20.00 per round, £25.00 per day weekdays; £25.00 per round weekends. *Eating facilities:* lunch available daily, dinner by arrangement. *Visitors:* welcome Monday to Friday without reservation, enquiry advised. *Society Meetings:* catered for Tuesday (pm only), Wednesday and Thursday. Professional: Murray Burgess (0423 872620). Manager/Secretary: W.K. Davies (0423 872628).

KIRKBYMOORSIDE. **Kirkbymoorside Golf Club,** Manor Vale, Kirkbymoorside, York YO6 6EG (0751 31525). Wooded course. 18 holes, 6027 yards. S.S.S. 69. *Green Fees:* £10.00 weekdays, £15.00 weekends and Public Holidays. *Eating facilities:* available. *Visitors:* welcome by arrangement with Steward. *Society Meetings:* catered for by arrangement with Steward. Secretary: D.G. Saunders (0439 71625).

KNARESBOROUGH. **Knaresborough Golf Club,** Boroughbridge Road, Knaresborough HG5 0QQ (Harrogate (0423) 863219). *Location:* one-and-a-half miles from town centre. A1 Boroughbridge.Wooded parkland. 18 holes, 6117 yards. S.S.S.70. Large prac-

tice area. *Green Fees:* weekdays £12.00 per round, £16.00 per day; weekends £20.00. *Eating facilities:* resident Steward provides full catering. *Visitors:* welcome without reservation. *Society Meetings:* catered for. Professional: Keith Johnstone. Secretary/Manager: J.I. Barrow (0423 862690).

MALTON. **Malton and Norton Golf Club,** Welham Park, Malton YO17 9QE (Malton (0653) 692959). *Location:* off A64 to Malton between York and Scarborough. One mile south on Welham road turn right at Norton level crossing. 18 holes, 6411 yards. S.S.S.71. Medal course; 6141 yards. S.S.S. 69 (club). Practice ground. *Green Fees:* weekdays £15.50, weekends and Public Holidays £20.00. *Eating facilities:* full bar and catering available. *Visitors:* welcome without reservation (except club match days and weekends from 1st November to 31st March, unless with member). *Society Meetings:* catered for by arrangement with Secretary. Professional: Malcolm Henderson (0653 693882). Secretary: W.G. Wade (0653 697912).

RICHMOND. **Richmond (Yorkshire) Golf Club,** Bend Hagg, Richmond D10 5EX (Richmond (0748) 2457). *Location:* A6108 from Scotch Corner. 18 holes, 5704 yards. S.S.S. 68. *Green Fees:* weekdays £10.00 per round, £12.00 per day, weekends £15.00 per round, £20.00 per day. *Visitors:* welcome without reservation (not before 11.30am on Sundays). *Society Meetings:* catered for. Professional: Paul Jackson. Secretary: B.D. Aston.

RIPON. **Masham Golf Club,** Masham, Ripon (Ripon (0765) 89379). *Location:* nine miles north of Ripon. 9 holes, 2622 yards. S.S.S. 66. *Green Fees:* £10.00 U/A. *Visitors:* welcome weekdays but must be accompanied by a member weekends and Bank Holidays, with reservation. Party visits by arrangement with Secretary. Secretary: Mrs M.A. Willis (0765 89491).

RIPON. **Ripon City Golf Club,** Palace Road, Ripon HG4 1UW (Ripon (0765) 3640). *Location:* one mile north on A6108. 9 holes, 5645 yards. S.S.S. 68. *Green Fees:* Saturday, Sunday and Bank Holidays £15.00 per day, £10.00 other days. *Visitors:* welcome Mondays, Tuesdays, Thursdays and Fridays. *Society Meetings:* catered for, apply in writing. Professional: S.T. Davis. Hon. Secretary: G. Crompton.

SCARBOROUGH. **Ganton Golf Club Ltd,** Ganton, Near Scarborough YO12 4PA. *Location:* on A64, nine miles west of Scarborough. 18 holes, 6693 yards. *Green Fees:* on request. *Eating facilities:* available. *Visitors:* welcome by prior arrangement. *Society Meetings:* catered for with reservation. Professional: Gary Brown. Secretary: Air Vice-Marshal R.G. Price, CB.

SCARBOROUGH. **Raven Hall Country House Hotel Golf Course,** Ravenscar, Near Scarborough YO13 0ET. *Location:* twelve miles north of Scarborough, off coastal road to Whitby. Cliff top. 9 holes, 1938 yards. *Green Fees:* £8.00 per day, every day. *Eating facilities:* full catering available in Hotel Restaur-

ant. Bar snacks. *Visitors:* welcome. *Society Meetings:* arranged through Mr Davies, General Manager. Prior booking not necessary. For further details (0723-870353).

SCARBOROUGH. **Scarborough North Cliff Golf Club,** North Cliff Avenue, Scarborough YO12 6PP (Scarborough (0723) 360786). *Location:* two miles north of Scarborough on coastal road to Whitby. Parkland. 18 holes, 6425 yards. S.S.S. 71. Practice area. *Green Fees:* (1990): weekdays £14.00, weekends and Public Holidays £18.00. Restrictions, not allowed before 10am on Sundays. *Eating facilities:* available. *Visitors:* welcome (after 10am Sundays and restrictions on competition days). *Society Meetings:* catered for, from 12 to 40. Prior booking through Secretary. Professional: S.N. Deller (0723 365920). Secretary: J.R. Freeman (0723 360786).

SCARBOROUGH. **Scarborough North Cliff Golf Club,** North Cliff Avenue, Scarborough YO12 6PP (Scarborough (0723) 360786). *Location:* two miles north of Scarborough on coastal road to Whitby. Parkland. 18 holes, 6425 yards. S.S.S. 71. Practice area. *Green Fees:* weekdays £14.00, weekends £18.00. *Eating facilities:* available. *Visitors:* welcome (restrictions on competition days). *Society Meetings:* catered for, from 12 to 40. Prior booking through Secretary. Professional: S.N. Deller (0723 365920). Secretary: J.R. Freeman (0723 360786).

SCARBOROUGH. **Scarborough South Cliff Golf Club Ltd,** Deepdale Avenue, Scarborough YO11 2UE (Scarborough (0723) 360522). *Location:* one mile south of town centre on Filey road. Parkland and clifftop with panoramic sea views. 18 holes, 6085 yards. S.S.S. 69. *Green Fees:* £14.00 weekdays, £18.50 weekends and Bank Holidays. *Eating facilities:* full restaurant service. *Visitors:* welcome, no restrictions. *Society Meetings:* catered for by arrangement. Professional: D.M. Edwards (0723 365150). Secretary: J.A. Sword (0723 374737).

SELBY. **Selby Golf Club,** Mill Lane, Brayton Barff, Brayton, Selby YO8 9LD (0757-82 622). *Location:* three miles south of Selby off A19 Selby-Doncaster road. Interesting bushes and copse, well draining. 18 holes, 6246 yards. S.S.S. 70. Practice ground. *Green Fees:* weekdays £13.00 per round, £16.00 per day; weekends casual visitors not accepted. *Eating facilities:*

pleasant restaurant and bar. *Visitors:* Wednesdays, Thursdays and Fridays, suitable dress both on course and in diningroom. All visitors to have Handicap Certificates if possible. Tuition available. Professional: A. Smith (0757-82 785). Secretary: Mr Barrie Moore.

SETTLE. **Settle Golf Club,** Giggleswick, Settle (Settle (07292) 3912). *Location:* one mile north of Settle on main A65. Parkland. 9 holes, 4600 yards. S.S.S. 62. *Green Fees:* £5.00. *Eating facilities:* bar facilities open Sundays only. *Visitors:* welcome, restrictions Sundays. *Society Meetings:* welcome, must book in advance through Secretary. Secretary: L. Whitaker (07292 3912).

SKIPTON. **Skipton Golf Club,** off North West Bypass, Skipton BD23 1LL (Skipton (0756) 793922). *Location:* one mile town centre on the Skipton northern bypass. High fell land course. 18 holes, 6191 yards. S.S.S. 70. *Green Fees:* weekdays £10.00, weekends and Bank Holidays £15.00. Half-price if playing with member or juniors (under 18 years). *Eating facilities:* every day except Mondays. *Visitors:* welcome, phone Professional to ensure availability. *Society Meetings:* welcome, phone General Manager/Secretary. Professional: J.L. Hammond (0756 793257). General Manager: J.C. Varley (0756 792128).

THIRSK. **Thirsk and Northallerton Golf Club,** Thornton le Street, Thirsk YO7 4AB (Thirsk (0845) 22170). *Location:* two miles north of Thirsk on the Northallerton road, on the left. Flat parkland. 9 holes, 6257 yards. S.S.S. 70. Small practice area. *Green Fees:* weekdays £10.00, weekends only with a member. *Eating facilities:* available. *Visitors:* only with a member at weekends, with notice (in writing) to Secretary well before intended date of visit. *Society Meetings:* catered for provided notice is given well in advance of arrival. Secretary: H.D. Swarbrick. Professional: Andrew Marshall.

THORNTON-IN-CRAVEN. **Ghyll Golf Club,** Ghyll Brow, Barnoldswick, Colne, Lancs. BB8 6JQ (Earby (0282) 842466). *Location:* M65 to Colne. Parkland, hilly course. 9 holes, 5706 yards, 5213 metres. S.S.S. 68. *Green Fees:* weekdays £6.00 (£4.00 with member), weekends and Bank Holidays £10.00 restricted (£8.00 with member). *Eating facilities:* bar, evening only.

ALDWARK MANOR

Victorian Country House Hotel set in 46 acres of parkland, with our own golf course.
★ 15 luxury bedrooms ★ Excellent cuisine ★ Conference and Banqueting for up to 90 people
Special Breaks available
For full details & Reservations contact: Aldwark Manor Hotel, Aldwark, Alne, Yorkshire YO6 2NF
Telephone: Tollerton (03473) 8146

Visitors: welcome except Sundays and some Saturdays. *Society Meetings:* catered for by arrangement. Secretary: John L. Gill (0282 813205).

WHITBY. **Whitby Golf Club,** Low Straggleton, Whitby YO21 3SR (Whitby (0947) 602768). *Location:* Sandsend Road out of Whitby. Coastal course. 18 holes, 5560 yards. S.S.S. 67. *Green Fees:* weekdays £10.00, weekends and Bank Holidays £15.00. *Eating facilities:* meals available daily except Mondays, bar facilities. *Visitors:* welcome without reservation, parties over 12 by prior reservation, must be bona fide golfers. *Society Meetings:* catered for with prior reservation. Professional: A.S. Brook (0947 602719). Secretary: Alan Dyson (0947 600660).

YORK. **Aldwark Manor,** Aldwark Manor Hotel, Ardwark Alne, York YO6 2NF (Tollerton (03473) 353). *Location:* in village of Aldwark, five miles from A1 and five miles from A19. Flat parkland. 9 holes, 2569 yards. S.S.S. 66. Practice ground. *Green Fees:* weekdays £10.00, weekends and Bank Holidays £15.00. *Eating facilities:* two restaurants and two bars. *Visitors:* always welcome weekdays, restricted weekends. 20 bedroomed hotel. *Society Meetings:* always welcome, restricted weekends. Golf Director: G. Platt (03473 8146).

YORK. **Fulford (York) Golf Club Ltd,** Heslington Lane, York YO1 5DY (York (0904) 413579. *Location:* A19 (Selby) from city, turn left to Heslington. 18 holes, 6775 yards. S.S.S. 72. *Green Fees:* weekdays £20.00, weekends £25.00. *Visitors:* welcome during week, prior reservation. *Society Meetings:* by prior reservation – enquiries to Secretary. Professional: B. Hessay. Secretary: J.C.A. Gledhill.

YORK. **Heworth Golf Club,** Muncaster House, Muncastergate, York YO3 9JX (York (0904) 424618). *Location:* within city boundaries, adjacent A1036 (A64) for Malton/Scarborough. Parkland. 11 holes, 6141 yards. S.S.S. 69. *Green Fees:* weekdays £10.00, weekends and Bank Holidays £12.00. *Eating facilities:* available every day except Monday. *Visitors:* generally welcome except Sunday mornings and competition days, but advisable to telephone. Professional: Steve Robinson (0904 422389). Secretary: J.R. Richards (0904 412452).

YORK. **Pike Hills Golf Club,** Tadcaster Road, Copmanthorpe, York YO2 3UW (York (0904) 706566). *Location:* four miles from York on Tadcaster Road, right hand side going west. 18 holes, 6048 yards. S.S.S. 69. *Green Fees:* £14.00 per day. *Eating facilities:* full catering except Mondays. *Visitors:* welcome but not weekends or summer evenings. *Society Meetings:* catered for. Professional: Ian Gradwell (0904 708756). Secretary: G. Wood.

YORK. **York Golf Club,** Lordsmoor Lane, Strensall, York YO3 5XF (York (0904) 490304). *Location:* six miles north-east of York. Wooded heathland. 18 holes, 6285 yards. S.S.S. 70. Practice ground; Professional shop. *Green Fees:* £17.00 weekdays, £21.00 weekends and Bank Holidays. *Eating facilities:* full catering except Fridays. *Visitors:* welcome, but advisable to ring before visiting. *Society Meetings:* catered for Mondays, Wednesdays, Thursdays and Sundays. Professional: A.B. Mason (0904 490304). Secretary/GP Captain: T. Appleyard (0904 491840).

South Yorkshire

BARNSLEY. **Barnsley Golf Club,** Wakefield Road, Staincross, Barnsley S75 6JZ (Barnsley (0226) 382856). *Location:* A61 three miles north of Barnsley, five miles south of Wakefield. Parkland course. 18 holes, 6048 yards, 5529 metres. S.S.S. 69. *Green Fees:* weekdays £4.00, weekends £5.00. *Eating facilities:* meals available. *Visitors:* welcome, no restrictions. *Society Meetings:* course extremely busy and not suitable for Societies. Professional: Mr M. Melling (0226 382954). Secretary: L.E. Lammas (0226 382856).

BARNSLEY. **Silkstone Golf Club,** Field Head, Elmhirst Lane, Silkstone, Barnsley S75 4OD (Barnsley (0226) 790328). *Location:* one mile beyond Dodworth village on the A628 and one mile from M1. Parkland. 18 holes, 6045 yards. S.S.S. 70. *Green Fees:* weekdays £12.00 per day/round. Special £19.00 Day Package including meals. *Eating facilities:* available. *Visitors:* welcome weekdays only. *Society Meetings:* by arrangement. Professional: Kevin Guy (0226 790128). Secretary: L. Depledge (0226 287053).

DONCASTER. **Austerfield Park Golf Club**, Cross Lane, Austerfield, Doncaster DN10 6RF (Doncaster (0302) 710841). *Location:* two miles from Bawtry on the A614. Parkland. 18 holes, 6828 yards. S.S.S. 73. Driving range, practice area. *Green Fees:* midweek £10.00 per day, weekends £14.00 per day. *Eating facilities:* bar snacks and full restaurant. *Visitors:* welcome without reservation. *Society Meetings:* welcome, special package rates. Professional: Andrew Stothard (0302 710695). Secretary: Alan Bradley (0709 540928).

DONCASTER. **Crookhill Park (Municipal) Golf Club**, Crookhill Park, Conisborough, Doncaster (Rotherham [0709] 862974). *Location:* leave A1(M) Doncaster by-pass, on to A630 Sheffield, in 2 miles turn left in Conisborough on to B60694. 18 holes, 5846 yards. S.S.S. 68. Practice area. *Green Fees:* £5.00. *Eating facilities:* buffet lunches at club. *Visitors:* welcome. Professional: Richard Swaine 0709 862979.

DONCASTER. **Doncaster Town Moor Golf Club**, c/o Belle Vue Club, Belle Vue, Doncaster DN4 5HT (Doncaster (0302) 535286). *Location:* clubhouse approximately 300 yards from racecourse roundabout travelling south towards Bawtry, same entrance as Doncaster Rovers Football Club. Flat wooded parkland. 18 holes, 6112 yards. S.S.S. 69. *Green Fees:* weekdays £9.00, £5.00 with a member; weekends and Public Holidays £11.00, £7.00 with a member. *Eating facilities:* available except Sundays. *Visitors:* welcome without reservation, not before 11.30am Sundays. *Society Meetings:* catered for by arrangement with Secretary. Professional: Steve Poole (0302 535286). Secretary: John Padley (0302 535458).

DONCASTER. **Hickleton Golf Club**, Hickleton, Near Doncaster (Rotherham (0709) 892496). *Location:* six miles from Doncaster on A635 to Barnsley. In Hickleton village turn right to Thurnscoe, 500 yards on right. Undulating parkland. 18 holes, 6403 yards. S.S.S. 71. Practice facilities. *Green Fees:* weekdays £10.00, weekends and Bank Holidays £15.00. *Eating facilities:* available by arrangement with Stewardess (not Mondays). *Visitors:* welcome by arrangement, restricted times at weekends. *Society Meetings:* welcome by arrangement. Professional: Paul Shepherd (0709 895170). Secretary: R. Jowett.

DONCASTER. **Serlby Park Golf Club**, Serlby, Doncaster DN10 6BA (Retford (0777) 818268). *Location:* 12 miles south of Doncaster, between A614 and A638. 9 holes, 5370 yards. S.S.S. 66. *Green Fees:* information not provided. *Visitors:* welcome only if playing with member. *Society Meetings:* not available. Hon Secretary: R. Wilkinson.

DONCASTER. **Thorne Golf Club**, Kirkton Lane, Thorne, Near Doncaster (Thorne (0405) 815173). *Location:* A18, 10 miles from Doncaster, 15 from Scunthorpe. Parkland. 18 holes, 5522 yards. S.S.S. 66. Practice ground. *Green Fees:* weekdays £4.00 per round, weekends and Bank Holidays £5.00 per round. *Eating facilities:* full Clubhouse amenities. *Visitors:* welcome, no restrictions. *Society Meetings:* welcome. Professional: R.D. Highfield (0405 812084). Secretary: P. Kettridge (0405 812084).

DONCASTER. **Wheatley Golf Club**, Armthorpe Road, Doncaster DN2 5QB (Doncaster (0302) 831655). *Location:* follow East Coast route alongside Racecourse boundary to water tower at first crossroads. Flat parkland. 18 holes, 6169 yards. S.S.S. 69 (yellow markers). Practice area and putting green. *Green Fees:* weekdays £12.00 per round, £15.00 per day. Weekends and Bank Holidays £16.00 per round, £18.50 per day. Reductions if playing with member. *Eating facilities:* restaurant and bars. *Visitors:* welcome if member of another club. Non-members may play in the company of a member. *Society Meetings:* catered for weekdays only on written application. Professional: T.C. Parkinson. Bookings Secretary: Mrs B. Morton (0302 831655).

ROTHERHAM. **Grange Park Golf Club**, Upper Wortley Road, Rotherham (Rotherham (0709) 55884). Municipal golf course, private clubhouse. *Location:* A629 from Rotherham, easy access from M1. Parkland. 18 holes, 6353 yards. S.S.S. 71. Practice ground. *Green Fees:* £2.95 weekdays, £3.60 weekends. *Eating facilities:* bar and full catering, except Mondays. *Visitors:* welcome without restriction. *Society Meetings:* contact Secretary in first instance. Professional: Eric Clark (0709 559497). Secretary: R. Charity (0709 583400).

ROTHERHAM. **Phoenix Golf Club**, Pavilion Lane, Brinsworth, Rotherham (Rotherham (0709) 363864). *Location:* M1 Tinsley roundabout, Bawtry Road, Pavilion Lane one mile on left. 18 holes, 6145 yards. S.S.S. 69. *Green Fees:* weekdays £10.00, £5.00 with a member; weekends £14.00, £6.00 with a member. *Eating facilities:* snacks or full meals. *Visitors:* welcome weekdays. *Society Meetings:* welcome, reduced rates for parties. Professional: A. Limb (0709 382624). Secretary: J. Burrows: (0709 370759).

ROTHERHAM. **Rotherham Golf Club Ltd**, Thrybergh Park, Thrybergh, Rotherham S65 4NU (Rotherham (0709) 850466). *Location:* three and a half miles east of Rotherham on main Rotherham to Doncaster Road A630. Parkland. 18 holes, 6324 yards, 5701 metres. S.S.S. 70. Practice ground. *Green Fees:* weekdays £17.00, weekends £20.00. Reductions for parties over 20. *Eating facilities:* full catering, bar and restaurant. *Visitors:* welcome all days by prior arrangement with Professional. *Society Meetings:* catered for every day except Wednesdays (Ladies Day) by arrangement with Secretary. Professional: Simon Thornhill (0709 850480). Secretary: F. Green: (0709 850812).

ROTHERHAM. **Sitwell Park Golf Club**, Shrogswood Road, Rotherham S60 4BY (Wickersley (0709) 700799). *Location:* A631 off M18, Bramley turn off to Rotherham, exit 33 off M1, follow A631 to Bawtry. Undulating parkland. 18 holes, 6203 yards. S.S.S. 70. Practice ground available. *Green Fees:* weekdays £14.00 per round £18.00 per day, weekends and Bank Holidays £16.00 per round, £20.00 per day. *Eating facilities:* stewardess catering. *Visitors:* welcome with reservation, no catering Tuesday. *Society Meetings:* catered for if pre-arranged with Secretary. Professional: N.J. Taylor (0709 540961). Secretary: J. Straffen (0709 541046).

ROTHERHAM. **Wath Golf Club,** Abdy, Rawmarsh, Rotherham S62 7SJ (Rotherham (0709) 872149). *Location:* A633 from Rotherham, through Rawmarsh, taking B6090 towards Wentworth, right along B6089 taking signed road to Clubhouse 300 yards on right. Flat parkland course. 18 holes, 5737 yards. S.S.S. 68. *Green Fees:* information not available. *Eating facilities:* lounge bar and dining area with seating for up to 200 people. *Visitors:* weekdays only. No jeans or collarless shirts allowed. *Society Meetings:* welcome weekdays only. Professional: Steven Poole (0709 526727). Secretary: Brian Lawrence (0709 878677).

SHEFFIELD. **Abbeydale Golf Club,** Twentywell Lane, Dore, Sheffield S17 4QA (Sheffield (0742) 360763). *Location:* A621 five miles south of Sheffield. Parkland. 18 holes, 6419 yards. S.S.S. 71. *Green Fees:* weekdays £20.00, weekends and Bank Holidays £25.00. *Eating facilities:* restaurant and bar meals. *Visitors:* welcome, preferably by arrangement. Starting time restrictions April-October. *Society Meetings:* catered for Tuesdays and Fridays by arrangment. Professional: S. Cooper (0742 365633). Secretary: Mrs K.M. Johnston (0742 360763).

SHEFFIELD. **Beauchief Municipal Golf Club,** Abbey Lane, Beauchief, Sheffield S8 0DB (Beauchief (0742) 620040 (Clubhouse) or 387274 (Booking Office). *Location:* course lies between the A61 and the A625 on the outer ring road, Abbey Lane. Adjacent landmark Beauchief Abbey. Mainly flat parkland course. 18 holes, 5462 yards, 4984 metres. S.S.S. 66. Practice area. *Green Fees:* £4.50 per round. No day ticket. *Eating facilities:* cafe and bar open until dusk every day except Tuesday.. *Visitors:* welcome anytime but starting times get booked up early and cannot be booked by telephone. *Society Meetings:* can be booked through Sheffield City Council Recreation Department, Meersbrook Park, Sheffield S8 9FL. Professional: B.T. English (0742 620648). Secretary: J.G. Pearson (0742 306720).

SHEFFIELD. **Birley Wood Golf Course,** Birley Lane, Sheffield S12 3BP (0742 647262). *Location:* four and a half miles south east of city centre, off A616 from Mosborough. Undulating meadowland course with well varied features, open plan and good views. 18 holes, 5452 yards. S.S.S. 67. Practice field near course. *Green Fees:* £5.40 per round. *Eating facilities:* bar and snacks at nearby Fairway Inn. *Visitors:* welcome with prior notice. *Society Meetings:* by prior arrangement. Professional: P. Ball (0742 647262). Secretary: D. Cronshaw (0742 471258).

SHEFFIELD. **Concord Park Golf Club,** Shiregreen Lane, Sheffield S5 6AE. *Location:* one-and-a-half miles from M1 Junction 34. Hilly wooded parkland. 18 holes, 4321 yards, 3929 metres. S.S.S. 62. *Green Fees:* £5.00. *Eating facilities:* available at adjacent Sports Centre. *Visitors:* welcome any time. Secretary: B. Shepherd (0742 456806).

SHEFFIELD. **Dore and Totley Golf Club,** The Clubhouse, Bradway Road, Bradway, Sheffield S17 4QR (Sheffield (0742) 360492). *Location:* leave M1 at Junction 33. Parkland. 18 holes, 6265 yards. S.S.S. 70. *Green Fees:* weekdays £15.00 per round, £18.00 per day. *Eating facilities:* bar available, catering facilities available except Mondays. *Visitors:* unintroduced visitors restricted to the hours of 9.30am to 12 noon and after 2pm. Restrictions also exist on Wednesday (Ladies Day). *Society Meetings:* catered for Tuesday, Thursday, Friday by prior arrangement. Professional: Mr M. Pearson (0742 366844). Secretary: Mrs C. Milner (0742 369872).

SHEFFIELD. **Hallamshire Golf Club Ltd,** Sandygate, Sheffield S10 4LA (Sheffield (0742) 301007). *Location:* A57 out of Sheffield four miles then fork left for Lodge Moor. Moorland course. 18 holes, 6396 yards. S.S.S. 71. *Green Fees:* £17.00 weekdays, £25.00 weekends. *Eating facilities:* full catering except Tuesdays - prior notice required. *Visitors:* welcome weekdays by arrangement, some weekends. Snooker table. *Society Meetings:* catered for by arrangement with Secretary. Professionals: Geoffrey Tickell (0742 305222). Secretary: R. Burns (0742 302153).

SHEFFIELD. **Hallowes Golf Club,** Hallowes Lane, Dronfield, Sheffield S18 6UA (Dronfield (0246) 413149). *Location:* six miles south of Sheffield on old A61 (not by-pass to Chesterfield). Moorland. 18 holes, 6342 yards. S.S.S. 70. Large practice area. *Green Fees:* weekdays £15.00 per day. *Eating facilities:* bars, dining room (no catering Mondays). *Visitors:* no visitors at weekends or Bank Holidays except with a member. *Society Meetings:* limited number allowed. Professional: Martin Heggie (0246 411196). Secretary: Keith Dowswell (0246 413734).

SHEFFIELD. **Hillsborough Golf Club Ltd,** Worral Road, Sheffield S6 4BE (Sheffield (0742) 343608). *Location:* three miles from city centre. Worral Road via Middlewood Road, Dykes Hall Road. Undulating grassland. 18 holes, 5662 yards. S.S.S. 70. *Green Fees:* weekdays £14.00, weekends £20.00. *Eating facilities:* snacks available; lunches, teas, evening meals by arrangement (not Fridays). *Visitors:* welcome without reservation. *Society Meetings:* catered for. Professional: G. Walker (0742 332666). Secretary: A. Platts (0742 349151).

SHEFFIELD. **Lees Hall Golf Club Ltd,** Hemsworth Road, Norton, Sheffield S8 8LL (0742 554402). *Location:* three miles south of Sheffield, between A61 and A6102 ring road. Undulating parkland with extensive views over Sheffield. 18 holes, 6137 yards. S.S.S. 69. *Green Fees:* weekdays £13.00 per day; weekends and Bank Holidays £20.00 *Eating facilities:* available daily except Tuesdays. *Visitors:* welcome, except Saturday and Sunday before 10.30am. *Society Meetings:* by arrangement only. Professional: J.R. Wilkinson (0742 551526). Secretary: N.E. Westworth (0742 552900).

SHEFFIELD. **Stocksbridge and District Golf Club Ltd,** 30 Royd Lane, Deepcar S30 5RZ (Sheffield (0742) 882003). *Location:* 10 miles from Sheffield on A616 heading towards Manchester. Parkland. 18 holes, 5200 yards. S.S.S. 65. Practice ground. *Green Fees:* £10.00 weekdays, £15.00 weekends. *Eating facilities:* available. *Visitors:* welcome, restrictions weekends. *Society Meetings:* catered for by arrangment. Secretary: Stuart Lee (0742 882408).

SHEFFIELD. **Tankersley Park Golf Club,** High Green, Sheffield S30 4LG (Sheffield (0742) 468247). *Location:* take M1 north round to Junction 35a off at 35a to island, straight on from island approximately quarter of a mile and turn right into golf club. Parkland. 18 holes, 6212 yards. S.S.S. 70. *Green Fees:* £12.00 per round, £15.00 per day weekdays; £15.00 weekends. *Eating facilities:* sandwiches, bar meals, full evening meals. *Visitors:* welcome on weekdays without reservation but not before 3pm weekends. *Society Meetings:* catered for by prior arrangement. Professional: I. Kirk (0742 455583). Secretary: S. Jessop (0742 468247).

SHEFFIELD. **Tinsley Park Golf Club (Municipal),** High Hazels Park, Darnall (0742 560237). *Location:* three miles from Junction 33 M1. Entry from A6102 in Darnall. Wooded course. 18 holes, 6086 yards. S.S.S.

69. *Green Fees:* £3.00 weekdays, £4.50 weekends. *Eating facilities:* cafe (closed Tuesday) meals if ordered from Stewardess. Time must be booked on arrival. *Visitors:* welcome without reservation. *Society Meetings:* not catered for. Professional: Mr A.P. Highfield. Secretary: Mr S.H. Conroy.

SHEFFIELD. **Wortley Golf Club,** Hermit Hill Lane, Wortley, Near Sheffield S30 4DF (Sheffield (0742) 882139). *Location:* leave M1 junction 35 or 35A, A629 to Wortley Village, turn right after leaving village. Parkland. 18 holes, 5983 yards, 5469 metres. S.S.S. 69. *Green Fees:* per day or round: £14.00 weekdays, £20.00 weekends and Bank Holidays. *Eating facilities:* order in advance, not Mondays. *Visitors:* welcome. *Society Meetings:* catered for by arrangement Wednesdays and Fridays. Professional: Jeremy Tilson (0742 886490). Secretary: J. Lewis Dalby (0742 885294).

West Yorkshire

BEESTON PARK. **Middleton Park (Municipal) Golf Club,** The Ring Road, Beeston Park, Middleton, Leeds (0532 700449). 18 holes, 6120 yards. S.S.S. 69. *Green Fees:* information not provided.

BINGLEY. **Bingley (St. Ives) Golf Club,** The Mansion, St. Ives, Harden, Bingley (Bradford (0274) 562436). Parkland/moorland. 18 holes, 6480 yards. S.S.S. 71. Practice ground. *Green Fees:* weekdays £10.50 per round, £16.00 per day; weekends and Bank Holidays £18.50 per round. *Eating facilities:* daily except Mondays. *Visitors:* welcome weekdays, limited availability weekends. *Society Meetings:* welcome, book through Professional. Professional: R.K. Firth (0274 562506). Secretary: J. Crolla (0535 274231).

BRADFORD. **Clayton Golf Club,** Thornton View Road, Clayton, Bradford BD14 6JX (Bradford (0274) 880047). *Location:* two miles south west of Bradford, via Thornton Road, then Listerhills Road. Moorland course, testing par 3 at third hole. 9 holes, 5515 yards. S.S.S. 67. *Green Fees:* weekdays £6.00 per round, £8.00 per day; weekends £8.00. *Eating facilities:* bar snacks, meals if notice given. No bar Mondays. *Visitors:* welcome at all times except before 4.00pm on Sundays. *Society Meetings:* catered for by arrangement. Secretary: F. V. Wood (0274 574203).

BRADFORD. **East Bierley Golf Club,** South View Road, East Bierley, Bradford (Bradford (0274) 681023). *Location:* situated about three miles east of Bradford on the Wakefield/Heckmondwike road. Turn off at Bierley Bar and down South View Road. Undulating semi-moorland course. 9 holes, 4308 metres. S.S.S. 63. *Green Fees:* £8.00 per round. *Eating*

facilities: light refreshments and meals to order in advance. Secretary: M. Welch.

BRADFORD. **Headley Golf Club,** Headley Lane, Thornton, Bradford BD13 3LX (Bradford (0274) 833481). *Location:* five miles west of Bradford. Hilly parkland. 9 holes, 4914 yards. S.S.S. 64. *Green Fees:* weekdays £5.00, weekends £5.00 with member only. *Eating facilities:* dining and bar. *Visitors:* weekdays only. *Society Meetings:* restricted facilities. Hon Secretary: J.P. Clark (0274 832571).

BRADFORD. **Northcliffe Golf Club,** High Bank Lane, Shipley BD18 4LJ (Bradford (0274) 584085). *Location:* three miles west of Bradford on A650 Bradford-Keighley. Undulating wooded parkland. 18 holes, 6065 yards, 5546 metres. S.S.S. 69. *Green Fees:* weekdays £12.00, weekends and Bank Holidays £17.00. *Eating facilities:* bars, dining room (no catering Mondays). *Visitors:* Wednesdays to Fridays preferred. Special Package £20.00. *Society Meetings:* welcome, discount for parties over 24. Professional: Simon Poot (0274 587193). Secretary: Ralph Anderson (0274 596731).

BRADFORD. **Queensbury Golf Club,** Brighouse Road, Queensbury, Bradford BD13 1QF (Bradford (0274) 882155). *Location:* on A647, four miles from Bradford. Wooded course. 9 holes, 5102 yards. S.S.S. 65. *Green Fees:* weekdays £8.00, weekends £15.00. *Eating facilities:* lunches, teas except Monday. Bar available. *Visitors:* welcome without restriction. *Society Meetings:* by arrangement. Professional: Nigel Barber (0274 816864). Secretary: Allen Robinson (0274 882956).

BRADFORD. **Shipley Golf Club,** Beckfoot Lane, Cottingley Bridge, Bingley BD16 1LX (Bradford (0274) 563212). *Location:* off A650 at Cottingley Bridge, Bradford six miles, Bingley one mile (from Bradford left before Cottingley Bridge). Slightly undulating parkland. 18 holes. S.S.S. 70. Practice area and net putting green. *Green Fees:* weekdays £15.00, weekends and Bank Holidays £20.00. *Eating facilities:* available by arrangement with Steward, except Mondays. *Visitors:* welcome (Tuesdays after 2.00pm, Saturdays after 4.00pm). *Society Meetings:* catered for by arrangement. Professional: David Sutcliffe (0274 563674). Hon. Secretary: Stuart Holman (0274 568652).

BRADFORD. **South Bradford Golf Club,** Pearson Road, Odsal, Bradford BD6 1BH (Bradford (0274) 679195). *Location:* take Stadium Road to Pearson Road, from Cleckheath Road, Odsal, Bradford. Slightly hilly and wooded in parts. 9 holes, 6004 yards. S.S.S. 69. Practice ground. *Green Fees:* weekdays £9.00, weekends £15.00. *Eating facilities:* available except Mondays. *Visitors:* welcome. Must conform with club rules on dress. *Society Meetings:* catered for on application. Professional: M. Hillas (0274 673346). Secretary: H.H. Kellett (0274 676911).

BRADFORD. **West Bowling Golf Club Ltd,** Newall Hall, Rooley Lane, Bradford BD5 8LB (Bradford (0274) 724449). *Location:* take M606 off the M62, course at top of M606. 18 holes, 5769 yards. S.S.S. 67. *Green Fees:* weekdays £15.00, weekends and Bank Holidays £20.00 (restricted). *Eating facilities:* luncheons served, excluding Monday. *Visitors:* individuals welcome without reservation. *Society Meetings:* societies and visiting parties accepted with reservation. Professional: A. Swaine (0274 728036). Secretary: M.E. Lynn (0274 393207).

BRADFORD. **West Bradford Golf Club Ltd,** Chellow Grange Road, Haworth Road, Bradford BD9 6NP (Bradford (0274) 542767). *Location:* three miles west of city centre off Haworth Road. Undulating course. 18 holes, 5752 yards. S.S.S. 68. *Green Fees:* £12.00 weekdays, £18.00 weekends, including VAT. *Eating facilities:* available every day except Mondays. *Visitors:* welcome, except Saturdays. *Society Meetings:* welcome Wednesday to Friday. Golf package deals Wednesday to Friday £16.00. Professional: S.J. Longster (0274 542102). Secretary: D. Ingham (0274 542767).

BRIGHOUSE. **Castlefields Golf Club,** Rastrick Common, Rastrick, Brighouse WD6 3HL. *Location:* one mile out of Brighouse on A643. Parkland. 6 holes, 2406 yards. S.S.S. 50. *Green Fees:* £1.50 weekdays, £3.00 weekends. £1.50 Juniors. *Eating facilities:* Globe Inn 200 yards away. *Visitors:* welcome at all times but must be accompanied by a member. Secretary: P. Bentley (0484 712108).

CLECKHEATON. **Cleckheaton and District Golf Club Ltd,** Bradford Road, Cleckheaton BD19 6BU (0274 874118). *Location:* four miles south of Bradford on A638, Junction 26 M62. Parkland course. 18 holes, 5847 yards. S.S.S. 69. Practice area. *Green Fees:* £15.00 weekdays, £21.00 weekends and Bank Holidays. *Eating facilities:* available (except Mondays).

Visitors: welcome all year, suggest prior enquiry weekends. *Society Meetings:* catered for, except Mondays, Saturdays or Sundays. Professional: Mike Ingham (0274 851267). Secretary: Herbert Thornton (0274 851266).

DEWSBURY. **Hanging Heaton Golf Club,** White Cross Road, Dewsbury WF12 7DT (Dewsbury (0924) 461606). *Location:* one mile from town centre on main A653 Dewsbury to Leeds road. 9 holes, 5870 yards (for 18 holes). S.S.S. 67. *Green Fees:* weekdays £10.00 (£6.00 with member); weekends with member £8.00. Green fees not taken weekends or Bank Holidays without member's introduction. *Eating facilities:* available. *Visitors:* welcome without reservation, except weekends. *Society Meetings:* catered for by arrangement with Steward. Professional: J. Allott. Secretary: S.M. Simpson.

ELLAND. **Elland Golf Club,** Hammerstones, Leach Lane, Elland HX5 0QP (0422 372505). *Location:* M62 Junction 24 exit off roundabout for Blackley. Parkland. 9 holes, 5630 yards. S.S.S. 66. *Green Fees:* weekdays £8.00, weekends £12.00. *Eating facilities:* meals/bar snacks except Mondays. *Visitors:* welcome mid-week. *Society Meetings:* by arrangement. Professional: J. Tindall (0422 374886). Secretary: W.H. Pearson (0422 373276).

GUISELEY. **Bradford Golf Club,** Hawksworth Lane, Guiseley, Leeds LS20 8NP (Guiseley (0943) 77239). *Location:* Shipley to Ilkley road, left at top of Hollins Hill, one mile up Hawksworth Lane. Moorland/parkland. 18 holes, 6259 yards. S.S.S. 70. *Green Fees:* weekdays £18.00, weekends £25.00 (half-price with member). *Eating facilities:* every day, preferably by prior arrangement. *Visitors:* welcome without reservation weekdays, not on weekends without prior arrangement. *Society Meetings:* catered for on weekdays, prior arrangements. Professional: Sydney Weldon (0943 73719). Secretary: (0943 75570).

HALIFAX. **Bradley Hall Golf Club,** Holywell Green, Halifax (0422 374108). *Location:* three miles south of Halifax on B6112. Moorland, undulating. 18 holes, 6213 yards. S.S.S. 70. *Green Fees:* weekdays £11.00, weekends £18.00. *Eating facilities:* full catering except Mondays and Tuesdays. *Visitors:* welcome. *Societies:* welcome with prior reservation weekdays. Professional: P. Wood (0422 372103). Secretary: P.M. Pritchforth.

HALIFAX. **Halifax Golf Club Ltd,** Union Lane, Ogden, Halifax (Halifax (0422) 244171). *Location:* three miles out of Halifax, A629 towards Keighley. Moorland. 18 holes, 6037 yards. S.S.S. 70. *Green Fees:* weekdays £10.00, weekends £15.00. *Eating facilities:* luncheons and dinners served. Good restaurant facilities. *Visitors:* welcome most days by arrangement. All-in Day £20.00. *Society Meetings:* catered for by arrangement. Professional: Mr Steve Foster (0422 240047). Secretary: Mr J.P. Clark (0422 244171).

HALIFAX. **Lightscliffe Golf Club,** Knowle Top Road, Lightscliffe, Halifax (Halifax (0422) 202459). *Location:* three miles east of Halifax on A58 (Leeds) road. 9 holes, 5368 metres. S.S.S. 68. *Green Fees:*

weekdays £6.00, weekends £10.00. *Eating facilities:* snacks available, other meals to order (except Mondays). *Visitors:* welcome without reservation but must confirm with Professional. Professional: J.R. Parry. Secretary: T.H. Gooder.

HALIFAX. **Ryburn Golf Club,** The Shaw, Norland, Near Halifax (Halifax (0422) 831355). *Location:* Station Road Halifax to Sowerby Bridge, turn right up hill, right towards Hobbit Inn (signposted), left after cottages. Demanding, hilly, windy course. 9 holes, 5002 yards. S.S.S. 65. *Green Fees:* weekdays £8.00 (£4.00 with a member), weekends £11.00 (£5.00 with a member). *Eating facilities:* good catering facilities (except Mondays) and bar. *Visitors:* welcome weekdays, weekends by prior arrangement. *Society Meetings:* welcome by prior arrangement. Secretary: Jack Hoyle (0422 843070 home).

HALIFAX. **West End Golf Club (Halifax) Ltd,** Paddock Lane, Highroad Well, Halifax HX2 0NT (Halifax (0422) 353608). *Location:* two miles from town centre. Parkland. 18 holes, 6003 yards. S.S.S. 69. *Green Fees:* weekdays £10.00, weekends £12.00. *Eating facilities:* full bar and catering except Mondays. *Visitors:* welcome without reservation. *Society Meetings:* catered for by arrangement. Professional: D. Rishworth (0422 363293). Secretary: B.R. Thomas (0422 367145).

HEBDEN BRIDGE. **Mount Skip Golf Club Ltd,** Wadsworth, Hebden Bridge HX7 8PH (Hebden Bridge (0422) 842896). *Location:* one mile upwards past Birchcliffe Centre. Moorland with superb Pennine views. 9 holes, 5202 yards. S.S.S. 66. *Green Fees:* £6.00, half-price if playing with member, Junior discounts. *Eating facilities:* bar and diningroom facilities. *Visitors:* welcome, please check first at weekends. *Society Meetings:* welcome by prior arrangement. Secretary: Dr R.G. Pogson.

HUDDERSFIELD. **Bradley Park Golf Course,** Off Bradley Road, Huddersfield HD2 1PZ (Huddersfield (0484) 539988). *Location:* Exit 25 on A62, follow signs for Brighouse, then Huddersfield, signposted from R.A.B. Parkland with panoramic views, slightly hilly. 18 holes, 6201 yards. S.S.S. 70. 9 hole, par 3 course, 14 bay floodlit driving range. *Green Fees:* weekdays £5.25, weekends £6.75. *Eating facilities:* lounge with bar and separate diningroom. *Visitors:* casual visitors welcome everyday. *Society Meetings:* mid-week only (12 to 50). Professional: P.E. Reilly. Secretary: J. Murphy.

HUDDERSFIELD. **Crosland Heath Golf Club Ltd,** Felk Stile Road, Crosland Hill, Huddersfield HD4 7AF (0484 653216). *Location:* three miles from town centre off A62 Oldham road. Flat heathland with extensive views. 18 holes, 5963 yards. S.S.S. 70. Practice facilities. *Green Fees:* on application. *Eating facilities:* full catering except Mondays. *Visitors:* welcome, suggest prior enquiry. *Society Meetings:* catered for by arrangement. Professional: John Andrew (0484 653877). Secretary: D. Walker (0484 653262).

HUDDERSFIELD. **Huddersfield Golf Club,** Fixby Hall, Lightridge Road, Fixby, Huddersfield HD2 2EP

(Huddersfield (0484) 420110). *Location:* A643 from The Hilton National Hotel. 18 holes, 6402 yards. S.S.S. 71. *Green Fees:* weekdays £18.50 per round, £24.00 for more than one round; £20.00 per round, £26.00 for more than one round weekends and Public Holidays, £6.00 playing with a member. *Eating facilities:* available. *Visitors:* always welcome, reservation advised but not essential. Tuesday is Ladies' day and no visitors Saturdays. *Society and Company Days:* catered for, well appointed private rooms. Catering to suit all occasions. Professional: P. Carman (0484 426463). Secretary: D. Rose (Miss) (0484 426203).

HUDDERSFIELD. **Longley Park Golf Club,** Off Somerset Road, Huddersfield (Huddersfield (0484) 22304). *Location:* one mile town centre, Wakefield side. 9 holes, 5324 yards. S.S.S. 66. *Green Fees:* weekdays £6.50 per round, weekends and Bank Holidays £8.00. *Eating facilities:* available. *Visitors:* welcome, special party package available. Professional: John Andrew. Secretary: K.L.W. Ireland.

HUDDERSFIELD. **Marsden Golf Club,** Hemplow, Marsden, Huddersfield (Huddersfield (0484) 844253). *Location:* eight miles south of Huddersfield on A64 to Manchester. Moorland. 9 holes, 5702 yards. S.S.S. 68. *Green Fees:* weekdays £6.00, weekends £12.00. *Eating facilities:* lunches and snacks available except Tuesdays. *Visitors:* welcome with reservation. *Society Meetings:* catered for by arrangement. Professional: T. Morley. Secretary: G.C. Scott.

HUDDERSFIELD. **Woodsome Hall Golf Club,** Woodsome Hall, Fenay Bridge, Huddersfield HD8 0LQ (Huddersfield (0484) 602971). *Location:* to the west of the A629 Huddersfield to Sheffield Road. Parkland. 18 holes, 6080 yards. S.S.S. 69. Practice ground *Green Fees:* weekdays £16.00, weekends and Public Holidays £20.00. *Eating facilities:* full facilities except Mondays. *Visitors:* not on Tuesdays Ladies Day or Saturdays. *Society Meetings:* by booking before November for the following year. Professional: Karl Scarr (0484 602034). Secretary: Mrs P. Bates (0484 602739). Hon Secretary: E.V. Hartley.

ILKLEY. **Ben Rhydding Golf Club,** High Wood, Ben Rhydding (0943 608759). 9 holes, 4711 yards (18 holes). S.S.S. 64. *Green Fees:* weekdays £5.00, weekends and Public Holidays £7.50. *Visitors:* welcome without reservation, no visitors Wednesday afternoons, Saturdays and Sundays. Secretary: J.D.B. Watts (0943 462178).

ILKLEY. **Ilkley Golf Club,** Nesfield Road, Ilkley (Ilkley (0943) 607277). *Location:* 15 miles north of Bradford. 18 holes, 6328 yards. S.S.S. 70. *Green Fees:* information not provided. *Eating facilities:* by arrangement. *Visitors:* welcome with reservation. *Society Meetings:* catered for. Professional: J. L. Hammond (0943 607463). Secretary: G. Hirst (0943 600214).

KEIGHLEY. **Branshaw Golf Club,** Branshaw Moor, Oakworth, Keighley BD22 7ES (Haworth (0535) 43235). *Location:* B6143 south west of Keighley. Moorland with extensive views. 18 holes, 5858 yards. S.S.S. 69. *Green Fees:* weekdays £8.00, weekends £12.00. *Eating facilities:* meals and bar snacks served (except Monday). *Visitors:* welcome weekdays, limited Saturdays. *Society Meetings:* catered for if application tendered four weeks in advance. Secretary: Mr D.A. Town (0535 605003).

KEIGHLEY. **Keighley Golf Club,** Howden Park, Utley, Keighley BD20 6DH (Keighley (0535) 603179). *Location:* one mile west of Keighley on A629. Parkland. 18 holes, 6139 yards, 5615 metres. S.S.S. 70. *Green Fees:* weekdays £15.00 per round/day, weekends £18.00 per round/day. *Eating facilities:* full catering available. *Visitors:* welcome by prior arrangement. Ladies' day, Tuesday. *Society Meetings:* catered for by arrangement. Professional: D. Walker (0535 665370). Secretary: D.F. Coyle (0535 604778).

KEIGHLEY. **Riddlesden Golf Club,** Howden Rough, Riddlesden, Keighley BD20 5QN (Keighley (0535) 602148). *Location:* A650 Keighley-Bradford road, left into Bar Lane, left on Scott Lane, which leads on to Scott Lane West and Elam Wood Road approximately two miles. Moorland. 18 holes, 4247 yards. S.S.S. 61. *Green Fees:* weekdays £4.00 (£3.00 with a member), weekends £7.00 (£5.00 with a member). *Eating facilities:* available weekends or by prior arrangement. *Visitors:* welcome with very little reservation. *Society Meetings:* catered for. Secretary: Mrs K.M. Brooksbank (0535 607646).

KEIGHLEY. **Silsden Golf Club,** High Brunthwaite, Silsden, Near Keighley (Sleeton (0535) 52998). *Location:* five miles north of Keighley. Undulating downland. 14 holes, 4870 yards. S.S.S. 64. Putting green. *Green Fees:* £5.00 per round weekdays, £10.00 weekends. *Eating facilities:* not available. *Visitors:* welcome, Sundays after 1.00pm only. *Society Meetings:* by arrangement with Secretary. Secretary: G. Davey.

KNOTTINGLEY. **Ferrybridge "C" P.S. Golf Club,** PO Box 39, Stranglands Lane, Knottingley WF11 8SQ. *Location:* off the A1 at Ferrybridge and quarter of a mile towards Castleford on the B6136. Undulating land within the boundaries of and surrounding the power station. 9 holes, 5138 yards. S.S.S. 65. Practice ground. *Green Fees:* £2.00 weekdays, £3.00 weekends. *Visitors:* welcome when accompanied by a member only because of security restrictions. *Society Meetings:* by special arrangment in parties of not more than 12. Secretary: Mr N.E. Pugh (0977 674188 extension 2851).

LEEDS. **Alwoodley Golf Club,** Wigton Lane, Alwoodley, Leeds LS17 8SA (Leeds (0532) 681680). *Location:* five miles north of Leeds on A61 (Leeds to Harrogate). 18 holes, 6686 yards. S.S.S. 72. *Green Fees:* £25.00 summer weekdays. *Eating facilities:* available. *Visitors:* welcome by arrangement. *Society Meetings:* catered for by arrangement. Professional: J.R. Foss. Secretary: George Turnbull.

LEEDS. **Garforth Golf Club Ltd,** Garforth, Leeds LS25 2DS (Leeds (0532) 863308). *Location:* six miles east of Leeds on A63, then turn left on to A642. 18 holes, 6327 yards. S.S.S. 70. *Green Fees:* £17.00 per day. *Eating facilities:* full catering except Tuesday. *Visitors:* welcome weekdays, weekends and Public

Holidays only if playing with a member. *Society Meetings:* catered for. Professional: K. Findlater. Secretary: F.A. Readman.

LEEDS. **Gotts Park Municipal Golf Club,** Gotts Mansion, Gotts Park, Armley Ridge Road, Armley, Leeds LS12 2QX (Leeds (0532) 310492). *Location:* two miles west of Leeds on Stanningley Road A647 towards Bradford. Parkland, tight, hilly, some very steep. 18 holes, 4960 yards. S.S.S. 64. Practice area and putting green. *Green Fees:* £3.70 weekdays, £4.20 weekends. *Eating facilities:* cafe open most days for light meals and snacks, bar evenings only. *Visitors:* unrestricted except at weekends when booking system applies – no phone bookings. Professional: J.K. Simpson (0532 636600). Secretary: M. Gill (0532 562994).

LEEDS. **Headingley Golf Club,** Back Church Lane, Adel, Leeds LS16 8DW (Leeds (0532) 673052). *Location:* leave Leeds/Otley road (A660) at Church Lane, Adel about five miles from city centre. 18 holes, 6298 yards. S.S.S. 70. *Green Fees:* £15.00 per round, £20.00 per day (weekdays), £25.00 per round or per day (weekends and Bank Holidays). *Eating facilities:* full catering except Fridays. *Visitors:* members of other golf clubs welcome, preferably with prior reservation. *Society Meetings:* catered for by arrangement. Professional: Andrew Dyson (0532 675100). Secretary: R.W. Hellawell (0532 679573).

LEEDS. **Horsforth Golf Club Ltd,** Layton Rise, Layton Road, Horsforth, Near Leeds. *Location:* northwest of Leeds on A65 to Ilkley. 18 holes, 6293 yards. S.S.S. 70. *Green Fees:* £14.00 weekdays, £18.00 weekends and Bank Holidays. *Eating facilities:* full catering (except Monday), order in advance for dinner. *Visitors:* welcome, must be bona fide member of another club. *Society Meetings:* catered for by arrangement with Secretary. Professional: G. Howard (0532 585200). Secretary: C.B. Carrington (0532 586819).

LEEDS. **Howley Hall Golf Club,** Scotchman Lane, Morley, Leeds (Batley (0924) 472432). *Location:* turn off the Bradford/Wakefield road at the Halfway House Public House. 18 holes, 6421 yards. S.S.S. 71. *Green Fees:* information not provided. *Eating facilities:* available up to 7.00pm. *Visitors:* welcome, parties with reservation. *Society Meetings:* catered for by reservation. Professional: S.A. Spinks. Secretary: Mrs A. Pepper.

LEEDS. **Leeds Golf Club,** Cobble Hall, Elmete Lane, Leeds LS8 2LJ (Leeds (0532) 658775). *Location:* Leeds ring road to A58, turn left if from east, right if from west, fork right at next roundabout, turn right after 250 yards. 18 holes, 6097 yards. S.S.S. 69. *Green Fees:* £17.00 per day, £14.00 per round. *Eating facilities:* full catering, apply in advance. *Visitors:* welcome. *Society Meetings:* catered for. Professional: S. Thornhill. Secretary: G.W. Backhouse.

LEEDS. **Moor Allerton Golf Club,** Coal Road, Wike, Leeds LS17 9NH (Leeds (0532) 661154). *Location:* accessible from A61 at Alwoodley or from Harvester Scarcroft on A58. Undulating parkland, designed by Robert Trent Jones. 18 holes, 6552 yards. S.S.S. 72. 9 holes, 3541 yards. S.S.S. 37. Large practice area and driving range. *Green Fees:* £25.00 per day weekdays. Reduced rate November to March. *Eating facilities:* bars, full restaurant and snack facilities. *Visitors:* welcome weekdays with reservation. Tennis courts. *Society Meetings:* catered for weekdays by arrangement, brochure available. Professional. Peter Blaze (0532 665209). Secretary: (0532 661154). Executive Vice-President: J.J. Harris.

LEEDS. **Moortown Golf Club,** Harrogate Road, Alwoodley, Leeds LS17 7DB (Leeds (0532) 681682). *Location:* five miles north of Leeds centre, A61 Leeds to Harrogate road. 18 holes, 6544 yards. S.S.S. 72. Large practice field. *Green Fees:* weekdays £25.00 per round, £32.00 per day, weekends £32.00 per day. *Eating facilities:* lunches except Mondays, evening meals Tuesday to Saturday. *Visitors:* welcome weekdays, some tee-off time restrictions. *Society Meetings:* catered for. Professional: B. Hutchinson (0532 683636). Secretary: R.H. Brown (0532 686521).

LEEDS. **Rawdon Golf and Lawn Tennis Club,** Buckstone Drive, Micklefield Lane, Rawdon, Leeds LS19 7EZ (Leeds (0532) 506040). *Location:* eight miles north of Leeds on A65, left at Rawdon traffic lights on to Micklefield Lane. Undulating parkland, with trees a special feature. 9 holes (18 tees), 5964 yards. S.S.S. 69. *Green Fees:* weekdays £12.00, weekends with member only. *Eating facilities:* meals and bar snacks except Mondays. *Visitors:* welcome, weekends must play with a member. Facilities for tennis, visitors welcome with members. *Society Meetings:* catered for on application to Secretary. Professional: John Clapham (0532 505017). Secretary: Ray Adams (0532 506064).

LEEDS. **Roundhay Municipal Golf Club,** Park Lane, Leeds LS8 3QW (Leeds (0532) 662695). *Location:* four miles north of Leeds city centre, leave A58 to Wetherby at Oakwood. Wooded parkland. 9 holes, 5166 yards, 4701 metres. S.S.S. 65. Practice ground. *Green Fees:* weekdays £3.75, weekends and Bank Holidays £4.10. *Eating facilities:* bar for members and guests, restaurant in evenings. *Visitors:* welcome without reservation. *Society Meetings:* arrangements to be made with Leeds City Council. Professional: awaiting appointment (0532 661686). Hon. Secretary: R.H. McLauchlan (0532 492523).

LEEDS. **Sand Moor Golf Club,** Alwoodley Lane, Leeds LS17 7DJ (Leeds (0532) 681685). *Location:* five miles north of Leeds off A61. Moorland, overlooking picturesque Wharfedale. 18 holes, 6429 yards, 5876 metres. S.S.S. 71. *Green Fees:* £24.00 per round. *Eating facilities:* lunches daily, evening meals Tuesday to Friday. *Visitors:* welcome most weekdays by arrangement. *Society Meetings:* catered for. Pro-

fessional: J.R. Foss (0532 683925). Secretary: D. Warboys (0532 685180).

LEEDS. **Scarcroft Golf Club,** Syke Lane, Leeds LS14 3BQ (Leeds (0532) 892263). *Location:* A58 Wetherby road; turn left at New Inn, Scarcroft village seven miles north of Leeds. Undulating parkland. 18 holes, 6426 yards. S.S.S. 71. Practice ground and indoor net. *Green Fees:* £20.00 per round, £24.00 per day weekdays; £27.50 per round weekends. *Eating facilities:* bar and restaurant except Mondays. *Visitors:* casuals after 9.30am. *Society Meetings:* catered for Tuesdays and Thursdays only April to October, must have official Handicaps. Professional: Martin R. Ross (0532 892780). Secretary: R.D. Barwell (0532 892311).

LEEDS. **South Leeds Golf Club,** Parkside Links, Gipsy Lane, Off Middleton Ring Road, Leeds LS11 5TU (Leeds (0532) 700479). *Location:* M62 and M1 within five minutes' drive, Leeds City Centre 10 minutes' drive. Links course with undulating fairways. 18 holes, 5835 yards. S.S.S. 68. Practice fairway. *Green Fees:* £12.00 weekdays, £16.00 weekends and Bank Holidays (rates may change). Special rates for visiting parties numbering 40 or more. *Eating facilities:* full catering and bar except Mondays. *Visitors:* welcome most days except Saturdays or before 2.00pm on Sundays. *Society Meetings:* catered for by prior arrangement. Professional: Mike Lewis (0532 702598). Secretary: J. McBride (0532 771676).

LEEDS. **Temple Newsam Golf Club,** Temple Newsam, Leeds 15 (Leeds (0532) 645624). *Location:* easily reached by public transport from City (to Temple Newsam or Halton). Two 18 hole courses. No. 1 Course 6448 yards. S.S.S. 71. No. 2 course 5731 yards. S.S.S. 70. *Green Fees:* as decided by City Council. *Eating facilities:* cafe open Saturdays and Sundays 7.30am till 4.00pm. *Visitors:* welcome without reservation, except that parties must book in advance. *Society Meetings:* catered for. Professional: David Bulmer (0532 641464). Secretary: G. Gower.

MELTHAM. **Meltham Golf Club,** Thick Hollins Hall, Meltham, Huddersfield HD7 3DQ (Huddersfield (0484) 850227). *Location:* half mile east of Meltham, 6 miles south west of Huddersfield (B6107). Gently sloping course in wooded valley from Meltham. 18 holes, 6145 yards. S.S.S. 70. Restricted practice area. *Green fees:* weekdays £13.50, weekends £16.50. *Eating facilities:* lunches, dinners (with reservation). *Visitors:* welcome weekdays without reservation, not Saturday and with member Sunday. *Society Meetings:* catered for by arrangement, except Wednesday or Saturday. Professional: (0484 851521). Secretary: B. F. Precious (0484 682106).

MIRFIELD. **Dewsbury District Golf Club.** The Pinnacle, Sands Lane, Mirfield WF14 8HJ (0924 492399). *Location:* turn off A644 opposite Swan Inn, two miles west of Dewsbury. Undulating moorland/parkland with panoramic views over surrounding countryside. 18 holes, 6256 yards. S.S.S. 71. *Green Fees:* £11.00 weekdays. *Eating facilities:* full catering except Monday – order in advance. *Visitors:* welcome without reservation except weekends unless with member. Two full size snooker tables. *Society Meetings:* welcome. Professional: N.P. Hirst (0924 496030). Secretary: P. Croft.

NORMANTON. **Normanton Golf Club,** Snydale Road, Normanton WF6· 1PA (Wakefield (0924) 892943). *Location:* one mile from Junction 31 M62 Motorway towards Wakefield. Flat with internal out of bounds. 9 holes, 6284 yards. S.S.S. 66. Large practice area. *Green Fees:* £5.00 weekdays, weekends £9.00. £1.00 off if playing with a member. No green fees Sundays. *Eating facilities:* full catering and bar facilities. *Visitors:* no visitors on Sundays. *Society Meetings:* catered for weekdays only. Professional: Martin Evans (0924 220134). Secretary: Jack McElhinney (0977 702273).

OTLEY. **Otley Golf Club,** West Busk Lane, Otley (0943 461015). *Location:* off Bradford/Otley road. 18 holes, 6229 yards. S.S.S. 70. *Green Fees:* weekdays £17.00, weekends £22.00. *Eating facilities:* large dining room. *Visitors:* welcome without reservation except Tuesday mornings and Staurdays. *Society Meetings:* catered for by arrangement. Professional: Stephen McNally. Secretary: A.F. Flowers.

OUTLANE. **Outlane Golf Club,** Slack Lane, Outlane, Near Huddersfield (Halifax (0422) 74762). *Location:* from Huddersfield (A640) through Outlane Village, entrance on left just after bus terminus. 18 holes, 5862 yards. S.S.S. 68. *Green Fees:* information not provided. *Eating facilities:* available except Mondays. *Visitors:* welcome without reservation (but advisable to phone). Professional: D. Chapman. Secretary: P. Sykes.

POLLARD LANE. **Bradford Moor Golf Club,** Scarr Hill, Pollard Lane, Bradford 2 (Bradford (0274) 638313). *Location:* A658 two miles from M62. 9 holes, 5854 yards. *Green Fees:* weekdays £7.50, weekends £8.80. *Eating facilities:* available, order in advance. *Visitors:* welcome except on competition days. Professional: Mr R.J. Hughes. Secretary: D. Armitage.

PONTEFRACT. **Pontefract and District Golf Club,** Park Lane, Pontefract WF8 4QS (Pontefract (0977) 792241). *Location:* M62 exit 32, one mile from Pontefract. Parkland. 18 holes, 6227 yards. S.S.S. 70. Practice ground. *Green Fees:* weekdays £14.00, weekends £18.00. *Eating facilities:* available except Mondays. *Visitors:* welcome must be members of a golf club. *Society Meetings:* catered for Tuesdays, Thursdays and Fridays by arrangement. Professional: J. Coleman (0977 706806). Secretary: W. T. Smith (0977 792115).

PUDSEY. **Fulneck Golf Club Ltd,** Fulneck, Pudsey S28 8NT (Pudsey (0532) 565191). *Location:* between Leeds and Bradford. Undulating wooded parkland course. 9 holes, 5564 yards. S.S.S. 67. *Green Fees:* £8.00 (£5.00 with member) weekdays, weekends with a member only. *Society Meetings:* catered for by arrangement. Secretary: J.A. Broaden.

PUDSEY. **Woodhall Hills Golf Club Ltd,** Woodhall Road, Calverley, Pudsey (Pudsey (0532) 564771). *Location:* one mile from Pudsey roundabout on A647 Leeds to Bradford road, signposted Calverley. 18 holes, 6102 yards. S.S.S. 69. *Green Fees:* weekdays £11.00 per round, £15.00 per day; weekends £15.00 per round, £20.00 per day; Juniors £4.00 per round, £6.00 per day. *Eating facilities:* available daily except Mondays. *Visitors:* welcome without reservation. *Society Meetings:* catered for by previous arrangement. Professional: M.D. Lord (0532 562857). Secretary: D. Harkness (0532 554594).

SHIPLEY. **Baildon Golf Club,** Moorgate, Baildon BD17 5PP (0274 584266). *Location:* five miles north-west of Bradford via Shipley. Hilly, moorland course. 18 holes, 6085 yards. 5692 metres. S.S.S. 70. *Green Fees:* weekdays £9.00, weekends and Bank Holidays £12.00. Reduced rates for groups of 12 and over. *Eating facilities:* catering except Mondays. Bar and separate restaurant. *Visitors:* welcome, restricted at weekends and Tuesdays. *Society Meetings:* welcome weekdays only, by written application. Professional: R. Masters (0274 595162). Secretary: D. Farnsworth (0274 584684/567545).

TODMORDEN. **Todmorden Golf Club,** Rive Rocks, Cross Stone Road, Todmorden (Todmorden (0706) 812986). *Location:* A646 Halifax road, one mile left Cross Stone Road, one mile, bear left at top. Moorland. 9 holes, 5818 yards. S.S.S. 68. *Green Fees:* weekdays £6.00, weekends and Bank Holidays £8.00. *Eating facilities:* available except Monday, order in advance. *Visitors:* welcome without reservation. *Society Meetings:* catered for Tuesday to Friday. Secretary: R.A. Ward.

WAKEFIELD. **City of Wakefield Golf Club,** Lupset Park, Horbury Road, Wakefield WF2 8QS (Wakefield (0924) 374316). *Location:* one mile from city centre, two miles from M1 Junctions 39/40. Undulating partially wooded parkland. 18 holes, 6299 yards, 5760 metres. S.S.S. 70/71. *Green Fees:* weekdays £3.80, weekends and Bank Holidays £5.90; Juniors half price. *Eating facilities:* full or snack catering, bar available. *Visitors:* weekdays only – ball chute operates, weekends – booked times only. *Society Meetings:* only by arrangement with Secretary – not weekends. Professional: Roger Holland (0924 360282). Secretary: Mrs P. Ambler (0924 367442 club or 0924 375008 home).

WAKEFIELD. **Low Laithes Golf Club Ltd,** Golf House, Parkmill Lane, Flushdyke, Ossett, Wakefield (Wakefield (0924) 273275). *Location:* one mile from Junction 40 M1, or along A638 Dewsbury to Wakefield road. Parkland, undulating. 18 holes, 6456 yards. S.S.S. 71. Limited practice area and net. *Green Fees:* £12.00 weekdays, £16.00 weekends and Bank Holidays. Reduced rates if playing with a member (£8.00 and £12.00). *Eating facilities:* bar, good eating facilities.

Visitors: no restriction, weekends and Bank Holidays prefer prior arrangement if possible. *Society Meetings:* by arrangement welcome. Professional: Paul Browning (0924 274667). Secretary: Donald Walker (0924 376553).

WAKEFIELD. **Painthorpe House Country and Golf Club,** Painthorpe Lane, Painthorpe, Wakefield (Wakefield (0924) 255083). *Location:* off A636 two miles south of Wakefield (Grigglestone). One mile from M1, Junction 39. 9 holes, 4008 yards. S.S.S. 60. Bowling green. *Green Fees:* weekdays £3.00, Saturdays £4.00 (no visitors Sunday). *Eating facilities:* extensive catering for private functions up to 400. Two ballrooms, Saturday dinner dances. *Visitors:* welcome with reservation. Secretary: H. Kershaw (0924 274527).

WAKEFIELD. **Wakefield Golf Club,** Woodthorpe Lane, Sandal, Wakefield WF2 6JH (Wakefield (0924) 255104). *Location:* three miles south of Wakefield.

Parkland. 18 holes, 6626 yards. S.S.S. 72. *Green Fees:* weekdays £15.00 per round/day, weekends and Bank Holidays £18.00 per round/day. *Eating facilities:* full catering available. *Visitors:* visiting parties by arrangement Wednesdays, Thursdays and Fridays. *Society Meetings:* catered for by arrangement. Professional: I.M. Wright (0924 255380). Secretary: D.T. Hall (0924 258778).

WETHERBY. **Wetherby Golf Club,** Linton Lane, Wetherby LS22 4JF (Wetherby (0937) 62527). *Location:* off the A1 at Wetherby. Parkland course. 18 holes, 6244 yards. S.S.S. 70. Two practice grounds. *Green Fees:* weekdays £15.00 per round, £20.00 per day; weekends £25.00 per round/day. *Eating facilities:* available except Mondays. *Visitors:* welcome, advisable to phone first. *Society Meetings:* catered for Wednesdays, Thursdays and Fridays. Professional: D. Padgett (0937 63375). Secretary: W.F. Gibb (0937 63375).

Golf in Scotland
WHERE TO PLAY • WHERE TO STAY

The main event on the golfing scene in Scotland has probably been the 'Open' at St Andrews in July 1990, with record-breaking attendances once again. Bell's 'Scottish Open' at Gleneagles is rapidly establishing itself and there is also important news of golf developments at such diverse locations as Loch Lomond, Cumbernauld and Dalmahoy.

The arrival of fresh golfing venues and accommodation adds to an already rich stock of golfing hospitality available for the visitor. *THE GOLF GUIDE* is delighted to include such internationally famous names as Turnberry and Gleneagles, joined for 1991 by the equally prestigious Sheraton group with their recently opened new hotel in Edinburgh. From Dornoch Castle and Alton Burn, Nairn in the north to the very southernmost borders of Scotland with Beachcomber House in Berwick-on-Tweed, there are old and new Scottish hotels closely associated with golf.

Indeed, local tourism authorities often lend their support and nowhere more strongly than in Fife with its wealth of courses and hotels, and in the Ayrshire and Burns country whose golfing jewels sparkle around Troon, Prestwick and Ayr.

Scotland has long laid claim to the title 'Home of Golf'. If the quality and quantity of the clubs, courses and hotels featured in this current edition of *THE GOLF GUIDE* is any measure, there's unlikely to be a serious competitor!

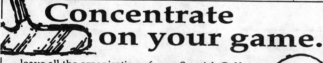

Aberdeenshire

ABERDEEN. Auchmill Golf Course, Aberdeen District Council, Aberdeen Leisure, Howes Road, Buckburn, Aberdeen. *Location:* approximately four miles from city centre, turn off A96 into Aberdeen at Howes Road. Open, fairly flat. 18 holes, 5952 yards, 5439 metres. S.S.S. 69. *Green Fees:* information not provided. *Visitors:* welcome. Contact: Outdoor Activities Officer, Aberdeen Leisure, Bon Accord Baths, Justice Mill Lane, Aberdeen AB1 2EQ (0224 587920).

ABERDEEN. Balnagask Golf Course, Aberdeen District Council, Aberdeen Leisure, Grey Hope Road, Aberdeen. *Location:* on coast beside Girdleness Lighthouse between Aberdeen Harbour and Nigg Bay, south east side of city. Seaside links. 18 holes, 5986 yards, 5472 metres. S.S.S. 69. *Green Fees:* information not provided. *Visitors:* welcome. Contact: Outdoor Activities Officer, Aberdeen Leisure, Bon Accord Baths, Justice Mill Lane, Aberdeen (0224 587920).

ABERDEEN. Bon Accord Municipal Golf Club, 19 Golf Road, Aberdeen (0224 633464). *Location:* next to Pittodrie Stadium at Aberdeen beach. Seaside links. 18 holes, 6433 yards, 5880 metres. S.S.S. 71. *Green Fees:* £4.80. *Eating facilities:* meals on request. *Society Meetings:* bookings in advance. Professional: Bruce Davidson (0224 641577). Secretary: J.T. Burnett (0224 682604).

ABERDEEN. Caledonian Golf Club, Kings Links, Aberdeen (Aberdeen (0224) 632443). 18 holes, 6396 yards. S.S.S. 71. *Green Fees:* information not provided. *Visitors:* welcome.

ABERDEEN. Deeside Golf Club, Haughton, Bieldside, Aberdeen (Aberdeen (0224) 867697). *Location:* three miles west of Aberdeen on A93. Parkland. 18 holes, 5972 yards, 5460 metres. S.S.S. 69. New 9 hole course. Practice area. *Green Fees:* £15.00 weekday, £17.00 weekends and Public Holidays. Weekly tickets £60.00. *Eating facilities:* diningroom and bar. *Visitors:* not permitted to play after 4pm weekdays nor before 4pm weekends or before 9am weekdays. *Society Meetings:* by arrangement, Thursdays only. Professional: F.G. Coutts (0224 861041). Secretary: Dr N.M. Scott (0224 869457).

ABERDEEN. Hazlehead Golf Club, Aberdeen District Council, Aberdeen Leisure, Groats Road, Aberdeen. *Location:* situated on west edge of city, four miles from city centre. From A944 into Aberdeen turn off into Groats Road. No. 1 course 18 holes, 6204 yards, 5673 metres. S.S.S. 70. No 2 course 18 holes, 5801 yards, 5303 metres. S.S.S. 68. 9 hole course, 2770 yards, 2531 metres. S.S.S. 34. *Green Fees:* Information not provided. *Eating facilities:* restaurant adjoining park. *Visitors:* welcome. Professional: Iain Smith. Contact: Outdoor Activities Officer, Aberdeen Leisure, Bon Accord Baths, Justice Mill Lane, Aberdeen AB1 2EQ (0224 587920).

ABERDEEN. King's Links Golf Course, Aberdeen District Council, Aberdeen Leisure, Golf Road, Aberdeen (0224 641577). *Location:* city centre, beside Beach Esplanade. Seaside links course – flat. 18 holes, 6384 yards, 5835 metres. S.S.S. 70. *Green Fees:* information not provided. *Visitors:* welcome. Professional: Mr R. MacDonald. Contact: Outdoor Activities Officer, Aberdeen Leisure, Bon Accord Baths, Justice Mill Lane, Aberdeen AB1 2EQ (0224 587920).

ABERDEEN. Murcar Golf Club, Murcar, Bridge of Don, Aberdeen (0224 704345). *Location:* five miles from Aberdeen on Peterhead – Fraserburgh road. 18 holes, 6240 yards. S.S.S. 70. *Green Fees:* weekdays £16.00 per day, weekends £18.00 per day, before 11.30 a.m. £10.00 per round. *Eating facilities:* meals served at club except Tuesday. *Visitors:* welcome without reservation. *Society Meetings:* catered for. Professional: A. White (0224 704370). Secretary: R. Matthews (0224 704354).

ABERDEEN. Northern Aberdeen (Municipal) Golf Club, 22 Golf Road, Aberdeen AB2 1QB (0224 636440). *Location:* off Beach Esplanade near Pittodrie Stadium. Seaside course – flat. 18 holes, 7204 yards. S.S.S. 70. *Green Fees:* information not available. *Eating facilities:* snacks available at the bar. *Visitors:* welcome. *Society Meetings:* catered for, contact Leisure and Recreation Department. Professional: Ronnie McDonald. Secretary: F. Sutherland. Steward (0224 632134).

ABERDEEN. Royal Aberdeen Golf Club, Balgownie, Bridge of Don, Aberdeen (Aberdeen (0224) 702571). *Location:* on A92, north side of Aberdeen, cross Bridge of Don, second right. Seaside links. Main course Balgownie, alternative Silverburn course. 18 holes, 6372 yards. S.S.S. 71. 18 holes, 4033 yards. S.S.S. 60. *Green Fees:* weekdays £18.00 per round, £22.00 per day; weekends and Public Holidays £22.00 per round/day. (Silverburn course green fees are half those quoted for Balgownie). *Eating facilities:* meals at lunchtime and by arrangement with Club Steward. *Visitors:* welcome with reservation. Telephone Secretary or Professional. Saturdays after 3.30 pm only. *Society Meetings:* catered for by arrangement with Secretary. Professional: R. A. Macaskill (0224 702221). Hon. Secretary: F. Webster (0224 702571).

ABERDEEN. Tarland Golf Club, Aberdeen Road, Tarland, Aboyne (03398 81413). *Location:* from Aberdeen – A944 then A974. Parkland/wooded, easy walking, difficult upland course. 9 holes, 5816 yards for 18 holes, S.S.S. 68. Small practice area. *Green Fees:* weekdays £6.00, weekends £8.00. Weekly £25.00; Fortnightly £40.00 (all rates to be reviewed). *Eating facilities:* catering available, bar 11.00am to 11.00pm, midnight Saturdays and Sundays. *Visitors:* welcome without reservation, phone call advisable due to club competitions. *Society Meetings:* catered for except weekends. Secretary: Mr J.H. Honeyman.

ABOYNE. **Aboyne Golf Club,** Formaston Park, Aboyne (Aboyne (0339) 2328). *Location:* A93, 30 miles west of Aberdeen. Part park land, part hilly with lovely views. 18 holes, 5330 yards. S.S.S. 66. Practice ground. *Green Fees:* weekdays £8.00 per day, weekends £13.00 per day. *Eating facilities:* full restaurant and bar service. *Visitors:* welcome without reservation. *Society Meetings:* catered for weekdays, restricted size of party on Saturdays. Professional: Innes Wright. Secretary: Mrs M. MacLean (03398 86755).

ALFORD. **Alford Golf Club,** Montgarrie Road, Alford AB3 8AE (09755 62178). *Location:* A944 from Aberdeen, golf course situated middle of the village. Flat course. 9 holes, 5964 yards. S.S.S. 69. *Green Fees:* £5.50 weekdays, £9.50 weekends. Weekly tickets available. *Eating facilities:* available. *Visitors:* always welcome. *Society Meetings:* catered for. Secretary: Mrs M.J. Ball.

BALLATER. **Ballater Golf Club,** Victoria Road, Ballater AB3 5QX (Ballater (0338) 55200). *Location:* 40 miles west of Aberdeen on A93 in Upper Deeside. Wooded parkland course. 18 holes, 5704 yards. S.S.S. 67. *Green Fees:* £10.00 per round, £15.00 for two rounds weekdays; £12.00 per round, £18.00 for two rounds weekends. Weekly £36.00, fortnightly £60.00, season ticket £120. Reductions for under 18 players. *Eating facilities:* restaurant, dining room – April to October, bar. *Visitors:* welcome, but advise phone call first, can be very busy especially weekends. *Society Meetings:* catered for. Professional: F. Mann (0338 55658). Secretary: Bert Ingram (0338 55567).

BRAEMAR. **Braemar Golf Club,** Cluniebank Road, Braemar AB3 5XX (03397 41618). *Location:* about one mile from centre of the village, signposted. Flat parkland, 18 holes, 5011 yards. S.S.S. 64. Practice net. Highest 18 hole course on mainland of Great Britain *Green Fees:* weekdays £5.00 per round, £8.00 per day; weekends £8.00 per round, £10.00 per day. Parties of 12 or more £2.00 reduction on day ticket. *Eating facilities:* restaurant (limited menu midweek) and bar. *Visitors:* welcome (prior booking for weekends). *Society Meetings:* welcome, prior booking advised. Secretary: George A. McIntosh (0224 733836).

ELLON. **McDonald Golf Club,** Ellon Hospital Road, Ellon AB4 9AW (Ellon (0358) 20576). *Location:* A92 from Aberdeen to Ellon. One mile down A948, on left. Flat parkland with trees, stream and pond. 18 holes, 5986 yards, 5473 metres. S.S.S. 69. Practice putting green and 2 practice nets. *Green Fees:* information not available. *Eating facilities:* full catering and bars, 11am – 2.30pm and 5pm – 11pm. *Visitors:* welcome at all times, but booking advisabie weekend mornings. Round ticket available after 4.00 p.m. without reservation. *Society Meetings:* must book in advance. Club Steward: Bill Polson. Professional: Ronnie Urquhart (0358 22891). Secretary: Fred Chadwick (0358 21397).

ELLON. **Newburgh-on-Ythan Golf Club,** c/o Andrew C. Stevenson, 51 Mavis Bank, Newburgh, Ellon, Aberdeen AB4 0FB (03586 89438). *Location:* 12 miles north of Aberdeen. Seaside links course. 9 holes, 6300 yards, 5758 metres. S.S.S. 70. *Green Fees:* weekdays £7.00, weekends £9.00. Reduction of £2 for Senior Citizens. *Eating facilities:* at local hotels. *Visitors:* welcome, but tee reserved Tuesday evenings (Club competitions) and Monday evenings (Ladies and Juniors have priority). *Society Meetings:* by arrangement. Secretary: Andrew C. Stevenson.

FRASERBURGH. **Fraserburgh Golf Club,** Corbie Hill, Fraserburgh (0346 28287). *Location:* 38 miles north of Aberdeen. Seaside links. 18 holes, 6217 yards, 5688 metres. S.S.S. 70. Practice area. *Green Fees:* weekdays £7.00 per day, weekends £10.00 per day. Special rates for parties over 12 persons. *Eating facilities:* full catering provided, bar. *Visitors:* welcome, reservations at weekends. *Society Meetings:* catered for. Secretary: J. Grant (034665 2978).

HUNTLY. **Huntly Golf Club,** Cooper Park, Huntly (0466 2643). *Location:* on A96, 38 miles from Aberdeen. On right hand side of road towards castle from the square. Parkland. 18 holes, 5399 yards. S.S.S. 66. *Green Fees:* weekdays £7.00, weekends £10.00. Weekly ticket £20.00. *Eating facilities:* catering and bar. *Visitors:* welcome, no restriction but cannot book tee times. *Society Meetings:* catered for, not before 10am and 2pm, can book the tee. Secretary: George Angus (0466 3638).

INSCH. **Insch Golf Club,** Golf Road, Insch (0464 20363). *Location:* A96 from Aberdeen. Parkland – trees, water hazards. 9 holes, 2886 yards. S.S.S. 67. *Green Fees:* £5.00 per day weekdays, £6.00 per day weekends. £10.00 per week, £15.00 per fortnight. *Eating facilities:* catering and bar by prior arrangement with caterer. *Visitors:* welcome except Tuesday evenings. Secretary: Mrs Anne Sutherland (04644 315).

INVERALLOCHY. **Inverallochy Golf Club,** Inverallochy (03465 2324). *Location:* A92 from Aberdeen then B9107 for three and a half miles. Seaside links course. 18 holes, 5107 yards. S.S.S. 65. *Green Fees:* weekdays £4.00, weekends £5.00. *Eating facilities:* limited, advance booking required. *Visitors:* welcome. *Society Meetings:* catered for on limited basis. Secretary: George M. Young.

INVERURIE. **Inverurie Golf Club,** Davah Wood, Blackhall Road, Inverurie (Inverurie (0467) 20207). *Location:* main Aberdeen/Inverness trunk road, 16 miles west of Aberdeen. Parkland, partly wooded course. 18 holes, 6000 yards. S.S.S. 66. Practice area. *Green Fees:* weekdays £8.00, weekends £10.00. *Eating facilities:* bar lounge, catering. *Visitors:* welcome anytime – reserve through Golf Shop (0467 20193). *Society Meetings:* catered for. Secretary: John Ramage (0467 21291).

INVERURIE. **Kintore Golf Club,** Balbithan Road, Kintore, Inverurie AB5 0UR (0467 32631). *Location:* off A96 12 miles north of Aberdeen. Undulating moorland course. 18 holes, 5985 yards. S.S.S. 69 (9 holes until Spring 1991). *Green Fees:* weekdays £7.00

per day, weekends £8.00 per day. *Eating facilities:* bar available, catering if booked in advance. *Visitors:* welcome daily except Mondays, Wednesdays and Fridays after 4pm. *Society Meetings:* welcome weekdays. Secretary: James D. Black.

KEMNAY. **Kemnay Golf Club,** Monymusk Road, Kemnay (Kemnay (0467) 42225). *Location:* from A96 main Aberdeen/Inverness road. Take B994 sign posted Kemnay and pass through village of Kemnay to find golf course on left hand side on leaving village. Parkland. 9 holes, 5502 yards. S.S.S. 67. *Green Fees:* weekdays £5.00, weekends £6.00. *Eating facilities:* light snacks available at the bar. *Visitors:* welcome all week, Sundays if starting times available. *Society Meetings:* weekdays, maximum number 25. Secretary: Dr G. Young (0467 42681).

OLDMELDRUM. **Oldmeldrum Golf Club,** Kirk Brae, Oldmeldrum (06512 2648). *Location:* 17 miles north west of Aberdeen on A947 to Banff. Course is on a slight hill, many young trees planted this year. 18 holes, 5988 yards, 5479 metres. S.S.S. 69. Practice area. *Green Fees:* weekdays £6.00, weekends £8.00. *Eating facilities:* catering by arrangement, bar. *Visitors:* welcome by arrangement. *Society Meetings:* catered for by arrangement. Secretary: J.N.D. Duncan (06512 2626).

PETERHEAD. **Cruden Bay Golf Club,** Aulton Road, Cruden Bay, Peterhead AB4 7NN (Cruden Bay (0779) 812285). *Location:* seven miles south of Peterhead, 23 miles north east of Aberdeen. 18 holes and 9 holes. 6370 yards, 5859 metres. Par 70. S.S.S. 71. *Green Fees:* weekdays £13.50, weekends £18.00. *Eating facilities:* full bar and catering facilities. *Visitors:* welcome but restricted at weekends. *Society Meetings:* welcome weekdays only. Professional: David Symington. Manager: Ian A.D. McPherson.

PETERHEAD. **Peterhead Golf Club,** Craigewan Links, Peterhead (Peterhead (0779) 72149). 9 holes and 18 holes. S.S.S. 70. *Green Fees:* £6.00 weekdays, £10.00 weekends. *Eating facilities:* to be booked in advance. *Visitors:* welcome without reservation except Saturdays. *Society Meetings:* catered for. Secretary: A. Brandie.

TORPHINS. **Torphins Golf Club,** 26 Beltie Road, Torphins AB3 4JT (03398 82115). *Location:* Torphins is five miles north-west of Banchory; Club in Torphins, north-west of village, well signed. Parkland/heather, good views of the Grampians. 9 holes, 2317 yards. S.S.S. 63. *Green Fees:* £4.00 weekdays, £5.00 weekends. *Eating facilities:* no licence but snacks served. *Visitors:* no play on Medal Days (one Saturday and one Sunday per month). *Society Meetings:* no restrictions. Secretary: Harry Shepherd (03398 82493).

TURRIFF. **Turriff Golf Club,** Rosehall, Turriff (0888 62745). *Location:* A947 signposted on south side of Turriff. Flat, parkland course. 18 holes, 6145 yards. S.S.S. 69. *Green Fees:* weekdays £7.00 per round, £10.00 per day; weekends £10.00 per round, £12.00 per day. *Eating facilities:* catering by arrangement. *Visitors:* no visitors before 10am weekends. Phone Professional for tee bookings. *Society Meetings:* welcome. Professional: Alan Hemsley (0888 63025). Secretary: James D. Stott (0888 62982).

WESTHILL. **Westhill Golf Club,** Westhill Heights, Westhill, Skene (0224 743361). *Location:* six miles from Aberdeen on A944. Undulating parkland course. 18 holes, 5921 yards. S.S.S. 69. Short practice area. *Green Fees:* weekdays £7.00 per round, £9.00 per day; weekends £8.00 per round, £11.00 per day. *Eating facilities:* lounge bar with dining area. *Visitors:* welcome except Saturdays and 4.30pm to 7.00pm Monday to Friday. Professional: Stewart Smith (0224 740159). Secretary: John L. Webster (0224 740957).

Angus

ARBROATH. **Arbroath Golf Course,** Elliot, By Arbroath (Arbroath (0241) 72069). *Location:* A92 one mile south of Arbroath on main coast road. Seaside links. 18 holes, 6095 yards. S.S.S 69. Practice area. *Green Fees:* £10.00 weekdays, £14.00 weekends. *Eating facilities:* available at Arbroath Artisan Golf Club. *Visitors:* welcome weekdays without reservation, booking times evenings and weekends. *Society Meetings:* all welcome (good rates midweek). Professional: L. Ewart (0241 75837). Secretary: Tom Pullar (0241 74604).

ARBROATH by. **Letham Grange Golf Club,** Colliston, By Arbroath DD11 4RL. *Location:* From Arbroath take the A933, Brechin/Forfar road. Approximately four miles turn right at Colliston (signposted). Parkland/wooded course with water features. 18 holes, 6789 yards. S.S.S. 73. Putting green and practice areas. *Green Fees:* weekdays £12.00 per round, £18.00 per day; weekends £15.00 per round. Juniors £3.00 weekday round and £4.00 weekend round. *Eating facilities:* available at Hotel – catering and bars. *Visitors:* welcome, with valid handicap. Except: Tuesdays 9-10am; weekends 7.30-10.30am and 1.00-2.00pm. Accommodation available. *Society Meetings:* welcome by arangement. Professional: David F.G. Scott (024 189 377). Secretary: Heather McDougall (024 189 373).

BARRY. **Panmure Golf Club,** Barry, Angus (Carnoustie (0241) 53120). *Location:* two miles from Carnoustie, south in centre at Barry village, then 200 yards turn right. Seaside course, 18 holes, 6302 yards. S.S.S. 70. *Green fees:* information not provided. *Eating facilities:* bar and diningroom. *Visitors:* welcome daily except Saturday. *Society Meetings:* catered for. Professional: T. Shiel. Secretary: Captain J.C. Ray.

BRECHIN. **Brechin Golf and Squash Club,** Trinity, By Brechin DD9 6BJ (Brechin (035-62) 2383). *Location:* Trinity Village, one mile north of Brechin on A94. Rolling parkland. 18 holes, 5287 yards. S.S.S. 66. *Green Fees:* weekdays £7.00 per round, £10.50 per day; weekends £8.00 per round, £11.50 per day. *Eating facilities:* excellent catering available at all times; large bar. *Visitors:* welcome without reservation. Squash courts, pool table available. *Society Meetings:* catered for, but prior booking necessary. Midweek packages for parties of 12 or more. Professional: Brian Mason (035-62 5270). Secretary: A.B. May (035-62 2326).

CARNOUSTIE. **Carnoustie Golf Links,** Links Parade, Carnoustie DD7 7JE (0241 53789). *Location:* 12 miles east of Dundee. Three 18-hole courses. Championship Course 6936 yards. S.S.S. 74; Burnside Course 6020 yards. S.S.S. 69; Buddon Links 5700 yards. S.S.S. 69. Golf trolleys permitted from May to October only. *Green Fees:* (1990 only) Championship Cup: Weekly tickets for play over three courses £100.00. Three-day tickets for play over three courses £70.00. Championship Course: Day ticket (Monday-Friday only) £35.00, single round £22.00. Burnside Course: Day ticket £15.00. Adult single round £10.00. Juvenile (under 14 yrs) £2.00. Buddon Links Course: Day ticket £7.50, single round £5.00. Juvenile (under 14 yrs) £0.50. *Eating facilities:* catering facilities can be arranged with the local golf clubs. *Visitors:* welcome, times must be booked and ballot system in operation. *Society Meetings:* catered for by arrangement. Secretary: Earle J.C. Smith.

DUNDEE. **Caird Park Golf Club,** Mains Loan, Dundee (0382 453606). *Location:* northern edge of city, off Kingsway. Wooded parkland. 18 holes, 6273 yards, 5740 metres. S.S.S. 70. Practice range on course. *Green Fees:* information not available. *Eating facilities:* at clubhouse. *Visitors:* welcome, must book in advance to ensure game. *Society Meetings:* see Dundee District Council, Parks Department. Professional: Jackie Black (0382 459438). Secretary: Douglas Farquhar Jnr.

DUNDEE. **Camperdown Golf Club,** Camperdown Park, Dundee (Dundee (0382) 623715). *Location:* two miles north-west of city, enter at Kingsway/Coupar Angus road junction. Wooded parkland, flat. 18 holes, 6561 yards. S.S.S. 72 par 71. *Green Fees:* £7.50. *Eating facilities:* (must be ordered beforehand) all year round. *Visitors:* welcome, bookable all week, contact Parks Department, 353 Clepington Road, Dundee. *Society Meetings:* by arrangement, catered for once booked by Parks Dept. for date and times. Professional: R. Brown (0382 623452). Secretary: K. McCreery (0382 642925).

DUNDEE. **Downfield Golf Club,** Turnberry Avenue, Dundee DD2 3QP (0382 825595). *Location:* north end Dundee off A923 (Timex Circle). Map available on request. By rail Dundee Tay Bridge Station. Undulating wooded heathland course. 18 holes, 6804 yards. S.S.S. 73. Extensive practice ground. *Green Fees:* weekdays £24.00 day, £16.00 round (inclusive of VAT). Weekends with members only. *Eating facilities:* full catering available. *Visitors:* welcome with reservation Monday-Friday 9.30-11.48am and 2.18-3.48pm. *Society Meetings:* catered for (reservation). Professional: C. Waddell (0382 89246). Managing Secretary: Brian F. Mole (0382 825595).

EDZELL. **Edzell Golf Club,** High Street, Edzell DD9 7TF (03564 235). *Location:* A94 north of Brechin by-pass on Forfar to Aberdeen road. Undulating heathland course. 18 holes, 6300 yards. S.S.S. 70. Practice area and putting green. *Green Fees:* weekdays £10.00 per round, £15.00 per day; weekends £12.00 per round, £18.00 per day. *Eating facilities:* dining room, lounge and bar. *Visitors:* welcome with some restrictions. *Society Meetings:* welcome with some restrictions, apply to Secretary. Professional: Jim Webster (03564 462). Secretary: J. M. Hutchison (03564 7283). Steward and Caterer: Mr and Mrs McArthur.

FORFAR. **Forfar Golf Club,** Cunninghill, Forfar (Forfar (0307) 62120). *Location:* one mile from Forfar on A932 to Arbroath. Undulating wooded heathland course. 18 holes, 5537 metres. S.S.S. 69. *Green Fees:* weekdays £12.00 per round, £18.00 per day; Sundays £20.00 per day. *Visitors:* welcome. *Society Meetings:* catered for. Professional: Peter McNiven. Secretary: P.H. Wallace (0307 63773).

KIRRIEMUIR. **Kirriemuir Golf Club Ltd,** Northmuir, Kirriemuir (Kirriemuir (0575) 72144). *Location:* on A926 and A928. Parkland and heathland course. 18 holes, 5591 yards, 5336 metres. S.S.S: 67. Practice area for members. *Green Fees:* £12.50, £7.00 after 4.00pm weekdays; weekends with member only. Weekly ticket £40.00 (including weekend). *Eating facilities:* fully licensed, all catering facilities. *Visitors:* welcome weekdays only. Professional: A. Caira (0575 73317). Secretaries: Irvine, Adamson & Co., 23 Bank Street, Kirriemuir (0575 72729).

MONIFIETH. **Ashludie Course,** (adjoining Medal Course), The Links, Monifieth (Monifieth (0382) 2767). *Location:* seven miles east of Dundee. 18 holes, 5123 yards. S.S.S. 64. *Green Fees:* Monifieth Medal Course – Monday to Saturday £10.00 per round, £15.00 per day; Sundays £11.00 per round, £17.00 per day; Weekly ticket £40.00. Monifieth Ashludie Course – Monday to Saturday £8.00 per round, £11.00 per day; Sundays £9.00 per round, £13.00 per day; Weekly ticket £26.00. *Eating facilities:* at Monifieth, Broughty Grange/Dundee, and Abertay Clubs by arrangement with Secretary. *Visitors:* welcome both courses weekdays at any time; Saturdays after 2.00 p.m.; Sundays after 10.00am. Professional: Ian McLeod (0382 532945). Secretary: J.A.R. Fraser (0383 78117).

MONIFIETH. **Broughty Golf Club,** 6 Princes Street, Monifieth, Dundee DD5 4AW (0382 532147). Starter (0382 532767). *Location:* eight miles east of Dundee, in village of Monifieth. Seaside links. Medal Course: 18 holes, 6657 yards, 6087 metres. S.S.S. 72. Ashludie

Course: 18 holes, 5123 yards. S.S.S. 66. Practice area. *Green Fees:* Medal Course £10.00 per round, £15.00 per day, £40 per week. Ashludie Course £8.00 per round, £11.00 per day, £26.00 per week. *Eating facilities:* full catering; lunches only Thursdays, no catering Tuesdays. *Visitors:* by prior arrangement with Club Secretary. *Society Meetings:* as visitors. Secretary: Samuel J. Gailey (0382 730014).

MONIFIETH. **Monifieth Golf Links,** The Links, Monifieth, Dundee (0382 532767). *Location:* seven miles east of Dundee. Medal Course 18 holes, 6657 yards. S.S.S. 72; Ashludie Course 18 holes, 5123 yards. S.S.S. 64. *Green Fees:* Medal Course £10.00 per round, £15.00 per day weekdays, £11.00 per round, £17.00 per day Sundays; Ashludie Course £8.00 per round, £11.00 per day weekdays, £9.00 per round, £13.00 per day Sundays. *Eating facilities:* at Monifieth, Broughty, Abertay, Grange and Dundee Clubs by arrangement through Secretary. *Visitors:* welcome Monday to Friday at any time; Saturdays after 2pm; Sundays after 10am. *Society Meetings:* contact Secretary. Professional: Ian McLeod (0382 532945). Secretary: J.A.R. Fraser (0382 78117).

MONTROSE. **Montrose Links Trust,** Starters Box, Traill Drive, Montrose DD10 8SW (Montrose (0674) 72634). *Location:* A92 runs from Dundee to Aberdeen, through Montrose. Links Medal Course 6451 yards. Par 71. S.S.S. 71. Broomfield Course 4815 yards. Par 66. S.S.S. 63. *Green Fees:* April 1990/March 1991. Medal: weekdays £14.00 per day, £9.00 per round, Juniors £4.50 per round. Weekends £18.00 per day, £11.50 per round, Juniors £5.50 per round. Weekly tickets £35.00 adult, £17.00 Juniors. Broomfield: weekdays £7.50 per day, £5.50 per round, Juniors £1.25 per round. Weekends £10.00 per day, £8.00 per round, Juniors £2.50 per round. Weekly ticket £26.00 adult, £12.00 Junior. 'Special Deal' to parties for two rounds plus catering from £14.50. Details on request. *Eating facilities:* catering facilities available by arrangement in golf clubs. *Visitors:* welcome, except on Medal Course Saturdays and before 10 am Sundays. *Society Meetings:* welcome by arrangement. Temporary membership available at the following clubs: Caledonia Golf Club (0674 72313); Mercantile Golf Club, Secretary: R.S. West (0674 72408); Royal Montrose, Secretary: J.D. Sykes (0674 72376). Professional: Alastair J. Webster. Secretary: Mrs Margaret Stewart (0674 72932).

MONTROSE. **Royal Montrose Golf Club,** Dorward Road, Montrose (Montrose (0674) 72376). Private club playing over the Montrose courses. 18 holes, 6442 yards. S.S.S. 71. *Green Fees:* information not provided. *Eating facilities:* meals at club for temporary members. Hon. Secretary: J D. Sykes.

Argyll

CAMPBELTOWN. **Machrihanish Golf Club,** Machrihanish, By Campbeltown (Machrihanish (058 681) 213). *Location:* five miles west of Campbeltown on B843 road. Championship standard, seaside links course. 18 holes, 6228 yards. S.S.S. 70. Also 9 holes, 2395 yards. Practice area. *Green Fees:* weekdays (18 holes) £10.00 per round, day ticket £13.00; weekends day ticket only, £15.00. Discounts for parties of 12 and over. Advance booking necessary. *Eating facilities:* full catering and bar facilities. *Visitors:* welcome without reservation. (Some restrictions on competition days. Open competitions in summer). Special Flight/Golf packages available through Loganair, Glasgow Airport, Paisley. *Society Meetings:* as visitors. Professional: Ken Campbell (058 681 277). Secretary: Mrs Anna Anderson.

CARRADALE. **Carradale Golf Club,** Carradale PA28 6QT. *Location:* 15 miles north of Campbeltown on B842. Seaside, short but very demanding, unbelievable views. 9 holes, 2700 yards. S.S.S. 63 (18 holes). *Green Fees:* £3.00 per day. *Eating facilities:* hotel at first tee. *Visitors:* all welcome, no restrictions. Secretary: J.A. Duncan (05833 387).

DUNOON. **Blairmore and Strone Golf Club,** Strone, by Dunoon (Kilmun (036-984) 676). *Location:* on high road above Strone village, nine miles north of Dunoon on A880. Scenic hilly course, heavily wooded. 9 holes, 2112 yards, 1933 metres. S.S.S. 62. *Green Fees:* £4.00 per day or round. *Eating facilities:* bar only. *Visitors:* welcome except Saturday afternoons. Secretary: A.B. Horton (036-984 217).

DUNOON. **Cowal Golf Club,** Ardenslate Road, Kirn, Dunoon PA23 8LT (Dunoon (0369) 2216). *Location:* quarter mile off A815 at Kirn (north-east boundary of Dunoon). Wooded parkland. 18 holes, 6251 yards. S.S.S. 70. *Green Fees:* weekdays £8.50 per round, £11.50 per day; weekends £13.00 per round, £16.50 per day. *Eating facilities:* full catering and bar facilities 11 a.m. to 11 p.m. *Visitors:* welcome most weekdays, some restrictions weekends. *Society Meetings:* welcome at special rates in groups of 12 (minimum) to 24 (maximum). Professional: R.D. Weir (0369 2395). Secretary: J. Bruce (0369 5673).

OBAN. **Glencruitten Golf Club,** Glencruitten Road, Oban (Oban (0631) 62868). *Location:* one mile from town centre. Hilly parkland. 18 holes, 4452 yards. S.S.S. 63. Practice area. *Green Fees:* £7.00 per round, £8.50 per day; weekends £8.50 per round, £9.50 per day. *Eating facilities:* full catering and bar facilities. *Visitors:* welcome, restrictions on Saturdays and Thursdays during competition times. Starter: (0631 64115). Secretary: C.M. Jarvie (0631 62308).

SOUTHEND. **Dunaverty Golf Club,** Southend, By Campbeltown *Location:* about 10 miles south of Campbeltown on B842. 18 holes, 4597 yards. S.S.S. 63. *Green Fees:* £4.00 per round, daily and weekly rates on application. *Eating facilities:* light snacks, tea and coffee on competition days only. *Visitors:* welcome without reservation. *Society Meetings:* catered for on limited basis on prior application. Secretary: J. Galbraith (0586 83698).

TARBERT. **Tarbert Golf Club,** Kilberry Road, Tarbert (0880 820565). *Location:* approximately one mile south of Tarbert, Loch Fyne on B8024 at head of West Loch Tarbert. Hilly wooded heathland. 9 holes, 4460 yards. S.S.S. 64. *Green Fees:* £3.00 per round, £5.00 per day. *Eating facilities:* licensed clubhouse open evenings and weekends. *Visitors:* welcome without introduction. *Society Meetings:* by arrangement. Secretary: John Reid (0880 820389).

TIGHNABRUAICH. **Kyles Of Bute Golf Club,** Tighnabruaich. *Location:* access from Dunoon and Strachur. Clubhouse by Kames Farm, turn south off B8000 Kames to Millhouse road. Hillside course with magnificent views. 9 holes, 4778 yards. S.S.S. 64. *Green Fees:* £4.00 per day (Juniors £2.00). *Eating facilities:* no bar, but snacks and soft drinks available. *Visitors:* welcome, except Sunday mornings. *Society Meetings:* by special arrangement only. Secretary: D.W. Gieve (0700 811355).

Ayrshire

AYR. **Belleisle Golf Club,** Doonfoot Road, Ayr (0292 41258). *Location:* two miles south of Ayr on A719 road. Parkland course, tree-lined. 18 holes, 5244 yards. S.S.S. 66. Practice area. *Green Fees:* Belleisle: weekdays £6.40 per round, £10.00 per day; weekends £7.80 per round, £12.20 per day. Seafield: weekdays £4.60 per round, £7.10 per day; weekends £5.40 per round, £8.90 per day. Tuition available from Professional. *Eating facilities:* public cafe available; bars and restaurants in hotel. *Visitors:* welcome without reservation. Juniors under 17 must have handicap of 12 or under. *Society Meetings:* catered for. Professional: John S. Easey (0292 41314). Secretary: F. Wilson (0292 42136).

AYR. **Dalmilling (Municipal) Golf Club,** Westwood Avenue, Ayr (0292 263893). *Location:* A77, on north-east boundary, one mile from town centre. Meadowland. 18 holes, 5401 yards. S.S.S. 66. Practice area. *Green Fees:* weekdays £5.00 per round, weekends £6.60 per round. Fifty per cent reduction for Senior Citizens. *Eating facilities:* snacks/lunches/high teas, table licence. *Visitors:* welcome without reservation. *Society Meetings:* catered for. Professional: D. Gemmell. Secretary: C. King (0292 268180).

AYR. **Seafield Golf Club,** Belleisle Park, Doonfoot Road, Ayr (0292 41258). *Location:* A77 from Glasgow, take main coast road from Ayr to Stranraer. Seaside links. 18 holes, 5600 yards. S.S.S. 67. *Green Fees:* weekdays £4.60 per round, £7.10 per day; weekends £5.40 per round, £8.50 per day. *Eating facilities:* available. *Visitors:* welcome at any time, advance booking preferable. *Society Meetings:* welcome. Professional: John S. Easy (0292 41314).

GALSTON. **Loudoun Gowf Club,** Galston (Galston (0563) 820551). 18 holes, 5820 yards. S.S.S. 68. *Green Fees:* Information not provided. *Eating facilities:* lunches and high teas at Club. Secretary: C.A. Bruce (0563 821993).

GIRVAN. **Girvan Golf Club,** Girvan (Girvan (0465) 4272). *Location:* A77 from Glasgow, through Ayr, on coast road to Stranraer. Links, parkland. 18 holes, 5078 yards. S.S.S. 65. Practice area. *Green Fees:* weekdays £8.00 per day, £5.00 per round; weekends £10.00 per day, £6.60 per round. Senior Citizens half price. *Eating facilities:* available. *Visitors:* welcome, book through Starter. *Society Meetings:* welcome. Secretary: W.B. Tait (0465 2011).

Please mention this guide when you write or phone to enquire about accommodation.

IRVINE. **Glasgow Golf Club,** Gailes, Irvine KA11 5AE (0294 311347). *Location:* six miles from Kilmarnock, three miles south of Irvine, four miles north of Troon. Links. 18 holes, 6483 yards, 5928 metres. S.S.S. 71. *Green Fees:* £22.00 weekdays. *Eating facilities:* full catering and bar facilities. *Visitors:* welcome weekdays, not 4th Wednesday. *Society Meetings:* catered for. Professional: Jack Steven (041-942 8507). Secretary: (041-942 2011).

IRVINE. **Irvine Ravenspark Golf Club,** Municipal Clubhouse, Kidsneuk Lane, Irvine KA12 0SR (Irvine (0294) 71293 or 79550). *Location:* on A78 between Irvine and Kilwinning at Ravenspark Academy. Parkland course. 18 holes, 6453 yards. S.S.S. 71. *Green Fees:* weekdays £7.00, weekends £10 (day tickets). *Eating facilities:* entry to Club by arrangement with Secretary. *Visitors:* welcome, no jeans or training shoes allowed in the bar. *Society Meetings:* groups of up to 20 welcome weekdays and Sundays. Professional: P.J. Bond (0294 76467). Secretary: R.C. Palmer (0294 76983).

IRVINE. **The Irvine Golf Club,** Bogside, Irvine KA12 8SN (Irvine (0294) 78139). *Location:* through Irvine going towards Kilwinning, turn left at Ravenspark Academy. Fairly flat and deemed a links course. 18 holes, 6408 yards. S.S.S. 71. Practice ground. *Green Fees:* £15.00 per round, £20.00 per day. *Eating facilities:* full catering every day except Mondays. *Visitors:* welcome with reservation. *Society Meetings:* catered for. Professional: Keith Erskine. Secretary: Angus Macpherson (0294 75979).

IRVINE. **Western Gailes Golf Club,** Gailes, By Irvine (0294 311649). *Location:* west of A78 on Troon/Irvine main road, approximately 2 miles south of Irvine. 18 holes, 6763 yards. S.S.S. 72. *Green fees:* information not provided. *Eating facilities:* full service. *Visitors:* welcome with reservation, not on Saturdays unless playing with member. *Society Meetings:* catered for except on Thursday, Saturday and Sunday. Secretary: James A. Clement, CA.

KILBIRNIE. **Kilbirnie Place Golf Club,** Largs Road, Kilbirnie (Kilbirnie (0505) 683398). *Location:* situated on Largs Road, 25 miles from Glasgow. 18 holes, 5500 yards. S.S.S. 67. *Green Fees:* weekdays £3.75 per round, day ticket £6.50. Sundays £9.00 per round, day ticket £12.00. *Eating facilities:* catering facilities available only at weekends. *Visitors:* welcome except Saturdays. Secretary: A. Rice.

KILMARNOCK. **Annanhill Golf Club,** Irvine Road, Kilmarnock (0563 21644). *Location:* on main Kilmarnock to Irvine road. 18 holes, 6285 yards. S.S.S. 70. *Green Fees:* weekdays £6.20; weekends £9.45. *Eating facilities:* catering and bar facilities available by reservation only. *Society Meetings:* catered for. Secretary: R.M. Davidson.

KILMARNOCK. **Caprington Golf Club,** Ayr Road, Kilmarnock (0563 23702). Parkland/wooded course. *Green Fees:* £4.75 per round, £6.20 per day weekdays; £9.45 per day only weekends. *Eating facilities:* available. *Visitors:* welcome except Saturdays. *Society Meetings:* all welcome. Secretary: F. McCulloch (0563 25848).

LARGS. **Inverclyde National Golf Training Centre,** Scottish Sports Council, Burnside Road, Largs KA30 8RW (Largs (0475) 674666). *Location:* Largs-Greenock-Glasgow (M8). Parkland, links, training bunkers. 6 holes, driving range. *Green Fees:* on application. *Eating facilities:* cafeteria, dining room, accommodation and bar. *Visitors:* groups only – pre-booked on a weekly residential basis.. Professionals: Bob Torrance, Jack Steven, David Scott. Secretary: John Kent (Deputy Director).

LARGS. **Largs Golf Club,** Irvine Road, Largs KA30 8EU (Largs (0475) 673594).*Location:* on A78 28 miles from Glasgow. Parkland with scenic views. 18 holes, 6220 yards. S.S.S. 70. *Green Fees:* weekdays £18.00 per day, £12.00 per round; weekends £18.00 per round or day. *Eating facilities:* full facilities available. *Visitors:* welcome, restrictions Tuesdays and Thursdays (parties) and weekends. *Society Meetings:* catered for Tuesdays and Thursdays only by prior arrangement. Professional: R. Stewart (0475 686192). Secretary: F. Gilmour (0475 672497).

LARGS. **Routenburn Golf Club,** Routenburn, Largs (Largs (0475) 3230). Hill moorland course. 18 holes, 5765 yards. S.S.S. 67. *Green Fees:* information not provided. *Eating facilities:* lunches at club except Thursdays, order in advance. *Visitors:* welcome with reservation. *Society Meetings:* catered for on application to club. Professional: Greig McQueen (0475 687240). Secretary: J.E. Smeaton.

MAUCHLINE. **Ballochmyle Golf Club,** Mauchline KA5 6RR (Mauchline (0290) 50469). *Location:* turn left from A76 coming out of Mauchline from Kilmarnock, club adjacent to Ballochmyle Hospital. Wooded parkland course. 18 holes, 5952 yards. S.S.S. 69. *Green Fees:* £13.00 per day weekdays, £19.00 per day weekends. *Eating facilities:* all day bar opening from 1st April until 30th Sept, snacks and meals available during bar hours. *Visitors:* welcome every day except Saturdays. Dress both on and off the course must be adhered to. Two full size snooker tables and squash court. *Society Meetings:* all welcome to a total of 30 per party. Secretary: Douglas Munro (0290 52780).

MAYBOLE. **Maybole Golf Club,** Memorial Park, Kirkoswald Road, Maybole (0292 281511). *Location:* A77 from Glasgow. By-pass Ayr to Girvan road, on main Girvan road at Maybole. Hilly parkland. 9 holes, 5270 yards. S.S.S. 65. *Green Fees:* municipal rates. *Visitors:* welcome. *Society Meetings:* welcome.

NEW CUMMOCK. **New Cummock Golf Club,** Lochill, New Cummock. *Location:* one mile north of New Cummock on A76. Parkland. 9 holes, 2365 yards. S.S.S. 63. *Green Fees:* £4.00 weekdays, £5.00 weekends. Senior Citizens £1.00. Winter rates £3.00 weekdays, £4.00 weekends. *Visitors:* welcome at all times except Sunday competition days. Secretary: Peter Pollock (0290 21951).

PRESTWICK. **Prestwick Golf Club,** Links Road, Prestwick (Prestwick (0292) 77404). *Location:* one mile from Prestwick airport, 40 minutes by car from Turnberry Hotel, 10 minutes from Troon, 15 minutes from Ayr. 18 holes, 6544 yards. (No LGU tees). S.S.S. 72. *Green Fees:* information not provided. *Eating facilities:* dining room (male only) (prior booking required) open from 12.30 p.m. to 2.30 p.m. Cardinal Room (light lunches) open to ladies and gentlemen from 10.00 a.m. until 4.00 p.m. *Visitors:* welcome with reservation. *Society Meetings:* catered for. Professional: F.C. Rennie. Secretary: D.E. Donaldson.

PRESTWICK. **Prestwick St. Cuthbert Golf Club,** East Road, Prestwick KA9 2SX (0292 77101). *Location:* south-east area of Prestwick near A77 and Prestwick Airport. Flat, some trees; semi-parkland. 18 holes, 6470 yards, 6063 metres. S.S.S. 71. Limited practice area. *Green Fees:* £15.00 per day weekdays only. *Eating facilities:* full catering and bar service. *Visitors:* welcome without reservation except weekends unless introduced by and playing with member. *Society Meetings:* catered for. Secretary: R. Morton (0292 79120).

PRESTWICK **Prestwick St. Nicholas Golf Club,** Grangemuir Road, Prestwick KA9 1SN (0292 77608). *Location:* sea front. 18 holes, 5926 yards, 5418 metres. S.S.S. 68. *Green Fees:* weekdays £20.00 per day. *Eating facilities:* full service. *Visitors:* welcome weekdays with club introduction, reserved for members at weekends. *Society Meetings:* catered for by arrangement. Professional: I. Parker (0292 79755). Secretary: J.R. Leishman (0292 77608).

SKELMORLIE. **Skelmorlie Golf Club,** Beithglass, off Skelmorlie Castle Road, Upper Skelmorlie PA17 5ES (Wemyss Bay (0475) 520152). *Location:* five miles north of Largs, eight miles south of Gourock. Scenic hillside course. 13 holes, 5104 yards. S.S.S. 65. (play first 5 holes twice to make 18). *Green Fees:* weekdays £6.50 per round, £9.50 per day; Sundays only £9.00 per round, £13.00 per day. Five weekdays £25.00. *Eating facilities:* bar snacks and dining room facilities. *Visitors:* welcome except Saturdays before 4pm. Fishing available. *Society Meetings:* welcome except Saturdays before 4pm. Secretary: P. Griffin.

STEVENSTON. **Ardeer Golf Club,** Greenhead, Stevenston (0294 64542). *Location:* one mile east of the town of Stevenston on the A78, adjacent waterworks, Greenhead. 18 holes, 6630 yards. S.S.S. 72. *Green Fees:* weekdays £14.00 per day, weekends £18.00 per day. *Eating facilities:* full catering except Thursdays (or by arrangement). *Visitors:* welcome except Saturdays. *Society Meetings:* catered for. Golf Shop and Starter: P. Rodger (0294 601327). Secretary: William F. Hand (0294 63538).

If you are writing, a stamped, addressed envelope is always appreciated.

TROON. **Kilmarnock (Barassie) Golf Club,** Hillhouse Road, Barassie, Troon KA10 6SY (Troon (0292) 311077). *Location:* 100 yards from Barassie Railway Station. 18 holes, 6473 yards. S.S.S. 71. *Green Fees:* £23.00 per day or round. *Eating facilities:* coffee, lunches, snacks, high teas. *Visitors:* welcome except Wednesday, Saturday and Sunday. Visitors introduced by members can play on Wednesdays, Saturdays and Sundays if they play with the member. Professional: W.R. Lockie (0292 311322). Secretary: Robert L. Bryce (0292 313920).

TROON. **Royal Troon Golf Club,** Craigend Road, Troon KA10 6EP (0292 311555). *Location:* three miles from A77 (Glasgow/Ayr trunk road). Old Course 18 holes, 6641 yards, 6070 metres. S.S.S. 73. Portland Course 18 holes, 6274 yards, 5738 metres. S.S.S. 71. *Green Fees:* £40.00 (Old), £25.00 (Portland) per day (1990). *Eating facilities:* full restaurant service available, including bar snacks. *Visitors:* Monday to Thursday only between 9.30 and 11.00am and 14.30 and 15.00pm. Letter of introduction from own club and Handicap Certificate (maximum of 20). (No ladies or those under 18 years on Old Course). *Society Meetings:* parties in excess of 24 not accepted. Professional: R. Brian Anderson (0292 313281). Secretary/Manager: J.D. Montgomerie (0292 311555).

TROON. **Troon Darley,** Harling Drive, Troon (0292 312464). *Location:* on A77 from Glasgow. Pure links course. 18 holes, 6327 yards. S.S.S. 70. Practice ground. *Green fees:* weekdays £6.40, weekends £7.80. *Eating facilities:* available. *Visitors:* welcome. *Society Meetings:* welcome. Professional: Gordon McKinley (0292 315566).

TROON. **Troon Fullerton,** Harling Drive, Troon (0292 312464). *Location:* A77 from Glasgow, follow directions to Troon. Links course, ideal for juniors, ladies, beginners. 18 holes, 4784 yards. S.S.S. 63. Practice ground. *Green Fees:* Adults: weekdays £4.60, weekends £5.40; Juniors: weekdays £2.30, weekends £2.70. *Eating facilities:* available. *Visitors:* welcome. *Society Meetings:* welcome. Professional: Gordon McKinley (0292 315566).

TROON. **Troon Lochgreen,** Harling Drive, Troon (0292 312464). *Location:* A77 from Glasgow. Pure links, ex- Open qualifying course, very tough. 18 holes, 6687 yards. S.S.S. 72. Practice ground. *Green Fees:* weekdays £6.40, weekends £7.80. *Eating facilities:* available. *Visitors:* welcome. *Society Meetings:* welcome. Professional: Gordon McKinley (0292 315566).

TROON. **Troon Municipal Golf Course,** Harling Drive, Troon (0292 312464). *Location:* adjacent to railway station, one mile off the Ayr-Glasgow road. Three 18 hole courses. Lochgreen 6687 yards. S.S.S. 72. Darley 6327 yards. S.S.S. 70. Fullarton 4784 yards. S.S.S. 63. *Green Fees:* information not provided. *Eating facilities:* hot snacks, 8am – 6pm. Bar snacks and lunches, evening meals bookings only. *Visitors:* catered for. Broad wheeled trolleys only. *Society Meetings:* catered for. Caterer: John Darge. Professional: Gordon McKinley. Advance booking should be made in writing to Starter's Office, Troon Municipal Golf Courses, Harling Drive, Troon, Ayrshire.

PUBLISHER'S NOTE

While every effort is made to ensure accuracy, we regret that FHG Publications cannot accept responsibility for errors, omissions or misrepresentation in our entries or any consequences thereof. Prices in particular should be checked because we go to press early. We will follow up complaints, but cannot act as arbiters or agents for either party.

TURNBERRY. **Turnberry Hotel and Golf Courses,** Turnberry KA26 9LT (0655 31000). Telex: 777779. Facsimile 0665 31706. *Location:* between Girvan and Maidens on the West Coast of Scotland. Seaside links with magnificent views over Turnberry Bay to Arran and Ailsa Craig. 2 Championship Courses, Ailsa and Arran, each of 18 holes. Ailsa S.S.S. 72, Arran S.S.S. 70. *Green Fees:* (non resident's) £35.00 per person – one round Ailsa Course, and optional round on Arran Course, Monday to Friday. £40.00 per person for one round on Ailsa Course and optional round on Arran Course weekends. £26.00 per person for two rounds on Arran Course only. £21.00 per person for one round on Arran Course. (Special rates for Hotel residents). Rates to be reviewed for 1991. *Eating facilities:* at Clubhouse bar and restaurant, and within the Hotel.

Day visitors welcome. Golf Societies and Company Golf days catered for by prior arrangement. Professional: Bob Jamieson. Golf Club Manager: R. L. Hamblett. General Manager: C. J. Rouse.

WEST KILBRIDE. **West Kilbride Golf Club,** 33-35 Fullerton Drive, Seamill, West Kilbride KA23 9HT (0294 823128). *Location:* on A78 Greenock to Ayr Road, leave at Seamill. Seaside links course. 18 holes, 6247 yards. S.S.S. 70. Practice area. *Green Fees:* on application. *Eating facilities:* diningroom and bar. *Visitors:* welcome weekdays only. Dormie House available sleeps four. *Society Meetings:* catered for Tuesdays and Thursdays. Professional: George Howie (0294 823042). Secretary: E.D. Jefferies (0294 823911).

Culzean Castle near Turnberry

Banffshire

BANFF. **Duff House Royal Golf Club,** The Barnyards, Banff (02612 2062). *Location:* two minutes from town centre, A97, A98. Level parkland with two-tier greens. 18 holes, 6161 yards. S.S.S. 69. *Green Fees:* weekdays £7.50 per round, £10.00 per day; weekends £10.00 per round, £12.00 per day. *Eating facilities:* lounge bar and full catering service. *Visitors:* welcome without reservation except restricted weekends. *Society Meetings:* catered for by prior arrangement. Professional: R.S. Strachan (02612 2075). Secretary: M. Pierog (02612 2461).

BUCKIE. **Buckpool Golf Club (Buckie),** Barhill Road, Buckie (0542 32236). *Location:* turn off A98 signposted Buckpool. Links course with superlative view over Moray Firth. 18 holes, 6257 yards. S.S.S. 70. *Green Fees:* £5.00 per round, £6.00 per day weekdays; £7.00 per round, £8.00 per day weekends. *Eating facilities:* full catering weekends, weekdays by prior arrangement. Normal bar hours. *Visitors:* no restrictions except when there are scheduled competitions. Squash, snooker and indoor bowling. *Society Meetings:* welcome by prior arrangement. Secretary: F. MacLeod OBE (0542 35368).

CULLEN. **Cullen Golf Club,** The Links, Cullen (0542 40685). *Location:* half-mile west of Cullen, off A98. 18 holes, 4610 yards. *Green Fees:* information not available. *Eating facilities:* lunchtime only. *Visitors:* unrestricted. *Society Meetings:* catered for. Secretary: J. Douglas.

DUFFTOWN. **Dufftown Golf Club,** Mether Cluny, Tomintoul Road, Dufftown (Dufftown (0340) 20325). *Location:* one mile from Dufftown on Tomintoul Road. Hilly course, spectacular views. 18 holes, 5308 yards. S.S.S. 67. *Green Fees:* weekdays £5.00, weekends £6.00, weekly (seven day) ticket £25.00. *Eating facilities:* bar open evenings, clubhouse facilities available all day. *Visitors:* unrestricted except Tuesdays and Wednesdays 5.00pm to 8.00pm. *Society Meetings:* welcome by arrangement with Secretary, catering available. Secretary: Mr W. Garden (0340 20439).

KEITH. **Keith Golf Club,** Fife-Keith, Banffshire (Keith (05422) 2469). *Location:* off the Keith-Dufftown Road. 18 holes, 5745 yards. S.S.S. 68. *Green Fees:* Day ticket: weekdays £5.00, weekends £6.00. *Eating facilities:* only for organised parties. *Visitors:* welcome without reservation at all times. *Society Meetings:* catered for. Secretary: A. Stronach.

MACDUFF. **Royal Tarlair Golf Club,** Buchan Street, Macduff (Macduff (0261) 32897). *Location:* A98 Fraserburgh to Inverness trunk road – A947 Aberdeen to Banff road. Seaside links. 18 holes, 5866 yards, 5373 metres. S.S.S. 68. *Green Fees:* weekdays £6.00 per day, weekends £8.00 per day. *Eating facilities:* full catering and bar available. *Visitors:* welcome. *Society Meetings:* catered for (bookings through Secretary). Secretary: Mrs E. Black (02615 221).

Berwickshire

COLDSTREAM. **Hirsel Golf Club,** Kelso Road, Coldstream (0890 2678). *Location:* A697 west of Coldstream. Parkland. 9 holes, 5830 yards. S.S.S. 72 (ladies), 68 (men). *Green Fees:* weekdays £6.00, weekends £8.00. Weekly tickets £35.00. *Eating facilities:* can be arranged. *Visitors:* welcome without reservation. *Society Meetings:* catered for by arrangement with Secretary. Secretary: G.H. Toyne (0890 2568).

DUNS. **Duns Golf Club,** Hardens Road, Duns. *Location:* about one mile west of Duns just off A6105. 9 holes, 5826 yards (2913 x 2). S.S.S. 68. *Green Fees:* £6.00 (half-price 1st November to 15th March). *Visitors:* welcome without reservation. *Society Meetings:* catered for. Secretary: A. Campbell (0361 82733).

EYEMOUTH. **Eyemouth Golf Club,** Gunsgreen House, Eyemouth (Eyemouth (08907) 50551). *Location:* six miles north of Berwick-on-Tweed, off the A1 towards the coast. 9 holes, 5000 metres. S.S.S. 66.

Green Fees: £5.00. *Eating facilities:* bar closed duing the day weekdays. *Visitors:* welcome weekdays; tee restricted until 12 noon Saturday and Sunday. *Society Meetings:* by prior arrangement. Professional: Craig Maltman (08907 50261). Secretary: J. Fleming (08907 50887).

JEDBURGH. **Jedburgh Golf Club,** Dunion Road, Jedburgh, Roxburghshire (0835 63587). Hilly course. *Location:* one mile from town via Castlegate. 9 holes, 5492 yards. S.S.S. 67. *Green Fees:* weekdays £5.00, weekends £6.00. *Eating facilities:* catering if required. *Visitors:* welcome especially weekends. *Society Meetings:* catered for. Secretary: Robert Strachan.

LAUDER. **Lauder Golf Club,** Lauder. *Location:* off A68, course half a mile from Lauder on Galashiels road. 9 holes, 6002 yards. S.S.S. 70. *Green fees:* information not available. *Eating facilities:* none; good Hotels in Lauder. *Visitors:* welcome without reservation.

Caithness

LYBSTER. **Lybster Golf Club,** Main Street, Lybster. *Location:* 14 miles south from Wick on A9, half-way down village street. One of smallest courses in Scotland. Heathland/parkland. 9 holes, 1896 yards. S.S.S. 62. *Green Fees:* £3.00 per day adults; Juniors (under 16) £2.00). *Eating facilities:* at nearby hotels in village. *Visitors:* welcome anytime. *Society Meetings:* welcome any time. Secretary: M. Bowman, Quatre Bras, Lybster (no phone).

THURSO. **Reay Golf Club,** Clubhouse, Reay (Reay (084-781) 288). *Location:* 11 miles west of Thurso, two miles west of Dounreay. Seaside links. 18 holes, 5865 yards. S.S.S. 68. *Green Fees:* visitors £6.00 per day, reduced rates for week, fortnight or month. *Visitors:* welcome except during competitions (usually Saturday mornings); bar. Secretary: Ron Jones M.B.E. (0847-63340).

THURSO. **Thurso Golf Club,** Newlands of Geise, By Thurso (Thurso (0847) 3807). *Location:* two miles south west of Railway Station. Flat parkland, wonderful views of Pentland Firth and Orkneys. 18 holes, 5610 yards. S.S.S. 67. *Green Fees:* £6.00, with member £3.00 (clubs provided). *Eating facilities:* Tuesdays and Thursday evenings and weekends. *Visitors:* welcome without reservation. *Society Meetings:* catered for. Shop Manager: Mr D. Hall. Secretary: Dr G. Birnie (0847 65716).

WICK. **Wick Golf Club,** Reiss, By Wick KW1 4RW (0955 2726). *Location:* three miles north of Wick on A9. Seaside links course. 18 holes, 5976 yards. S.S.S. 69. *Green Fees:* weekdays £5.00 per round, £8.00 per day; weekends £6.00 per round, £10.00 per day. Weekly £20.00, fortnightly £30.00. *Eating facilities:* licensed; snacks available. *Visitors:* welcome without reservation. *Society Meetings:* catered for. Secretary: Mrs M.S.W. Abernethy.

Please mention this guide when you write or phone to enquire about accommodation.

Clackmannanshire

ALLOA. **Alloa Golf Club**, Shawpark, Sauchie (Alloa (0259) 722745). *Location:* on A908 between Alloa and Tillicoultry. Parkland. 18 holes, 6240 yards. S.S.S. 70. Two practice grounds. *Green Fees:* weekdays £12.00 day ticket. *Eating facilities:* dining room, bar meals. *Visitors:* welcome. *Society Meetings:* catered for. Professional: Bill Bennett (0259 724476). Secretary: A.M. Frame (0259 50100).

ALLOA. **Braehead Golf Club**, Cambus, By Alloa (0259 722078). *Location:* one mile from Alloa (West) on A907. Parkland. 18 holes, 6013 yards. S.S.S. 69. Practice area. *Green Fees:* weekdays £8.00 per round, £10.00 per day; weekends £10.00 per round, £14.00 per day. Weekly ticket (Monday to Friday) £30.00. *Eating facilities:* catering and bar in the evening during the week, all day at weekends. *Visitors:* no restrictions provided prior telephone or written booking. *Society Meetings:* catered for with prior booking. Secretary: June A. Harrison (0259 215135).

ALVA. **Alva Golf Club**, Beauclerc Street, Alva FK12 5LD (0259 60431). *Location:* seven miles from Stirling on A91 Stirling to St. Andrews road – course lies at foot of Ochil Hills. Inland wooded hillside course with fast greens. 9 holes, 2407 yards, 2207 metres. S.S.S. 64. *Green Fees:* £3.50 weekdays, £4.50 weekends. *Eating facilities:* bar snacks only. *Visitors:* welcome at all times. Lounge and changing rooms available. Secretary: Mrs A. McGuire (0259 60455).

DOLLAR. **Dollar Golf Club**, Brewlands House, Dollar (Dollar (025-94) 2400). *Location:* on A91. 18 holes, 5144 yards. S.S.S. 66. *Green Fees:* weekdays £5.50 round, £7.00 day; weekends £9.00. *Eating facilities:* lunches served at club. *Visitors:* welcome. *Society Meetings:* catered for. Secretary: M.B. Shea.

DOLLAR. **Muckhart Golf Club**, Muckhart, By Dollar (Muckhart (025 981) 423). *Location:* on A91, 14 miles east of Stirling. 18 holes, 6112 yards. S.S.S. 70. *Green Fees:* weekdays £8.00 per round, £14.00 per day; weekends £12.00 per round, £18.00 per day. Morning coffee, lunch and high tea plus 36 holes golf: £21.00 weekdays, £25.00 weekends. *Eating facilities:* meals available in clubhouse. *Visitors:* welcome without reservation except before 9.45am and 12.00 noon to 2.30pm weekends. *Society Meetings:* catered for. Professional: Keith Salmoni. Secretary: A.B. Robertson.

Dumfriesshire

ANNAN. **Powfoot Golf Club**, Cummertrees, Annan (Cummertrees (046-17) 227). *Location:* off Annan/Dumfries Road B724, signpost to course approximately three miles from Annan. Semi links course. 18 holes, 6266 yards. S.S.S. 70. *Green Fees:* weekdays £13.00, weekends £15.00 (additional £1.00 per person for parties of 12 and over). *Eating facilities:* morning coffee, lunches and teas in clubhouse – ordering in advance essential for large parties. *Visitors:* welcome weekdays but restrictions at weekends, no formal introduction required. *Society Meetings:* catered for; limited number by prior arrangement. Professional: Gareth Dick (046-17 327). Secretary: R.G. Anderson (046-12 2866/7).

DUMFRIES. **Dumfries and County Golf Club**, Nunfield, Edinburgh Road, Dumfries DG1 1JX (Dumfries (0387) 53585). *Location:* one mile north-east town centre on Edinburgh Road. 18 holes, 5928 yards. S.S.S. 68. Limited practice facilities. *Green Fees:* information not provided. *Eating facilities:* restaurant and bar snacks. *Visitors:* welcome except on Saturdays. *Society Meetings:* catered for by arrangement. Professional: G. Gray (0387 68918). Secretary: J.K. Wells (0387 53585).

PUBLISHER'S NOTE

While every effort is made to ensure accuracy, we regret that FHG Publications cannot accept responsibility for errors, omissions or misrepresentation in our entries or any consequences thereof. Prices in particular should be checked because we go to press early. We will follow up complaints, but cannot act as arbiters or agents for either party.

DUMFRIES. **Dumfries and Galloway Golf Club,** Laurieston Avenue, Dumfries (Dumfries (0387) 53582). *Location:* on Castle Douglas/Stranraer road, A75. Parkland course, 18 holes, 5803 yards. S.S.S. 68. Practice area. *Green Fees:* £12.00 weekdays, £15.00 weekends. *Eating facilities:* full catering during bar hours except Mondays. *Visitors:* welcome, except on competition days. *Society Meetings:* catered for weekdays, except Tuesdays. Secretary: Jack Donnachie (0387 63848). Professional: Joe Fergusson (0387 56902).

DUMFRIES. **Southerness Golf Club,** Southerness, Kirkbean, Dumfries DG2 8AZ (Kirkbean (038 788) 677). *Location:* 16 miles south of Dumfries on A710 (Solway Coast Road). Natural challenging links, designed by MacKenzie Ross with panoramic views of Solway Firth and Galloway hills. 18 holes, 6554 yards. S.S.S. 72. Large practice area. *Green Fees:* weekdays £12.00 per day, weekends £15.00 per day. Weekly ticket £50.00. *Eating facilities:* full bar and catering facilities. *Visitors:* welcome after 10am. *Society Meetings:* on application to Secretary. Secretary: Major (rtd) D.D.F. Palmer.

LANGHOLM. **Langholm Golf Club,** Whitaside, Langholm (Langholm (03873) 80559). *Location:* On A7 Carlisle-Edinburgh road. Turn off at market place in centre of town. 9 holes, 5744 yards. S.S.S. 69. *Green Fees:* £5.00 per round or day. *Eating facilities:* on request. *Visitors:* welcome without reservation. *Society Meetings:* welcome to enquire. Secretary: Mr A. Edgar (03873 80878).

LOCKERBIE. **Lochmaben Golf Club,** Back Road, Lochmaben, Lockerbie DG11 1NT (Lochmaben (0387) 810552). *Location:* A709 Dumfries – Lockerbie Road. Parkland with panoramic views adjacent to Loch. 9 holes, 5304 yards, 4616 metres. S.S.S. 66. *Green Fees:* weekdays £8.00, weekends £10.00. *Eating facilities:* on request, lunch/evening. *Visitors:* welcome except on competition days and not after 5pm. Fishing. *Society Meetings:* welcome. Secretary: B.J. Graham (0387 810552).

LOCKERBIE. **Lockerbie Golf Club,** Corrie Road, Lockerbie (Lockerbie (057-62) 3363). 18 holes, 5418 yards. S.S.S. 66. *Green Fees:* £7.00 per day Monday to Sunday. Weekly ticket £30.00. *Visitors and visiting parties:* welcome. Catering for visiting parties arranged on request. Secretary: Mr J.A. Carruthers (0387 810352).

MOFFAT. **Moffat Golf Club,** Coatshill, Moffat DG10 9SB (Moffat (0683) 20020). *Location:* leave A74 at Beattock on A701, club notice one mile on left. Scenic moorland course. 18 holes, 5218 yards. S.S.S. 66. Putting green; small practice area. *Green Fees:* weekdays £9.00 per day; weekends £13.50 per day; 5-day ticket £30.00. *Eating facilities:* bar meals served all day. *Visitors:* welcome without reservation, except Wednesday after 12 noon. *Society Meetings:* catering provided. Secretary: T.A. Rankin (0683 20043). Clubmaster: Mr Ian Preston.

SANQUHAR. **Sanquhar Golf Club,** Euchan Course, Sanquhar (Sanquhar (0659) 50577). *Location:* situated quarter-of-a-mile from A76 Dumfries-Kilmarnock trunk road. 9 holes, 5144 metres. S.S.S. 68.*Green Fees:* weekdays £6.00 per round, weekends £8.00 per round. *Eating facilities:* bar available if requested in advance. *Visitors:* welcome without reservation. *Society Meetings:* catered for with advance notice. Licensed clubhouse with full size snooker table. Secretary: Mrs J. Murray (0659 58181).

THORNHILL. **Thornhill Golf Club,** Thornhill (Thornhill (0848) 30546) *Location:* 14 miles north of Dumfries on A76. Parkland. 18 holes, 6011 yards. S.S.S. 69. Par 71. Practice ground. *Green Fees:* weekdays £9.00, weekends £12.00, £40.00 per week. *Eating facilities:* catering available, except Mondays, bar facility. *Visitors:* welcome without reservation, except on Open Competition Days. *Society Meetings:* welcome, contact club Steward. Secretary: Stuart Moscrop (0848 30151).

Dunbartonshire

ALEXANDRIA. **Vale of Leven Golf Club,** Northfield Road, Bonhill, Alexandria (Alexandria (0389) 52351). *Location:* off A82 at Bonhill. Parkland, overlooking Loch Lomond with splendid views. 18 holes, 5165 yards. S.S.S. 66. *Green Fees:* weekdays £6.00 per round, weekends £10.00 per round. *Eating facilities:* catering and bar available. *Visitors:* welcome except Saturdays between April 1st and September 30th. Full changing and locker facilities. *Society Meetings:* catered for, special rates available on application to Secretary. Secretary: W. McKinlay (0389 52508).

CARDROSS. **Cardross Golf Club,** Main Road, Cardross G82 5LB (Cardross (0389) 841213). *Location:* on A814 west of Dumbarton. Parkland course. 18 holes, 6466 yards. S.S.S. 71. Practice ground. *Green Fees:* weekdays £13.00 per round, £20.00 day ticket. *Eating facilities:* lunches/bar snacks available during bar hours. *Visitors:* weekdays only (by phoning Professional to book time). *Society Meetings:* catered for weekdays by application to Secretary. Professional: Robert Craig (0389 841350). Secretary: R. Evans C.A. (0389 841754).

CLYDEBANK. **Clydebank and District Golf Club,** Glasgow Road, Hardgate, Clydebank G81 5QY (0389 73289). *Location:* Hardgate village. Off A8 10 miles west of Glasgow (off Great Western Road). 18 holes, 5832 yards, 5325 metres. S.S.S. 68. *Green Fees:* £10.00 per day. *Eating facilities:* catering as required. *Visitors:* welcome weekdays. Professional: Campbell Elliot (0389 738086). Secretary: W. Manson (0389 72832).

CLYDEBANK. **Clydebank Municipal Golf Course,** Overtoun Road, Dalmuir, Clydebank G81 3RE (041-952 6372). *Location:* one mile west of Clydebank centre off Duntocher Road. Parkland course - one of the best Par 3's in Scotland. 18 holes, 5349 yards. S.S.S. 67. *Green Fees:* £2.85 weekdays, £3.25 Sundays. *Eating facilities:* unlicensed cafeteria. *Visitors:* municipal, tee closed Saturdays in Summer 11am to 2pm. *Society Meetings:* contact District Council. Professional: Richard Bowman (041-952 6372). Secretary: District Council (041-941 1331).

CUMBERNAULD. **Palacerigg Golf Club,** Palacerigg Country Park, Cumbernauld, Near Glasgow G67 3HU (0236 743969). *Location:* Palacerigg Road, three miles south of Cumbernauld. Wooded parkland. 18 holes, 6440 yards. S.S.S. 71. Practice area. *Green Fees:* £5.00 per day weekdays, £6.00 per day weekends. *Eating facilities:* bar seven days, all day opening from March to October; meals available Wednesdays to Sundays or by arrangement. *Visitors:* welcome weekdays only. *Society Meetings:* applications by letter to Secretary. Secretary: John H. Dunsmore (0236 726572).

DUMBARTON. **Dumbarton Golf Club,** Broadmeadow, Dumbarton (Dumbarton (0389) 32830). *Location:* Dumbarton – A84. Flat course. 18 holes, 5992 yards. S.S.S. 69. *Green Fees:* £10.00 per round/day, weekdays only. *Eating facilities:* available. *Visitors:* welcome, Monday to Friday only. *Society Meetings:* catered for weekdays. Secretary: R. Turnbull.

GLASGOW by. **Westerwood Golf Course,** Westerwood, Cumbernauld, By Glasgow (0236 725 281). *Location:* off M80 towards Dullatur. Undulating wooded course. 18 holes, 6980 yards. S.S.S. 73. *Green Fees:* £15.00 per round, £25.00 per day weekdays; £20.00 per round, £30.00 per day weekends. *Eating facilities:* available. *Visitors:* welcome at all times, no restrictions. Westerwood Hotel newly opened. *Society Meetings:* welcome by prior arrangement. Secretary: Neil I. MacKintosh.

HELENSBURGH. **Helensburgh Golf Club,** 25 East Abercrombie Street, Helensburgh G84 9JD (Helensburgh (0436) 74173). *Location:* A82 Dumbarton Clyde Submarine Base. Moorland course with panoramic views. 18 holes, 6058 yards. S.S.S. 69. Practice area. *Green Fees:* £8.00 per round, £12.00 per day weekdays. *Eating facilities:* full catering and bar. *Visitors:* welcome weekdays only, dress in recognised golfing attire. Golfing parties day ticket £10.00. Professional: Robert Farrell (0436 75505). Secretary: Mrs A. McEwan (0436 74173).

KIRKINTILLOCH. **Kirkintilloch Golf Club,** Campsie Road, Kirkintilloch G66 1RN (041-776 1256). *Location:* from Glasgow to Bishopbriggs, then straight on to Kirkintilloch. Undulating, parkland course. 18 holes, 5900 yards. S.S.S. 66. Par 70. Putting green and practice areas. *Green Fees:* information not provided. *Eating facilities:* available only for members and their guests. *Visitors:* weekdays only, must be introduced by member. *Society Meetings:* catered for Mondays and Tuesdays, information from Secretary including catering. Secretary: Mr H. Bannerman (041-777 7971).

LENZIE. **Lenzie Golf Club,** 19 Crosshill Road, Lenzie, Glasgow (041-776 1535). *Location:* six miles north-east of Glasgow. 18 holes, 5977 yards. S.S.S. 69. *Green Fees:* weekdays only, £10.00 per round, £16.00 per day. *Eating facilities:* dining room available. *Visitors:* welcome if introduced with reservation. *Society Meetings:* catered for. Professional: Jim McCallum (041-777 7748) Secretary: A.W. Jones (041-776 4377).

Edinburgh and the Lothians

ABERLADY. **Kilspindle Golf Club,** Aberlady. *Location:* on the south bank of the River Forth Estuary. 18 holes, 5417 yards, 4957 metres. S.S.S. 66. *Green Fees:* weekdays £10.50 per round, £15.00 per day, Saturday and Sunday £12.50 per round, £17.50 per day. *Eating facilities:* full catering except Fridays. *Visitors:* welcome. Secretary: Hugh F. Brown (087-57 358).

ABERLADY. **Luffness New Golf Club,** Aberlady EH32 0QA (Gullane (0620) 843114). Clubmaster (0620) 843376). *Location:* A198 – 17 miles east of Edinburgh. One mile from Gullane. Links course. 18 holes, 6122 yards. S.S.S. 69. *Green Fees:* provided on application. *Eating facilities:* dining room except Mondays. *Visitors:* weekdays only (require introduction). *Society Meetings:* by prior arrangement. Secretary: Lt. Col. J.G. Tedford (0620 843336).

BATHGATE **Bathgate Golf Club,** Edinburgh Road, Bathgate EH48 1BA (0506 52232). *Location:* 400 yards east towards Edinburgh from George Square, the town centre. 18 holes, 6328 yards. S.S.S. 70. *Green Fees:* weekdays £10.00 per day, weekends £15.00 per day. *Eating facilities:* by arrangement with Steward. *Visitors:* welcome without reservation except on Competition days. Professional: Sandy Strachan (0506 630553). Secretary: Dick Smith (0506 630505).

BROXBURN. **Uphall Golf Club,** Uphall, Broxburn (Broxburn (0506) 856404). *Location:* on outskirts of Uphall adjacent to A8 Edinburgh to Glasgow road. 18 holes, 5567 yards. S.S.S. 67. *Green fees:* information not available. *Eating facilities:* available at The Houston House Hotel situated within the grounds of the golf course. *Visitors:* welcome without reservation. *Society Meetings:* catered for. Secretary: Aidin Dobie.

DALKEITH. **Newbattle Golf Club Ltd,** Abbey Road, Dalkeith (031-663 2123). *Location:* approximately seven miles south-east of Edinburgh A7 to Eskbank Toll (Newbattle exit). Parkland course. 18 holes, 6012 yards, 5498 metres. S.S.S. 69. Small practice area. *Green Fees:* £9.00 per round, £15.00 per day. *Eating facilities:* full catering available on request. *Visitors:* weekdays only. No jeans/trainers on course or in clubhouse. *Society Meetings:* restricted. Professional: John Henderson (031-660 1631). Secretary: H.G. Stanners (031-663 1819).

DUNBAR. **Dunbar Golf Club,** East Links, Dunbar (Dunbar (0368) 62317). *Location:* on sea side on eastern end of Dunbar. 18 holes, 6441 yards. S.S.S. 71. *Green Fees:* weekdays £15.00 per day, weekends £25.00. *Visitors:* welcome without reservation weekdays. *Society Meetings:* catered for. Professional: Derek Small. Secretary: Arnold J.R. Poole.

DUNBAR. **Winterfield Golf Club,** North Road, Dunbar (0368 62280). Seaside course. 18 holes, 4686 metres. S.S.S. 65. *Green Fees:* information not available. *Eating facilities:* available, except Thursdays. *Visitors:* welcome without reservation. The Pro Shop: (0368 63562). Professional: John Sandilands. Secretary: Michael O'Donnell.

EDINBURGH. **Baberton Golf Club,** Baberton Avenue, Juniper Green, Edinburgh EH14 5DU (031-453 3361). *Location:* five miles west of Edinburgh on the A70. 18 holes, 6140 yards. S.S.S. 69. *Green Fees:* information not provided. *Eating facilities:* by arrangement. *Society Meetings:* catered for. Professional: K. Kelly (031-453 3555). Secretary: D.M. McBain (031-453 4911).

EDINBURGH. **Braids United Golf Club,** 22 Braid Hills Approach, Morningside, Edinburgh 10. Starters box (031-447 6666). *Location:* Braid Hills on south side of Edinburgh. Two 18 hole courses. No. 1 – 5880 yards. S.S.S. 68. No. 2 – 4495 yards. S.S.S. 64. *Green Fees:* £3.30 per round. *Visitors:* welcome without reservation (Accommodation in Braid Hills Hotel – 400 yards). Public courses, clubs on hire. Sunday golf on No. 2 course only. Professional: John Boath.

EDINBURGH. **Broomieknowe Golf Club Ltd,** 36 Golf Course Road, Bonnyrigg (031-663 9317). *Location:* south of Edinburgh, A6094 from Dalkeith. 18 holes, 6046 yards. S.S.S. 69. *Green Fees:* £8.00 per round, £12.00 per day. £10.00 per round at weekends. *Eating facilities:* lunches, high teas. *Visitors:* welcome Monday to Friday. *Society Meetings:* catered for by arrangement. Professional: Mark Patchett. Secretary: Dr J. Symonds.

EDINBURGH. **Bruntsfield Links Golfing Society,** 32 Barnton Avenue, Edinburgh EH4 6JH (031-336 2006). *Location:* off A90 to Davidson's Mains. Parkland course. 18 holes, 6402 yards. S.S.S. 71. *Green Fees:* information not provided. *Eating facilities:* lunches served at club. *Visitors:* welcome on weekdays if playing with a member, or if suitably introduced. *Society Meetings:* catered for. Professional: Brian MacKenzie. Secretary: M.W. Walton (031-336 1479).

EDINBURGH. **Craigmillar Park Golf Club,** 1 Observatory Road Edinburgh EH9 3HG (031-667 2837). *Location:* A702 from City centre on Mayfield Road, right at King's Buildings. Parkland. 18 holes, 5846 yards. S.S.S. 68. *Green Fees:* £10.00 per round, £15.00 per day. *Eating facilities:* lunches, snacks, high teas and dinners. *Visitors:* welcome with reservation on production of Handicap Certificate. Weekdays only before 3.30p.m. *Society Meetings:* catered for by previous arrangement. Professional: B. McGee (031-667 0047). Secretary: Mrs J.H. Smith (031-667 0047).

EDINBURGH. **Duddingston Golf Club Ltd,** Duddingston Road West, Edinburgh EH15 3QD (031-661 1005). *Location:* adjacent to A1 Willowbrae Road, turn right at Duddingston crossroads then one mile on Duddingston Road West. Undulating parkland with stream. 18 holes, 6647 yards. S.S.S. 72. *Green Fees:* weekdays only £14.00 per round, £19.00 per day. *Eating facilities:* full catering and bar facilities. *Visitors:*

welcome weekdays only. *Society Meetings:* catered for Tuesdays and Thursdays (rates on request). Professional: Alistair McLean (031-661 4301). Secretary: John C. Small (031-661 7688).

EDINBURGH. **Kingsknowe Golf Club,** 326 Lanark Road, Edinburgh EH14 2JD (031-441 1144). *Location:* on Edinburgh Corporation Bus No. 44 route. Parkland course. 18 holes, 5979 yards, 5466 metres. S.S.S. 69. Practice area. *Green Fees:* weekdays £10.00 per round, £15.00 per day, weekends £15.00 per round. *Eating facilities:* lounge bar, snacks and meals available. *Visitors:* welcome Monday to Friday, also weekends subject to availability. *Society Meetings:* catered for. Professional: W. Bauld (031-441 4030). Secretary: S. McMichael (031-441 1145)

EDINBURGH. **Liberton Golf Club,** 297 Gilmerton Road, Edinburgh EH16 4UJ (031-664 8580). *Location:* Corporation transport to Lodge Gate, buses 3 and 8 from Edinburgh. By car on A7 (Visitors' car park). 18 holes, 4845 metres. S.S.S. 66. *Green fees:* information not provided. *Eating facilities:* meals or snacks by arrangement, bar. *Visitors:* not after 5.00pm on Mondays, Wednesdays and Fridays. Juveniles restricted unless playing with an adult. Charges reduced if introduced by a member. *Society Meetings:* catered for by arrangememt. Professional: P.J. Fielding. Secretary: T.J. Muirhead (031-664 3009).

EDINBURGH. **Lothianburn Golf Club,** 106a Biggar Road, Edinburgh EH10 6HG (031-445 2206). *Location:* south on the A702 approximately four miles from city centre or easily reached from Edinburgh by pass road coming off at Lothianburn junction. Hill course in Pentland Hills. 18 holes, 5750 yards. S.S.S. 69. Two practice grounds. *Green Fees:* weekdays £7.50 per round, £12.00 per day; weekends £10.00 per round, £13.00 per day. *Eating facilities:* normal bar hours, no cooked food on Wednesdays. *Visitors:* welcome without restrictions except weekends. *Society Meetings:* catered for, but no parties weekends. Professional: Paul Morton (031-445 2288). Secretary: Eric W. Horberry (031-445 5067).

EDINBURGH. **Merchants Of Edinburgh Golf Club,** Craighill Gardens, Edinburgh (031-447 1219). *Location:* car park, Glenlockhart Road, Edinburgh EH10. Hilly parkland. 18 holes, 4889 yards. S.S.S. 64. *Green Fees:* £8.00 per round, £10.00 per day weekdays; £10 per round weekends. *Eating facilities:* by arrangement with Clubmaster – J. Wilson. *Visitors:* welcome, not Saturdays, Sunday a.m. *Society Meetings:* catered for except weekends. Professional: Robin Smith (031-447 8709). Secretary: A.M. Montgomery.

EDINBURGH. **Mortonhall Golf Club,** 231 Braid Road, Edinburgh, EH10 6PB (031-447 2411). *Location:* take A702 south from City to Morningside traffic lights, up Braid Road 1 mile, course on left. 18 holes, 6548 yards, 5987 metres. S.S.S. 71. *Green Fees:* Information not provided. *Eating facilities:* lunch, tea and snacks every day (no lunches Mondays). *Visitors:* welcome with introduction. *Society Metings:* catered for (not at weekends). Professional: D. Horn. Secretary: Mr P. T. Ricketts (031-447 6974).

EDINBURGH. **Murrayfield Golf Club,** 43 Murray-field Road, Edinburgh EH12 6EU (031-337 0019). *Location:* two miles west of city centre. Parkland on east side of Corstorphine Hill. 18 holes, 5725 yards. S.S.S. 68. Practice area and putting green. *Green Fees:* weekdays £15.00 per round, £21.00 per day. *Eating facilities:* lunch each day, snacks in casual bar also full bar facilities. *Visitors:* welcome playing with member or by prior arrangement only. No visitors weekends. *Society Meetings:* catered for by prior arrangement. Professional: J. Fisher (031-337 3479). Secretary: J.P. Bullen (031-337 3478).

EDINBURGH. **Portobello Golf Club,** Stanley Street, Portobello, Edinburgh EH15 1JJ (031-669 4361). *Location:* on A1 at Milton Road East. Parkland course. 9 holes, 2400 yards, 2167 metres. S.S.S. 32. *Green Fees:* £3.50 per round (18 holes). *Visitors:* welcome without reservation. *Society Meetings:* not catered for. Professional: J. Boath. Secretary: B. Duffy (031-652 2266).

EDINBURGH. **Prestonfield Golf Club,** 6 Priestfield Road North, Edinburgh EH16 5HS (031-667 1273). *Location:* off Dalkeith Road, near Royal Common-wealth Pool on A68. Parkland. 18 holes, 6216 yards. S.S.S. 70. Practice area. *Green Fees:* weekdays £10.00 per round, £15.00 per day; weekends and Bank Holidays £15.00 per round, £20.00 per day. *Eating facilities:* full catering. *Visitors:* welcome weekdays anytime, weekends and Bank Holidays (Saturday not between 12 noon and 1.30pm, Sunday not before 10.30am. *Society Meetings:* welcome weekdays. Pro-

fessional: Brian Commins (031-667 8597). Secretary: M.D.A.G. Dillon (031-667 9665).

EDINBURGH. **Ravelston Golf Club Ltd,** 24 Ravel-ston Dykes Road, Blackhall, Edinburgh EH4 5NZ (031-315 2486). *Location:* A90 Queensferry Road (leading to Forth Road Bridge). Left pedestrian crossing, Blackhall, into Craigcrook Road, then second left. Parkland course. 9 holes, 2600 yards, 2377 metres. S.S.S. 33. *Green Fees:* £10.00 weekdays. *Eating facilities:* tea, coffee and snacks. *Visitors:* normally introduced by club members. *Society Meetings:* per-mitted by special application only. Secretary: Frank Phillip (031-312 6850).

EDINBURGH. **Royal Burgess Golfing Society of Edinburgh,** 181 Whitehouse Road, Barnton, Edin-burgh EH4 6BY (031-339 2075). *Location:* A90 to Queensferry, behind Barnton Hotel. Parkland. 18 holes, 6494 yards. S.S.S. 71. *Green Fees:* on request. *Eating facilities:* snacks and lunches available. *Visitors:* welcome weekdays, male only. *Society Meetings:* male only, catered for Tuesdays, Thursdays and Fridays. Professional: George Yuille (031-334 6474). Secretary: John Audis (031-334 5270).

EDINBURGH: **Silverknowes Golf Club,** Silver-knowes, Parkway, Edinburgh (031-336 3843). *Loca-tion:* beside Firth of Forth. Links type course. 18 holes, 6206 yards. S.S.S. 71. Practice area. *Green Fees:* information not provided. Reductions for Senior Citi-zens and Juniors. *Visitors:* must have own clubs. *Society Meetings:* by arrangement. Secretary: J. Munro.

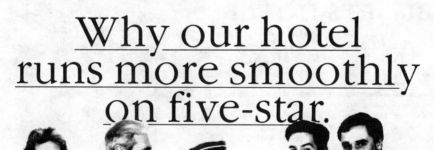

EDINBURGH. **Swanston Golf Club,** 111 Swanston Road, Edinburgh EH10 7DS (031-445 2239). *Location:* five miles from centre of Edinburgh on the lower slopes of the Pentland Hills. Parkland course. 18 holes, 5024 yards. S.S.S. 66. *Green Fees:* weekdays £6.00 per round, £8.00 day ticket; weekends £8.00 per round, £12.00 per day. *Eating facilities:* full catering facilities. *Visitors:* welcome without reservation weekdays, weekends restricted. *Society Meetings:* catered for. Professional: Ian Seith (031-445 4002). Secretary: John Allan.

EDINBURGH. **Torphin Hill Golf Club,** Torphin Road, Edinburgh EH13 0PG (031-441 1100). *Location:* south west of Colinton Village at terminus of No. 9 and No. 10 bus. 18 holes, 5020 yards. S.S.S. 66. *Green Fees:* weekdays £5.00, weekends £8.00. *Eating facilities:* dining room and bar snacks. *Visitors:* welcome without reservation except on Competition Days. *Society Meetings:* catered for weekdays only, not at weekends. Secretary: D.O. Campbell.

EDINBURGH. **Turnhouse Golf Club,** Turnhouse, Edinburgh (031-339 1014). *Location:* on road from Edinburgh to Turnhouse Airport. 18 holes, 6171 yards. S.S.S. 69. *Green Fees:* information not provided. *Eating facilities:* full service. *Visitors:* welcome with reservation with member or by letter of introduction from Secretary. Professional: K. Whitson. Secretary: A.B. Hay.

FAULDHOUSE. **Greenburn Golf Club,** Greenburn, Bridge Street, Fauldhouse (Fauldhouse (0501) 70292). *Location:* midway Glasgow-Edinburgh. 18 holes, 6013 yards. S.S.S. 69. *Green Fees:* information not available. *Eating facilities:* weekend only. *Visitors:* welcome without reservation. *Society Meetings:* catered for including Sat/Sun. Secretary: Alistair Morrison.

GULLANE. **Gullane Golf Club,** Gullane EH31 2BB (0620 843115). *Location:* 18 miles east of Edinburgh on A198 Edinburgh to North Berwick Road. Links. Three 18 hole courses. No. 1 – 6466 yards, 5913 metres. S.S.S. 71. No. 2 – 6219 yards, 5690 metres. S.S.S. 70. No. 3 – 5128 yards, 4692 metres. S.S.S. 65. *Green Fees:* no 1 course £26.00, no 2 course £12.00, no 3 course £8.00 weekdays; no 1 course £35.00, no 2 course £15.00, no 3 course £10.00 weekends. *Eating*

facilities: lunches and snacks daily except Mondays. *Visitors:* welcome with reservation. No. 1 Course visitors only in Clubhouse. *Society Meetings:* catered for. Professional: Jimmy Hume (0620 843111). Secretary: A.J.B. Taylor (0620 842255).

GULLANE. **The Honourable Company Of Edinburgh Golfers,** Muirfield, Gullane EH31 2EG (Gullane (0620) 842123). *Location:* 20 miles from Edinburgh along the coast road to North Berwick. 18 holes, 6601 yards. *Green Fees:* information not provided. *Eating facilities:* luncheons (except Mondays) men only. *Visitors:* on Tuesdays, Thursdays or the mornings of Fridays by introduction of a member or by previous arrangement with the Secretary: Major J.G. Vanreenen.

HADDINGTON. **Haddington Golf Club,** Amisfield Park, Haddington, East Lothian (062-082 3627). *Location:* on A1 Edinburgh. Wooded parkland. 18 holes, 6280 yards. S.S.S. 71. *Green Fees:* weekdays £8.00 per round, £11.00 per day (approx.); weekends £10.00 per round, £13.00 per day (approx.). Practice facilities. *Eating facilities:* full catering available every day except Tuesday; bar. *Visitors:* welcome weekdays and 10am – 12 noon and 2 – 4pm Saturdays and Sundays. *Society Meetings:* catered for. Secretary: T. Shaw (062-082 2584). Starter: (062-082 2727).

KIRKNEWTON. **Dalmahoy Hotel, Golf and Country Club,** Kirknewton, Midlothian EH28 8EB (031-333 1845). *Location:* on A71, 7 miles west of Edinburgh, 3 miles from ring road. Two courses: East

The Queen's Hotel
Gullane, East Lothian
Telephone: 0620 842275

* Only eighteen miles east of Edinburgh
* Nine golf courses within a radius of ten miles * Ideal base for walking or touring in the Border Country * New wing with twenty-two bedrooms, sixteen of which have private bathrooms, six with showers * TVs * Telephones * Tea/coffee making facilities in all bedrooms * Renowned for fine cuisine * Fully licensed * Dogs allowed * Reductions for children under twelve years sharing parents' room * Open all year.   RAC ★★

HOTEL AND RESTAURANT

Uphall, West Lothian EH52 6JS
Telephone: Broxburn (0506) 853831
Telex: 727148
10 Minutes from Edinburgh Airport

A CENTRE OF EXCELLENCE

From Houstoun House, it's only a short drive to some of Scotland's most prestigious golf clubs. Dalmahoy 6 miles; Muirfield 30 miles; St. Andrews 50 miles. On the doorstep is Uphall Golf Club and hotel patrons have access to the course.

ACCOMMODATION

The hotel's 30 bedrooms are appointed, to international standard, with private bathroom or shower, direct dial telephone, colour television, radio, hairdryer, trouser press and tea and coffee facilities. 12 are in modern style and 18 traditionally furnished. Many have four-poster beds and retain their original 18th century wood panelling.

DINING

The chefs of Houstoun have always sought to achieve excellence, and Head Chef Ian McDonald and his brigade continue that tradition. In the three intimate dining rooms, Ian offers only the finest fresh produce, woven imaginatively into luncheon and dinner menus which change daily. The choice of dishes on each menu reflects the international influences in Ian's repertoire, gathered during his time at Gleddoch House, Houstoun's sister hotel in Langbank.

HOUSTOUN'S WEEKEND PACKAGE: Two nights stay (Fri/Sat or Sat/Sun) in a superbly appointed twin or double room, including breakfast and dinner each day: £55.00 per person per night.

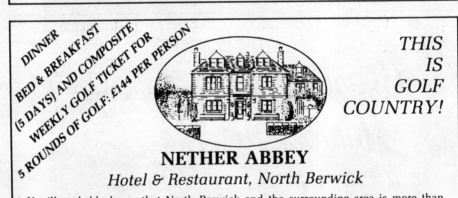

Course, 18 holes, 6664 yards. S.S.S. 72. West Course, 18 holes, 5317 yards. S.S.S. 66. Extensive practice area. *Green Fees:* East Course: weekdays £25.00 per round; West Course: weekdays £18.00 per round. *Eating facilities:* excellent choice of dining facilities. *Visitors:* weekend play restricted to members and hotel residents only. Tee off times bookable in advance (031-333 4501). Professional: Brian Anderson (031-333 1436). Secretary: Isabel Auld (031-333 1845).

LINLITHGOW. **Linlithgow Golf Club,** Braehead, Linlithgow EH49 6QF (Linlithgow (0506) 842585). *Location:* M8, M9, 20 miles west of Edinburgh, west end of Linlithgow – fork left. Parkland and wooded course with panoramic views. 18 holes, 5858 yards, 5359 metres. S.S.S. 68. Small practice area and net. *Green Fees:* weekdays £7.00 per round, £9.00 per day; weekends £9.00 per round, £12.00 per day. *Eating facilities:* full facilities available. *Visitors:* welcome except Saturdays. *Society Meetings:* welcome. Professional: Derek Smith (0506 844356). Secretary: Mrs A. Bird (0506 842585).

LINLITHGOW. **West Lothian Golf Club,** Airngath Hill, By Linlithgow (Bo'ness (0506) 826030). *Location:* situated midway between Linlithgow and Bo'ness. Undulating parkland course. 18 holes, 6629 yards. S.S.S. 72. Practice area. *Green Fees:* weekdays £7.00 per round, £10.00 per day, weekends £9.00 per round, £15.00 per day. *Eating facilities:* available. *Visitors:* welcome, no restrictions before 4 pm midweek. After 4 pm and at weekends by arrangement only. *Society Meetings:* by arrangement. Secretary: T.B. Fraser (0506 825476).

LIVINGSTON. **Deer Park Golf & Country Club.** Golf Course Road, Knightsridge, Livingston EU54 9PG (0506 38843). *Location:* eleven miles outside Edinburgh on M8. Parkland course. 18 holes, 6775 yards. S.S.S. 72. *Green Fees:* weekdays £16.00, weekends £18.00. *Eating facilities:* catering available every day; bar open all day. *Visitors:* welcome without reservation. Snooker, squash, swimming pool, ten pin bowling etc, available at club. *Society Meetings:* catered for. Professional: W.J. Yule (0506 38843). Secretary: C. Clark (0506 34482).

LIVINGSTON. **Pumpherston Golf Club,** Drumshoreland Road, Pumpherston, Livingston EH53 0LF (0506 32869). *Location:* one mile east of Livingston, one and a half miles south of M8. Undulating parkland course, well bunkered. 9 holes, 5154 yards, 4712 metres. S.S.S. 65. Small practice area. *Green Fees:* information not supplied. *Eating facilities:* snack meals, lounge bar. *Visitors:* only when introduced by member. *Society Meetings:* Mondays to Thursdays, maximum number 24. Secretary: A.H. Docharty (0506 854652).

LONGNIDDRY. **Longniddry Golf Club Ltd,** The Clubhouse, Links Road, Longniddry EH32 0NL (Longniddry (0875) 52228). *Location:* from Edinburgh by A1, left for Longniddry, A198 at Wallyford roundabout or left off A1 one mile after MacMerry. 18 holes, 6219 yards, 5678 metres. S.S.S. 70. Practice ground and putting green. *Green Fees:* weekdays £14.00 per round, £20.00 per day, weekends £28.00 per day. *Eating facilities:* every day, bar snacks only on Fridays. *Visitors:* Monday to Thursday parties booked, otherwise all days casual bookings within the previous seven days except on Public Holidays and competition days. *Society Meetings:* catered for (except Friday – Sunday and Monday pm). Professional: John Gray (0875 52228). Secretary: G.C. Dempster, C.A. (0875 52141).

MUSSELBURGH. **Musselburgh Golf Club,** Monktonhall, Musselburgh (031-665 2005). *Location:* six miles east of Edinburgh on A1. Wooded parkland, rivers. 18 holes, 6600 yards. S.S.S. 72. *Green Fees:* on application. *Visitors:* welcome with reservation. *Society Meetings:* catered for. Professional: T. Stangoe (031-665 7055). Secretary: J.R. Brown (031-553 1701).

MUSSELBURGH. **Musselburgh Old Course Golf Club,** Silver Ring Clubhouse, 3B Millhill, Musselburgh EH21 7RG. *Location:* A1 road at Mussleburgh racecourse one-and-a-half miles east of town centre. Seaside links course. 9 holes, 2690 yards. S.S.S. 67. Extensive practice area. *Green Fees:* £1.65. *Eating facilities:* available. *Visitors:* welcome except during club competitions. *Society Meetings:* book through Mr Smith, Brunton Hall, Musselburgh (031-665 3711). Secretary: W. Finnigan (031-665 6014).

NEWBRIDGE. **Ratho Park Golf Club Ltd,** Ratho, Newbridge (031-333 1252). *Location:* eight miles west of Edinburgh G.P.O., access from A71 or A8. Flat parkland. 18 holes, 6028 yards, 5514 metres. S.S.S. 69. *Green Fees:* weekdays £14.00 per round, £20.00 per day; weekends £27.00 per day. All inclusive of "Strokesaver" booklet. *Eating facilities:* full catering available. *Visitors:* welcome without reservation. *Society Meetings:* catered for Tuesdays, Wednesdays and Thursdays. Professional: Alan Pate (031-333 1406). Secretary: J.C. McLafferty (031-333 1752).

NORTH BERWICK. **Glen Golf Club,** East Links, Tantallon Terrace, North Berwick EH39 4LE (0620 2221). *Location:* Firth of Forth – opposite Bass Rock, A198 one mile east of Railway Station. Seaside links with superb views. 18 holes, 6086 yards. S.S.S. 69. Practice area on course. Practice putting green at Clubhouse. *Green Fees:* weekdays £6.25 per round, £9.00 per day, weekends £8.00 per round, £11.50 per day. (Composite tickets available from hotels in East Lothian). Half price for Senior Citizens and Juniors weekdays. *Eating facilities:* full catering available plus

bar service. *Visitors:* welcome anytime. *Society Meetings:* catered for with advance booking. Professional: (shop only) D. Huish (0620 3323). Secretary: D.R. Montgomery (0620 3323). Starter: (0620 2726).

NORTH BERWICK. **North Berwick Golf Club,** New Clubhouse, Beach Road, North Berwick EH39 4BB (0620 2135). *Location:* golf course stretches along the coast. First tee five minutes from town centre. Accessible from A198. Seaside links. 18 holes, 6315 yards. S.S.S. 70. *Green Fees:* (1990) weekdays £12.00 per round, £17.50 per day; weekends and Public Holidays £17.50 per round, £25.00 per day. *Eating facilities:* diningrooms and bar available. *Visitors:* welcome without restrictions. *Society Meetings:* catered for. Professional: D. Huish (0620 3233). Secretary: R. Russell (0620 2135).

PENICUIK. **Glencorse Golf Club,** Milton Bridge, Penicuik EH26 0RD (0968 77177). *Location:* A701 nine miles south of Edinburgh on Peebles road. Parkland course with stream affecting 10 holes. 18 holes, 5205 yards. S.S.S. 66. *Green Fees:* weekdays £8.00 per round, £12.00 per day, weekends £12.00 per round. *Eating facilities:* full catering and bar. *Visitors:* welcome most days and times subject to Club Competitions. *Society Meetings:* catered for Tuesdays, most Wednesdays, Thursdays, most Fridays. Professional: C. Jones (0968 76481). Secretary: D.A. McNiven (0968 77189).

PRESTONPANS. **Royal Musselburgh Golf Club,** Prestongrange House, Prestonpans EH32 (Prestonpans (0875) 810276). *Location:* A198 North Berwick road near Prestonpans. Parkland, 18 holes, 6237 yards. S.S.S. 70. *Green Fees:* weekdays £12.000 per round, £20.00 per day, weekends £20.00 per round. (No day tickets). *Eating facilities:* full catering and licence (no meals on Tuesdays). *Visitors:* welcome weekdays not before 9.30am, not after 3pm, not Friday afternoons. *Society Meetings:* catered for weekdays only – book in advance. Professional: Allan Minto (0875 810139). Secretary: T.H. Hardie.

SOUTH QUEENSFERRY. **Dundas Parks Golf Club,** Dundas Estate, South Queensferry, West Lothian. *Location:* five miles west of Edinburgh, on South Queensferry to Kirkliston road on right of A8000. Parkland course in open countryside. 9 holes (x 2). Small practice area. *Green Fees:* weekdays £6.00. *Eating facilities:* not available. *Visitors:* welcome with member, or by prior arrangement with Secretary. *Society Meetings:* by prior arrangement with Secretary. Secretary: R.H. Crowe (031-331 1601).

WEST CALDER. **Harburn Golf Club,** Harburn, West Calder EH55 8RS (West Calder (0506) 871256). *Location:* two miles south of West Calder on B7008. Parkland course. 18 holes, 5843 yards, 5340 metres. S.S.S. 68. Practice ground and net. *Green Fees:* £7.50 per round, £10.00 per day weekdays; £10.00 per round, £14.00 per day weekends. *Eating facilities:* full catering and bar service. *Visitors:* welcome any time – no restrictions. *Society Meetings:* catered for by advance arrangement. Professional: R. Redpath (0506 871582). Secretary: Frank Vinter (0506 871131).

WHITBURN. **Polkemmet Golf Course,** Polkemmet Country Park, Whitburn, West Lothian (Whitburn (0501) 43905). *Location:* off B7066, one mile west of Whitburn. 9 holes, 2969 metres. Par 37. Driving range. *Green Fees:* Monday to Saturday £1.70, Sunday £2.20. Juniors, Senior Citizens and unemployed: Monday to Saturday £0.95, Sunday £1.25. *Eating facilities:* restaurant and bar complex. *Visitors:* welcome. Facilities include bowling green, picnic areas, etc. Secretary: West Lothian District Council, Department of Leisure and Recreation, County Buildings, Linlithgow.

WINCHURCH. **Niddry Castle Golf Club,** Castle Road, Winchurch EH52. *Location:* ten miles west of Edinburgh on A803 between Kirkliston and Linlithgow. Wooded, natural parkland. 9 holes, 5450 yards. S.S.S. 67. *Green Fees:* £5.00 weekdays, £7.50 weekends. *Eating facilities:* none – but bar lunches available in village. *Visitors:* welcome anytime except not until 2.00pm on Saturdays of Club Competitions. *Society Meetings:* by arrangement. Secretary: Alan M. Lamont (0506 890185).

FASCINATING FIFE FOR GOLF – PAR EXCELLENCE!

THIRTY-SEVEN CRACKING COURSES IN THE ANCIENT HOME OF GOLF AND A TOTAL OF MORE THAN 100 WITHIN AN HOUR'S CAR DRIVE OF ANYWHERE IN FIFE, INCLUDING ST. ANDREWS, GLENEAGLES, CARNOUSTIE, GLENROTHES – A GOLFER'S PARADISE, 'WAY ABOVE PAR.

EXCELLENT LINKS AND INLAND COURSES WITH GREEN FEES THAT WILL PLEASANTLY SURPRISE YOU.

OTHER ACTIVITY HOLIDAYS INCLUDE FLYING, SHOOTING, FISHING, GLIDING, 10-PIN BOWLING, CLAY PIGEON SHOOTING.

Free colour brochure – Ring 0592 756684 or write to Glenrothes Tourist Promotions Ltd., Department GG, Glenrothes House, North Street, Glenrothes, Fife KY7 5PB.

5996

Fife

ABERDOUR. **Aberdour Golf Club,** Seaside Place, Aberdour KY3 0TX (0383 860256). Parkland course situated by the River Forth. 18 holes, 5496 yards. S.S.S. 67. *Green Fees:* £10.00 per round, £14.00 per day. *Eating facilities:* full catering except Tuesdays. *Visitors:* welcome on weekdays. *Society Meetings:* catered for on weekdays and Sundays. On Sundays, maximum size of group 24. Professional: Alan Hope (0383 860256). Secretary: B.P. Drever (0383 860353).

ANSTRUTHER. **Anstruther Golf Club,** Marsfield, Shore Road, Anstruther (0333 310956). *Location:* nine miles south of St. Andrews. Seaside links course. 9 holes, 4144 yards. S.S.S. 63. *Green Fees:* weekdays £6.00, weekends £8.00. *Eating facilities:* lounge bar and dining room. *Visitors:* welcome except during club competitions. *Society Meetings:* outwith May/September and competition days. Secretary: Mrs M. Yuill (0333 312055).

BURNTISLAND. **Burntisland Golf House Club,** Dodhead, Burntisland (Burntisland (0592) 873247). *Location:* on B923, one mile north-east of town centre. Parkland. 18 holes, 5897 yards, 5391 metres. S.S.S. 69. *Green Fees:* weekdays £10.00 per round, £14.00 per day, weekends £13.00 per round, £19.00 per day. *Eating facilities:* meals and snacks in clubhouse. *Visitors:* welcome with advance bookings. *Society Meetings:* advance booking. Professional: Sandy Walker. Secretary: Arthur W. Mann (0592 874093).

CARDENDEN. **Auchterderran Golf Club,** Woodend Road, Cardenden (0592 721579). *Location:* seven miles on A910 from Kirkcaldy. 9 holes, 5250 yards. S.S.S. 66. *Green fees:* information not provided. *Visitors:* welcome without reservation. Secretary: S. G. Miller.

CRAIL. **Crail Golfing Society,** Balcomie Clubhouse, Fifeness, Crail KY10 3XN (Crail (0333) 50278). Instituted 1786. *Location:* eleven miles south-east of St. Andrews on A917. Parkland/seaside links. 18 holes, 5720 yards. S.S.S. 68. Practice ground. *Green Fees:* weekdays £10.00 per round, £15.00 per day; weekends £12.00 per round, £18.00 per day. 3 consecutive weekdays £30.00. Week (excluding Sunday) £50.00. *Eating facilities:* quality catering and bar. *Visitors:* welcome. *Society Meetings:* advance booking available for parties except latter half of July and first half August. Professional: Graeme Lennie (0333 50960). Secretary: G. Thomson (0333 50686).

CUPAR. **Cupar Golf Club,** Hilltarvit, Cupar (Cupar (0334) 53549). *Location:* 10 miles west of St. Andrews. Hillside course. 9 holes, 5168 yards. S.S.S. 65. *Green Fees:* weekdays £8.00, weekends £10.00. *Eating facilities:* bar snacks available. *Visitors:* welcome, except Saturdays. *Society Meetings:* made very welcome. Secretary: I.R. Wilson (0334 53254).

DUNFERMLINE. **Canmore Golf Club,** Venture Fair, Dunfermline (Dunfermline (0383) 724969). *Location:* one mile north of town centre on A823. 18 holes, 5347 yards. S.S.S. 66. *Green Fees:* weekdays £8.00 per round, £12.00 per day. *Eating facilities:* full catering and bar. *Visitors:* welcome except on weekends. *Society Meetings:* visiting societies with prior reservation (not at weekends). Professional: Stephen Craig (0383 728416). Secretary: J.C. Duncan (0383 726098).

DUNFERMLINE. **Dunfermline Golf Club,** Pitfirrane, Crossford, By Dunfermline KY12 8QU (0383 723534). *Location:* two miles west of Dunfermline on main road to Kincardine Bridge. Undulating parkland. 18 holes, 6217 yards, 5739 metres. S.S.S. 70. *Green Fees:* £10.00 per round, £18.00 per day weekdays. *Eating facilities:* catering except Mondays, bar snacks available. *Visitors:* welcome weekdays only when course is quiet. Visiting groups by application. *Society Meetings:* by previous application, up to 36 in numbers. Professional: Jacky Montgomery (0383 723534).

DUNFERMLINE. **Pitreavie (Dunfermline) Golf Club,** Queensferry Road, Dunfermline KY11 5PR (0383 722591). *Location:* M90 Edinburgh/Perth, leave at Rosyth for Dunfermline. Undulating wooded parkland with magnificent views. 18 holes, 6074 yards. S.S.S. 69. Practice range. *Green Fees:* weekdays £9.00 per round, £13.00 per day; weekends £12.00 per round, £16.00 per day. *Eating facilities:* full catering available. *Visitors:* welcome, must have recognised Golf Union Handicap. *Society Meetings:* catered for, must be booked through Secretary. Professional: Jim Forrester (0383 722591/723151). Secretary: W.P. Syme (0383 722591).

DUNFERMLINE. **Saline Golf Club,** Kinneddar Hill, Saline (New Oakley (0383) 852591). *Location:* four miles north-west of Dunfermline. 9 holes, 5302 yards. S.S.S. 66. *Green Fees:* £5.00 daily, £7.00 Sundays. *Eating facilities:* bar snacks, meals by prior arrangement. *Visitors:* welcome without reservation except Saturdays, April to October. *Society Meetings:* catered for midweek or Sundays; maximum 30. Secretary: R. Hutchison (0383 852344).

ELIE. **Earlsferry Thistle Golf Club,** Melon Park, Rotton Row, Elie (0333 310053). 18 holes, 6241 yards. S.S.S. 70. *Green Fees:* set by Elie Golf House Club, on application. *Visitors:* welcome mid-week. Secretary: (0334 76770). The course belongs to Elie Golf House Club, Earlsferry Thistle play the same course.

ELIE. **Elie Sports Club,** Elie. *Location:* ten miles south of St. Andrews on A917. 9 holes, 2277 yards. S.S.S. 32. *Green Fees:* information not provided. *Eating facilities:* light snacks available. *Visitors:* welcome without reservation. Professional: R. Wilson. Secretary: J. Fyall (0333 330955).

ELIE. **Golf House Club,** Elie (Elie (0333) 330327). *Location:* ten miles south of St. Andrews on A917. Links course. 18 holes, 6253 yards. S.S.S. 70. *Green Fees:* weekdays £12.00 per round, £18.00 per day; weekends £16.00 per round, £24.00 per day. *Eating facilities:* lunches, teas, etc. *Visitors:* welcome with reservation. Elie Sports Centre nearby with leisure facilities and cafeteria. *Society Meetings:* catered for except at weekends. Professional: Robin Wilson (0333 330955). Secretary: G.A. Forgie (0333 330301).

FALKLAND. **Falkland Golf Club,** The Myre, Falkland KY7 7AA (0337 57404). *Location:* entrance on A912. Last right hand turn before leaving village travelling north. 12 miles from Kirkcaldy. Flat course. 9 holes, 2608 yards, 2384 metres. S.S.S. 66 for 18 holes. *Green Fees:* £5.00 weekdays, £7.00 weekends. Weekly ticket £17.50. *Eating facilities:* meals by arrangement, snacks available at weekends; bar available for golfers. *Visitors:* welcome, no problem during weekdays. Changing rooms available. *Society Meetings:* must book in advance. Secretary: Mrs C.R. Forsythe (0337 57356).

GLENROTHES. **Glenrothes Golf Club,** Golf Course Road, Glenrothes (Glenrothes (0592) 758686). *Location:* west Glenrothes. Hilly wooded parkland. 18 holes, 6444 yards. S.S.S. 71. *Green Fees:* weekdays £3.20 per round, weekends £4.40 per round. *Eating facilities:* two licensed lounges, dining room. *Visitors:* welcome any time. *Society Meetings:* book one month in advance, minimum 12, maximum 40. Secretary: Leslie Dalrymple (0592 754561).

KINCARDINE. **Tulliallan Golf Club,** Alloa Road, Kincardine, by Alloa (0259 30396). *Location:* on A908 five miles east of Alloa, one mile north of Kincardine Bridge. Parkland slightly wooded, burn winds through the course. 18 holes, 5892 yards, 5463 metres. S.S.S. 69. *Green Fees:* weekdays: round £9.00, day £13.00; weekends: round £11.00, day £15.00. *Eating facilities:* diningroom, bar 11am to 11pm. *Visitors:* no visiting parties on Fridays, Saturdays or on local holidays. *Society Meetings:* catered for with reservation, 24 limit on Sundays. Professional: Steven Kelly (992 30798). Secretary: J.S. McDowall (992 485420).

KINGHORN. **Kinghorn Municipal Golf Club,** MacDuff Crescent, Kinghorn (0592 890345/80242). *Location:* bus stop at course, railway station 3 mins. 18 holes, 5217 yards. S.S.S. 67. *Green Fees:* weekdays £3.20 per round, weekends £4.40 per round. *Eating facilities:* meals at clubhouse (not Saturdays), local hotels. *Visitors:* welcome with prior reservation if large

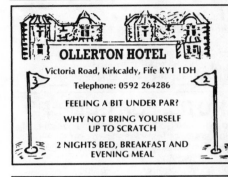
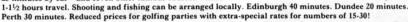
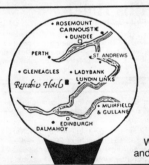

party (up to 30). *Society Meetings:* catered for by arrangement. Secretary: J.P. Robertson (0592 890345).

KIRKCALDY. **Dunnikier Park Golf Club,** Dunnikier Way, Kirkcaldy (Kirkcaldy (0592) 261599). *Location:* M90. Parkland course. 18 holes, 6601 yards, 6036 metres. S.S.S. 72. *Green Fees:* weekdays £3.20 per round, weekends £4.40 per round. *Eating facilities:* dining and bar facilities. *Visitors:* welcome by arrangement with Secretary, no restrictions. Adjacent to private hotel. *Society Meetings:* catered for. Secretary: R.A. Waddell (0592 200627).

KIRKCALDY. **Kirkcaldy Golf Club,** Balwearie, Kirkcaldy (0592 260370). *Location:* west end of town. Wooded parkland with stream. 18 holes, 6004 yards. S.S.S. 70. Practice ground. *Green Fees:* weekdays £7.00 per round, £12.00 per day; weekends £8.00 per round, £14.00 per day. *Eating facilities:* full catering facilities available. *Visitors:* welcome. Professional's shop. *Society Meetings:* catered for. Professional: Brian Lawson (0592 203258). Secretary: J.I. Brodley (0592 263316).

LADYBANK. **Ladybank Golf Club,** Annsmuir, Ladybank KY7 7RA (Ladybank (0337) 30320). *Location:* on B9129 off A91, 15 miles St. Andrews. Wooded heathland. 18 holes, 6617 yards. S.S.S. 72. Practice ground. *Green Fees:* weekdays £12.00 per round, £18.00 per day; weekends £14.00 per round, £21.00 per day. *Eating facilities:* full catering facilities and bar. *Visitors:* welcome without reservation. Party bookings by arrangement with Secretary. *Society Meetings:* by arrangement. Professional: Martin J. Gray (0337 30725). Secretary: D. Downie (0337 30814).

LESLIE. **Leslie Golf Club,** Balsillie, Leslie. 9 holes, 4940 yards. S.S.S. 64. *Green Fees:* £4.00 weekday, £5.00 weekend. *Visitors:* welcome without reservation. Treasurer: Jack Ganson.

LEUCHARS. **St. Michaels Golf Club,** Leuchars (Leuchars (033483) 365). *Location:* on main road St. Andrews to Dundee, north end of Leuchars village. Undulating parkland with plantation surroundings. 9 holes, 5510 yards. S.S.S. 68. *Green Fees:* £8.00 day ticket, Juniors £4.00. *Eating facilities:* bar facilities and meals available. *Visitors:* welcome without reservation except Sundays before 1.00 p.m. Changing rooms and showers. *Society Meetings:* by reservation with green fee deposit £2.00 per head. Secretary: A.J.R. MacKenzie (0334 54044 office hours).

LEVEN. **Leven Golfing Society,** Links Road, Leven KY8 4HS (Leven (0333) 26096). *Location:* nine miles east of Kirkcaldy on the A955. Links course, flat. 18 holes, 6434 yards, 5939 metres. S.S.S. 71. *Green Fees:*

weekdays £11.00 round, £16.00 day; weekends £14.00 round, £19.00 day. *Eating facilities:* full catering available. *Visitors:* welcome (except Saturdays). *Society Meetings:* by arrangement (0333 23509). Parties of under 12 persons (0333 21390). Secretary: John W. Bennett (0333 23898).

LEVEN. **Leven Thistle Golf Club,** Balfour Street, Leven (0333 26397). *Location:* eight miles east of Kirkcaldy, 14 miles west of St. Andrews. Seaside links, top championship links used for national and international events including Open qualifying. 18 holes, 6434 yards. S.S.S. 71. *Green Fees:* weekdays £16.00 per day, £11.00 per round; weekends £19.00 per day, £14.00 per round. *Eating facilities:* full catering available, two bars, function hall. *Visitors:* welcome without reservation, except Saturdays. *Society Meetings:* for group bookings contact Mr M. Innes, Clydesdale House, Duries Street, Leven, Fife. Secretary: J. Scott.

LEVEN. **Lundin Golf Club,** Golf Road, Lundin Links KY8 6BA (0333 320202). *Location:* three miles east of Leven on the A915 (Leven to St. Andrews). Seaside links. 18 holes, 6377 yards. S.S.S. 71. Practice ground. *Green Fees:* £15.00 per round, £22.50 per day weekdays; £18.00 Saturdays after 2.30pm. *Eating facilities:* bar and diningroom. *Visitors:* welcome except Saturdays before 2.30pm and Sundays. *Society Meetings:* limited numbers. Professional: David K. Webster (0333 320051). Secretary: A.C. McBride (0333 320202).

LEVEN. **Scoonie Golf Club,** North Links, Leven KY8 4SP (Leven (0333) 27057). *Location:* five minutes from centre of town. Interesting course, ideal for 36 hole events. 18 holes, 5410 yards. S.S.S. 66. Practice area available. *Green Fees:* weekdays £3.00 round (approximately), weekends £4.00. Reduced rates for Senior Citizens, Juniors. *Eating facilities:* bar meals served all day. *Visitors:* welcome. *Society Meetings:* parties of 12 or more by prior arrangement. Secretary: D.K. Davidson (0592 714232).

LOCHGELLY. **Lochgelly Golf Club,** Cartmore Road, Lochgelly (Lochgelly (0592) 780174). *Location:* take M90 to Junction 4 Halbeath Interchange, follow signs. Flat parkland. 18 holes, 5580 yards. S.S.S. 67. *Green Fees:* £5.00 per round, £9.00 per day weekdays; £7.00 per round, £12.00 per day weekends. *Eating facilities:* meals available on request. *Visitors:* welcome anytime; maximum number for outings 24. Secretary: R.F. Stuart (0383 512238).

LOCHGELLY. **Lochore Meadows Golf Course,** Lochore Meadows Country Park, Crosshill, Lochgelly KY5 8BA (0592 860086). *Location:* B920 two miles north of Lochgelly. 9 holes, 3241 yards. S.S.S. 35, 71 (18). *Green Fees:* weekdays £3.80, weekends £5.00.

"Heading for Home" on the 18th on the Old Course, St. Andrews.

Putting green. *Eating facilities:* available. *Visitors:* unrestricted. *Society Meetings:* by arrangement through Park Manager: B. Wilson.

MARKINCH. **Balbirnie Park Golf Club,** Club House, Markinch (0592 752006). *Location:* outside Markinch near the A92. Wooded parkland course. 18 holes, 6210 yards. S.S.S. 72. *Green Fees:* £9.00 per round, £12.00 per day weekdays; £12.50 per round, £15.00 per day weekends. *Eating facilities:* by prior arrangement with Steward. *Visitors:* no restrictions at present other than maximum number of 24 at weekends and no visitors before 10.00am weekends. *Society Meetings:* welcome. Secretary: A.G. Grant.

ST. ANDREWS. **Balgove Course,** St. Andrews. *Location:* outskirts of St. Andrews on Dundee road. 9 hole beginners' course. *Green Fees:* £2.00 per 18 holes. *Eating facilities:* hotels and restaurants in the vicinity. Secretary: A. Beveridge, Links Management Committee of St. Andrews (0334 75757).

ST. ANDREWS. **Eden Course,** St. Andrews (Starter – 0334 74296). *Location:* follow A91 trunk road to St. Andrews, directions to golf courses are clearly marked. Seaside links. 18 holes, 6401 yards, 5852 metres. S.S.S. 71. Practice facilities. *Green Fees:* £9.00 per round weekdays. *Eating facilities:* hotels and restaurants in the vicinity. *Visitors:* welcome with or without reservation. *Society Meetings:* catered for. Secretary:

A. Beveridge, Links Management Committee of St. Andrews (0334 75757).

ST. ANDREWS. **Jubilee Course,** West Sands, St. Andrews KY16 9JA (Starter (0334) 73938). *Location:* follow A91 trunk road to St. Andrews, directions to golf course are clearly marked. Seaside links. 18 holes, 6805 yards. S.S.S. 73. Practice facilities available. *Green Fees:* £10.00 per round weekdays. *Eating facilities:* hotels and restaurants in the vicinity. *Visitors:* welcome with or without reservation. *Society Meetings:* catered for. Secretary: A. Beveridge, Links Management Committee of St. Andrews (0334) 75757).

ST. ANDREWS. **New Course,** West Sands, St. Andrews (Starter: 0334 73938). *Location:* follow A91 trunk road to St. Andrews – directions to golf courses are clearly marked. Seaside links. 18 holes, 6604 yards, 6036 metres. S.S.S. 72. Practice facilities available. *Green Fees:* £11.50 per round weekdays. *Eating facilities:* hotels and restaurants in vicinity. *Visitors:* welcome with or without reservation. *Society Meetings:* catered for except Saturday. Secretary: A. Beveridge, Links Management Committee of St. Andrews (0334 75757).

ST. ANDREWS. **St. Andrews Links,** Old Course, St. Andrews KY16 9JA (0334 73393). Seaside links. 18 holes, 6566 yards. S.S.S. 72. Practice area and driving range available. *Green Fees:* £25.00 per round.

Visitors: welcome. *Society Meetings:* welcome. Secretary: Alec Beveridge (0334 75757).

ST. ANDREWS. **The Old Course,** St. Andrews KY16 9JA (0334 73393). *Location:* follow A91 trunk road to St. Andrews – directions to golf course are clearly marked. Seaside links. 18 holes, 6566 yards, 6004 metres. S.S.S. 72. Practice facilities. *Green Fees:* £22.50 per round weekdays. *Visitors:* Handicap Certificate or letter of introduction required from recognised golf club. *Society Meetings:* welcome. Secretary: A. Beveridge (0334 75757).

TAYPORT. **Scotscraig Golf Club,** Tayport (Dundee (0382) 552515). *Location:* ten miles north of St. Andrews. Seaside links. 18 holes, 6486 yards. S.S.S. 71. *Green Fees:* weekdays £18.00 per round, £24.00 per day; weekends £23.00 per round, £30.00 per day. *Eating facilities:* lunches and high teas, except Tuesdays. *Visitors:* welcome on weekdays or weekends by prior arrangement. *Society Meetings:* catered for subject to approval. Secretary: K. Gourlay (0382 552515).

THORNTON. **Thornton Golf Club,** Thornton KY1 4DW (Glenrothes (0592) 771111). *Location:* south east Fife located off A92, midway between Glenrothes and Kirkcaldy. Undulating, wooded, parkland. 18 holes, 6177 yards. S.S.S. 69. *Green Fees:* weekdays £6.00 per round, £9.50 per day, weekends £10.00 per round, £15.00 per day. *Eating facilities:* full catering service and bar. *Visitors:* welcome anytime, booking advisable. *Society Meetings:* catered for. Secretary: Neil Robertson.

Glasgow & District

BISHOPBRIGGS. **Bishopbriggs Golf Club,** Brackenbrae Road, Bishopbriggs (041-772 1810). Location: quarter mile from Bishopbriggs Cross on Glasgow-Kirkintilloch road. 18 holes, 6041 yards. S.S.S. 69. *Green Fees:* information not provided. *Eating facilities:* full service available when prior notice given. *Visitors:* welcome with reservation, application to Committee for parties. *Society Meetings:* catered for. Secretary: Hugh G. Simpson.

GLASGOW. **Alexandra Golf Club,** Alexandra Park, Alexandra Parade, Glasgow G31 3SE (041-554 1204). *Location:* off M8. Wooded parkland. 9 holes, 1965 yards. *Green Fees:* weekdays adults £1.40, weekends £1.70. Senior Citizens and UB40 45p. *Eating facilities:* rooms available for functions. *Visitors:* welcome anytime. Blind club, Unemployed club. Professional: G. Campbell. Secretary: G. Arthur.

GLASGOW. **Bearsden Golf Club.** Thorn Road, Bearsden, Glasgow G61 4BP (041-942 2351). *Location:* seven miles north-west of Glasgow. Parkland. 9 holes, 6014 yards. S.S.S. 69. *Green Fees:* information not provided. *Visitors:* welcome, but must be accompanied by member. Secretary: W.S. Chalmers (041-942 4480).

GLASGOW. **Blairbeth Golf Club,** Fernhill, Rutherglen, Glasgow (041-634 3355). *Location:* two miles south of Rutherglen off Stonelaw Road. Parkland. 18 holes, 5800 yards. S.S.S. 67. *Green Fees:* information not provided. *Eating facilities:* available. *Visitors:* welcome with reservation, by introduction. *Society Meetings:* not catered for. Secretary: F.T. Henderson (041-632 0604).

GLASGOW. **Bonnyton Golf Club,** Eaglesham, Glasgow G76 0QA (03553 2645). *Location:* B764. Moorland. 18 holes, 6252 yards. S.S.S. 71. *Green Fees:* £14.00 per day. *Eating facilities:* full diningroom and snack facilities. *Visitors:* welcome except weekends. Professional: Joe Pearston (03553 2256). Secretary: (03553 2781).

GLASGOW. **Bothwell Castle Golf Club,** Blantyre Road, Bothwell (Bothwell (0698 853177). *Location:* adjacent to M74, three miles north of Hamilton. Parkland course. 18 holes 6240 yards. S.S.S. 70. Golf clubs and caddy cars for hire. *Green Fees:* weekdays (8.00am to 3.30pm) £8.00 per round, £12 per day. (Playing times must be booked with Professional). *Eating facilities:* lunches and dinners available, bar. *Visitors:* welcome with reservation. *Society Meetings:* catered for, courtesy of course granted by committees to societies. Professional: William Walker (0698 852052). Secretary: A.D.C. Watson (0698 852395).

GLASGOW. **Buchanan Castle Golf Club,** Drymen, Glasgow (0360 60369). *Location:* half mile from Drymen on the Glasgow/Drymen road. Flat parkland course. 18 holes, 6086 yards. S.S.S. 69. Practice area. *Green Fees:* £16.00 per round, £20.00 per day. *Eating facilities:* by arrangement. *Visitors:* welcome by arrangement or if introduced by member. *Society Meetings:* welcome by arrangement. Professional: Charles Dernie (0360 60330). Secretary: J. Iain Hay (0360 60307).

GLASGOW. **Cambuslang Golf Club,** Westburn, Cambuslang (041-641 3130). *Location:* one mile from Station. 9 holes, 6146 yards. S.S.S. 69. *Visitors:* welcome when accompanied by member. *Society Meetings:* by arrangement. Secretary: William Lilly.

GLASGOW. **Cathcart Castle Golf Club,** Mearns Road, Clarkston, Glasgow (041-638 0082). *Location:* A77. Parkland course. 18 holes, 5818 yards. S.S.S. 68. *Green Fees:* information not provided. *Eating facilities:* lunches served at club. *Visitors:* welcome on weekdays if playing with member. *Society Meetings:* on Tuesdays and Thursdays by application. Professional: David Naylor. Secretary: W.G. Buchan.

GLASGOW. **Cathkin Braes Golf Club,** Cathkin Road, Rutherglen, Glasgow G73 4SE (041-634 6605). 18 holes, 6266 yards. S.S.S. 71. Practice ground. *Green Fees:* £12.00 per round, £17.00 per day. *Eating facilities:* available. *Visitors:* welcome Monday to Friday by prior arrangement. *Society Meetings:* catered for. Professional: Stephen Bree (041-634 0650). Secretary/Treasurer: G.L. Stevenson.

GLASGOW. **Cawder Golf Club,** Cadder Road, Bishopbriggs, Glasgow G64 3QD (041-772 7101). *Location:* A803 north of city. Parkland. Cawder: 18 holes, 6305 yards, 5737 metres. S.S.S. 71. Keir: 18 holes, 5891 yards, 5373 metres. S.S.S. 68. Practice area. *Green Fees:* £16.50. *Eating facilities:* lunches, high teas, dinners available. *Visitors:* welcome when playing with member. *Society Meetings:* catered for mid-week. Professional: Ken Stevely (041-772 7102). Secretary: G.T. Stoddart (041-772 5167).

GLASGOW. **Clober Golf Club,** Craigton Road, Milngavie G62 7HP (041-956 1685). *Location:* five minutes from Milngavie centre, seven miles from Glasgow city centre. 18 holes, 5068 yards. S.S.S. 65. *Green Fees:* weekdays £7.00 per round. *Eating facilities:* morning coffee, lunches, high teas. *Visitors:* welcome weekdays before 4.30pm (Fridays 4.00pm), weekends if introduced by a member. *Society Meetings:* catered for. Professional: G.Lyle (041-956 1685). Secretary: G. Buchanan (041-956 5839).

GLASGOW. **Cowglen Golf Club**, 301 Barrhead Road, Glasgow G43 (041-632 0556). *Location:* southwest Glasgow. 18 holes, 6033 yards. S.S.S. 69. *Green Fees:* information not provided. *Eating facilities:* dining room and bar snacks. *Visitors:* welcome if playing with member. Professional: John McTear. Secretary: R.J.G. Jamieson C.A.

GLASGOW. **Crow Wood Golf Club**, Muirhead, Chryston, Glasgow (041-799 2011). Parkland. 18 holes, 6249 yards, 5875 metres. S.S.S. 70. Practice area. *Green Fees:* weekdays £8.00 per round, £12.00 per day. *Eating facilities:* bar open 11am to 11pm; catering 11am to 9pm. *Visitors:* welcome weekdays only by arrangement with Secretary. Professional: Ronnie Gregan (041-779 1943). Secretary: R. Britton (041-248 4523).

GLASGOW. **Deaconsbank Golf Course**, Rouken Glen Golf Centre, Stewarton Road, Thornliebank, Glasgow G46 7UZ (041-638 7044). *Location:* on Stewarton Road at Rouken Glen Park, only 250 yards from the A726. Parkland with wooded features, designed by James Braid. 18 holes, 4800 yards. S.S.S. 64. 15-bay floodlit driving range. *Green fees:* weekdays £4.00 per round, £6.00 per day; weekends £8.50 day ticket. *Eating facilities:* catering and bar facilities available. *Visitors:* welcome all year round. *Society Meetings:* catered for all year round. Professional: (041-638 7044). Secretary: Christine Cosh (041-620 0926).

GLASGOW. **Dougalston Golf Course**, Strathblane Road, Milngavie, Glasgow G62 (041-956 5750). *Location:* A81 half a mile Milngavie. Wooded – water; three ponds. 18 holes, 6683 yards. S.S.S. 72. Practice ground. *Green Fees:* £6.00 weekdays, £9.00 weekends. *Eating facilities:* restaurant and bar. *Visitors:* no restrictions, open to the general public. Secretary: W. McInnes.

GLASGOW. **Douglas Park Golf Club**, Hillfoot, Bearsden (041-942 2220). *Location:* adjacent to railway station, Hillfoot, Bearsden, 20 yards past traffic lights at Milngavie Road/Boclair Road. 18 holes. S.S.S. 68. *Green Fees:* information not provided. *Eating facilities:* full service available. *Visitors:* must be introduced and play with member. *Society Meetings:* Mondays, Wednesdays and Thursdays on application to Secretary. Professional: David B. Scott. Secretary: J.R. Thornburton.

GLASGOW. **Dullatur Golf Club**, Dullatur, Glasgow G68 0AR (0236 723230). *Location:* 12 miles east of Glasgow, north of Cumbernauld on Kilsyth road via Dullatur. 18 holes, 6229 yards. S.S.S. 70. *Green Fees:* £14.00 per day, £8.00 per round after 1.30pm. *Visitors:* welcome weekdays. Professional: Duncan Sinclair.

GLASGOW. **East Kilbride Golf Club**, Nerston, East Kilbride G74 4PF (03552 20913). 18 holes, 6384 yards. S.S.S. 71. *Green Fees:* £8.00 per round, £12.00 per day. *Eating facilities:* full catering except Tuesdays and Thursdays. *Visitors:* welcome weekdays only on application if members of an official club. Weekends no visitors unless accompanied by a member. *Society Meetings:* catered for on application, limit of 30. Professional: A.R Taylor. Secretary: J.H. King.

GLASGOW. **Eastwood Golf Club**, Muirshield, Loganswell, Newton Mearns, Glasgow G77 6RX (035-55 261). *Location:* on main A77 road to Kilmarnock two miles south of Newton Mearns. Parkland. 18 holes, 5864 yards. S.S.S. 68. *Green Fees:* £10.00 per round. *Eating facilities:* snacks or full meals available. *Visitors:* welcome on application to Secretary. *Visiting parties:* welcomed on prior application. Professional: K. McWade (035-55 285). Secretary: C.B. Scouler (035-55 280).

GLASGOW. **Glasgow Golf Club**, Killermont, Bearsden, Glasgow G61 2TW (041-942 2011). *Location:* from Glasgow head towards Bearsden, (Aberfoyle). Tree-lined, parkland. 18 holes, 5968 yards. S.S.S. 69. *Green Fees:* weekdays £25.00. Weekends members only. *Eating facilities:* available. Smart dress obligatory. *Visitors:* only if introduced by member. *Society Meetings:* by application to Club Secretary. Professional: Jack Steven (041-942 8507). Secretary: I.A.D. Mann.

GLASGOW: **Haggs Castle Golf Club**, Dumbreck Road, Dumbreck, Glasgow G41 4SN (041-427 0480). *Location:* straight ahead at roundabout at end of M77 from Glasgow. Flat, tree-lined course. 18 holes, 6464 yards. S.S.S. 71. Practice area and putting green. *Green Fees:* weekdays £16.00 per round, £24.00 per day. Weekends, members only. *Eating facilities:* available. *Visitors:* welcome, must book through Secretary, golf shoes must be worn. *Society Meetings:* by arrangement through Secretary. Professional: J. McAlister (041-427 3355). Secretary: I. Harvey (041-427 1157).

GLASGOW. **Hayston Golf Club**, Campsie Road, Kirkintilloch, Glasgow G66 1RN (041-776 1244). *Location:* 10 miles north-east of Glasgow and one mile north of Kirkintilloch. Undulating course with tree-lined fairways. 18 holes, 6042 yards. S.S.S. 69. Practice area. *Green Fees:* weekdays £9.00 per round, £15.00 per day. *Eating facilities:* lunches and bar snacks available; high tea or dinner if ordered in advance. *Visitors:* welcome weekdays before 4.30pm with letter of introduction from own club. Weekends only if introduced by member. *Society Meetings:* Tuesdays and Thursdays only. Professional: Steve Barnett (041-775 0882).

GLASGOW. **Hilton Park Golf Club**, Stockiemuir Road, Milngavie, Glasgow G62 7HB (041-956 5124). *Location:* on A809. Moorland courses. Allander course: 18 holes, 5409 yards. S.S.S. 67. Hilton course: 18 holes, 6021 yards. S.S.S. 70. Practice area. *Green Fees:* £12.00 per round, £18.00 per day. *Eating facilities:* full catering and bar. *Visitors:* on application to the Secretary (not at weekends). *Society Meetings:* as visitors. Professional: W. McCondichie (041-956 5125). Secretary: Ms J.A. Dawson (041-956 4657).

GLASGOW. **Kirkhill Golf Club**, Greenlees Road, Cambuslang, Glasgow (041-641 3083 or 8499). 18 holes, 5862 yards. S.S.S. 69. *Green Fees:* £12.00 per day, £8.00 per round. *Eating facilities:* dining room and bar snacks. *Visitors:* welcome when introduced by member or on written application to the Secretary. Secretary: C.C. Stanfield.

GLASGOW. **Knightswood Golf Club**, Lincoln Avenue, Glasgow G13 (041-959 5610). *Location:* four miles west of city centre. Flat parkland course. 9 holes, 2717 yards. S.S.S. 66 (33). *Green Fees:* £1.40 weekdays, £1.60 weekends. *Visitors:* welcome anytime, medals and tournaments most weekends. Secretary: D.M. Hill (041-334 0562).

GLASGOW. **Linn Park Golf Club**, Simshill Road, Glasgow G44 (041-637 5871). *Location:* five miles south of city centre. 18 holes, 4952 yards. S.S.S. 65. Practice nets, putting green. *Green Fees:* weekdays £2.75, weekends £3.25 (Special rates Senior Citizens midweek). *Eating facilities:* snacks available all week from March to October, weekends only from November to February. *Visitors:* welcome without restrictions. *Society Meetings:* not catered for. Secretary: Robert Flanagan.

GLASGOW. **Littlehill Golf Club**, Auchinairn Road, Bishopbriggs, Glasgow (041-772 1916). *Location:* close to Stobhill General Hospital, north of city centre. 18 holes, 6364 yards. S.S.S. 70. Golf shop. *Green Fees:* information not available. *Eating facilities:* restaurant within clubhouse. *Visitors:* welcome without reservation. *Society Meetings:* not catered for. Secretary: D.K. Hughes.

GLASGOW. **Milngavie Golf Club**, Laigh Park, Milngavie, Glasgow (041-956 1619). *Location:* situated off Glasgow to Drymen road approximately one mile past Stockiemuir Service Station, turn right at signpost. 18 holes, 5818 yards. S.S.S. 68. *Green Fees:* information not provided. *Eating facilities:* catering available. *Visitors:* welcome when introduced by member only. *Society Meetings:* catered for. Secretary: W.D. Robertson.

GLASGOW. **Pollok Golf Club**, 90 Barrhead Road, Glasgow G43 1BG (041-632 1080). *Location:* A736, four miles south of Glasgow, near end of M77. Wooded parkland. 18 holes, 6257 yards. S.S.S. 70. *Green Fees:* £18.00 per round, £22.00 per day. *Eating facilities:* dining room and bar. *Visitors:* welcome with reservation by letter to Secretary. No visitors Saturday or Sunday. No Ladies. *Society Meetings:* catered for by letter. Secretary: A. Mathison Boyd (041-632 1453).

GLASGOW. **Sandyhills Golf Club**, 223 Sandyhills Road, Glasgow G32 9NA (041-778 1179). *Location:* three miles east from centre of Glasgow. 18 holes, 6253 yards. S.S.S. 70. *Green Fees:* information not provided. *Eating facilities:* lunches at club except Mondays, order in advance. *Visitors:* welcome when introduced by a member.

GLASGOW. **The White Craigs Golf Club**, 72 Ayr Road, Giffnock, Glasgow G46 6SW (041-639 1681). *Location:* on A77 south of city. Parkland course, 18 holes. *Green Fees:* information not provided. *Eating facilities:* dining room, lounge bar. *Visitors:* letter of introduction required. *Society Meetings:* catered for Wednesday only. Professional: William Watson (041-639 2140). Secretary: W. Miller (041-639 4530).

GLASGOW. **Williamwood Golf Club**, Clarkston Road, Glasgow G44 (041-637 1783). *Location:* beside Clarkston Toll on Clarkston Road. Attractive parkland course designed by James Braid. 18 holes, 5878 yards. S.S.S. 68. Practice area and putting. *Green Fees:* £12.00 per round, £18.00 per day. Members only at weekends. *Eating facilities:* meals must be ordered. *Visitors:* must have Handicap Certificate, and proof of club membership. *Society Meetings:* weekdays only by arrangement. Professional: J. Gardner (041-637 2715). Secretary: R.G. Cuthbert CA (041-226 4311).

GLASGOW. **Windyhill Golf Club**, Baljaffray Road, Bearsden, Glasgow G61 4QQ (041-942 2349). *Location:* eight miles north-west of Glasgow. Undulating parkland, moorland course. 18 holes, 6254 yards, 5765 metres. S.S.S. 70. Practice area, caddy cars available. *Green Fees:* £10.00 per day, weekends with member only. *Eating facilities:* full catering and bar. *Visitors:* welcome weekdays, by prior arrangement with Secretary. *Society Meetings:* welcome weekdays by arrangement. Professional: R.Collinson (041-942 7157). Secretary: A.J. Miller (041-942 2349).

KILSYTH. **Kilsyth Lennox Golf Club**, Tak-Ma-Doon Road, Kilsyth, Glasgow G65 0RS (Kilsyth (0236) 822190). *Location:* 12 miles from Glasgow on A80. Parkland/moorland, undulating ground with superb views across central Scotland. 9 holes, 5934 yards. S.S.S. 69. (Second 9 hole course currently under construction). *Green Fees:* £8.00 per round. *Eating facilities:* bar and lounge, bar snacks available. *Visitors:* welcome weekdays up to 5.00pm, Saturdays after 5.00pm, not Sundays. Professional: R. Abercrombie. Secretary: A.G. Stevenson (0236 823213).

NEWTON MEARNS. **The East Renfrewshire Golf Club**, Pilmuir, Newton Mearns, Glasgow G77 6RT (035 55 256). *Location:* on A77, one and a half miles south of Newton Mearns. Moorland course. 18 holes, 6097 yards, 5577 metres. S.S.S. 70. *Green Fees:* £15.00 weekdays, £20.00 weekends. *Eating facilities:* by prior arrangement with Clubmaster. *Visitors:* welcome except Saturdays but always by prior arrangement with Professional. *Society Meetings:* welcome by prior arrangement with Secretary. Professional: Gordon D. Clark (035 55 206). Secretary: A. Lindsay Gillespie (041 226 4311).

If you are writing, a stamped, addressed envelope is always appreciated.

Inverness-shire

BOAT OF GARTEN. **Boat of Garten Golf and Tennis Club,** Boat of Garten PH24 3BQ (Boat of Garten (047-983) 351). *Location:* 27 miles south of Inverness (A9), Boat one mile off A9. 18 holes, 5720 yards. S.S.S. 68. *Green Fees:* information not provided. *Eating facilities:* catering facilities open 10am to 6pm, bar facilities open 11am to 11pm daily. *Visitors:* welcome without reservation except weekends, when tee-off times must be booked. *Society Meetings:* catered for. Secretary: J.R. Ingram. Golf shop: (047-983 282).

CARRBRIDGE. **Carrbridge Golf Club,** Carrbridge (047-984 674). *Location:* eight miles north of Aviemore adjacent to A9, 23 miles south of Inverness. Moorland/parkland course. 9 holes, 2630 yards. S.S.S. 66. *Green Fees:* weekdays £5.50 per day, weekends £6.50 per day. *Eating facilities:* snacks, coffee etc. No bar. *Visitors:* unrestricted except Competition days – mainly Sundays. Secretary: E.G. Drayson (047-984 674).

FORT AUGUSTUS. **Fort Augustus Golf Club,** Fort Augustus (Fort Augustus (0320) 6460). *Location:* new entrance 500 yards south of village on Fort William road. 9 holes, 18 tees, 5454 yards. S.S.S. 68. *Green Fees:* information not provided. *Visitors:* welcome without reservation. *Society Meetings:* catered for. Secretary: I. Aitchison (0320 6460).

INVERNESS. **Inverness Golf Club,** Culcabock Road, Inverness IV2 3XQ (Inverness (0463) 233422). *Location:* one mile south of town centre. Parkland course. 18 holes, 6226 yards. S.S.S. 70. *Green Fees:* weekdays £14.00 (£10.00 per round). weekends and Bank Holidays £16.00 (£12.00 per round). *Eating facilities:* sandwiches, lunches, high teas and dinners served at club. *Visitors:* welcome but not on Saturdays from 25th March to 20th October. *Society Meetings:* catered for, pre-booking preferred. Professional: A.P. Thomson (0463 231989). Secretary/Manager: T. Crane (0463 239882).

INVERNESS. **Torvean Golf Club,** Glenurquhart Road, Inverness (0463 237543). *Location:* on A82 towards Fort William, approximately one mile from town centre. Flat course. 18 holes, 4682 yards. S.S.S. 63. Practice area and putting green. *Green Fees:* information not provided. *Eating facilities:* all meals and bar available. *Visitors:* booking preferred, especially at weekends. *Society Meetings:* by arrangement through District Council. Secretary: A. Menzies (0463 238541).

KINGUSSIE. **Kingussie Golf Club,** Gynack Road, Kingussie (0540-661 374). *Location:* signposted at the Duke of Gordon Hotel, just outside centre of village. Moorland. 18 holes, 5555 yards, 5079 metres. S.S.S.

67. *Green Fees:* £7.00 per round, £9.00 per day. *Eating facilities:* can be arranged. *Visitors:* welcome without reservation. Caravan site. *Society Meetings:* catered for. Secretary: Mr William Cook (0540-661 600).

NETHYBRIDGE. **Abernethy Golf Club,** Nethybridge, PH25 3EB (Nethybridge [047982] 305). *Location:* 10 miles from Aviemore lying between Boat-of-Garten and Grantown on Spey. 9 holes, 2484 yards. S.S.S. 33. *Green Fees:* £6.00 per day. *Eating facilities:* meals snacks, coffees available. *Visitors:* welcome. *Society Meetings:* by arrangement. Contact the Secretary, Barbara Douglas.

Kincardineshire

BANCHORY. **Banchory Golf Club,** Kinneskie Road, Banchory AB3 3TA (Banchory (033 02) 2365). *Location:* 18 miles west of Aberdeen on Deeside, 100 yards south west Banchory town centre. Parkland. 18 holes, 5305 yards, 4850 metres. S.S.S. 66. *Green Fees:* weekdays £12.00, weekends £14.00. *Eating facilities:* full catering service and lounge bar. *Visitors:* welcome. *Society Meetings:* catered for. Professional: D.W. Smart (033 02 2447). Secretary: E. Girvan (033 02 2365).

LAURENCEKIRK. **Auchenblae Golf Club,** Auchenblae, Laurencekirk AB3 1JT. *Location:* five miles north of Laurencekirk, on A94, two miles west of Fordoun.

Parkland. 9 holes, 2174 yards. S.S.S. 30. *Green Fees:* Mondays to Saturdays £4.00, Juniors £1.00 and Senior Citizens £2.00; Sundays £6.00, Juniors £1.50 and Senior Citizens £3.00. *Eating facilities:* two hotels in nearby village. *Visitors:* restrictions Wednesday and Friday evenings (competitions); very busy Sundays. *Society Meetings:* small groups welcome. Secretary: A.I. Robertson (05612 407).

STONEHAVEN. **Stonehaven Golf Club,** Cowie, Stonehaven AB3 2RH (Stonehaven (0569) 62124). *Location:* A92, one mile north of town. 18 holes, 5128 yards. S.S.S. 65. *Green Fees:* £10.00 weekdays, £12.50 weekends. *Eating facilities:* full catering including bar lunches. *Visitors:* welcome, only a few with reservation. *Society Meetings:* catered for except for Saturday and all Sundays in July and August. Secretary: E.A. Ferguson. Club Manager: R.O. Blair.

Kinross-shire

KINNESSWOOD. **Bishopshire Golf Club,** Kinnesswood. (Scotlandwell [059-284] 395). *Location:* approximately three miles east of M90 travelling north, coming off at Kinross interchange. 9 holes, 4546 yards.

S.S.S. 63. *Green fees:* information not available. *Eating facilities:* available at the Lomond Hotel, two minutes from course. *Visitors:* welcome without reservation. Secretary: A.B. Moffat.

KINROSS. **Green Hotel Golf Course,** Green Hotel, Kinross (0577 63467). *Location:* turn left in Kinross off M90, course 500 yards on right. 18 holes, 6111 yards. S.S.S. 70. *Green Fees:* available from Secretary. *Eating facilities:* in clubhouse or hotel. *Visitors:* welcome with reservation. *Society Meetings:* catered for. Secretary: Mrs Stewart, Green Hotel.

MILNATHORT. **Milnathort Golf Club Ltd,** South Street, Milnathort (Kinross (0577) 64069). Parkland course. 9 holes, 5962 yards. S.S.S. 69. *Green Fees:* weekdays £6.00, weekends £10.00. *Eating facilities:* by arrangement. *Visitors:* welcome without reservation. *Society Meetings:* must be booked in advance. All enquiries phone Clubhouse.

Kirkcudbrightshire

CASTLE DOUGLAS. **Castle Douglas Golf Club,** Abercromby Road, Castle Douglas (0556 2801). *Location:* in town. Parkland. 9 holes, 5408 yards. S.S.S. 66. *Green Fees:* £8.00 per round or day. *Eating facilities:* some catering may be available during season. *Visitors:* welcome without reservation, except Thursdays after 4.00pm and Competition Days. *Society Meetings:* not catered for. Secretary: A.J. Guy (0556 2307).

DALBEATTIE. **Colvend Golf Club,** Sandyhills, By Dalbeattie (0556-63 398). *Location:* six miles from Dalbeattie on the A710, Solway Coast road, between Dalbeattie and Dumfries. Picturesque seaside course on a hill. 9 holes, 2322 yards. S.S.S. 63. *Green Fees:* £5.00 per day; weekly ticket £20.00 (approximately). *Eating facilities:* excellent catering available. *Visitors:* welcome almost anytime. Course must be vacated by 4.30pm on Tuesdays and 5.30pm on Thursdays from April to September. Secretary: J.B. Henderson (0556 610878).

GATEHOUSE OF FLEET. **Gatehouse of Fleet Golf Club,** Laurieston Road, Gatehouse of Fleet, Castle Douglas. *Location:* quarter of a mile from Gatehouse.

Sloping and wooded. 9 holes, 2500 yards. S.S.S. 63. *Green Fees:* £6.00 per day. *Visitors:* welcome, enquiries to the Secretary. Secretary: William McMillan (055 74 252).

KIRKCUDBRIGHT. **Kirkcudbright Golf Club,** Stirling Crescent, Kirkcudbright (0557 30314). *Location:* signposted near centre of town. Hilly parkland. 18 holes, 5598 yards. S.S.S. 67. *Green Fees:* £8.00 per round or day. Reductions for parties of 20 or more. *Eating facilities:* available. *Visitors:* welcome without reservation most days. Secretary: A. Gordon (0557 30542).

NEW GALLOWAY. **New Galloway Golf Club,** New Galloway, Castle Douglas (Castle Douglas (0556) 2794). *Location:* one mile off A731, Ayr to Dumfries road. Scenic with fine turf. 9 holes, 5058 yards. S.S.S. 65. *Green Fees:* £5.00 per round/day. *Eating facilities:* bar. *Visitors:* welcome without reservation. Accommodation and meals available in village. *Society Meetings:* by arrangement. Secretary: John T. Watson (0556 2794).

Lanarkshire

AIRDRIE. **Airdrie Golf Club,** Glenmavis Road, Airdrie (Airdrie (0236) 62195).*Location:* one mile north of Airdrie Cross. 18 holes, 6004 yards. S.S.S. 69. *Green Fees:* £12.00 per day, £8.00 per round (both inclusive of VAT). *Eating facilities:* available. *Visitors:* welcome only on application to the Secretary. Professional: A. McCloskey. Secretary: W.R. Thomson.

AIRDRIE. **Easter Moffat Golf Club,** Plains, Airdrie ML6 8NP (0236 842878). *Location:* three miles east of Airdrie on old Edinburgh Road. 18 holes, 6221 yards. S.S.S. 70. Practice ground. *Green Fees:* £8.00 per round, £10.00 per day (lower rate if visited previous year). *Eating facilities:* bar and dining room. *Visitors:* welcome except weekends. *Society Meetings:* welcome. Professional: Brian Dunbar (0236 843015). Secretary: J.G. Timmons (0236 61440).

BELLSHILL. **Bellshill Golf Club,** Community Road, Orbiston, Bellshill ML4 2RZ (Bellshill (0698) 745124). *Location:* Bellshill to Motherwell road, turn right. Parkland course. 18 holes, 6604 yards, 6057 metres. S.S.S. 72. *Green Fees:* weekdays £11.00, weekends £15.00. *Visitors:* casual visitors welcome; parties by prior application (not competition days or Sundays). Secretary: A.M. Currie (03552 23101).

BIGGAR. **Biggar Golf Club,** Broughton Road, Biggar ML12 6HA (0899 20618). *Location:* from Edinburgh A702, from Glasgow A74 or M8, turn off at Newhouse. Flat, scenic parkland course. 18 holes, 5416 yards. S.S.S. 66. *Green Fees:* weekdays £6.50, weekends £8.50. Reductions for Juniors and Senior Citizens. *Eating facilities:* all day licence, full catering (not Mondays). *Visitors:* unrestricted, casual dress – no jeans. All weather tennis courts and caravan park. *Society Meetings:* welcome, early reservation essential. Secretary: W.S. Turnbull (0899 20319). Tee Reservations: (0899 20566).

CARLUKE. **Carluke Golf Club,** Maudslie Road, Hallcraig, Carluke ML8 5HG (0555 71070). *Location:* one and a quarter mile from Carluke cross, through Clyde Street. Parkland course. 18 holes, 5800 yards. S.S.S. 68. Practice area. *Green Fees:* £8.00 per round, £12.00 per day weekdays. *Eating facilities:* available. *Visitors:* till 4.30pm weekdays, no visitors weekends. Tuition. *Society Meetings:* by written application to the Secretary. Professional: A. Brooks (0555 51053). Secretary: J. Kyle (0555 70366).

COATBRIDGE. **Coatbridge Golf Club,** Townhead Road, Coatbridge ML5 2HX (0236 28975). *Location:* one and a half miles west of town centre. Wooded. 18 holes, 6026 yards, 5562 metres. S.S.S. 69. Large practice area. *Green Fees:* £1.75. *Eating facilities:* all catering facilities and bar facilities available. *Visitors:* no restrictions. Professional: Mr George Weir (0236 21492). Secretary: Mr Owen Dolan (0236 26811).

COATBRIDGE. **Drumpellier Golf Club,** Coatbridge (Coatbridge (0236) 28723). *Location:* one mile from town. 18 holes, 6227 yards. S.S.S. 70. *Green Fees:* £12.50 per round, £18.00 per day. *Eating facilities:* catering available except Thursdays. *Visitors:* welcome with reservation. *Society Meetings:* catered for by arrangement. Professional: I. Collins. Secretary: W. Brownlie.

DOUGLAS WATER. **Douglas Water Golf Club,** Ayr Road, Rigside, Douglas Water (055 588 361). *Location:* seven miles south-west of Lanark on A70. 9 holes, 2832 yards. S.S.S. 69. *Green Fees:* weekdays £3.50, weekends £5.00. *Eating facilities:* by arrangement. *Visitors:* welcome without reservation except Saturdays. *Society Meetings:* contact Secretary. Secretary: (0555 2295).

EAST KILBRIDE. **Torrance House Golf Club,** Strathaven Road, East Kilbride (03552 49720). *Location:* East Kilbride boundary on main Strathaven road. Parkland. 18 holes, 6423 yards. S.S.S. 71. Practice area. *Green Fees:* information on request. *Eating facilities:* bar and dining room. *Visitors:* welcome with reservation. *Society Meetings:* details on request. Professional: John Dunlop (03552 33451). Secretary: Duncan A. MacIver (03552 49720).

GARTCOSH. **Mount Ellen Golf Club,** Johnstone House, Johnstone Road, Gartcosh (Glenboig (0236) 872277). *Location:* approximately six miles north-east of Glasgow, near old Gartcosh steelworks. Parkland. 18 holes, 5525 yards. S.S.S. 68. *Green Fees:* information not available. *Eating facilities:* bar and catering. *Visitors:* welcome weekdays only. *Society Meetings:* not catered for. Professional: G. Reilly. Secretary: W.J. Dickson (041 778 7464).

HAMILTON. **Hamilton Golf Club,** Riccarton, Ferniegair, Hamilton ML3 7PZ (0698 282872). *Location:* off M74 Hamilton turn-off, one and a half miles up Larkhall road. Parkland course. 18 holes, 6700 yards. S.S.S. 70. Practice area and putting. *Green fees:* information not provided. *Eating facilities:* meals must be ordered. *Visitors:* must be accompanied by a member. *Society Meetings:* by arrangement with Secretary. Professional: M.J. Moir (0698 282324). Secretary: P. Soutar (0698 286131).

HAMILTON. **Strathclyde Park Golf Club,** Mote Hill, Hamilton (0698 66155). *Location:* five minutes from town centre. Parkland, wooded course. 9 holes, 3147 yards. S.S.S. 70. Practice area and golf range. *Green Fees:* adults approximately £1.50, Juniors/Senior Citizens 80p. *Eating facilities:* bar and cafe available within main complex. *Visitors:* book in advance through Secretary. *Society Meetings:* by arrangement with J. Rankin (0698 66155). Professional: Ken Davidson (0698 283994). Secretary: Andrew J. Duncan (0698 459201).

LANARK. **Carnwath Golf Club,** 1 Main Street, Carnwath (Carnwath (0555) 840251). Fairly hilly inland course. 18 holes, 5860 yards. S.S.S. 69. *Green Fees:* £11.00 weekdays, £13.00 Sundays and Bank Holidays. *Eating facilities:* lounge bar and dining room daily. *Visitors:* welcome Mondays, Wednesdays, Fridays and Sundays with prior booking. *Society Meetings:* catered for by prior arrangement. Secretary: G.P. Pollock (0555 4359).

LANARK. **Lanark Golf Club,** The Moor, Whitelees Road, Lanark ML11 7RX (Lanark (0555) 3219). *Location:* off A73. Tough moorland course. 18 holes, 6423 yards. S.S.S. 71. Two practice grounds. *Green Fees:* £14.00 per round, £20.00 per day weekdays. *Eating facilities:* full catering by resident chef; bar. *Visitors:* welcome daily until 4.00pm, no visitors weekends. *Society Meetings:* groups of 24 and over catered for Mondays and Tuesdays. Professional: Ron Wallace (0555 61456). Secretary: W.W. Law.

LARKHALL. **Larkhall Golf Club,** Burnhead Road, Larkhall (0698 881113). *Location:* on A74, close to M74. Parkland. 9 holes, 6684 yards. S.S.S. 72. *Green fees:* information not provided. *Eating facilities:* meals weekends; bar normal hours. *Visitors:* welcome, but check beforehand; every second Saturday course closed to visitors. Secretary: I. Gilmour (0698 881755).

LEADHILLS. **Leadhills Golf Club,** Leadhills, Biggar (0659 74222). *Location:* seven miles south of Abington on B797. This short but testing course is the highest in Britain. 9 holes, 2400 yards. S.S.S. 62. *Green Fees:* weekdays £2.50, weekends £3.50. *Eating facilities:* not available. *Visitors:* welcome any time. *Society Meetings:* welcome. Secretary: Harry Shaw.

LESMAHAGOW. **Hollandbush Golf Club,** Acretophead, Lesmahagow (Lesmahagow (0555) 893484). *Location:* off M74 between Lesmahagow and Coalburn. 18 holes, 6110 yards. S.S.S. 70. Practice area. *Green Fees:* £6.00 weekdays, £8.00 weekends. (Special tourist rates available). *Eating facilities:* meals at club. *Visitors:* welcome without restriction. *Society Meetings:* catered for. Professional: Ian Rae (0555 893646). Secretary: James Hamilton (055 582 222).

MOTHERWELL. **Colville Park Golf Club,** Jerviston Estate, Motherwell (Motherwell (0698) 63017). *Location:* one mile from station (Merry Street, Motherwell). 18 holes, 6265 yards. S.S.S. 70. *Green Fees:* information not provided. *Eating Facilities:* licensed and full catering facilities. *Visitors:* prior written arrangement or when accompanied by member. *Society Meetings:* prior written arrangement. Secretary: Mr Scott Connacher.

SHOTTS. **Shotts Golf Club,** Blairhead, Benhar Road, Shotts ML7 5BJ (Shotts (0501) 20431). *Location:* off M8 at junction B7057. Semi-flat moorland/wooded course. 18 holes, 6125 yards. S.S.S. 70. Practice area. *Green Fees:* weekdays £12.00 per day, weekends £15.00 per day. *Eating facilities:* full catering, all day licence. *Visitors:* welcome anytime except weekends or Public Holidays. *Society Meetings:* weekdays only. Professional: Gordon Graham (0501 22658). Secretary: Jack McDermott (0501 20431).

STRATHAVEN. **Strathaven Golf Club,** Overton Avenue, Glasgow Road, Strathaven ML10 6NR (Strathaven (0357) 20539). *Location:* on A726 on outskirts of town. 18 holes, 6226 yards. S.S.S. 70. *Green Fees:* please contact Secretary for information. *Eating facilities:* full catering and bar. *Visitors:* welcome weekdays, casual visitors before 4.30pm; party bookings Tuesdays only by prior arrangement. *Society Meetings:* catered for weekdays only, by prior arrangement. Professional: M.R. McCrorie (0357 21812). Secretary: A.W. Wallace (0357 20421).

UDDINGSTON. **Calderbraes Golf Club,** 57 Roundknowe Road, Uddingston (Uddingston (0698) 813425). *Location:* at end of M74, overlooking Calderpark Zoo. 9 holes, 3425 yards. S.S.S. 67. *Green Fees:* £6.00 per day. *Visitors:* welcome weekdays only. Secretary: S. McGuigan.

WISHAW. **Wishaw Golf Club,** 55 Cleland Road, Wishaw (Wishaw (0698) 372869). *Location:* centre of town, five miles from M74. Tree lined parkland course. 18 holes, 6137 yards. S.S.S. 69. Practice area. *Green Fees:* weekdays £7.50 per round, £10.50 per day; Sundays £15.50 per day. *Eating facilities:* full catering and two bars. *Visitors:* welcome before 4pm weekdays, after 11am Sundays. *Society Meetings:* by application to Secretary. Professional: J.G. Campbell (0698 358247). Secretary: J.W. Douglas (0698 351047).

If you are writing, a stamped, addressed envelope is always appreciated.

Morayshire

ELGIN. **Elgin Golf Club,** Hardhillock, Birnie Road, Elgin IV30 3SX (Elgin (0343) 542338). *Location:* one mile south of Elgin on Birnie Road. Undulating parkland, sandy subsoil. 18 holes, 6401 yards, 5853 metres. S.S.S. 71. Practice ground. *Green Fees:* weekdays £7.50 per round, £12.50 per day; weekends £10.00 per round, £15.00 per day. Discount for parties over 30 persons. *Eating facilities:* bar and catering every day. *Visitors:* no restrictions. *Society Meetings:* by arrangement with Secretary. Professional: Ian Rodger (0343 542884).

ELGIN. **Hopeman Golf Club,** Hopeman, Elgin IV30 2YA (Hopeman (0343) 830578). *Location:* 7 miles north-east of Elgin on B9012. Seaside links, with spectacular 12th hole. 18 holes, 5474 yards, 5003 metres. S.S.S. 67. *Green Fees:* weekdays £6.00 per day, weekends £9.00 per day. Reductions for Senior Citizens. *Eating facilities:* bar, catering. *Visitors:* welcome, some restrictions weekends. *Society Meetings:* by arrangement. Secretary: J. Blyth (0343 830336).

FOCHABERS. **Garmouth & Kingston Golf Club,** Garmouth, Fochabers (Speybay (0343-87) 388). *Location:* west bank of River Spey, 300 yards from North Sea. Seaside links (tidal). 18 holes, 5649 yards, 5164 metres. S.S.S. 67. *Green Fees:* £4.00 per round, £6.00 per day. Reduced fees from October to March. *Eating*

facilities: bar facilities and catering by arrangement. *Visitors:* welcome, except during local competitions. *Society Meetings:* by arrangement. Secretary: A. Robertson (0343-87 231).

FOCHABERS. **Spey Bay Golf Club,** Spey Bay Hotel, Spey Bay, Fochabers IV32 7JP (0343 820424). *Location:* four miles off A96 at Fochabers (signposted). Seaside links. 18 holes, 6059 yards. S.S.S. 69. *Green Fees:* Monday to Saturday £5.50, Sundays £7.00. *Eating facilities:* all meals available at the adjoining hotel. *Visitors:* welcome weekdays without reservation, advise prior phone call on Sundays. *Society Meetings:* catered for by prior arrangement. Special weekend terms including full board and golf available. Any enquiries to the Hotel Manager.

FORRES. **Forres Golf Club,** Muiryshade, Forres (Forres (0309) 72949). *Location:* one mile south from clock tower in town centre. Part parkland and wooded. 18 holes, 6141 yards, 5615 metres. S.S.S. 69. Practice ground and putting green. *Green Fees:* weekdays £7.00, weekends £8.00. *Eating facilities:* bar snacks, meals by arrangement. *Visitors:* welcome without reservation. *Society Meetings:* catered for on weekdays. Professional: Sandy Aird (0309 72250). Secretary: D.F. Black (0309 72949).

GRANTOWN-ON-SPEY. **Grantown-on-Spey Golf Club,** The Clubhouse, Golf Course Road, Grantown-on-Spey (Grantown-on-Spey (0479) 2079). *Location:* situated at north end of town, turn off A95, off Police Station. Parkland and woodland. 18 holes, 5745 yards. S.S.S. 67. *Green Fees:* weekdays £7.00, weekends £9.00; weekly ticket £38.00, fortnightly ticket £50.00. *Eating facilities:* bar and catering available. *Visitors:* welcome anytime during week, after 10.00am weekends. Course and clubhouse closed November to March. *Society Meetings:* catered for. Professional: W. Mitchell (0479 2398). Secretary: D. Elms (0479 2715).

LOSSIEMOUTH. **Moray Golf Club,** Stotfield Road, Lossiemouth IV31 6QS (034-381 2018). *Location:* six miles north of Elgin. Old Course 18 holes, 6643 yards, 6074 metres. S.S.S. 72. New Course 18 holes, 6005 yards, 5491 metres. S.S.S. 69. *Green Fees: on request.* *Eating facilities:* full catering and bar facilities. *Visitors:* welcome weekdays after 9.30 (not between 1pm–2pm); weekends: Saturday (New Course only), Sunday not before 10am and not between 1pm to 2pm. *Society Meetings:* all welcome. Professional: Alastair Thomson (034-381 3330). Secretary: James Hamilton (034-381 2018).

Nairnshire

NAIRN. **Nairn Dunbar Golf Club,** Lochloy Road, Nairn IV12 5AE (Nairn (0667) 52741). *Location:* on A96, one mile east of town. Seaside links. 18 holes, 6431 yards. S.S.S. 71. *Green Fees:* weekdays £10.00, weekends £12.00. *Eating facilities:* available. *Visitors:* welcome. *Society Meetings:* catered for. Professional: B. Mason (0667 53964). Secretary: Mrs S.J. MacLennan.

NAIRN. **Nairn Golf Club,** Seabank Road, Nairn IV12 4HB. *Location:* Nairn West Shore, on the southern shore of the Moray Firth, 16 miles east of Inverness, five miles from Inverness Airport. Seaside links. 18 holes, 6556 yards. S.S.S. 71. Large practice ground. *Green Fees:* weekdays £16.00 per round, weekends £20.00. *Eating facilities:* full catering service except Thursdays; two bars open 11am to 11pm. *Visitors:* welcome, no restrictions. *Society Meetings:* catered for. Professional: Robin Fyfe (0667 52787). Secretary: D. Patrick (0667 53208).

Peebles-shire

PEEBLES. **Peebles Municipal Golf Club,** Kirkland Street, Peebles (Peebles (0721) 20153 (office), (0721) 20197 (clubhouse). *Location:* 51 miles from Glasgow, off A72 at west side of town, 23 miles from Edinburgh. 18 holes, 6137 yards. S.S.S. 69. *Green Fees:* information not provided. *Eating facilities:* food available 11.30am – 7.00pm. *Visitors:* welcome. *Society Meetings:* catered for subject to prior bookings. Secretary: Mr G. Garvie, District Offices, Rosetta Road, Peebles.

WEST LINTON. **West Linton Golf Club,** West Linton EH46 7HN (0968 60463). *Location:* A702 road 17 miles south west of Edinburgh. Moorland. 18 holes, 6132 yards, 5607 metres. S.S.S. 69. Two practice areas. *Green Fees:* weekdays £9.00 per round, £11.00 per day; weekends £11.00 per round, £14.00 per day. *Eating facilities:* diningroom, lunches, high tea, morning coffee, afternoon tea and bar. *Visitors:* welcome at all times except on medal days. *Society Meetings:* catered for weekdays except Tuesdays. Professional: Douglas Stewart (0968 60256). Secretary: Grahame Scott (0968 75843).

Perthshire

ABERFELDY. **Aberfeldy Golf Club,** Taybridge Road, Aberfeldy (Aberfeldy (0887) 20535). *Location:* on A827, leave A9 at Ballinluig. 9 holes, 5466 yards. S.S.S. 67. *Green Fees:* information not provided. *Eating facilities:* snacks and bar. *Visitors:* welcome without reservation. *Society Meetings:* limited number catered for. Contact the Secretary at Aberfeldy Golf Club. Secretary: (0887 20117).

ABERFELDY. **Taymouth Castle Golf Course,** Kenmore, by Aberfeldy PH15 2NT (Kenmore (08873) 228). *Location:* six miles west of Aberfeldy. Flat parkland set in scenic mountain terrain. 18 holes, 6066 yards. S.S.S. 69. Good practice ground. *Green Fees:* weekdays, £11.00 per round, £16.00 per day; weekends and Bank Holidays, £14.00 per round, £20.00 per day. Half price for Juniors (under 15). *Eating facilities:* restaurant and bar. *Visitors:* welcome except competition days, tee reservations necessary (phone or letter). *Society Meetings:* catered for by previous arrangement only. Director of Golf/Professional and Bookings: Alex Marshall.

AUCHTERARDER. **Auchterarder Golf Club,** Orchil Road, Auchterarder PH3 1LS (Auchterarder (0764) 62804). *Location:* off A9 to south-west of town, next to Gleneagles. Flat parkland, part wooded. 18 holes, 5757 yards. S.S.S. 68. *Green Fees:* weekdays £8.50 per round, £11.00 per day; weekends £12.00 per round, £17.00 per day. *Eating facilities:* full catering and bar. *Visitors:* welcome without reservation except major competition days. *Society Meetings:* welcome, must book three months in advance. Professional: K. Salmoni (0764 63711). Secretary: J.I. Stewart (0764 63840).

AUCHTERARDER. **Gleneagles Hotel Golf Courses,** Auchterarder PH3 1NF (Auchterarder (0764) 62231). Telex 76105. *Location:* A9 from Perth, 16 miles south-west: bus meets trains at Gleneagles Station. Gleneagles offer two moorland 18 hole courses. **King's Course: 6471 yards, par 70; **Queen's Course: 5965 yards, par 68. *Green Fees:* on request. *Eating facilities:* at Dormy House (Bar & Restaurant) and The Gleneagles Hotel. *Visitors:* strictly Hotel residents. Professional: Ian Marchbank. Hotel General Manager: Ms Vivien Sirotkin (0764 62231). Golf Manager: Tom Younger (0764 63543).

BLAIRGOWRIE. **Alyth Golf Club,** Alyth, Blairgowrie (Alyth (08283) 2268). *Location:* A926 or A927 to Alyth, B958 one mile to Club (five miles from Blairgowrie/ Coupar Angus). 18 holes, 6226 yards. S.S.S. 70. *Green Fees:* weekdays £16.00 per day; weekends £20.00 per day, £16.00 per round after 3pm. *Eating facilities:* full catering facilities. *Visitors:* welcome with reservation. *Society Meetings:* catered for. Secretary: H. Sullivan.

BLAIRGOWRIE. **Blairgowrie Golf Club,** Rosemount, Blairgowrie PH10 6LG (0250 2383). *Location:* take A923 out of Perth, turn right at "Rosemount" sign. Flat wooded moorland. Rosemount Course: 18 holes, 6588 yards. S.S.S. 72. Lansdowne Course: 18 holes, 6895 yards. S.S.S. 73. Three practice grounds. Wee Course: 9 holes, 2307 yards. S.S.S. 65. *Green Fees:* weekdays £18.00 - £27.00, weekends £25.00 per round. No advance booking Wednesdays/Saturdays/Sundays. *Eating facilities:* full catering available. *Visitors:* advance booking Mon/Tues/Thurs/part Fri, 8.30am-4.00pm (through Secretary). Handicap Certificate required. *Society Meetings:* catered for by application to the Secretary. (Maximum 32 without prior permission.) Professional: Gordon Kinnoch (0250 3116). Secretary/ Manager: John N. Simpson (0250 2622).

BLAIRGOWRIE. **Dalmunzie Golf Course,** Spittal O' Glenshee, Blairgowrie PH10 7QG (025-085 226). *Location:* A93 Blairgowrie to Braemar road, left at Spittal O' Glenshee. A small well-kept hill course amid glorious scenery. 9 holes, 2035 yards. Practice area. *Green Fees:* on application. Under 7 free, 7 - 14 half price (we like young golfers.) *Eating facilities:* restaurant facilities at Dalmunzie Hotel. Bar. *Visitors:* welcome without reservation. Self-catering cottages available. *Society Meetings:* catered for. Secretary: Simon Winton.

CALLANDER. **Callander Golf Club,** Aveland Road, Callander FK17 8EN (0877 30090). *Location:* M9 (Stirling) leave by Crianlarich exit on to A84 to Callander, at east end of town, just off Main Street Golf Course. Parkland, partly wooded with panoramic views. 18 holes, 5125 yards. S.S.S. 66. Practice ground. *Green Fees:* weekdays £9.00 per round, £11.00 per day; weekends £13.00 per round, £17.00 per day. *Eating facilities:* full catering and bar always available. *Visitors:* welcome without reservation. *Society Meetings:* welcome, arrange with Secretary. Professional: W. Kelly (0877 30975). Secretary: J. McClements (0877 30090). Booking Secretary: 10.00am to 2.00pm (0877 30090), 7.00pm to 9.00pm (0877 30866).

CRIEFF. **Comrie Golf Club,** Comrie (Comrie (0764) 70544). *Location:* six miles from Crieff on Crieff/ Lochearnhead road at east end of Comrie village. 9 holes, 5966 yards. S.S.S. 69. *Green Fees:* weekdays £6.00, weekends £7.00. *Eating facilities:* light refreshments during summer months. *Visitors:* welcome without reservation. *Society Meetings:* by arrangement with Secretary. Professional: Hunter Donaldson. Secretary: D.G. McGlashan (0764 70544).

CRIEFF. **Crieff Golf Club,** Perth Road, Crieff PH7 3LR (Crieff (0764) 2909). *Location:* A85 north-east outskirts of Crieff. Ferntower Course - 18 holes, 6402 yards. S.S.S. 71. Dornock Course - 9 holes, 2386 yards. S.S.S. 63. Two practice areas. *Green Fees:* Ferntower: weekdays £12.00 per round, £20.00 per day; weekends £15.00 per round, £22.00 per day. Dornock - per 18 holes: weekdays £8.00; weekends £9.00. *Eating facilities:* full restaurant facilities by arrangement (phone 0764 2397) and bar snacks. *Visitors:* welcome with reservation, prior arrangement advisable by phone. *Society Meetings:* book by phone and confirm in writing. Senior Professional: John Stark (0764 2909). Club Professional: David Murchie. Secretary: L.J. Rundle (0764 3300).

CRIEFF. **Muthill Golf Club,** Peat Road, Muthill, Crieff PH5 2AD (076481 523). *Location:* 500 yards off main Crieff/Stirling road at west end of village. Parkland (noted for panoramic views of Strathearn). 9 holes, 2350 yards. S.S.S. 63 for 18 holes. *Green Fees:* £5.00 per day. *Eating facilities:* none, tea, coffee, soft drinks only. *Visitors:* restricted when competitions and matches are being played, notice displayed at clubhouse. Changing and toilet facilities available. Secretary: W.H. Gordon (0764 3319).

CRIEFF. **St. Fillans Golf Club,** South Loch Earn Road, St. Fillans PH6 2NG (St. Fillans (0764-85) 312). *Location;* thirteen miles west of Crieff on A85 between Crieff and Lochearnhead. M9 nearest motorway. Parkland with one small hill. 9 holes, 5268 yards. S.S.S. 66 (18 holes). Practice green. *Green Fees:* weekdays £6.00 per day, weekends £7.00. *Eating facilities:* light meals, teas, coffees, snacks. No bar. *Visitors:* welcome at all times. *Society Meetings:* welcome with advance booking (not July and August). Hon. Professional: John Stark. Secretary: A.J.N. Abercrombie (0764 3643).

DUNBLANE. **Dunblane New Golf Club,** Perth Road, Dunblane (Dunblane (0786) 822343). *Location:* six miles north of Stirling on main road north. 18 holes, 5876 yards. S.S.S. 68. *Green Fees:* information not provided. *Eating facilities:* available at clubhouse. *Visitors:* welcome with reservation. *Society Meetings:* catered for weekdays only. Professional: R.M. Jamieson. Secretary: Mr J.C. Allan.

DUNKELD. **Dunkeld and Birnam Golf Club,** Fungarth, Dunkeld PH8 0HU (Dunkeld (03502) 524). *Location:* turn right one mile north of Dunkeld on A9. Heathland course with panoramic views, testing. 9 holes, 5264 yards. S.S.S. 66. *Green Fees:* weekdays £7.00 per round, £9.00 per day; weekends £12.00. *Eating facilities:* meals available and bar. *Visitors:* welcome. *Society Meetings:* catered for. Secretary: Mrs W.A. Sinclair (03502 564).

DUNNING. **Dunning Golf Club,** Rollo Park, Dunning. *Location:* off A9, nine miles south west Perth. Parkland. 9 holes, 4836 yards. S.S.S. 64. *Green Fees:* £5.00. Juniors £2.50. *Eating facilities:* soft drinks, crisps, sweets. *Visitors:* no play before 1pm Sundays, no visitors after 5pm weekdays, no visitors before 4pm Saturday unless accompanied by a member. *Society Meetings:* welcome weekdays. Secretary: Miss C. Westwood (076484 312).

KILLIN. **Killin Golf Club,** Killin Golf Course, Killin (Killin (056-72) 312). 9 holes, 2865 yards. S.S.S. 65. *Green Fees:* information available on request at clubhouse. *Eating facilities:* light snacks. *Visitors:* welcome. *Society Meetings:* catered for during May, June, September and October. Secretary: Mr John Blyth.

PERTH. **Craigie Hill Golf Club (1982) Ltd,** Cherrybank, Perth PH2 0NE (Perth (0738) 24377). *Location:* at west end of town, easy access from M90 and A9. Hilly course with lovely scenery. 18 holes, 5379 yards. S.S.S. 66. Practice ground and putting green. *Green Fees:* weekdays £7.00 per round, £10.00 per day, weekends £12.00 per day. Visitors with member £2.00, Juniors (weekdays) £1.50. *Eating facilities:* full catering and bars. *Visitors:* welcome Mondays to Fridays and Sundays. *Society Meetings:* catered for. Professional: Frank L. Smith (0738 22644). Secretary: William A. Miller (0738 20829).

PERTH. **King James VI Golf Club,** Moncrieffe Island, Perth PH2 8NR (Perth (0738) 25170). Starter (0738 32460). Parkland course. 18 holes, 6026 yards. S.S.S. 69. *Green Fees:* weekdays £11.00, weekends £15.00. *Eating facilities:* lunches and high teas available. *Visitors:* welcome without reservation. *Society Meetings:* catered for by prior arrangement. Fully stocked golf shop. Professional: Tony Coles (0738 32460). Secretary: Dorothy Barraclough (0738 32460).

PITLOCHRY. **Blair Atholl Golf Club,** Blair Atholl, Pitlochry (Blair Atholl (0796) 81407). *Location:* off A9, seven miles north of Pitlochry. Flat parkland. 9 holes. S.S.S. 69. Clubs for hire. *Green Fees:* weekdays £6.00 per day, weekends £7.00 per day. *Eating facilities:* bar meals and snacks. *Visitors:* welcome at all times. *Society Meetings:* by arrangement with Secretary. Secretary: Mr J.A. McGregor (0796 81274).

PITLOCHRY. **Pitlochry Golf Course,** Pitlochry (Pitlochry (0796) 2792). *Location:* half mile from centre of Pitlochry on A9. 18 holes, 5811 yards, S.S.S. 68. *Green Fees:* 1st April to 31st October: weekdays £11.00 per day (£3.00 juniors), £6.00 per round after 5pm; Saturdays £14.00 per day (£5.00 juniors), £9.00 per round, £6.00 after 5pm; Sundays £14.00 per day, £9.00 per round, £6.00 after 5pm. Restricted course (1st November to 31st March). Day ticket (any day) Adult £5.00, Junior £1.50. *Eating facilities:* catering and refreshments available in licensed clubhouse, except mid-October to end of March. *Visitors:* welcome. Caddy cars available for hire. *Society Meetings:* catered for. Professional: James Wilson (0796 2792). Secretary: D.C.M. McKenzie (0796 2114 for Group bookings).

PUBLISHER'S NOTE

While every effort is made to ensure accuracy, we regret that FHG Publications cannot accept responsibility for errors, omissions or misrepresentation in our entries or any consequences thereof. Prices in particular should be checked because we go to press early. We will follow up complaints, but cannot act as arbiters or agents for either party.

— THE —
MURRAYSHALL
COUNTRY HOUSE HOTEL,
RESTAURANT AND
GOLF COURSE

SCONE, PERTH, SCOTLAND
Tel: 0738 51171. Fax: 0738 52595

19 Bedrooms with immaculate 18 Hole Par 73
Golf Course. A variety of Holes, Tree Lined
Fairways and Water Holes, all make a real
sporty challenge to the discerning Golfer.
Green Fees   £15.00 – £35.00
Golf Societies, Company Golf Days welcome
Golf Packages available
Telephone for our Brochure and Tariff

SCONE. **Murrayshall Golf Course,** Murrayshall, Scone PH2 7PH (0738 51171). *Location:* three miles north of Perth on Coupar Angus road. Undulating wooded parkland. 18 holes, 6460 yards. S.S.S. 70. Golf range. *Green Fees:* £12.00 per round, £18.00 per day weekdays; £15.00 per round, £25.00 per day weekends. *Eating facilities:* full catering service every day. *Visitors:* welcome at all times, no restrictions – advance booking advisable. Hotel. *Society Meetings:* welcome at all times by prior arrangement. Professional: Neil I.M. Mackintosh (0738 52784).

STRATHTAY. **Strathtay Golf Club,** Strathtay. *Location:* from A9 four miles west from Ballinluig, four miles east of Aberfeldy. Wooded hilly course with beautiful views. 9 holes, 4082 yards. S.S.S. 63. *Green Fees:* information not provided. *Eating facilities:* local hotel and cafe nearby. *Visitors:* no restrictions except at competition times (mostly Sundays). Very young (pre-teenage) require adult with them. *Society Meetings:* notice required. Secretary: J.B. Armstrong-Payne (08874 367).

Renfrewshire

BARRHEAD. **Fereneze Golf Club,** Fereneze Avenue, Barrhead, Glasgow (041-881 1519). *Location:* nine miles south west of Glasgow. 18 holes, 5821 yards. S.S.S. 68. *Green Fees:* on application. *Eating facilities:* lunches served at club except Mondays, order in advance. *Visitors:* welcome by arrangement. *Society Meetings:* welcome, bookings arranged in advance. Professional: Andrew Armstrong.

BISHOPTON. **Erskine Golf Club,** Bishopton PA7 5PH (0505 862302). *Location:* north of M8, leave M8 at Bridge Toll barrier and turn left along B815 for one mile approximately. Parkland course. 18 holes, 6298 yards. S.S.S. 70. Putting green and practice area. *Green Fees:* £13.00 per round, £20.00 per day ticket. *Eating facilities:* restaurant and bar, lunches, teas and dinners served at club. *Visitors:* welcome but must play with a member or be introduced. Professional: Peter Thomson. Secretary: T.A. McKillop.

BRIDGE OF WEIR. **Ranfurly Castle Golf Club Ltd,** Golf Road, Bridge of Weir PA11 3HN (0505 612609). *Location:* M8 from Glasgow exit junction 29, A240 and A761 to Bridge of Weir. Moorland. 18 holes, 6284 yards. S.S.S. 70. Practice ground. *Green Fees:* weekdays £16.00 per round, £22.00 day ticket. *Eating facilities:* snack lunches, high teas, etc by arrangement. *Visitors:* welcome weekdays, at weekends only if accompanied by member. *Society Meetings:* catered for weekdays (preferably Tuesdays). Professional: (0505 614795). Secretary: Mr J. Walker (0505 612609).

ELDERSLIE. **Elderslie Golf Club,** 63 Main Road, Elderslie PA5 9AZ (0505 22835). *Location:* off M8 at Linwood turn-off, left at roundabout, continue along Linwood Road to main traffic lights, right at traffic lights. Woodland course. 18 holes, 6031 yards. S.S.S. 69. Putting green and practice areas. *Green Fees:* information not provided. *Eating facilities:* restaurant and bar. No catering on Thursdays. *Visitors:* welcome weekdays until 3.30 p.m., booking preferable. *Society Meetings:* welcome weekdays, book through Secretary. Professional: Gary Weir (0505 20032). Secretary: Mr W. Muirhead (0505 23956).

GOUROCK. **Gourock Golf Club,** Cowal View, Gourock (0475 31001). *Location:* two miles west of Gourock Station above Yacht Club. 18 holes, 6492 yards. S.S.S. 71. *Green Fees:* on application. *Eating facilities:* restaurant, full meals also bar snacks. *Visitors:* welcome with letter of introduction. *Society Meetings:* catered for on application. Professional: Robert M. Collinson. Secretary: C.M. Campbell.

GREENOCK. **Greenock Golf Club,** Forsyth Street, Greenock PA16 8RE (0475 20793). *Location:* one mile from town centre. Moorland course. 18 holes, 5835 yards. S.S.S. 68. *Green Fees:* £10.00 per round weekdays, £15.00 per day weekends. *Eating facilities:* available. *Visitors:* welcome weekdays, not Saturdays. *Society Meetings:* advance booking required. Professional: Graham Ross (0475 87236). Secretary: Eric J. Black (0475 26819).

GREENOCK. **Greenock Whinhill Golf Club,** Beith Road, Greenock (0475 24694). *Location:* 26 miles from Glasgow. Municipal course. 18 holes, 5454 yards. S.S.S. 68. *Green fees:* information not provided. Secretary: D. McConnell.

JOHNSTONE. **Cochrane Castle Golf Club,** Craigston, Johnstone PA5 0HF (0505 22010). *Location:* A737 off Beith Road, Johnstone. Parkland course. 18 holes, 6226 yards. S.S.S. 70. Practice ground. *Green Fees:* weekdays £13.00 per day, £8.00 per round. *Eating facilities:* full catering and bar snacks. *Visitors:* welcome weekdays, maximum 32 players. *Society Meetings:* catered for by arrangement, weekdays only. Professional: Stuart H. Campbell (0505 28465). Secretary: J.C. Cowan (0505 20146).

KILMACOLM. **Kilmacolm Golf Club,** Porterfield Road, Kilmacolm PA13 4PD (Kilmacolm (050 587) 2139). *Location:* A761. Moorland course. 18 holes, 5964 yards. S.S.S. 68. Practice area. *Green Fees:* £11.00 per round, £17.00 per day. *Eating facilities:* diningroom and bar. *Visitors:* welcome on weekdays. *Society Meetings:* catered for. Professional: D. Stewart (050 587 2695). Secretary: R.F. McDonald.

LANGBANK. **Gleddoch Golf and Country Club,** Langbank PA14 6YG (047554 304). *Location:* M8 west of Glasgow, past airport to Langbank, Langbank and Gleddoch House are both signposted. Moorland, woodland and parkland. 18 holes, 6332 yards. S.S.S. 71. Practice area, indoor driving bay and putting green. *Green Fees:* £16.50 day ticket. *Eating facilities:* bar, lounge and restaurant open all day. *Visitors:* welcome all week. Gleddoch House Hotel, 33 bedrooms. *Society Meetings:* welcome weekdays only. Professional: Keith Campbell (047554 704). Secretary: Tom McCartan (047554 304).

LOCHWINNOCH. **Lochwinnoch Golf Club,** Burnfoot Road, Lochwinnoch PA12 4AN (0505 842153). *Location:* between Johnstone and Beith, off A737 on Largs road A760. Parkland, extremely scenic, set in quiet country village. 18 holes, 6202 yards. S.S.S. 70. *Green Fees:* weekdays £7.00 per round, £9.00 per day; weekends £8.00 per round, £10.00 per day. *Eating facilities:* licensed bar and catering, except Mondays. *Visitors:* welcome every day, although weekends may be too busy. *Society Meetings:* welcome weekdays, telephone or write to the Secretary. Professional: Gerry

Reilly (0505 843029). Secretary: Mrs Evelyn McBride (0505 842153).

PAISLEY. **Barshaw Park Golf Course (Municipal),** Glasgow Road, Paisley (041-889 2908). *Location:* one mile from Paisley Cross travelling east towards Glasgow (Glasgow Road). Parkland course. 18 holes, 5703 yards. S.S.S. 68. *Green Fees:* £2.70, O.A.Ps and Juniors £1.35. *Eating facilities:* none. *Visitors:* welcome anytime, must have a bag of clubs. *Society Meetings:* apply to Superintendent Parks Department (Leisure and Recreation). Secretary: Mr W. Collins (041-884 2533).

PAISLEY. **Paisley Golf Club,** Braehead, Paisley PA2 8TZ (041-884 2292). *Location:* up Causeyside Street, Neilston Road, turn right into Glenburn, left at roundabout. Moorland course. 18 holes, 6424 yards. S.S.S. 71. Practice area. *Green Fees:* weekdays £10.00 per round, £14.00 per day. *Eating facilities:* bar snacks and full meals. *Visitors:* welcome with reservation (except weekends, Bank Holidays and weekdays after 4.00pm). *Society Meetings:* catered for by prior arrangement. Secretary: W.J. Cunningham (041-884 3903).

PAISLEY. **Ralston Golf Club,** Strathmore Avenue, Ralston, Paisley (041-882 1349). *Location:* two miles east of Paisley. *Green Fees:* information not provided. *Visitors:* welcome by introduction by members only. *Society Meetings:* catered for on application. Professional: Derek Barbour. Secretary: John W. Home.

PORT GLASGOW. **Port Glasgow Golf Club,** Devol Road, Port Glasgow PA14 5XE (0475 704181). *Location:* M8 to Newark Castle to roundabout, follow signs for Industrial Estate. Heathland. 18 holes, 5712 yards, 5224 metres. S.S.S. 68. *Green Fees:* weekdays £8.00 per round, £12.00 per day. *Eating facilities:* meals by arrangement. *Visitors:* welcome weekdays until 4 pm, weekends must be introduced. *Society Meetings:* welcome weekdays. Secretary: N.L. Mitchell. (0475 706273).

RENFREW. **Renfrew Golf Club,** Blythswood Estate, Inchinnan Road, Renfrew PA4 9EG (041-886 6692). *Location:* A8 Renfrew, turn in at Stakis Normandy Hotel. Wooded parkland with featured rivers. 18 holes, 6818 yards, 6231 metres. S.S.S. 73. Small practice

area. *Green Fees:* weekdays £14.00 per round, £22.00 per two rounds. No green fees accepted at weekends. *Eating facilities:* daily restaurant facilities and bar. *Visitors:* welcome on introduction by members. Visiting parties by arrangement. *Society Meetings:* catered for by written application to Secretary. Golf Shop: Mr David Grant (041-885 1754). Secretary: Andrew Kerr.

UPLAWMOOR. **Caldwell Golf Club,** Uplawmoor, Glasgow G78 (050 585 329). *Location:* five miles south of Barrhead, Glasgow on A736 Irvine Road. Parkland/moorland. 18 holes, 6046 yards. S.S.S. 69. Practice area. *Green Fees:* £10.00 per round, £15.00 per day weekdays. *Eating facilities:* everyday bar menu – filled rolls on Thursdays. *Visitors:* welcome weekdays only before 4.30pm. *Society Meetings:* weekdays only. Professional: Keith Baxter (050 585 616). Secretary: Mr Donald McLean (041-333 9770).

Ross-shire

ALNESS. **Alness Golf Club,** Ardross Road, Alness (0349 883877). *Location:* on A9 ten miles north east of Dingwall. 9 holes, 2359 yards (twice round 4718 yards). S.S.S. 63. *Green Fees:* weekdays, Adults (day ticket) £3.00, Juniors £1.25, O.A.Ps £2.00; weekends and Bank Holidays Adults (day ticket) £4.00, Juniors £1.50, O.A.Ps £3.00. *Eating facilities;* licensed bar and snacks served. *Visitors:* welcome without reservation. *Society Meetings:* catered for if notice given. Secretary: J.G. Miller (0349 883877).

FEARN. **Tarbat Golf Club,** Portmahomack, Fearn IV20 17B (086 287 273). *Location:* ten miles east of Tain. B9165 off A9. Seaside links course. 9 holes, 4657 yards, 4219 metres. S.S.S. 63. Practice area. *Green Fees:* £4.00, no Sunday golf. *Eating facilities:* local hotels. *Visitors:* welcome without reservation. *Society Meetings:* by arrangement. Secretary: D. Wilson (086·287 236).

FORTROSE. **Fortrose and Rosemarkie Golf Club,** Ness Road East, Fortrose (Fortrose (0381) 20529). *Location:* on the Black Isle. A9 north from Inverness, across Kessock Bridge, through Munlochy, follow signs to Fortrose. Good links course, sea both sides. 18 holes, 5462 yards. S.S.S. 69. *Green Fees:* weekdays £8.50 per round, weekends £10.00 per round. *Eating facilities:* bar snacks available all year round. *Visitors:* welcome without reservation. *Society Meetings:* catered for. Professional: George Hampton (0381 20733). Secretary: Mrs M. Collier.

GAIRLOCH. **Gairloch Golf Club,** Gairloch IV21 2BE (Gairloch (0445) 2407). *Location:* 75 miles west of Inverness on the A832. Seaside links, extensive views. 9 holes, 2093 yards, 1770 metres. S.S.S. 63 over 18 holes. *Green Fees:* daily £6.00, weekly £25.00. No Sunday golf. *Visitors:* welcome without reservation. Secretary: B. Lawrence (0445 2407).

INVERGORDON. **Invergordon Golf Club,** King George Street, Invergordon (0349 852715). *Location:* two miles from A9. 9 holes, 3000 yards. S.S.S. 69 over 18 holes. *Green fees:* information not provided. *Eating facilities:* bar lunches. New clubhouse with bar facilities. Changing rooms with showers. *Visitors:* welcome without reservation. *Society Meetings:* catered for. Secretary: Bruce Gibson.

MUIR OF ORD. **Muir of Ord Golf Club,** Great North Road, Muir of Ord IV6 7SX (0463 870825). *Location:* 15 miles north of Inverness beside A862, 12 miles north of Inverness on A9/A832. Heathland, moorland course, five holes hilly, excellent greens. 18 holes, 5202 yards. *Green Fees:* October to March weekdays £6.00, weekends £7.00; April to September weekdays £7.00, weekends £8.00. *Eating facilities:* snacks, bar lunches or full meals. *Visitors:* visiting parties welcome. *Society Meetings:* catered for. Administrator: Mrs C. Moir.

STRATHPEFFER. **Strathpeffer Spa Golf Club,** Strathpeffer IV14 9AS (0997 21219). *Location:* 20 minutes north of Inverness by A9, five miles west of

Dingwall, quarter of a mile north of Strathpeffer Square (signposted). Upland course, panoramic views of moorland and mountain. No bunkers but plenty of natural hazards. 18 holes, 4792 yards. S.S.S. 65. Small practice area. *Green Fees:* £6.00 per round, £8.00 per day. Weekly (Monday to Friday) £20.00. Groups of 10 or over £4.50 per day. *Eating facilities:* snacks, morning coffee, lunches, high teas except Mondays. Bar open seven days. *Visitors:* welcome without reservation, but check weekends and competition days. *Society Meetings:* catered for by arrangement. Secretary: Norman Roxburgh (0997 21396).

TAIN. **Tain Golf Club,** The Clubhouse, Tain IV19 1PA (Tain (0862) 2314). *Location:* A9, 36 miles north of Inverness. Travelling north, turn right in middle of High Street - Golf Club one mile. Parkland and seaside links. 18 holes, 6207 yards. S.S.S. 70. *Green Fees:* weekdays £7.50 per round, £11.00 per day; weekends £8.50 per round, £13.00 per day. Special rates for parties over 10. *Eating facilities:* morning coffee, lunch, snacks available at clubhouse. Seven-day licence. *Visitors:* welcome subject to availability of tee. More tee time available weekdays. *Society Meetings:* catered for. Secretary: W.W. Russell.

Roxburghshire

HAWICK. **Hawick Golf Club,** Vertish Hill, Hawick (0450 72293). *Location:* north along A7 from Carlisle for 40 miles or south on A7 from Edinburgh for 50 miles. Wooded parkland, 18 holes, 5929 yards. S.S.S. 69. *Green Fees:* weekdays £6.00 per round, £9.00 per day; weekends £10.00 per day only. Visiting parties £18.00 per day, including meals. *Eating facilities:* available all day. *Visitors:* welcome without reservation. *Society Meetings:* catered for. Hon. Secretary: G.A. Rennie (0450 76945).

HAWICK. **Minto Golf Club,** Denholm, Hawick (Hawick (0450) 87220). *Location:* five miles north-east of Hawick leaving A698 at Denholm. Wooded parkland. 18 holes, 5460 yards. S.S.S. 68. Practice ground. *Green Fees:* weekdays £7.00, weekends £10.00. *Eating facilities:* available. *Visitors:* welcome. *Society Meetings:* catered for. Secretary: Mrs E. Mitchell (0450 72180).

KELSO. **Kelso Golf Club,** Berrymoss, Kelso (0573 23009). *Location:* one mile north-east of town within Kelso Racecourse. Flat parkland within racecourse. 18 holes, 6066 yards. S.S.S. 69. Practice ground. *Green Fees:* weekdays £7.00 per round, £10.00 per day; weekends £8.00 per round, £12.00 per day. *Eating facilities:* catering Wednesday to Sunday. *Visitors:* welcome without reservation. *Society Meetings:* welcome with reservation. Secretary: J.P. Payne (0573 23259).

MELROSE. **Melrose Golf Club,** Dingleton, Melrose (Melrose (089 682) 2855). *Location:* A68 or A7 from Edinburgh/Carlisle. Wooded/hilly course. 9 holes, 5579 yards, 5098 metres. S.S.S. 68. *Green Fees:* weekdays £5.00, weekends £6.00. Half price if playing with a member. *Eating facilities:* at restricted times. *Visitors:* welcome anytime when no competitions taking place. *Society Meetings:* catered for. Secretary: W.G. MacRae (089-682 2855).

MELROSE. **St. Boswells Golf Club** St. Boswells, Melrose TD6 0AT (0835 22359). *Location:*quarter of a mile off trunk route A68 at St. Boswells Green. Flat attractive scenery along the banks of the River Tweed. 9 holes, 5206 yards. S.S.S. 65. *Green Fees:* weekdays £5.00 per round/day, weekends £6.00 per round/day. *Visitors:* welcome without reservation except for groups which should contact Secretary. Secretary: G.B. Ovens (0835 22359).

NEWCASTLETON. **Newcastleton Golf Club,** Holm Hill, Newcastleton. *Location:* A7 Carlisle to Hawick road, Newcastleton is on B6357. Hilly course with splendid views. 9 holes, 2884 yards. S.S.S. 72. *Green Fees:* £3.00. *Eating facilities:* not available. *Visitors:* welcome, no restrictions. *Society Meetings:* welcome. Secretary: F.J. Ewart (03873 75257).

Selkirkshire

GALASHIELS. **Galashiels Golf Club,** Ladhope Recreation Ground, Galashiels TD1 2JJ (Galashiels (0896) 3724). *Location:* north east of town, quarter of a mile off A7. Parkland, hilly – municipal course. 18 holes, 5309 yards. S.S.S. 67. Practice area. *Green Fees:* weekdays £5.00, weekends £5.70. *Eating facilities:* bar and bar snacks; bar open 7.30pm. *Visitors:* welcome without restriction. *Society Meetings:* catered for. Professional: (0896 3431). Secretary: W.D. Millar (0750 21669).

GALASHIELS. **Torwoodlee Golf Club,** Edinburgh Road, Galashiels (Galashiels (0896) 2260). *Location:* leave Galashiels on A7 for Edinburgh, entrance to course one mile on left. Parkland, with splendid par 5 designed by Braid. 9 holes, 5720 yards. S.S.S. 68. *Green Fees:* weekdays £8.00, weekends £10.00 per round. *Eating facilities:* bar, dining room. *Visitors:* welcome without reservation. *Society Meetings:* catered for weekdays. Secretary: A. Wilson (089-682 2146).

SELKIRK. **Selkirk Golf Club,** Selkirk Hills, Selkirk (Selkirk (0750) 20621). *Location:* one mile south of Selkirk on A7 road. Undulating parkland. 9 holes, 5560 yards. S.S.S. 67. *Green Fees:* under review. *Eating facilities:* lounge bar. *Visitors:* welcome without reservation. *Society Meetings:* catered for. Secretary: R. Davies (0750 20427).

Stirlingshire

DRYMEN. **Strathendrick Golf Club,** Glasgow Road, Drymen, Glasgow G63 (0360 40582). *Location:* one mile south of Drymen on Glasgow Road. Inland – hilly course. 9 holes, 4962 yards. S.S.S. 65. *Green Fees:* information not provided. *Visitors:* accompanied by a member welcome all week, restrictions on competition days. Secretary: Ronald H. Smith (0360 40582).

FALKIRK. **Bonnybridge Golf Club,** Larbert Road, Bonnybridge FK4 1NV (0324 812822). *Location:* five miles west of Falkirk. Parkland. 9 holes, 6060 yards. S.S.S. 69. *Green Fees:* information not provided. *Eating facilities:* bar facilities available seven days, catering facilities available weekends only. *Visitors:* welcome with prior arrangement for visitors from outwith Scotland, otherwise must be accompanied by a member. *Society Meetings:* not catered for. Secretary: J.J. Keilt (0324 822697).

FALKIRK. **Falkirk Golf Club,** 136 Stirling Road, Camelon, Falkirk (Falkirk (0324) 611061). *Location:* one and a half miles west of town centre on A9. Parkland with streams. 18 holes, 6267 yards. S.S.S. 69. Large practice area. *Green Fees:* weekdays £7.50 per round, £12.00 per day. *Eating facilities:* full catering and bar facilities. *Visitors:* welcome Monday to Friday up to 4.00pm unaccompanied, with member only at weekends. *Society Meetings:* weekdays only except Wednesday (after 10.30am), arrangements with Clubmaster. Secretary: A. Bennie (0324 21388 or 031-557 6868).

FALKIRK. **Polmont Golf Club,** 56 Manvelrigg, Maddiston, Falkirk (Polmont (0324) 711277). *Location:* first turn to the right past fire brigade headquarters in Maddiston. Undulating course. 9 holes. 6603 yards. S.S.S. 70. *Green Fees:* Monday to Friday £3.00 per day, Saturday £4.00 per day, Sunday £5.00 per day. *Eating facilities:* lunches and high teas. *Visitors:* welcome without reservation. *Society Meetings:* catered for. Secretary: Peter Lees (0324 713811).

LARBERT **Falkirk Tryst Golf Club,** 86 Burnhead Road, Stenhousemuir, Larbert FK5 4BD (Larbert (0324) 562415). *Location:* three miles from Falkirk (M9), one mile from Larbert Station. Flat/seaside links style surface. 18 holes, 6053 yards, 5533 metres. S.S.S. 69. Practice area. *Green Fees:* £13.00 per day weekdays. *Eating facilities:* full catering – lunches, high teas, bar service. *Visitors:* welcome weekdays except Wednesday, not weekends. *Society Meetings:* catered for Tuesdays, Thursdays and Fridays only. Professional: Donald Slicer (0324 562091). Secretary: J.A. Stevenson (0324 562054).

LARBERT. **Glenbervie Golf Club Ltd,** Stirling Road, Larbert FK5 4SJ (Larbert (0324) 562983). *Location:* one mile north of Larbert on A9 Falkirk to Stirling road. Parkland course. 18 holes, 6469 yards, 5873 metres. S.S.S. 71. Two practice areas. *Green Fees:* £15.00 one round, £20.00 for day ticket. *Eating facilities:* lunches and high teas available, bar. *Visitors:* welcome weekdays only with reservation, letter of introduction. Weekends as members' guests only. *Society Meetings:* up to 40 competitors catered for, Tuesdays and Thursdays only. Professional: George McKay (0324 562725). Secretary: Mrs Mary Purves (0324 562605).

LENNOXTOWN. **Campsie Golf Club,** Crow Road, Lennoxtown, Glasgow G65 7HX (0360 310244). *Location:* on B822 out of Lennoxtown. Hillside course with panoramic views. 18 holes, 5517 yards, 5045 metres. S.S.S. 67. Practice fairway and putting green. *Green fees:* weekdays £6.50 per round, weekends £10.00 per round. Reduced rates for pre-booked parties of over 12. *Eating facilities:* full catering available for parties. *Visitors:* welcome, weekdays unrestricted, weekends by prior arrangement. *Society Meetings:* catered for. Secretary: J. M. Donaldson (0360 312249).

POLMONT. **Grangemouth Golf Club,** Polmont Hill, Polmont FK2 0YE (0324 711500). *Location:* M9, off Lothallan roundabout, near Grangemouth. Mixed course. 18 holes, 6033 yards. S.S.S. 71. *Green Fees:* weekdays £5.00 per round, £8.00 per day, weekends £5.75 per round, £10.00 per day. Reductions for juniors and OAP's. *Eating facilities:* available all day. *Visitors:* welcome, bookings preferred; golf shoes must be worn. *Society Meetings:* by arrangement through Professional. Professional: Stuart Campbell (0324 714355). Secretary: J.H. Black (0324 483842).

STIRLING. **Aberfoyle Golf Club,** Braeval, Aberfoyle, By Stirling FK8 3UY (Aberfoyle (08772) 493). *Location:* A81 Glasgow – Stirling. Parkland. 18 holes, 5204 yards. S.S.S. 66. Practice facilities available. *Green Fees:* £12.00. *Eating facilities:* catering by arrangement, bar facilities all day in Summer. *Visitors:* welcome anytime but must not tee off before 9.30am at weekends. Secretary: Alan McDonald (08772 441).

STIRLING. **Bridge Of Allan Golf Club,** Sunnylaw, Bridge of Allan (Bridge of Allan (0786) 832332). *Location:* from Stirling, three miles, turn right at Bridge, keep taking the high road. Hilly course. 9 holes, 2462 yards. S.S.S. 65. *Green Fees:* weekdays £5.00,

weekends £7.00. *Eating facilities:* by arrangement. *Visitors:* welcome without reservation, no visitors on Saturdays. *Society Meetings:* catered for by arrangement. Secretary: J.C. Whaley (0786 833914).

STIRLING. **Stirling Golf Club,** Queen's Road, Stirling (Stirling (0786) 73801). *Location:* one mile from town centre, rail and bus stations; two miles from Junction 10 M9. Parkland with superb panoramic views. 18 holes, 6095 yards. S.S.S. 69. Practice area. *Green Fees:* weekdays £12.00 per round, £18.00 per day; weekends £15.00 per round, £22.00 per day. *Eating facilities:* dining area, mixed lounge, men's bar. *Visitors:* welcome except Saturdays. *Society Meetings:* catered for except weekends. Professional: John Chillas (0786 71490). Secretary: W. McArthur (0786 64098).

STIRLING. **Tillicoultry Golf Club,** Alva Road, Tillicoultry FK13 6EB (Tillicoultry (0259) 50124). *Location:* on A91, nine miles from Stirling. Parkland. 9 holes, 5358 yards. S.S.S. 66. *Green Fees:* weekdays £4.00 per round, £6.00 per day; weekends £6.00 per round, £8.00 per day. *Eating facilities:* licensed bar, snacks; meals by prior arrangement. *Visitors:* welcome at all times outwith competitions. No children under 15 weekends until 4.00pm. *Society Meetings:* catered for on application to the Secretary. Secretary: R. Whitehead (0259 51337).

TORRANCE. **Balmore Golf Club,** Balmore, Torrance (041-332 0392). *Location:* A803 then A807 from Glasgow. 18 holes, 5641 yards. S.S.S. 67. *Green Fees:* information not provided. *Eating facilities:* full service available. *Visitors:* welcome if introduced by member. *Society Meetings:* catered for. Secretary: G. P. Woolard.

Sutherland

BONAR BRIDGE. **Bonar Bridge-Ardgay Golf Club,** Migdale Road, Bonar Bridge. *Location:* driving north cross Bonar Bridge, straight up hill for half-a-mile. Mainly flat wood and heathland. 9 holes, 4626 yards. S.S.S. 63. *Green Fees:* £4.00 per day. Reduced rates for week/fortnight. *Eating facilities:* not available. *Visitors:* always welcome. *Society Meetings:* limited. Joint Secretaries: A. Turner (054 982 248), H. Sutherland, 8 Carron Place, Ardgay, Sutherland IV24 3BQ.

BRORA. **Brora Golf Club,** Golf Road, Brora KW9 6QS (0408 21417). *Location:* approximately 65 miles north of Inverness on the A9. Seaside links, 18 holes, 6110 yards. S.S.S. 69. Practice ground available. *Green Fees:* £8.00 per day, £35.00 per week, £45.00 per fortnight, £50.00 for three weeks, £60.00 per month. *Eating facilities:* lunches and snacks May to August. *Visitors:* welcome, only restriction on tournament days. Welcome to participate in opens with

Certificate of Handicap. *Society Meetings:* catered for by arrangement. Secretary: Iain G. Smith (0408 21417).

DORNOCH. **Royal Dornoch Golf Club,** The Clubhouse, Golf Road, Dornoch (Dornoch (0862) 810219). *Location:* one mile from A9 to Wick. Links course. 18 holes, 6577 yards, 6014 metres. S.S.S. 72. Practice area. *Green Fees:* £25.00. *Eating facilities:* available. *Visitors:* welcome with advance reservation. *Society Meetings:* catered for with advance reservation. Pro-

fessional: W.E. Skinner (0862 810902). Secretary/Manager: I.C.R. Walker (0862 810219).

DURNESS. **Durness Golf Club,** Balnakiel, Durness. *Location:* 57 miles north-west of Lairg on A838. Links course with final hole played over deep gully. 9 holes, 2734 yards. S.S.S. 68. *Green Fees:* £5.00 per day. Weekly ticket £20.00. *Visitors:* welcome without reservation. *Society Meetings:* by arrangement. Secretary: Lucy MacKay (097181 364).

GOLSPIE. **Golspie Golf Club,** Ferry Road, Golspie (Golspie (04083) 3266). *Location:* off A9 half a mile from Golspie. Fairly flat course, seaside links and wooded. 18 holes, 5836 yards. S.S.S. 68. Practice area available. *Green Fees:* £10.00 per day. *Eating facilities:* bar and catering service. *Visitors:* welcome, no restrictions except on competition days. *Society Meetings:* welcome by prior arrangement. Secretary: J.L. Catchpole.

HELMSDALE. **Helmsdale Golf Club,** Golf Road, Helmsdale KW8 6JA. *Location:* on A9, 28 miles north of Dornoch. Parkland course. 9 holes, 1825 yards. S.S.S. 62 (2 x 9 holes). *Green Fees:* £3.00 per round or day, £10.00 weekly, £15.00 fortnightly. *Eating facilities:* Bridge Hotel, Helmsdale (04312 219). *Visitors:* welcome at all times. Secretary: Jim Mackay (04312 240).

Wigtownshire

NEWTON STEWART. **Newton Stewart Golf Club,** Kirroughtree Avenue, Minnigaff, Newton Stewart DG8 6ND (0671 2172). *Location:* from South leave A75 at sign to Minnigaff village. Parkland, mainly flat, set in Galloway hills and with a forest backdrop. 9 holes, 5646 yards, 5160 metres. S.S.S. 67, par 68. *Green Fees:* weekdays £6.00, weekends and Bank Holidays £8.00 per day. 20 per cent discount for groups. *Eating facilities:* bar lounge, bar snacks and meals available. *Visitors:* welcome without restriction, but busy at weekends. *Society Meetings:* all welcome. Discounts available. Secretary: D.F. Buchanan (0671 2292).

NEWTON STEWART. **Wigtownshire County Golf Club,** Glenluce, Newton Stewart (Glenluce (05813) 420). *Location:* A75 two miles west Glenluce, eight miles east Stranraer. Seaside links. 18 holes, 5715 yards, 5226 metres. S.S.S. 68. *Green Fees:* weekdays £8.00, weekends £10.00, after 5pm £5.00, weekly £35.00, juniors half-price. Parties of 10 and over, fees reduced by £1.00 each. *Eating facilities:* April to October (inc). *Visitors:* unrestricted except Wednesday evenings. *Society Meetings:* catered for. Secretary: R. McCubbin (05813 277).

PORT WILLIAM. **St. Medan Golf Club,** Monreith, Port William, Newton Stewart DG8 8NJ (09887 358). *Location:* on A747, three miles south of Port William. 9 holes, 4552 yards. S.S.S. 62. *Green Fees:* £4.00, 18 holes £7.00. £10.00 per day. £30.00 per week. *Eating facilities:* available April to September. *Visitors:* welcome. Parties please book. Secretary: D. O'Neill (09885 555).

PUBLISHER'S NOTE

While every effort is made to ensure accuracy, we regret that FHG Publications cannot accept responsibility for errors, omissions or misrepresentation in our entries or any consequences thereof. Prices in particular should be checked because we go to press early. We will follow up complaints, but cannot act as arbiters or agents for either party.

PORTPATRICK. **Portpatrick (Dunskey) Golf Club,** Golf Course Road, Portpatrick, Stranraer DG9 8TB (Portpatrick (0776-81 273). *Location:* A75 or A77 to Stranraer then A77 to Portpatrick, fork right at War Memorial, then signposted. Cliff top links course. 18 holes, 5644 yards. S.S.S. 67. Also short 9 hole course, 1442 yards. S.S.S. 27. Practice ground. *Green Fees:* fortnightly £50.00, weekly £35.00. Daily Monday to Friday £12.00, £8.00 per round. Weekends £14.00 per day, £10.00 per round. Juniors half price if accompanied by adult. 9 hole course £4.00, Juniors £2.00. *Eating facilities:* lunches and teas all days without reservation. Order before playing. *Visitors:* welcome by prior booking to be sure of tee time. *Society Meetings:* catered for by prior arrangement. Hon Secretary: J.A. Horberry (0776-81 273 or 231 home).

STRANRAER. **Stranraer Golf Club,** Creachmore, Stranraer (Leswalt (077 687) 245). *Location:* three miles from Stranraer on the Kirkcolm road (A718). Parkland. 18 holes, 6300 yards. S.S.S. 71. Practice ground. *Green Fees:* weekdays £10.00 per round, £12.50 per day; weekends £12.50 per round, £17.00 per day. *Eating facilities:* meals available, order in advance. *Visitors:* welcome. No reservations for individuals but parties require to book. *Society Meetings:* catered for. Secretary: W.I. Wilson C.A. (0776 3539).

WIGTOWN. **Wigtown and Bladnoch Golf Club,** Wigtown (09884 3354). *Location:* 200 yards from square in Wigtown. Parkland course. 9 holes, 5400 yards. S.S.S. 67. *Green Fees:* weekdays £4.50, Sundays £6.00. *Eating facilities:* bar only. *Visitors:* welcome any time. *Society Meetings:* welcome by arrangement. Secretary: J. Alexander (09884 3209).

Please mention this guide when you write or phone to enquire about accommodation.

Scottish Islands

ARRAN

BLACKWATERFOOT. **Shiskine Golf and Tennis Club,** Blackwaterfoot (Shiskine (077 086) 226). *Location:* off B880 at Blackwaterfoot. Seaside links with only par 5 on island. 12 holes, 3900 yards. S.S.S. 42. Putting green, tennis and bowls. *Green Fees:* £4.00 per round, £6.00 per day. During July and August £6.00 per round, £7.50 per day. *Eating facilities:* available May to September. *Visitors:* welcome. *Society Meetings:* on application. Match Secretary: J.R. Liddell (077 086 293). Treasurer: J. Allison (077 086 346).

BRODICK. **Brodick Golf Club,** Brodick (Brodick (0770) 2349). *Location:* by ferry from Ardrossan. 18 holes, 4404 yards. S.S.S. 62. *Green Fees:* £8.00 per day. *Eating facilities:* bar snacks available. *Visitors:* welcome without restriction. *Society Meetings:* welcome with reservation by letter. Professional: P.S. McCalla (0770 2513). Secretary: H.M. Macrae (0770 2181).

CORRIE. **Corrie Golf Club,** Sannox, Corrie KA97 8JD (077 081 223). *Location:* seven miles north of Brodick. Hilly course. 9 holes, 1948 yards. S.S.S. 61. *Green Fees:* £3.00 daily. *Eating facilities:* meals available March to September. *Visitors:* very welcome bar a Saturday afternoon. *Society Meetings:* catered for. Secretary: J. Kerr (077 081 215).

LAMLASH. **Lamlash Golf Club,** Lamlash KA27 8JU (Lamlash (07706) 296). *Location:* A841 three miles south of Brodick Pier ferry terminal. Undulating

heathland course. 18 holes, 4611 yards. S.S.S. 63. *Green Fees:* £5.00 per day. Three day weekend £12.00. *Eating facilities:* full facilities. *Visitors:* welcome without reservation. *Society Meetings:* catered for. Secretary: J. Henderson (07706 272).

LOCHRANZA. **Lochranza Golf Club,** Lochranza, Isle of Arran (077083 273). *Location:* at north end of Island of Arran. Flat - presently being improved with new tees, etc. 9 holes, 1790 yards. S.S.S. 29. *Green Fees:* £2.50 for 9 holes, £4.00 for 18 holes. *Eating facilities:* tearoom, meals and snacks. Home cooking. *Visitors:* singles to parties always welcome. Introduction sessions for novices. Regular competitions, visitors welcome to participate. Caravan for hire, caravan site adjacent. *Society Meetings:* catered for by arrangement, short notice if necessary. Transport can be provided for parties leaving their cars on the mainland. Secretary: I.M. Robertson.

MACHRIE. **Machrie Bay Golf Club,** Machrie, Near Brodick (077-084 267). *Location:* on A841, three and a half miles north from Blackwaterfoot. Flat seaside course. 9 holes, 2082 yards. S.S.S. 32. *Green Fees:* £3.00 per day. *Eating facilities:* available Summer season. *Visitors:* welcome anytime except on club competition days. *Society Meetings:* catered for if pre-booked. Secretary: Mrs M. Tunnell (077-084 267).

WHITING BAY. **Whiting Bay Golf Club,** near Brodick (07707 487). *Location:* approximately eight miles south of Brodick. 18 holes, 4406 yards, S.S.S. 63. *Green fees:* £5 per day, £17.50 weekly. *Visitors:* welcome, unrestricted. *Eating facilities:* available April to October. *Society Meetings:* by arrangement with Secretary. Secretary: Irene l'Anson (07707 307/326).

BUTE

ISLE OF BUTE. **Bute Golf Club,** West Shore Sands, Stravanan, Kingarth, Rothesay. *Location:* 8 miles from Rothesay on the A845 situated on shores of Stravanan Bay. Flat seaside links in beautiful setting. 9 holes, 2497 yards, 2284 metres. S.S.S. 64 (18 holes). *Green Fees:* £3.00 adults, 50p juniors. *Visitors:* welcome any day, Saturdays after 12.30pm. *Society Meetings:* catered for by arrangement. Secretary: J.M. Burnside (070 083 648).

ROTHESAY. **Port Bannatyne Golf Club,** Bannatyne Mains Road, Port Bannatyne. *Location:* two miles north of Rothesay (ferry terminal). Seaside course, hilly. 13 holes, 4654 yards, 4256 metres. S.S.S. 63. *Green Fees:* £5.50 per day, Juniors £3.00; weekly £20.00, Juniors £10.00. *Eating facilities:* in village, quarter-of-a-mile from course. *Visitors:* welcome without reservation. *Society Meetings:* by arrangement with Secretary. Secretary: Iain L. MacLeod (0700 2009).

ROTHESAY. **Rothesay Golf Club,** Canada Hill, Rothesay (0700 2244). *Location:* access to Island by steamer from Wemyss Bay (May to October every hour). 18 holes, 5370 yards. S.S.S. 67. *Green Fees:* weekdays £7.50 per day, weekends £10.50 per day. *Eating facilities:* full facilities at clubhouse. *Visitors:* welcome without reservation. *Society Meetings:* maximum 40 people catered for. Professional: Gordon McKinlay (0700 3554). Secretary: Alan M. Thom (0700 2244).

COLONSAY

ISLE OF COLONSAY. **Colonsay Golf Club,** Isle of Colonsay PA61 7YP. *Location:* two miles west of pier. Traditional links course, reputedly 200 years old. 18 holes, 4775 yards. *Green Fees:* no green fees, membership fee of £5.00 per family per year (payable at Colonsay Hotel). *Eating facilities:* none. *Visitors:* always welcome. Secretary: Kevin Byrne (09512 316).

CUMBRAE

MILLPORT. **Millport Golf Club,** Golf Road, Millport (Millport (0475) 530311). *Location:* Caledonian McBrayne car ferry Largs slip to Cumbrae slip (seven minutes). On hill overlooking Firth of Clyde over Bute to Mull of Kintyre. 18 holes, 5831 yards. S.S.S. 68. Large practice area. *Green Fees:* maximum charge £10.50 per day. Other charges pro rata. *Eating facilities:* full catering facilities. *Visitors:* welcome without reservation. Tee reservations available for parties. *Society Meetings:* catered for. Special open amateur competition, Cumbrae Cup. Secretary: W.D. Patrick C.A. (0475 530308).

ISLAY

PORT ELLEN. **Islay Golf Club,** Machrie Links, Port Ellen. C/o The Secretary, Western Cottage, Port Ellen (0496 2409). *Location:* adjacent Airport, 4 miles from Port Ellen. 18 holes, 6226 yards. S.S.S. 71. *Green Fees:* information not provided. *Eating facilities:* full service in hotel. *Visitors:* welcome any day without reservation. *Society Meetings:* any number catered for. Secretary: Thomas Dunn.

LEWIS

STORNOWAY. **Stornoway Golf Club,** Lady Lever Park, Stornoway, Isle of Lewis (0851 2240). *Location:* close proximity to town of Stornoway, in grounds of Lewis Castle. Inland course, hilly parkland, scenic. 18 holes, 5119 yards. S.S.S. 66. *Green Fees:* £5.00 per round, £7.50 per day. Weekly tickets £25.00. *Eating facilities:* available. *Visitors:* welcome, but no Sunday golf. Car ferry daily (except Sunday) from Ullapool. British Airways service daily (except Sunday) from Glasgow and Inverness. *Society Meetings:* welcome, book through Secretary. Secretary: Mr P. Dickie.

MULL

ISLE OF MULL. **Craignure Golf Club,** Scallastle, Craignure (Craignure (06802) 370). *Location:* one mile from ferry terminal at Craignure. Seaside links. 9 holes, 2218 metres. S.S.S. 64. *Green Fees:* £4.00. *Eating facilities:* not available. *Visitors:* always welcome, no restrictions. Secretary: Sheila M. Campbell (06802 370).

TOBERMORY. **Tobermory Golf Club,** Tobermory PA75 6PE. *Location:* situated on a hill north west of Tobermory. Clifftop course with panoramic views of Sound of Mull; testing terrain, not suitable for trolleys. 9 holes, 4921 yards, 4362 metres. S.S.S. 64. *Green Fees:* £5.00 per day, £20.00 per week, £30.00 per two weeks (clubhouse under construction). *Eating facilities:* none available. *Visitors:* unrestricted except for some competition days. *Society Meetings:* welcome. Secretary: Dr W.H. Clegg (0688 2013 or 2020).

ORKNEYS

KIRKWALL. **Orkney Golf Club Ltd,** Grain Bank, Kirkwall (Kirkwall (0856) 2457). *Location:* half-a-mile west of Kirkwall. 18 holes, 5406 yards. S.S.S. 68. *Green Fees:* £5.00 per day including Sunday. *Visitors:* welcome without reservation. Secretary: J. Sim (0856 2435).

STROMNESS. **Stromness Golf Club Ltd,** Ness, Stromness (0856 850772). *Location:* Stromness. Parkland/seaside links course. 18 holes, 4822 yards. S.S.S. 64. *Green fees:* information not available. *Eating facilities:* bar, and there are hotels nearby. *Visitors:* welcome. *Society meetings:* by arrangement through Secretary. Secretary: F.J. Groundwater (0856 850662).

SHETLAND

LERWICK. **Dale Golf Club,** PO Box 18, Lerwick, Shetland (Lerwick (0595) 369). *Location:* four miles north of Lerwick on main road. Hilly, undulating course. Excellent greens. 18 holes, 5776 yards. S.S.S. 68. *Green Fees:* £5.00 per day including weekends. Juniors and OAP's half-price. *Eating facilities:* bar snacks available. *Visitors:* welcome. *Society Meetings:* by arrangement with Course Manager. Course Manager: E. Groat.

SKYE

SCONSER. **Isle of Skye Golf Club,** Sconser. *Location:* 20 miles from ferry on road to Portree. Seaside course with spectacular views. 9 holes (18 tees), 4798 yards, 4385 metres. S.S.S. 63. *Green Fees:* £6.00 weekdays, £12.00 for three days, £20.00 per week. *Visitors:* no restrictions. Changing and toilet facilities. Secretary: I. Stephen (0478 2000).

TIREE

ISLE OF TIREE. **Vaul Golf Club,** Gott Bay, Isle of Tiree, Argyll. *Location:* two miles from Scarinish, Isle of Tiree. 9 holes, 3123 yards. S.S.S. 70 over 18 holes. *Green fees:* information not provided. *Visitors:* welcome without reservation. *Society Meetings:* catered for. No Sunday play allowed. Secretary: P. Robertson. Secretary: D. M. Farquhar.

Wonderful views on the seaside course at Nefyn (Gwynedd) near Pwllheli.

Golf in Wales
WHERE TO PLAY • WHERE TO STAY

It's a fact that the 'Open' has never been won by a golfer from Wales! The English, the Scots and the Irish have all shared this honour but surprisingly none of the many good Welsh golfers has hit form at exactly that right moment. Fortunately that statistic is no reflection on the state of golf in Wales and courses like Royal St David's and Royal Porthcawl will always attract visitors and demand a high standard of play.

Given this pattern of courses, there is a natural bias for golf in Wales to gravitate to the extreme north and south. You'll find plenty of accommodation for golfers in Llandudno and Pwllheli, for example, and also in Chepstow and Bridgend. Fortunately there are a few other courses in Wales! What about a few days at the Bull Bay Hotel in Anglesey and the White Lion Royal in Bala – you could introduce a 'birdie' or even an 'eagle' for a change!

Clwyd

ABERGELE. **Abergele and Pensarn Golf Club,** Tan-y-Gopa Road, Abergele LL22 8DS (Abergele (0745) 824034). *Location:* below Gwrych Castle, Abergele. Parkland in scenic setting. 18 holes, 6520 yards, 5961 metres. S.S.S. 71. Practice area. *Green Fees:* £13.00 weekdays, £15.00 weekends. *Eating facilities:* full catering facilities except Mondays, two bars. *Visitors:* welcome weekdays, Bank Holidays and weekends with official club Handicap. *Society Meetings:* catered for, by arrangement with Secretary. Professional: I. Runcie (0745 823813). Secretary: Mr H.E. Richards.

COLWYN. **Old Colwyn Golf Club,** The Clubhouse, Woodland Avenue, Old Colwyn LL29 9NL (Colwyn Bay (0492) 515581). *Location:* signposted at main Abergele road, Old Colwyn. Parkland. 9 holes (x 2), 5268 yards. S.S.S. 66. Practice area. *Green Fees:* information not available. *Eating facilities:* bar and meals by arrangement. *Visitors:* welcome except weekend afternoons and Tuesday, Wednesday evenings. *Society Meetings:* welcome by arrangement. Secretary: M. Davies.

DENBIGH. **Denbigh Golf Club,** Henllan Road, Denbigh (Denbigh (0745-71) 3888). *Location:* one mile from Denbigh town centre on the 5382 road. Wooded/undulating parkland with magnificent scenery. 18 holes, 5582 yards. S.S.S. 67. *Green Fees:* £12.00 weekdays, £15.00 weekends and Bank Holidays. *Eating facilities:* catering daily except Mondays, bar open seven days. *Visitors:* welcome, no restrictions. *Society Meetings:* catered for. Professional: M.D. Jones (0745-71 4159). Secretary: G.C. Parry (0745-71 4159).

DENBIGH near. **Bryn Morfydd Hotel Golf Course,** Llanrhaeadr, Near Denbigh LL.16 4NP (074578 280). *Location:* south off A525 between Denbigh and Ruthin. Parkland course with beautiful views of Vale of Clwyd. 9 holes, 1190 yards. *Green Fees:* £4.00. *Eating facilities:* course attached to Country House Hotel. *Visitors:* welcome all year. *Society Meetings:* welcome. Manager: D.J. Willmore.

FLINT. **Flint Golf Club,** Cornist Park, Flint (Flint (03526) 2327). *Location:* M56, A55, one mile from town centre. Parkland. 9 holes, 5819 yards. S.S.S. 68. Practice area. *Green Fees:* weekdays £6.00 per day, weekends only with member £6.00. Special rate for golf parties numbering 12 or more. *Eating facilities:* snacks, lunches, evening meals, day's golf £12.00; bar. *Visitors:* welcome weekdays (no restrictions), weekends with member only. *Society Meetings:* catered for – advance booking (not Sundays). Professional: M. Staton. Secretary: H. Griffith (03526 2186).

HAWARDEN. **Hawarden Golf Club,** Groomsdale Lane, Hawarden, Deeside CH5 3EH (Hawarden (0244) 531447). *Location:* A55, first left at Hawarden Station going west. Wooded parkland. 9 holes, 5630 yards. S.S.S. 67. *Green Fees:* £5.00 per day with member only, or by arrangement with Secretary. *Eating facilities:* full catering available. *Visitors:* welcome with reservation, with member only. *Society Meetings:* catered for by arrangement with Secretary. Professional: M. Carty. Secretary: T. Hinks-Edwards.

HOLYWELL. **Holywell Golf Club,** Brynford, Holywell (0352 710040). *Location:* at Brynford two miles south of Holywell, turn at traffic lights on A5206 at Holywell. Flat natural terrain. 18 holes, 5960 yards. S.S.S. 70. Par 70. *Green Fees:* weekdays £7.00, weekends and Bank Holidays £10.00. *Eating facilities:* full bar facilities and catering on request. *Visitors:* welcome weekdays without reservation. *Society Meetings:* by arrangement. Secretary: E.K. Carney (0352 710539).

LLANGOLLEN. **Vale of Llangollen Golf Club,** The Clubhouse, Llangollen (Llangollen (0978) 860613). *Location:* one mile east of town on the A5. 18 holes, 6617 yards. S.S.S. 72. *Green Fees:* on application. *Eating facilities:* full catering service. *Visitors:* welcome. *Society Meetings:* welcome. Professional: D.I. Vaughan (0978 860040). Secretary: T.F. Ellis (0978 860040).

MOLD. **Gwesty Chequers,** Northophall, Mold. *Location:* on the A55. Formerly the old manor house and situated in 40 acres of wood and pastureland. Special golf holidays by arrangement with Chester Golf Club (eight miles). For details of golf and other activity holidays contact Chris Wood (0244 816181). Telex: 617112. FAX 0244 814661.

MOLD. **Mold Golf Club,** Pantymwyn, Mold (Mold (0352) 740318). 18 holes, 5521 yards. S.S.S. 67. Par 67. Open to visitors and Societies 7 days a week. *Green Fees:* weekdays £10.00, Saturday, Sunday and Bank Holidays £12.50. *Eating facilities:* bar snacks available, full catering by arrangement with the Steward. Professional: Martin Carty (Lessons by appointment). Secretary: A. Newall.

MOLD. **Padeswood and Buckley Golf Club,** The Caia, Station Lane, Padeswood, Mold. *Location:* eight miles west from Chester, four miles from Mold on the A5118. 18 holes, 5823 yards. S.S.S. 68. *Green Fees:* weekdays £11.00, Saturdays and Bank Holidays £13.00. *Eating facilities:* by arrangement with Steward.

Visitors: welcome except on Sundays. *Society Meetings:* weekdays only. Professional: David Ashton (0244 543636). Secretary: R. McLauchlan (0244 550537).

PADESWOOD. **Old Padeswood Golf Club,** Station Road, Padeswood, Near Mold CH7 4JL (Buckley (0244) 547401). *Location:* off A5118 Chester to Mold road, three miles from Mold. Undulating meadowland. 18 holes, 6668 yards, 6079 metres. S.S.S. 72. Practice ground. *Green Fees:* weekdays £8.00 per round, £12.00 per day; weekends £10.00 per round, £14.00 per day. *Eating facilities:* diningroom meals plus two bars. *Visitors:* welcome anytime except on competition days and weekends. *Society Meetings:* catered for weekdays only. Professional: Tony Davies (0244 547401). Secretary: Bernard Hellen (0352 770506).

PRESTATYN. **Prestatyn Golf Club,** Marine Road East, Prestatyn LL19 7HS (Prestatyn (07456) 4320). *Location:* A483, on approaching Prestatyn from Chester direction turn right at sign for Pontins Holiday Village and follow club sign. Seaside links Championship course. 18 holes, 6517 yards, 5959 metres. S.S.S. 72. Practice areas. *Green Fees:* £10.00 weekdays, £14.00 weekends and Bank Holidays. *Eating facilities:* full catering available, bar. *Visitors:* welcome weekdays and Sundays if bona fide members of golf club, with Handicap Certificate. *Society Meetings:* special "all-in" arrangement for 27 holes. Professional: G. Hutchinson (07456 4320). Secretary: Roy Woodruff (07456 88353).

PRESTATYN. **St. Melyd Golf Club,** The Paddock, Meliden Road, Prestatyn (Prestatyn (07456) 4405). *Location:* beside Prestatyn to Rhuddlan main road (near Meliden village). Parkland. 9 holes, 18 tees, 5811 yards. S.S.S. 68. *Green Fees:* on application. *Eating facilities:* full range of catering facilities except Tuesdays. *Visitors:* welcome. *Society Meetings:* catered for by arrangement with Secretary (various golf packages). Professional: N.H. Lloyd (07456 88858). Secretary: C.S. McKechnie.

RHUDDLAN. **Rhuddlan Golf Club,** Meliden Road, Rhuddlan LL18 6LB (0745 590217). *Location:* between Rhyl and St. Asaph, leave A55 at St. Asaph for Rhuddlan. Gently undulating, parkland course with natural hazards. 18 holes, 6435 yards, 5900 metres. S.S.S. 71. Extensive practice ground. *Green Fees:* £13.00 weekdays, £16.00 Saturdays and Bank Holidays. *Eating facilities:* available daily except Monday. *Visitors:* at all times when course demand permits. Sundays with member only. No denim. Snooker table. *Society Meetings:* weekdays only, maximum 50. Professional: Gerry Cox (0745 590898). Secretary: David Morris (0745 590217).

RHYL. **Rhyl Golf Club,** Coast Road, Rhyl (Rhyl (0745) 353171). *Location:* one mile east of Rhyl on A548. Seaside links. 9 holes, 6153 yards, 5623 metres. S.S.S. 70. *Green Fees:* £7.00 weekdays, £8.00 weekends and Bank Holidays. Discounts for parties over 20. *Eating facilities:* snacks and meals available, bar. *Visitors:* welcome any time except when competitions in progress. *Society Meetings:* catered for by arrangement. Secretary: G.K. Watkin.

RUTHIN. **Ruthin Pwllglas Golf Club,** Pwllglas, Near Ruthin (Ruthin (0842) 2296). *Location:* two miles south of Ruthin off A494. Hilly parkland. 10 holes, 5418 yards. S.S.S. 66. Practice area. *Green Fees:* weekdays £6.00, weekends and Bank Holidays £12.00 (with member £8.00). *Eating facilities:* none. *Visitors:* welcome without reservation except on major competition or match days. Phone call advisable in high season. *Society Meetings:* catered for midweek. Hon. Secretary: R.D. Roberts (0842 4659).

WREXHAM. **Wrexham Golf Club,** Holt Road, Wrexham LL13 9SB (Wrexham (0978) 261033). *Location:* A543 north east of Wrexham. 18 holes, 6139 yards. S.S.S. 69. Practice facilities. *Green Fees:* weekdays £12.00, weekends £15.00. *Eating facilities:* daily, subject to functions and visiting Societies. *Visitors:* welcome, subject to competitions and Society bookings. Proof of Golf Club membership and/or Handicap Certificate required. *Society Meetings:* catered for, Mondays and Fridays preferred. Professional: D.A. Larvin (0978 351476). Secretary: K.B. Fisher (0978 364268).

Dyfed

ABERYSTWYTH. **Aberystwyth Golf Club,** Bry-y-mor, Aberyswyth SY23 2HY (Aberystwyth (0970) 615104). *Location:* north end of promenade access adjacent to cliff railway. Undulating meadowland. 18 holes, 5735 yards. S.S.S. 68. *Green Fees:* high season weekdays £10.00, weekends and Bank Holidays £12.00. Low season £8.00 weekdays, £9.00 weekends. *Eating facilities:* restaurant and bar. *Visitors:* welcome, no restriction, tee times, competition days. *Society Meetings:* catered for by arrangement. Professional: G. Brownlie (0970 625301). Secretary: W. Wynn Hughes.

AMMANFORD. **Glynhir Golf Club,** Glynhir Road, Llandybie, Ammanford SA18 2TF (Llandybie (0269) 850472). *Location:* seven miles from end of M4, between Ammanford and Llandybie on the A483. Turn right up Glynhir Road and proceed for about two miles. Undulating wooded parkland course. 18 holes, 6090 yards. S.S.S. 70. *Green Fees:* £9.00 (£8.00 with member) weekdays. £12.00 weekends and Bank Holidays (£8.00 with member). *Eating facilities:* full catering available. *Visitors:* welcome but preferably on weekdays. *Society Meetings:* welcome weekdays. Accommodation available. Bed and Breakfast at clubhouse (6 to 8 persons). Professional: Steve Rastall (0269 851010). Joint Secretaries: J. Trefor Thomas (0269 850571), E.P. Rees (0269 852345).

BORTH. **Borth and Ynyslas Golf Club Ltd,** Borth SY24 5JS (Borth (0970) 871202). *Location:* turn off A487 between Aberystwyth and Machynlleth, course is north of Borth village. Traditional seaside links course with natural hazards (oldest 18 hole course in Wales). 18 holes, 6100 yards, 5579 metres. S.S.S. 70. Practice area. *Green Fees:* weekdays £12.00, weekends £15.00 per day. *Eating facilities:* full bar, dining and snack services. *Visitors:* welcome at all times except when competitions in progress, open events held in holiday period. *Society Meetings:* by prior arrangement with the Secretary. Professional: J.G. Lewis (0970 871557). Secretary: R.B. Mair (065 474242).

CARDIGAN. **Cardigan Golf Club,** Gwbert-on-Sea, Cardigan SA43 1PR (Cardigan (0239) 612035). *Location:* two miles north-west of Cardigan. Seaside/meadowland links course on headland. 18 holes, 6641 yards. S.S.S. 72. *Green Fees:* £10.00 per day weekdays, £13.00 per day weekends and Bank Holidays. *Eating facilities:* snacks and meals available daily except Mondays. *Visitors:* welcome. Squash courts also available. *Society Meetings:* very welcome, catered for without restrictions. Professional: Colin Parsons. Hon. Secretary: J. Rhapps (0239 612035).

CARMARTHEN. **Carmarthen Golf Club**, Blaeny-coed Road, Carmarthen SA33 6EH (Conwyl Elfed 214). *Location:* north-west of Carmarthen by Water Street, Trevaughan Road signposted. 18 holes, 6212 yards. S.S.S. 71. *Green Fees:* information not provided. *Eating facilities:* meals at Clubhouse. *Visitors:* welcome with reservation. *Society Meetings:* catered for. Professional: Pat Gillis.

HAVERFORDWEST. **Haverfordwest Golf Club**, Arnolds Down, Haverfordwest SA61 2XQ (Haverford-west (0437) 763565). *Location:* one mile east of Haverfordwest on A40. Parkland, fairly flat. 18 holes, 5915 yards. S.S.S. 70. Practice fairway and putting green. *Green Fees:* £10.00 weekdays (£8.00 playing with a member), £15.00 weekends (£10.00 playing with member). *Eating facilities:* bar snacks available, meals by arrangement. *Visitors:* bona fide golfers welcome. *Society Meetings:* catered for by arrangement. Professional: A.J. Pile (0437 768409). Secretary: M.A. Harding (0437 764523).

LAMPETER. **Cilgwyn Golf Club**, Llangybi, Lampeter SA48 8NN (057045 286). *Location:* five miles north-east of Lampeter, off A485 at Llangybi. Flat parkland course. 9 holes, 5318 yards. S.S.S. 67. Practice area. *Green Fees:* weekdays £5.00, weekends £6.50. *Eating facilities:* available. *Visitors:* welcome without reservation. *Society Meetings:* catered for. Special rates available. Secretary: J.L. Jones (0570 422784).

LLANELLI. **Ashburnham Golf Club**, Cliffe Terrace, Burry Port SA16 0HN (05546 2466). *Location:* four miles west of Llanelli – eight miles from Exit 48 on M4. Seaside links with Championship status. 18 holes, 6916 yards. S.S.S. 73, Par 72. Practice area. *Green Fees:* weekdays £12.00 per round (£8.00 with member), £16.00 per day (£12.00 with member); weekends and Bank Holidays £16.00 per round (£12.00 with member), £20.00 per day (£16.00 with member). *Eating facilities:* full catering except Mondays, two bars. *Visitors:* welcome weekdays, Wednesday ladies' day, special arrangements weekends. *Society Meetings:* catered for with advance notification to Secretary only. Professional: Richard J. Playle (05546 3846). Secretary: D. Emrys Gravelle (05546 2269).

MILFORD HAVEN. **Milford Haven Golf Club**, Woobine House, Hubberston, Milford Haven (Milford Haven [0646] 692368). *Location:* one mile from Milford Haven on Dale Road. Parkland overlooking magnificent harbour. 18 holes, 6071 yards. S.S.S. 70.

Green Fees: weekdays £10; weekends £12. *Eating facilities:* lunches, bar snacks, dinners available at clubhouse. *Visitors:* welcome at all times. *Society Meetings:* welcome, special rates depending on numbers. Secretary: D.G. Britton, 22 Great North Road, Milford Haven (0646 697660 evenings).

NEWPORT. **Newport (Pembs) Golf Club**, The Golf Club, Newport SA42 0NR (Newport [Dyfed] (0239) 820244). *Location:* two miles off A487 Cardigan-Fish-guard at Newport, Dyfed. Flat seaside links course with mountain views. 9 holes, 3089 yards, S.S.S. 69. *Green Fees:* £8.00 weekdays and weekends. *Eating facilities:* full catering and bar facilities available. *Visitors:* welcome at all times, please telephone at weekends and Bank Holidays. Self-catering accommodation available adjoining clubhouse. *Society Meetings:* catered for at any time by arrangement with the Secretary. Professional: Mr Colin Parsons. Secretary: Ron Dietrich.

PEMBROKE. **South Pembrokeshire Golf Club**. Defensible Barracks, Pembroke Dock, Pembroke (Pembroke (0646) 683817). *Location:* on hilltop over-looking Pembroke Dock and Milford Haven waterway, near western end of A477. 9 holes, 5804 yards. S.S.S. 69. *Green Fees:* £8.00 per day. Weekly (Mondays to Fridays) rates available. *Eating facilities:* meals available. *Visitors:* welcome. *Society Meetings:* catered for by arrangement. Secretary: G.W. Thomas (0646 682035).

ST. DAVIDS. **St. Davids City Golf Club**, Whitesands Bay, St. Davids SA62 6QY. *Location:* left fork at Rugby Club, two miles to Whitesands Bay, turn left at sign for Whitesands Bay Hotel. Seaside links course with panoramic views of Whitesands Bay and St. Davids Head. 9 holes, 5911 yards. S.S.S. 70. *Green Fees:* £8.00 (£5.00 if playing with a member). *Eating facilities:* available at Whitesands Hotel – 200 yards from course. *Visitors:* no restrictions. No bag sharing, please. *Society Meetings:* welcome, preferably by prior arrangement with Secretary. Secretary: G.B. Lewis (04383 607).

TENBY. **Tenby Golf Club**, The Burrows, Tenby SA70 7NP (Tenby (0834) 2787). *Location:* on A478, near Tenby Railway Station. Seaside links, Championship course, oldest club in Wales. 18 holes, 6232 yards. S.S.S. 71. Practice area. *Green Fees:* weekdays £13.00, weekends £16.00. Reduced fees in winter and for Societies booked in advance. *Eating facilities:* complete dining facilities; licensed bars, snacks. *Visitors:* always welcome, subject to club competitions. Billiards room available. *Society Meetings:* catered for by advance booking. Professional: Terence Mountford (0834 4447). Secretary: T.R. Arnold (0834 2978).

Mid-Glamorgan

ABERDARE. **Aberdare Golf Club,** Abernant, Aberdare (0685 871188). *Location:* half a mile from Town Centre. Mountain course with parkland features and view of whole Cynon Valley. 18 holes, 5845 yards. S.S.S. 69. *Green Fees:* weekdays £11.00 (with member £7.00); weekends £14.00 (with member £9.00). *Eating facilities:* bar, lounge and diningroom. *Visitors:* welcome without reservation weekdays. No casual visitors on Saturdays, with member only. Snooker room, ladies' lounge and changing room. *Society Meetings:* catered for by prior arrangement with Secretary. Professional: A. W. Palmer (0685 878735): Secretary: Keith Lloyd (0685 871188 or 872842 home).

BARGOED. **Bargoed Golf Club,** Heolddu, Bargoed. (Bargoed (0443) 830143). *Location:* A469 to Bargoed town centre – Heolddu Road – Moorland Road. Mountain course. 18 holes, 6012 yards. S.S.S. 69. *Green Fees:* £12.00. *Eating facilities:* lunches, dinners and snacks. *Visitors:* welcome, only with member at weekends, no other restrictions. *Society Meetings:* catered for, no restrictions only at weekends. Secretary: W.R. Coleman (0443 830143 or 822377).

BLAENGWNLAIS. **Mountain Lakes Golf and Country Club,** Castell Heights Golf Club Ltd, Blaengwnlais CF8 1NG (0222 886666). *Location:* approximately four miles north of Cardiff on A469, two miles south of Caerphilly. Part parkland, part wooded, undulating – 17 lakes, large penncross greens. 18 holes, 6850 yards. S.S.S. 73. Large practice ground. weekdays £12.50 (£10.00 with member); weekends

£15.00 (£12.50 with member). *Eating facilities:* full restaurant and three bars. *Visitors:* welcome at all times but must have registered handicap. *Society Meetings:* welcome at all times but must have registered handicap. Professional: Robert Sandon (0222 886666). Secretary: Jean Bull (0222 861128).

BRIDGEND. **Southerndown Golf Club,** Ewenny, Bridgend (Southerndown (0656) 880326). *Location:* B4524, off A48 south of Bridgend, on coast, about five miles. Entrance to Club car park is the turn-off alongside the Pelican Inn at Ogmore by Sea (opposite ruins of Ogmore Castle). Seaside heathland course. 18 holes, 6613 yards. S.S.S. 73. Practice ground and putting green. *Green Fees:* £20.00 weekdays, £26.00 weekends. *Eating facilities:* diningroom facilities seven days a week; bars daily. *Visitors:* welcome if member of recognised golf club, on Sundays only with member. *Society Meetings:* catered for on Tuesdays and Thursdays. Special rates dependent on number. Professional: D. McMonagle (0656 880476). Secretary: R. Brickell (0656 880476).

CAERPHILLY. **Caerphilly Golf Club,** Pencapel, Mountain Road, Caerphilly CF8 1HJ (Caerphilly (0222) 883481). *Location:* seven miles north of Cardiff on A469. Mountainside course with two steep climb holes, otherwise wooded and undulating. 14 holes, 6028 yards. S.S.S. 71. Small practice area. *Green Fees:* weekdays £9.00, weekends only if playing with a member. *Eating facilities:* men's bar, mixed and ladies' lounges; lunches available except Saturdays, dinners by arrangement. *Visitors:* welcome at all times except

Bank Holidays and weekends and major club competitions. *Society Meetings:* £8.00 per player. Professional: E. McDonald (0222 869104). Secretary: H. Matthews (0222 863441).

CAERPHILLY. Castell Heights Public Golf Course, Blaengwynlais CF8 1NG (0222 861128). *Location:* approximately four miles north of Cardiff on A469, two miles south of Caerphilly. 9 holes, 2688 yards. S.S.S. 66 for 18 holes. *Green Fees:* information not available. *Eating facilities:* snacks, lunches and afternoon tea available. Restaurant meals booking only (0222 886686). *Visitors:* welcome booked times only. Professional: R. Sandow. Secretary: D. Philips.

DOWLAIS. Morlais Castle Golf Club, Pant, Dowlais, Merthyr Tydfil CF48 2UY (0685 722822). *Location:* near 'Heads of Valley Road', Dowlais roundabout, follow signs for Brecon Mountain Railway. Very pleasant moorland course with excellent views. 18 holes, 6320 yards, 5744 metres. S.S.S. 71. Practice area. *Green Fees:* £10.00 per day, £6.50 with member. *Eating facilities:* bar meals, for other meals contact Stewardess. *Visitors:* welcome except Saturday afternoons and Sunday mornings. *Society Meetings:* please contact Secretary. Secretary: J.M. Powell.

HENGOED. Bryn Meadows Golf and Country Club Hotel, The Bryn, Near Hengoed CF8 7SM (0495 225590/224103). FAX 0495 228272. *Location:* A472 between Maesycwmmer and Blackwood. 18 holes, 6200 yards. S.S.S. 69. *Green Fees:* weekdays £13.50, weekends £17.50. *Eating facilities:* restaurant, 70 covers. Functions up to 120. Conferences catered for from five to 120. Bar snacks served daily. *Visitors:* welcome, but not Sunday mornings. 20 bedrooms en-suite available. *Society Meetings:* welcome Tuesdays and Thursdays. Professional: B. Edwards (0495 221905). Secretary: B. Mayo.

KENFIG. Pyle and Kenfig Golf Club, Waun-y-Mer, Kenfig (Porthcawl (065 671) 3093). *Location:* south of A48 on B4283 between Cornelly and Nottage. 18 holes, 6085 metres. S.S.S. 73. *Green Fees:* £18.00 per day. *Eating facilities:* lunch and dinner except Mondays. *Visitors:* welcome if member of recognised golf club with reservation. Weekends by invitation only. *Society Meetings:* catered for except Mondays. Professional: R. Evans. Secretary/Manager: R.C. Thomas.

MAESTEG. Maesteg Golf Club, Mount Pleasant, Maesteg CF34 9PR (0656 732037). *Location:* half a mile out of Maesteg town centre on the Port Talbot road. Reasonably flat mountain course. 18 holes, 5845 yards. S.S.S. 69. *Green Fees:* weekdays £9.00, weekends £12.00. Special rates for Societies. *Eating facilities:* diningroom every day except Thursdays, lounge bar. *Visitors:* welcome without reservation, groups of more than eight by arrangement. *Society Meetings:* catered for by arrangement. Professional: Gary Hopkins (0656 735742). Secretary: W.H. Hanford.

MERTHYR TYDFIL. Merthyr Tydfil (Cilsanws) Golf Club, Cloth Hall Lane, Cerfn Coed, Merthyr Tydfil (0685 723308). *Location:* off A470 two miles north of Merthyr Tydfil town centre. Mountain course in National Park area with outstanding views. 11 holes, 5820 yards, 5305 metres. S.S.S. 68. *Green Fees:* £8.00 (£4.00 with a member) weekdays, £10.00 (£5.00 with a member) weekends. *Eating facilities:* weekends only. *Visitors:* welcome anytime except competition days (usually Sundays). *Society Meetings:* catered for by prior arrangement. Secretary: Vivian Price.

MOUNTAIN ASH. Mountain Ash Golf Club, Cefn Pennar, Mountain Ash (Mountain Ash (0443) 472265). *Location:* A470 Pontypridd to Aberdare road, approximately 10 miles from Pontypridd. 18 holes, 5575 yards. S.S.S. 68. *Green Fees:* weekdays £12.00, £6.00 with member, weekends and Bank Holidays £12.00 only with member. *Eating facilities:* catering at club. *Visitors:* welcome any time without reservation. *Society Meetings:* catered for. Professional: Jeff Sim (0443 478770). Secretary: Geoffrey Matthews.

NELSON. Whitehall Golf Club, The Pavilion, Nelson CF46 6FT (0443 740245). *Location:* Abercynon, three minutes from centre. Hilly course. 9 holes, 2856 yards. S.S.S. 34. *Green Fees:* £10.00 per day weekdays, also at weekends with Captain's permission. *Eating facilities:* available, meals must be ordered. *Visitors:* booking by telephone preferred. Professional: J. Sim. Secretary: V.E. Davies.

PONTYCLUN. Llantrisant and Pontyclun Golf Club, The Clubhouse, Talbot Green, Pontyclun (Llantrisant (0443) 222148). *Location:* 10 miles north of Cardiff, two miles north of Junction 34 M4. Parkland. 12 holes, 5712 yards. S.S.S. 68. *Green Fees:* weekdays £15.00, £7.50 with member; weekends and Bank holidays £10.00 with member only. *Eating facilities:* by arrangement with Steward. *Visitors:* welcome with proof of membership and weekends with member only. *Society Meetings:* catered for by arrangement. Professional: Nick Watson (0443 228169). Secretary: John Williams (0443 224601).

PONTYPRIDD. Pontypridd Golf Club, Ty Gwyn Road, Pontypridd CF37 4DJ (Pontypridd (0443) 402359). *Location:* east side of town centre, off A470, 12 miles from Cardiff. Wooded mountain course. 18 holes, 5650 yards, 5166 metres. S.S.S. 68. *Green Fees:* information not provided. *Eating facilities:* dining facilities and bar snacks. *Visitors:* welcome weekdays without member, weekends with member only. Must be member of recognised golf club. *Society Meetings:* catered for with prior reservation. Professional: K. Gittins (0443 491210). Secretary: J.G. Graham (0443 409904).

Pitching up at Bryn Meadows, Mid-Glamorgan.

THE PORTHCAWL HOTEL & FAIRWAYS HOTEL

**c/o PORTHCAWL HOTEL,
JOHN STREET, PORTHCAWL
MID-GLAMORGAN CF36 3AP**

The Porthcawl is situated in the main shopping centre close to the seafront whilst Fairways commands a magnificent panoramic view southwards across the adjacent foreshore and over the Bristol Channel towards the Devon hills.

Both hotels have first class facilities and serve excellent food and are licensed. The Porthcawl also has a nightclub and health club. Within easy reach of Royal Porthcawl Golf Club and Pyle & Kenfig Golf Club. Brochure available **(065671) 2257. Fax (0656) 772040.**

PORTHCAWL. **Royal Porthcawl Golf Club,** Porthcawl (0656 71 2251). *Location:* 25 miles west of Cardiff, 14 miles east of Swansea. Seaside links. 18 holes. Championship course 6691 yards. S.S.S. 74. Par 72. Medal course 6409 yards. S.S.S. 73. Par 72. Practice area. *Green Fees:* £24.00 weekdays, £35.00 weekends. *Eating facilities:* full catering and bar facilities. *Visitors:* playing with member only at weekends, reservations required and must have Handicap Certificate. *Society Meetings:* by arrangement. Professional: Mr Graham Poor (0656 71 6984). Secretary: A.W. Woolcott.

RHONDDA. **Rhondda Golf Club,** Pontygwaith, Ferndale, Rhondda CF43 3PW (Tonypandy (0443) 433204). *Location:* on the Penrhys road joining Rhondda Fach and Rhondda Fawr. Mountain course. 18 holes, 6428 yards. S.S.S. 71. *Green Fees:* £10.00 at all times, £7.00 with member. *Eating facilities:* all facilities every day except Mondays. *Visitors:* welcome without reservation at all times except mornings Saturday and Sunday and on special competition days. *Society Meetings:* catered for mid-week and by special arrangement. Secretary: G. Rees.

South Glamorgan

BARRY. **Brynhill (Barry) Golf Club,** Port Road East, Colcot, Barry (Barry (0446) 735061). *Location:* leave M4 at Cardiff, and follow signs to Barry, and Cardiff (Wales) Airport. Undulating meadowland course. 18 holes, 5511 metres. S.S.S. 69. Par 71. *Green Fees:* £15.00 per day, £8.00 with member. County Cards £7.50. Juniors £6.00. *Eating facilities:* the Steward Mr Barrie Cahill and his wife Ann extend a warm welcome, and will provide morning coffee, lunches between 12 noon and 2.00pm. Afternoon teas and dinner from 4.30 pm except Monday. Your order prior to playing is preferred. *Visitors:* welcome, except Sundays; Bank Holidays, guests must play with a member. *Society Meetings:* by arrangement with Secretary except Saturday and Sunday. Professional: Peter Fountain (0446 733660). Secretary: Mr Digby P. Lloyd. Clubhouse (0446 720277). Home: (0446 733587).

BARRY. **RAF St. Athan Golf Club,** Barry CF6 9WA (0446 751043). *Location:* first turning on right after driving through St. Athan Village, eight miles from Barry. Flat parkland. 9 holes, 5994 yards. S.S.S. 69. *Green Fees:* £6.00/£8.00 weekdays, £8.00/£10.00 weekends with or without member. *Eating facilities:* available Wednesdays, Fridays, Saturdays and Sunday lunch time. *Visitors:* green fee players welcome on display of Handicap Certificate except Sunday mornings. *Society Meetings:* apply through the Secretary. Professional: Neil Gillette (0222 373923). Secretary: Dai Llewellyn (0446 742142).

CARDIFF. **Cardiff Golf Club,** Sherborne Avenue, Cyncoed, Cardiff (Cardiff (0222) 753067). *Location:* two miles north of city centre on M4, A48 or A48M from east to Pentwyn exit on Eastern Avenue, and take Pentwyn Industrial Road to top of hill at Cyncoed Village, turn left at Spar shop into Sherborne Avenue. Undulating parkland, all greens bunkered. 18 holes. S.S.S. 70. *Green Fees:* £15.00 per round or day. *Eating facilities:* catering available lunchtime and evening weekdays except Mondays. Professional: Terry Hanson (0222 754772). Secretary: David Griffiths (0222 753320).

CARDIFF. **Creigiau Golf Club,** Cardiff Road, Creigiau, Cardiff CF4 8NN (Cardiff (0222) 890263). *Location:* seven miles north-west of Cardiff, two miles Exit 34 M4. 18 holes, 5786 yards. S.S.S. 68. *Green Fees:* £14.00 per day (£7.00 with member). *Eating facilities:* meals on request. *Visitors:* welcome without reservation except weekends when with members only. *Society Meetings:* catered for by arrangement at £12.00 per head. Professional: Colin Thomas (0222 891909). Secretary/Manager: D.Bryan Jones (0222 890263).

CARDIFF. **Llanishen Golf Club,** Cwm, Lisvane, Cardiff CF4 5UD (Cardiff (0222) 752205). *Location:* five miles north of Cardiff city centre, one mile north of Llanishen village. Wooded mountain course with spectacular views. 18 holes, 5296 yards, 4844 metres. S.S.S. 66. *Green Fees:* £20.00. Special rates for County Cards or playing with member. *Eating facilities:* full bar and catering except Mondays. *Visitors:* welcome weekdays; weekends only with member. Handicap Certificate required. *Society Meetings:* catered for Thursday only on written application. Visitors must be bona fide members of a golf club. Professional: R.A. Jones (0222 755076). Secretary/Manager: Elfed Davies (0222 755078).

CARDIFF. **Radyr Golf Club,** Drysgol Road, Radyr, Cardiff CF4 8BS (Cardiff (0222) 842442). *Location:* A470, five miles north of Cardiff, turn left at Taffs Well; or Cardiff to Llandaff then Llantrisant Road, fork right past Westward Ho! Garage for Radyr. Parkland course. 18 holes, 6031 yards. S.S.S. 70. *Green Fees:* £18.00 with Handicap Certificate. *Eating facilities:* snacks, lunches and evening meals except Thursdays. Please order in advance (0222 842735). *Visitors:* welcome without reservation, weekends only with member. *Society Meetings:* catered for Wednesdays and Fridays. Professional: Steve Gough (0222 842476). Club Manager: Major M.B. Richards (0222 842408).

CARDIFF. **St. Mellons Golf Club,** St. Mellons, Cardiff CF3 8XS (Castleton (0633) 680401). *Location:* just off M4 at Junction 28 on to A48. Parkland. 18 holes, 6225 yards. S.S.S. 70. *Green Fees:* £20.00 weekdays. *Eating facilities:* available. *Visitors:* welcome with Handicap Certificates weekdays only, weekends with member only. *Society Meetings:* catered for on written application. Professional: Barry Thomas (0633 680101). Secretary: Mrs K. Newling (0633 680408).

CARDIFF. **Wenvoe Castle Golf Club Ltd,** Wenvoe, Cardiff CF5 6BE (Cardiff (0222) 591094). *Location:* A48 west from Cardiff, left and A4050, about two miles. 18 holes, 6411 yards. S.S.S. 71. *Green Fees:* weekdays £17.00, weekends £12.00 with a member only. *Eating facilities:* bar snacks and restaurant meals. *Visitors:* welcome if introduced by a member or on presentation of recognised club card. *Society Meetings:* catered for Monday to Thursday, parties of 16 or more. Pro-

fessional: M. Pycroft (0222 593649). Secretary: E.J. Dew (0222 594371).

CARDIFF. **Whitchurch (Cardiff) Golf Club,** Whitchurch, Cardiff CF4 6XD (Cardiff (0222) 620125). *Location:* three-and-a-half miles from Cardiff on A470 Merthyr Tydfil road. 18 holes, 6245 yards. S.S.S. 70. *Green Fees:* £20.00 weekdays, £25.00 weekends and Bank Holidays. *Eating facilities:* full catering every day. *Visitors:* welcome, if members of recognised Golf Clubs. Restricted at weekends. Please telephone Professional prior to visit. *Society Meetings:* catered for Thursdays on written application. Professional: Eddie Clark (0222 614660). Secretary: Mrs P. Latham (0222 620985).

DINAS POWIS. **Dinas Powis Golf Club,** Old Highwalls, Dinas Powis CF6 4AJ (Cardiff (0222) 512157). *Location:* M4 Cardiff, thereafter signposted Dinas Powis, Penarth and Barry. Mostly parkland, three holes quite hilly. 18 holes, 5151 yards. S.S.S. 65. *Green Fees:* weekdays £12.00 (£8.00 with member), weekends £15.00 (£12.00 with member). *Eating facilities:* bar snacks, teas, à la carte – if required subject to notice. *Visitors:* welcome weekdays except Monday and Tuesday, weekends on special application. *Society Meetings:* welcome, no restrictions. Professional: G. Bennett (0222 512727). Secretary: J.D. Hughes (0222 512727).

PENARTH. **Glamorganshire Golf Club,** Lavernock Road, Penarth CF6 2UP (0222 707048). *Location:* one mile west of Penarth; M4 (Junction 33) then A4232. Parkland course overlooking Bristol Channel. 18 holes, 6150 yards. S.S.S. 70. *Green Fees:* weekdays £15.00, weekends and Bank Holidays £20.00. *Eating facilities:* full restaurant service and bar meals. Men's bar and mixed lounge bar. *Visitors:* welcome providing no competitions in progress and/or Societies on course, also must be a member of a bona fide golf club and show Handicap Certificate duly authorised by Secretary of club. *Society Meetings:* catered for with prior notice. Professional: A. Kerr Smith (0222 707401). Secretary/Manager: G.C. Crimp (0222 701185).

West Glamorgan

CLYDACH. **Inco Golf Club,** Clydach (0792 844216). *Location:* outskirts of Swansea, easily accessible from M4. Flat, tree-lined course, with river. 12 holes, 6230 yards. S.S.S. 70. *Green fees:* £8.00/£9.00 per round. *Eating facilities:* none. Bar only. *Visitors:* welcome. *Society Meetings:* by arrangement through Secretary: Mr S. Murdoch (0792 843336).

GLYNNEATH. **Glynneath Golf Club,** 'Penygraig', Pontneathvaughan, Near Glynneath SA11 5UH (Glynneath (0639) 720452). *Location:* turn off A465 into

Glynneath, right at traffic lights (east) onto B4242 for one and a half miles to Pentneathvaughan. Hillside course, fairly flat – half parkland and half wooded in Brecon National Park. 18 holes, 5456 yards, 4989 metres. S.S.S. 67. *Green Fees:* weekdays £6.00, weekends £10.00. £2.00 reduction if playing with a member. *Eating facilities:* catering available for societies, bar open every day. *Visitors:* welcome without reservation. *Society Meetings:* all welcome, but notify Secretary of date. Secretary: R.M. Ellis (0639 720679).

NEATH. **Neath Golf Club,** Cadoxton, Neath (Neath (0639) 643615). *Location:* two miles from Neath, signposted Pontardawe, Merthyr Road. 18 holes, 6436 yards. S.S.S. 72. *Green Fees:* weekdays £8.00, weekends £12.00. *Eating facilities:* available except Monday. *Visitors:* welcome without reservation. New snooker room. *Society Meetings:* catered for. Professional: E.M. Bennett. Hon. Secretary: J. Evans Esq (0639 52759).

NEATH. **Swansea Bay Golf Club,** Jersey Marine, Neath (Skewen (0792) 812198 and 814153). *Location:* on Neath to Swansea dual carriageway four miles from Neath. 18 holes, 6302 yards. S.S.S. 71. *Green Fees:* weekdays £12.00, weekends and Bank Holidays £15.00. *Eating facilities:* luncheons and teas available six days per week. *Visitors:* welcome without reservation. *Society Meetings:* catered for. Professional: M. Day. Secretary: D. Goatcher.

SWANSEA. **Clyne Golf Club,** 120 Owls Lodge Lane, The Mayals, Blackpyl, Swansea SA3 5DP (0792 401989). *Location:* west of Swansea, South Gower road before Mumbles. Moorland course. 18 holes, 6350 yards. S.S.S. 71. Large practice area and 18-hole putting green. *Green Fees:* weekdays £11.00, weekends £15.00. *Eating facilities:* full catering available. *Visitors:* welcome. *Society Meetings:* welcome by application. Professional: Mark Bevan (0792 402094). Secretary: B.R. Player.

SWANSEA. **Fairwood Park Golf Club Ltd,** Upper Killay, Swansea SA2 7JN (Swansea (0792) 203648). *Location:* from Swansea city centre, follow signs to 'Sketty' and 'Killay', road to club is opposite Swansea Airport. 18 holes, 6606 yards. S.S.S. 72. *Green Fees:* £15.00 weekdays, £20.00 weekends and Bank Holidays. *Eating facilities:* full range, from bar snacks to 3-course meals. (Order full meals before playing). *Visitors:* welcome (£1.00 reduction with member, on weekdays only). *Society Meetings:* welcome, other than Saturdays, Sundays and Bank Holidays, during time between April and September. Apply in first instance to Secretary. Secretary: J. Beer. Professional: Mark Evans.

SWANSEA. **Langland Bay Golf Club,** Mumbles, Swansea (Swansea (0792) 366023). *Location:* six miles west of Swansea. 18 holes, 5830 yards. S.S.S. 69. *Green Fees:* weekdays £15.00, weekends and Bank Holidays £17.00. *Eating facilities:* lunches, teas and supper, also bar snacks. *Visitors:* welcome without reservation. *Society Meetings:* restricted, by arrangement. Professional: T. Lynch (0792 366186). Secretary: T.J. Jenkins (0792 361721).

SWANSEA. **Morriston Golf Club,** 160 Clasemont Road, Morriston, Swansea (Swansea (0792) 771079). *Location:* three miles north of Swansea on A4067, then west on A48 for half a mile. 18 holes, 5773 yards. S.S.S. 68. *Green Fees:* weekdays £10.00 plus VAT, weekends and Bank Holidays £16.00 plus VAT. *Eating facilities:* lunches at club, 24 hours notice required. *Visitors:* welcome without reservation. *Society Meetings:* catered for by arrangement with Secretary. Professional: Derryl Rees (0792 772335). Secretary: Leonard T. Lewis (0792 796528).

SWANSEA. **Palleg Golf Club,** Lower Cwmtwrch, Swansea (Glantawe (0639 842193). *Location:* off A4067 (A4068) north of Swansea 14 miles, 25 miles Brecon. 9 holes, 6510 yards. S.S.S. 72. *Green Fees:* weekdays £6.00, weekends £8.00. *Eating facilities:* clubhouse open after 8.00pm; various public houses within two miles of club that do catering of a high standard. *Visitors:* welcome without reservation. *Society Meetings:* catered for Mondays. Secretary: A.W. Stanley.

SWANSEA. **Pennard Golf Club,** 2 Southgate Road, Southgate, Swansea SA3 2BT (044128 3131). *Location:* eight miles west of Swansea A4067, B4436. Seaside links. 18 holes, 6274 yards. S.S.S. 71. Practice areas. *Green Fees:* weekly ticket £30.00, daily – Monday/Friday £12.00, with member £8.00, daily weekends and Bank Holidays £15.00, with member £10.00. *Eating facilities:* dining room and bar snacks. *Visitors:* welcome at any time. Squash courts. *Society Meetings:* catered for weekdays only. Professional: M.V. Bennett (044128 3451). Secretary: J.D. Eccles (044128 3131).

SWANSEA. **Pontardawe Golf Club,** Cefn Llan, Pontardawe, Swansea (0792 863118). *Location:* four miles north of M4 Junction 45 on A4067 Swansea-Brecon road. 18 holes, 6162 yards. S.S.S. 70. *Green Fees:* £10.00 weekdays, £15.00 weekends. *Eating facilities:* restaurant open daily except Mondays. *Visitors:* welcome. Handicap Certificate required. *Society Meetings:* catered for by application. Professional: R.A. Ryder (0792 830977). Secretary: D.D. Abraham (0792 830041).

Gwent

ABERGAVENNY. **Monmouthshire Golf Club,** Llanfoist, Abergavenny NP7 9HE (Abergavenny (0873) 3171). *Location:* two miles out of Abergavenny on Llanfoist to Llanellen Road. Parkland with scenic mountain views. 18 holes, 6045 yards. S.S.S. 69. Practice ground. *Green Fees:* weekdays £16.00, weekends and Bank Holidays £21.00. *Eating facilities:* full meals except Tuesdays (order in advance). *Visitors:* welcome. Proof of membership of recognised golf club required. *Society Meetings:* catered for. Booking to be confirmed before Jan. 31st each year. Professional: P. Worthing (0873 2532). Secretary: G.J. Swayne (0873 2606).

BLACKWOOD. **Blackwood Golf Club,** Cwmgelli, Blackwood (0495 223152). *Location:* one mile north of Blackwood on Tredegar road A494. 9 holes, 5350 yards. S.S.S. 66. *Green Fees:* weekdays £8.00, weekends and Bank Holidays £10.00. *Visitors:* welcome weekdays only. *Society Meetings:* by arrangement. Secretary: A.M. Reed-Gibbs.

CAERLEON. **Caerleon Public Golf Course,** The Broadway, Caerleon, Newport (Caerleon (0633) 420342). *Location:* three miles off M4 at turnoff for Caerleon. Flat parkland. 9 holes, 3000 yards. S.S.S. 68. Driving range. *Green Fees:* information not provided. *Eating facilities:* cafe and bar. *Visitors:* no restrictions. *Society Meetings:* welcome. Professional: Alex Campbell. Secretary: P. Arnold.

CHEPSTOW. **St. Pierre Hotel Golf and Country Club Ltd,** St. Pierre Park, Chepstow NP6 6YA (Chepstow (02912) 5261). *Location:* five minutes from M4/Severn Bridge on A48 to Newport. Old course 18 holes, Championship/Medal 6700 yards, S.S.S. 73; standard tees 6285 yards, S.S.S. 71. New course 18 holes, 5762 yards, S.S.S. 68. *Green Fees:* information not provided. *Eating facilities:* restaurant, coffee shop. *Visitors:* welcome with current membership of a bona fide golf club. *Society Meetings:* weekdays only, except when resident in hotel which has 150 bedrooms with bathrooms, including 42 executive lodge bedrooms, conference rooms and extensive leisure facilities. Professional: Renton Doig. Secretary: T.J. Cleary.

CWMBRAN. **Greenmeadow Golf Club,** Treherbert Road, Croesygelliog, Cwmbran NP44 2BZ (06333 69321/2). *Location:* M4 Junction 26 north on A4042. Right turn-off Croesyceiliog by-pass. Next to Gwent Crematorium. Parkland course. 18 holes, 6140 yards. S.S.S. 69. Putting green. *Green fees:* information not provided. *Eating facilities:* all meals available, weddings and functions catered for. *Visitors:* welcome weekdays. Weekends by prior notice. No jeans, golf shoes must be worn. *Society Meetings:* by arrangement weekdays only. Professional: C. Coomes (06333 62626).

CWMBRAN. **Pontnewydd Golf Club,** Upper Cwmbran, Cwmbran (Cwmbran (0633) 2170). *Location:* two miles north of Cwmbran on B4244. 9 holes, 5403 yards. S.S.S. 67. *Green Fees:* £10.00. *Visitors:* welcome all week, must play with member at weekends. *Society Meetings:* not catered for. Secretary: H. R. Gabe.

LLANWERN. **Llanwern Golf Club,** Tennyson Avenue, Llanwern NP6 2DY (Newport (0633) 412380). *Location:* four miles east of Newport, one mile from M4 Junction 23. Parkland. 18 holes, 6202 yards, 5581 metres. S.S.S. 70. 9 holes, 5674 yards, 5186 metres. S.S.S. 69. Small practice area. *Green Fees:* £15.00 weekdays. *Eating facilities:* full catering and bar. *Visitors:* welcome weekdays and Thursdays especially, must have Handicap Certificate. No casual visitors at weekends. *Society Meetings:* catered for by arrangement. Professional: S. Price (0633 413233). Secretary: D.J. Peak (0633 412029).

MONMOUTH. **Monmouth Golf Club,** Leasbrook Lane, Monmouth (Monmouth (0600) 2212). *Location:* turn left (signposted) one mile along A40 (Monmouth to Ross road). 9 holes, 5424 yards. S.S.S. 66. *Green Fees:* weekdays £10.00, weekends and Bank Holidays £15.00 (inclusive of VAT). Weekly ticket (Monday/Friday inclusive) £35.00. *Eating facilities:* Clubhouse every day (except Mondays). *Visitors:* welcome. *Society Meetings:* catered for upon application. Secretary: K.A. Prichard (0594 33394).

MONMOUTH. **The Rolls of Monmouth Golf Club,** The Hendre, Monmouth NP5 4HG (Monmouth (0600) 5353). *Location:* three miles west of Monmouth on the B4233 Monmouth/Abergavenny road. Wooded, hilly parkland course on private estate. 18 holes, 6723 yards. S.S.S. 72. Practice area, practice net, putting

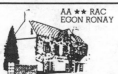

green. *Green Fees:* on request. *Eating facilities:* full catering. *Visitors:* welcome any day. *Society Meetings:* welcome on any day including weekends. Secretary: J.D. Ross.

NANTYGLO. **West Monmouthshire Golf Club,** Pond Road, Nantyglo NP3 4YX (Brynmawr (0495) 310233). *Location:* Heads of Valley Road to Brynmawr, Semtex factory, roundabout, signposted. Mountain and heathland course. 18 holes, 6118 yards. S.S.S. 69. *Green Fees:* weekdays £8.00, £2.00 less if playing with member, weekends and Bank Holidays £15.00 with member only. Weekly and monthly tickets available. *Eating facilities:* 24 hours notice required. *Visitors:* welcome weekdays without reservation, weekends with members only. *Society Meetings:* catered for, tee 9.30 to 11.30am; 2.00pm plus. Secretary: Colin Lewis (0495 312746).

NEWPORT. **Newport Golf Club,** Great Oak, Rogerstone, Newport NP1 9FX (Newport (0633) 892683). *Location:* four miles west of Newport, one and a half miles west of Exit 27 of M4 (signposted Highcross), on B4591. Flat parkland and wooded. 18 holes, 6314 yards, 5830 metres. S.S.S. 71. Two practice areas. *Green Fees:* £18.00 weekdays, £25.00 weekends. *Eating facilities:* full dining facilities at club. *Visitors:* welcome weekdays without reservation. *Society Meetings:* catered for weekdays (except Tuesdays). Professional: Roy Skuse (0633 893271). Hon. Secretary: Allen David Jones (0633 892643 and 896794).

NEWPORT. **Tredegar Park Golf Club Ltd,** Bassaleg Road, Newport NP9 3PX (Newport (0633) 895219).

Location: exit 27 M4, then via Western Avenue and Bassaleg Road. Parkland. 18 holes, 6097 yards, 5575 metres. S.S.S. 70. Two practice holes. *Green Fees:* weekdays £15.00, weekends and Bank Holidays £20.00. *Eating facilities:* lounge bar – 19th hole – and restaurant. *Visitors:* welcome with letter of introduction or membership card. *Society Meetings:* bona fide members of golf clubs catered for. Professional: M.L. Morgan (0633 894517). Secretary: A.A. Skinner, D.F.M.A.E. (0633 894433).

PONTYPOOL. **Pontypool Golf Club,** Lasgarn Lane, Trevethin, Pontypool NP4 8TR (Pontypool (0495) 763655). *Location:* St. Cadoc's Church A4042. Undulating hillside course, with mountain turf and fine view. 18 holes, 6013 yards. S.S.S. 69. Practice area. *Green Fees:* £13.00 weekdays, £17.50 weekends and Bank Holidays. *Eating facilities:* diningroom and bar snacks. *Visitors:* welcome with Handicap Certificates. *Society Meetings:* catered for by arrangement. Professional: Jim Howard (0495 55544). Secretary: Mrs E. Wilce (0495 763655).

RHYMNEY. **Tredegar and Rhymney Golf Club,** Cwmtysswg, Rhymney NP2 3BQ (0685 840743). *Location:* junction of A4048 and A465 Heads of the Valley road. 9 holes, 5564 yards. S.S.S. 68. *Green Fees:* weekends and Bank Holidays £7.50, weekdays £5.00. £3.00 if playing with a member. *Eating facilities:* bar snacks. *Visitors:* welcome without reservation weekdays only, must be member of a club. *Society Meetings:* catered for without reservation. Secretary: V. Davies (0495 6096).

Gwynedd

ABERDOVEY. **Aberdovey Golf Club,** Aberdovey LL35 0RT (Aberdovey (065 472) 210). *Location:* west end of Aberdovey on A493, adjacent to railway station. Links course. 18 holes, 6445 yards. S.S.S. 71. Practice ground. *Green Fees:* on application. *Eating facilities:* restaurant and bar. *Visitors:* welcome on providing proof of membership of bona fide Club. *Society Meetings:* catered for by previous arrangement (not August or Bank Holidays). Professional: J. Davies (065 472 602). Secretary: J.M. Griffiths (065 472 493).

ANGLESEY. **Baron Hill Golf Club,** Beaumaris, Anglesey (Beaumaris (0248) 810231). *Location:* one mile from Beaumaris centre. 9 holes, 5062 metres. S.S.S. 67. *Green Fees:* £6.00 per day, £7.00 weekends and Bank Holidays, £25.00 weekly ticket. *Eating facilities:* snacks during bar hours. *Visitors:* welcome without reservation. *Society Meetings:* catered for. Hon. Secretary: E.D. Thomas. Professional: Peter Maton.

ANGLESEY. **Bull Bay Golf Club Ltd,** Bull Bay, Amlwch, Anglesey LL68 9RY (Amlwch (0407) 830213). *Location:* A5025 coast road north west of Amlwch. Seaside links. 18 holes, 6160 yards. S.S.S. 70. Practice ground and putting green. *Green Fees:* £10.50 per day weekdays, £15.00 per day weekends (including Fridays). Discount for parties of 12 and over. *Eating facilities:* bar and bar snacks, dining room. *Visitors:* welcome, competitions permitting. *Society Meetings:* catered for by arrangement. Professional: Stephen Tarrant (0407 831188). Hon. Secretary: Rennie Tickle (0407 830960).

BALA. **Bala Golf Club,** Penlan, Bala (0678 520359). *Location:* turn right before coming to Bala Lake on the main Bala-Dolgellau road. Upland course with superb views in the Snowdonia National Park. 10 holes, 4934 yards, 4512 metres. S.S.S. 64. *Green Fees:* weekdays £5.00, weekends and Bank Holidays £7.00 per day. Weekly tickets £15.00. *Eating facilities:* bar with snacks available. *Visitors:* welcome all year, some restrictions on Bank Holidays and Sundays. Snooker table and small golf shop. *Society Meetings:* very welcome by prior arrangement. Professional: David Larvin (visiting). Secretary: Martin Wright (0678 520057 evenings).

BANGOR. **St. Deiniol Golf Club,** Penybryn, Bangor LL57 1PX (Bangor (0248) 353098). *Location:* at A5/A55 intersection, follow A5122 for one mile to eastern outskirts of Bangor. Parkland course with magnificent views. 18 holes, 5545 yards, 5068 metres. S.S.S. 67. *Green Fees:* £8.00 weekdays, £10.00 weekends. *Eating facilities:* two bars; full catering Mondays excepted. *Visitors:* welcome without reservation, restrictions at weekends. *Society Meetings:* welcome by prior arrangement. Professional: P. Lovell. Secretary: D.L. Davies.

BETWS-Y-COED. **Betws-y-Coed Golf Club,** Betws-y-Coed (Betws-y-Coed (069-02) 556). *Location:* turn north off A5 in village. Parkland, flat scenic course on valley floor of River Conwy. 9 holes, 4996 yards. S.S.S. 64. *Green Fees:* £10.00 weekdays, £12.00 weekends (reduction for parties). *Eating facilities:* catering, bar 12 – 2pm and from 4.30pm. *Visitors:* no restrictions provided there are no club competitions. *Society Meetings:* catered for, £8.00 weekdays, £10.00 weekends. Secretary: G.B. Archer (069-03 202).

CAERNARFON. **Caernarfon Golf Club,** Aberforeshore, Llanfaglan, Caernarfon (0286 3783). *Location:* two miles from town along the Menai Straits. Parkland course in superb sea and mountain setting. 18 holes, 5869 yards. S.S.S. 69. *Green Fees:* £8.00. *Eating facilities:* excellent catering and bar facilities. *Visitors:* welcome Monday to Friday. *Society Meetings:* welcome, subject to pre-arranged bookings. Secretary: J.I.Jones (0286 3783).

CONWY. **Conwy (Caernarvonshire) Golf Club,** Morfa, Conwy LL32 8ER (Aberconwy (0492) 593400). *Location:* quarter-of-a-mile west of Conwy off A55. Seaside links. 18 holes, 6901 yards. S.S.S. 73. Practice facilities. *Green Fees:* weekdays £12.00, weekends and Bank Holidays £16.00. Weekly ticket £48.00 (Monday to Friday). *Eating facilities:* available except Monday evening and all day Tuesday. *Visitors:* welcome with reservation, restrictions at weekends. *Society Meetings:* catered for on application to Secretary. Professional: Peter Lees (0492 593225). Secretary: E.C. Roberts (0492 592423).

CRICCIETH. **Criccieth Golf Club,** Ednyfed Hill, Criccieth (Criccieth (0766) 522154). *Location:* in High Street (A497) turn right past Memorial Hall, keep going up lane to Club. 18 holes, 5755 yards. S.S.S. 68. *Green Fees:* £7.00. *Eating facilities:* light meals available April to September. *Visitors:* welcome without reservation. *Society Meetings:* catered for with prior reservation. Secretary: M.G. Hamilton (0766 522697).

DOLGELLAU. **Dolgellau Golf Club,** Ffordd Pencefn, Dolgellau (0341 422603). *Location:* half-a-mile from town centre. 9 holes, 4671 yards. S.S.S. 63. *Green Fees:* weekdays £6.00 per day, weekends and Bank Holidays £7.50. *Eating facilities:* bar and catering facilities available. *Visitors:* welcome without reservation. *Society Meetings:* catered for. Secretary: D.W. Jones (0341 422603).

FFESTINIOG. **Ffestiniog Golf Club,** Y Cefn, Ffestiniog (0766 762637). *Location:* three miles from Blaenau Ffestiniog, near A470 north to south. Mountain course. 9 holes, 5032 yards. S.S.S. 66. *Green Fees:* £4.50. *Eating facilities:* available by prior arrangement. *Visitors:* welcome at any time. *Society Meetings:* by prior arrangement. Secretary: Andrew M. Roberts (0766 831829).

HARLECH. **Royal St. David's Golf Club,** Harlech LL46 2UB (Harlech (0766) 780203). Seaside links. 18 holes, 6427 yards. S.S.S. 71. Large practice ground. *Green Fees:* weekdays £16.00, weekends and Bank Holidays £20.00. *Eating facilities:* full catering and bar available in summer and by arrangement in winter (0766 780182). *Visitors:* welcome provided they are members of bona fide golf clubs, booking advisable. *Society Meetings:* catered for by prior arrangement. Professional (and Tee Bookings): John Barnett (0766 780857). Secretary/Manager: R.I. Jones (0766 780361).

LLANDUDNO. **Llandudno Golf Club (Maesdu) Ltd,** Hospital Road, Llandudno LL30 1HU (0492 76016). *Location:* Llandudno General Hospital. A55 and then A470. Parkland. 18 holes, 6513 yards. S.S.S. 72. *Green Fees:* weekdays £12.00 per day, weekends and Bank Holidays £16.00 per day. *Eating facilities:* full catering, bar (large) available. *Visitors:* welcome every-day, tee reservations for members. *Society Meetings:* must be booked, catered for. Professional: (0492 75195). Secretary: J. Hallam (0492 76450).

LLANDUDNO. **North Wales Golf Club Ltd,** 72 Bryniau Road, West Shore, Llandudno LL30 2DZ (Llandudno (0492) 75325). *Location:* one-and-a-half miles from Llandudno town centre on West Shore. Seaside links. 18 holes, 6132 yards, 5580 metres. S.S.S. 69. *Green Fees:* weekdays £10.00 per day, weekends and Bank Holidays £16.00 per day. Inclusive package available November to March. *Eating facilities:* full bar and catering facilities. *Visitors:* welcome with reservation after 9.45am. Some other time restrictions. *Society Meetings:* catered for by arrangement. Professional: J. Waugh (0492 76878). Secretary: G.D. Harwood (0492 75325).

LLANDUDNO. **Rhos-on-Sea Residential Golf Club,** Penrhyn Bay, Llandudno LL30 3PU (Llandudno (0492) 49100). *Location:* A55 to Colwyn Bay follow signs to Rhos-on-Sea, one mile past Rhos-on-Sea on coast road in Penrhyn Bay. Flat seaside parkland course. 18 holes, 6064 yards. S.S.S. 69. *Green Fees:* £10.00 weekdays, £13.00 weekends. *Eating facilities:* available, bar meals 12 – 2pm, teas, coffees, snacks available all day. Evening meals by arrangement. Licensed bar open 11am – 3pm lunch, 5.30pm – 11pm evenings; Sundays 12 – 2pm lunch, 7pm – 10.30pm evenings. *Visitors:* all welcome any time, prior booking required particularly weekends. 18 bedrooms, two full size snooker tables, small TV lounge. Two £100 jackpot fruit machines. *Society Meetings:* catered for. Professional: Mr Mike Greenough (0492 48115). Secretary: Mr Mike Poole (0492 49641). New Stewards: Mr and Mrs F. Nuttall.

LLANGEFNI. **Llangefni Public Golf Course,** Llangefni Isle of Anglesey. Short, parkland course. 9 holes, 1467 yards, 1342 metres. S.S.S. 28. Practice net. *Green fees:* information not provided. Reduced rates Juniors and OAP's. *Eating facilities:* light refreshments only. *Visitors:* welcome at all times, no booking. Golf equipment available for hire. Professional: Paul Lovell (0248 722193).

MORFA BYCHAN. **Porthmadog Golf Club,** Morfa Bychan, Porthmadog (0766 512037). *Location:* one mile from Porthmadog on the road to Black Rock Sands. First nine flat parkland, second nine links. 18 holes, 6309 yards. S.S.S. 70. Practice area. *Green Fees:* £10.00 weekdays, £15.00 weekends. *Eating facilities:* restaurant lunches, teas and evening meals by arrangement. Bar snacks. *Visitors:* welcome. *Society Meetings:* catered for by prior arrangement. Professional: Peter Bright (0766 513828). Secretary: Gareth W. Jones.

NEFYN. **Nefyn Golf Club,** Golf Road, Morfa Nefyn, Pwllheli LL53 6DA (Nefyn (0758) 720218). *Location:* north coast Lleyn Peninsula, two miles west of Nefyn, 20 miles west of Caernarfon. Seaside course. 18 holes, 6335 yards. S.S.S. 71. Practice area. *Green Fees:* weekdays £12.50, weekends £15.00. Reduction for parties over eight. *Eating facilities:* available. *Visitors:* welcome without reservation, except club competition days. Billiards room available. *Society Meetings:* catered for by arrangement with Secretary. Professional: J.R. Pilkington (0758 720218). Secretary: Lt Col R.W. Parry (0758 720966).

PENMAENMAWR. **Penmaenmawr Golf Club,** Cae Maen Pavilion, Conwy Old Road, Penmaenmawr LL34 6RD (Penmaenmawr (0492) 623330). *Location:* situated at the foot of Sychnant Pass between Conwy and Penmaenmawr (A55). Undulating parkland with panoramic views. 9 holes (alternate tees), 5223 yards. S.S.S. 66. Practice putting green. *Green Fees:* £8.00 weekdays, £10.00 weekends. *Eating facilities:* available by arrangement; bar open daily. *Visitors:* welcome subject to availability of tees. *Society Meetings:* welcome except Saturdays by arrangement. Secretary: Mrs J.E. Jones (0492 623330).

PWLLHELI. **Abersoch Golf Club,** Abersoch, Pwllheli (Abersoch (075 881) 2622). *Location:* beyond village

along the shore. 9 holes, 2896 yards. S.S.S. 68. *Green Fees:* information not provided. *Visitors:* welcome without reservation. *Society Meetings:* not catered for. Secretary: Peter Jones.

PWLLHELI. **Pwllheli Golf Club,** Pwllheli LL53 5PS (Pwllheli (0758) 613720). *Location:* first turning left when leaving island in Town Centre towards Abersoch. 18 holes, 6105 yards. S.S.S. 69. *Green Fees:* £10.00 weekdays, £12.00 weekends. *Eating facilities:* full catering service available. *Visitors:* welcome without reservation. *Society Meetings:* catered for. Professional: G.D. Verity. Secretary: Eric Williams (0758 612520).

RHOSNEIGR. **Anglesey Golf Club Ltd,** Station Road, Rhosneigr (Rhosneigr (0407) 810219). *Location:*

five miles off A5, eight miles from Holyhead. Links course. 18 holes, 5573 yards. S.S.S. 70. *Green Fees:* £6.00 weekdays, £8.00 weekends. *Eating facilities:* comprehensive. *Visitors:* welcome without reservation. *Society Meetings:* catered for. Professional: Paul Lovell (0407 811202). Secretary: R. D. Jones.

TREARDDUR BAY. **Holyhead Golf Club,** Trearddur Bay, Anglesey. 18 holes, 6058 yards. S.S.S. 70. *Green Fees:* on application to Secretary. *Eating facilities:* all catering facilities provided. *Visitors:* welcome, must be members of recognised golf clubs. *Society Meetings:* catered for if members of bona fide golf clubs. Dormy House accommodation available for up to 14. Professional: Paul Capper (0407 2119). Hon. Secretary/ Manager: L. Toth (0407 3279).

Powys

BRECON. **Brecon Golf Club,** Newton Park, Brecon (Brecon (0874) 2004). *Location:* on A40 west of town, half a mile from centre. 9 holes, 5208 yards. S.S.S. 66. *Green Fees:* £5.00 at all times. *Visitors:* welcome without reservation. *Society Meetings:* catered for. Secretary: D.H.E. Roderick.

BUILTH WELLS. **Builth Wells Golf Club,** Golf Club Lane, Builth Wells (Builth Wells (0982) 553296). *Location:* off A483, Builth Wells. Parkland. 18 holes, 5376 yards. S.S.S. 67. Practice area. *Green Fees:* £10.00 weekdays, £12.00 weekends and Bank Holidays. Five day ticket £40.00, seven day ticket £50.00. (Winter £6.00). *Eating facilities:* restaurant (not Mondays), bar. *Visitors:* limited only by tournaments. *Society Meetings:* size limited by catering facilities. Professional: Bill Evans (0982 553293). Secretary: M.A. Sanders (05913 562 – home).

BUILTH WELLS. **Rhosgoch Golf Club,** Rhosgoch, Builth Wells LD2 3JY (Painscastle (04975) 251). *Location:* near Hay-on-Wye. Parkland course. 9 holes 4842 yards. S.S.S. 64, *Green Fees:* £5.00 weekdays, £7.00 weekends. *Eating facilities:* bar/restaurant meals, two bars. *Visitors:* welcome anytime. Accommodation

arranged. *Society Meetings:* anytime. Secretary: N. Harley (04975 242).

CRADOC. **Cradoc Golf Club,** Penoyre Park, Cradoc, Brecon LD3 9LP (Brecon (0874) 3658). *Location:* situated in the Brecon Beacons National Park. Attractive parkland course. 18 holes, 6300 yards. S.S.S. 71. *Green Fees:* £10.00 weekdays, £14.00 weekends. *Eating facilities:* excellent facilities available. *Visitors:* welcome both weekend and weekdays. Professional: Douglas Beattie (0874 5524). Secretary: G.S.W. Davies. Host of 1982 Welsh Stroke Play Championships. Home of the Welsh Brewers Champion of Champions Tournament.

CRICKHOWELL. **Old Rectory Hotel and Golf Club,** Llangattock, Crickhowell NP8 1PH (Crickhowell (0873) 810373). *Location:* Crickhowell is between Abergavenny and Brecon. Course is on a hill with spectacular views. 9 holes, 2878 yards. S.S.S. 54. *Green Fees:* information not provided. *Eating facilities:* restaurant, bar meals, two bars. *Visitors:* welcome at all times. Accommodation available, outdoor swimming pool.

KNIGHTON. **Knighton Golf Club,** Ffrydd, Knighton LD7 1DG (Knighton (0547) 528646). *Location:* on ring road of town A488 towards Llandrindod Wells, turn left. Hill course, wooded. 9 holes, 5320 yards, 5014 metres. S.S.S. 66. *Green Fees:* weekdays £5.00, weekends and Bank Holidays £7.00. *Eating facilities:* bar only in evenings. *Visitors:* welcome every day except Sunday afternoons (Competitions). Secretary: E.J.P. Bright (0547 528684).

LLANDRINDOD WELLS. **Llandrindod Wells Golf Club,** Llandrindod Wells (Llandrindod Wells (0597) 2010). *Location:* well signposted from A483 and centre of town. 18 holes, 5687 yards. S.S.S. 68. *Green Fees:* £7.00 weekdays, £9.00 weekends. *Eating facilities:* every day (except Tuesday), order in advance. *Visitors:* welcome without reservation. *Society Meetings:* catered for, three months' notice required for weekends. Hon. Secretary: R.C. Jones.

LLANIDLOES. **St. Idloes Golf Club,** Pen-yr-Rhallt, Llanidloes (05512 2559). *Location;* take Trefeglwys Road from Llanidloes – one mile – turn left at cottage on top of hill. Slightly undulating terrain. 9 holes, 5300 yards. S.S.S. 66. *Green Fees:* £8.00 per round or day, £20.00 weekly. *Eating facilities:* full menu available. *Visitors:* welcome without reservation. *Society Meetings:* available Mondays to Fridays throughout the year. Secretary: D.N. Jones, "Hillcrest", 40 Caegwyn, Llanidloes (05512 3459).

MACHYNLLETH. **Machynlleth Golf Club,** Ffordd Drenewydd, Machynlleth SY20 8UH (0654 2000). *Location:* A489 from Newtown turn left hand turn before the speed restriction sign on entering Machynlleth. Undulating meadowland course. 9 holes, 5726 yards, 5285 metres. S.S.S. 67. Small practice area. *Green Fees:* £7.00. Reductions for groups of 10 or more. *Eating facilities:* by arrangement. Bar. *Visitors:* welcome except during competition days. *Society Meetings:* welcome. Secretary: Gary Holdsworth (0654 3264).

NEWTOWN. **St. Giles Golf Club,** Pool Road, Newtown (Newtown (0686) 25844). *Location:* convenient to town centre, quarter-of-a-mile on Welshpool Road from Newtown. Pleasant riverside course. 9 holes, 5864 yards. S.S.S. 68. *Green Fees:* weekdays £7.50 per day, weekends and Bank Holidays £10.00 per day. £40.00 per week. *Eating facilities:* bar and catering facilities. *Visitors:* welcome, with reservation Saturday afternoons and Sunday mornings. Golf shop and Professional. *Society Meetings:* catered for. Secretary: N.O. Davies.

WELSHPOOL. **Welshpool Golf Club,** Golfa Hill, Welshpool (Castle Caereinion (093 883) 249). *Location:* A458 West from Welshpool 4 miles signpost on right at junction with main road. 18 holes, 5708 yards. S.S.S. 69. *Green Fees:* information not provided. *Eating facilities:* lunches at club, bar open usual hours. Clubhouse closed Mondays. *Visitors:* welcome. *Society Meetings:* by arrangement. Secretary: R.G.D. Jones.

FOR THE MUTUAL GUIDANCE OF GUEST AND HOST

Every year literally thousands of holidays, short-breaks and overnight stops are arranged through our guides, the vast majority without any problems at all. In a handful of cases, however, difficulties do arise about bookings, which often could have been prevented from the outset.

It is important to remember that when accommodation has been booked, both parties — guests and hosts — have entered into a form of contract. We hope that the following points will provide helpful guidance.

GUESTS: When enquiring about accommodation, be as precise as possible. Give exact dates, numbers in your party and the ages of any children. State the number and type of rooms wanted and also what catering you require — bed and breakfast, full board, etc. Make sure that the position about evening meals is clear — and about pets, reductions for children or any other special points.

Read our reviews carefully to ensure that the proprietors you are going to contact can supply what you want. Ask for a letter confirming all arrangements, if possible.

If you have to cancel, do so as soon as possible. Proprietors do have the right to retain deposits and under certain circumstances to charge for cancelled holidays if adequate notice is not given and they cannot re-let the accommodation.

HOSTS: Give details about your facilities and about any special conditions. Explain your deposit system clearly and arrangements for cancellations, charges, etc, and whether or not your terms include VAT.

If for any reason you are unable to fulfil an agreed booking without adequate notice, you may be under an obligation to arrange alternative suitable accommodation or to make some form of compensation.

While every effort is made to ensure accuracy, we regret that FHG Publications cannot accept responsibility for errors, omissions or misrepresentation in our entries or any consequences thereof. Prices in particular should be checked because we go to press early. We will follow up complaints but cannot act as arbiters or agents for either party.

Royal Portrush, Co. Antrim.

Northern Ireland

Antrim

ANTRIM. **Massereene Golf Club,** 51 Lough Road, Antrim BT41 4DQ (Antrim (08494) 29293). *Location:* one mile S.W. of town, 3 miles from Aldergrove Airport, situated alongside the shores of Lough Neagh. Parkland. 18 holes, 6440 yards. S.S.S. 72. *Green Fees:* weekdays £11.00, weekends £13.00. *Eating facilities:* full catering facilities 12 noon till 9.00pm. *Visitors:* welcome any day except Saturday up to 4pm. *Society Meetings:* catered for Tuesdays, Wednesdays and Thursdays. Secretary: Mrs Marie Agnew (08494 28096). Professional: Jim Smyth (08494 64074).

BALLYCASTLE. **Ballycastle Golf Club,** Cushendall Road, Ballycastle (Ballycastle (02657) 62536). *Location:* approximately 50 miles along the coast road west of Larne Harbour. Seaside links/undulating. 18 holes, 5662 yards, 5177 metres. S.S.S. 68. *Green Fees:* weekdays £9.00 (with member £5.00), weekends £12.00 (with member £7.00 including Public Holi-

days). *Eating facilities:* catering by arrangement. *Visitors:* welcome, best days during the week, no particular restrictions. *Society Meetings:* by arrangement. Professional: Mr T. Stewart (02657 62506). Hon Secretaries: Mr T.J. Sheehan and Mr M.E. Page (02657 62536).

BALLYCLARE. **Ballyclare Golf Club,** 25 Springvale Road, Ballyclare BT39 9JW (Ballyclare (09603) 42352). *Location:* two miles north of Ballyclare. Parkland, lakes and river. 18 holes, 5840 metres. S.S.S. 71. *Green Fees:* weekdays £10.00, weekends £15.00. *Eating facilities:* catering available. *Visitors:* welcome weekdays except Thursday. *Society Meetings:* catered for. Secretary: Harry McConnell (09603 22696).

BALLYMENA. **Ballymena Golf Club,** 128 Raceview Road, Broughshane, Ballymena (Broughshane (0266) 861207). *Location:* two miles east of town on A42. Parkland. 18 holes, 5068 metres. S.S.S. 67. *Green Fees:* information not provided. *Eating facilities:* restaurant and bars. *Visitors:* welcome at all times. *Society Meetings:* catered for. Secretary Manager: W.R.G. Pogue (0266 861487). Professional: James Gallagher (0266 861652).

BELFAST. **Cliftonville Golf Club,** 44 Westland Road, Belfast BT14 6NH (Belfast (0232) 744158). Parkland with rivers bisecting three fairways. 9 holes, 6210 yards, 5672 metres. S.S.S. 70. Practice fairway and nets. *Green Fees:* weekdays £7.50, weekends £10.00. Special rates (25 per cent discount) for parties of 10 or over. *Eating facilities:* full catering available, restaurant, bar snacks. *Visitors:* welcome weekdays, after 5.00pm Saturdays. after 12 noon Sundays. *Society Meetings:* very welcome, especially by arrangement. Hon. Secretary: Martin Henderson (0232 746595).

BELFAST. **Dunmurry Golf Club,** 91 Dunmurry Lane, Dunmurry, Belfast BT17 9JS (Belfast (0232) 621402). *Location:* one mile off M1 (Dunmurry cut-off). Parkland – partially wooded. 18 holes, 5333 metres. S.S.S. 68. Practice area. *Green Fees:* weekdays £10.00 (with member £6.00), weekends £15.00 (with member £8.00). *Eating facilities:* catering (except Mondays) and bar facilities every day. *Visitors:* welcome on weekdays except Friday and Saturday, also Sundays after 1.00pm. *Society Meetings:* weekdays except Friday and Saturday, Sundays 11.30 – 12.30pm. Professional: Paul Leonard (0232 301179). Secretary: Mrs Mary Scott (0232 610834).

BELFAST. **Fortwilliam Golf Club,** Downview Avenue, Belfast BT15 4EZ (0232 776798). *Location:* one mile Fortwilliam Junction M2. Parkland. 18 holes, 5763 yards. S.S.S. 68. *Green Fees:* £11.00 weekdays, £15.00 weekends and Public Holidays. *Eating facilities:* available. *Visitors:* welcome most days. *Society Meetings:* catered for Tuesdays and Thursdays. Professional: Peter Hanna (0232 770980). Secretary: R.J. Campbell (0232 370770).

BELFAST. **Gilnahirk Golf Club,** Manns Corner, Upper Braniel Road, Gilnahirk, Belfast (0232 448351). *Location:* situated in the Castleriagh area of Belfast, off Ballygowan Road. Parkland. 9 holes, 5398 metres. S.S.S. 68. Practice areas, nets and putting green. *Green Fees:* £4.00 weekdays, £4.60 weekends. *Eating facilities:* at special times. *Visitors:* any day. *Society Meetings:* any day. Professional: Mr K. Gray (0232 448477). Secretary: Mr H. Moore (0232 659653).

BELFAST. **Malone Golf Club,** 240 Upper Malone Road, Dunmurry, Belfast BT17 9LB (Belfast (0232) 612695). Parkland course. 18 holes, 6476 yards. S.S.S. 71. 9 holes, 2895 yards. S.S.S. 72. Two practice grounds. *Green Fees:* £17.00 weekdays, £20.00 weekends. *Visitors:* no visitors on Wednesdays and Saturdays before 5.00pm. *Society Meetings:* Mondays and Thursdays. Professional: Peter O'Hagan (0232 614917). Secretary: Mr T. Aitken (0232 612758).

BUSHMILLS. **Bushfoot Golf Club,** Bushfoot Road, Portballintrae, Bushmills BT57 8RR (Bushmills (02657) 31317). *Location:* one mile north of Bushmills. Seaside course. 9 holes, 5552 yards. S.S.S. 67. *Green Fees:* £8.00 weekdays (£5.00 playing with a member), £10.00 weekends (£7.00 playing with a member). *Eating facilities:* bar and catering available. *Visitors:* welcome, but limited numbers at weekends. *Society Meetings:* welcome – rates negotiable. Secretary: Dr P. Ritchie.

CARRICKFERGUS. **Carrickfergus Golf Club,** 35 North Road, Carrickfergus BT38 8LP (Carrickfergus (09603) 62203). *Location:* one mile Carrickfergus via Albert Road. 18 holes, 5752 yards. S.S.S. 68. *Green Fees:* information not provided. *Eating facilities:* meals and snacks to order at club. *Visitors:* welcome. *Society Meetings:* catered for on weekdays. Professional: Ray Stevenson. Manager: J.H. Capper.

CARRICKFERGUS. **Greenisland Golf Club,** 156 Upper Road, Greenisland, Carrickfergus BT38 8RW (Whiteabbey (0232) 862236). 9 holes, 5596 metres. S.S.S. 68. *Green Fees:* weekdays £7.00, Sundays £10.00. *Eating facilities:* lunches at club, order in advance. *Visitors:* welcome except before 5.30pm Saturdays. Secretary: J. Wyness.

CARRICKFERGUS. **Whitehead Golf Club,** McCrae's Brae, Whitehead, Carrickfergus (Whitehead (096 03) 72792). *Location:* Whitehead 15 miles from Belfast, 10 miles from Larne. 18 holes, 6412 yards. S.S.S. 71. *Green Fees:* Information not provided. *Eating facilities:* by arrangement with Steward. *Visitors:* welcome without reservation. *Society Meetings:* by prior arrangement. Secretary/Manager: J.M. Niblock.

CUSHENDALL. **Cushendall Golf Club,** Shore Road, Cushendall (Cushendall (02667) 71318). *Location:* 25 miles north on Antrim coast road from Larne Harbour. Seaside – wooded. River comes into play in seven out of nine holes. 9 holes, 4678 yards 4030 metres. S.S.S. 63. *Green Fees:* weekdays £8.00 per day, weekends and Bank Holidays £10.00; £3.00 concession if playing with member. *Eating facilities:* normal bar hours – by arrangement with caterers. *Visitors:* welcome without reservation, time sheet in operation on Sundays. *Society Meetings:* by arrangement. Hon. Secretary: Shaun McLaughlin (0266 73366).

LARNE. **Cairndhu Golf Club Ltd,** 192 Coast Road, Ballygally, Larne (0574 83324). *Location:* three and a half miles north of Larne. Parkland course. 18 holes, 6112 yards, 5589 metres. S.S.S. 69. Practice area. *Green Fees:* £9.00 weekdays, £12.50 weekends. *Eating facilities:* dining and bar facilities available. *Visitors:* welcome except Saturdays. *Society Meetings:* welcome. Professional: R. Walker (0574 83417). Secretary: Mrs Josephine Robinson (0574 83248).

LARNE. **Larne Golf Club,** 54 Ferris Bay Road, Islandmagee, Larne BT40 3RT (Islandmagee (09603) 82228). *Location:* Larne town. Seaside links/parkland. 9 holes, 6114 yards. S.S.S. 69. Practice field. *Green Fees:* weekdays £6.00. weekends £8.00. Special rates (20 per cent reduction) for parties over 25. *Eating facilities:* restaurant on request/bar. *Visitors:* welcome weekdays, Sundays on application. *Society Meetings:* welcome weekdays. Sundays on application. Secretary: J.B. Stewart (09603 72043).

LISBURN. **Lisburn Golf Club,** Blaris Lodge, 68 Eglantine Road, Lisburn BT27 5RQ (0846 662186). *Location:* three miles south of Lisburn on A1. Parkland. 18 holes, 6556 yards. S.S.S. 72. Practice area. *Green Fees:* £12.00 weekdays, £15.00 weekends. *Eating facilities:* bar and restaurant. *Visitors:* welcome. *Society*

Meetings: catered for. Professional: B. R. Campbell (0846 677217). Secretary/Manager: T. C. McCullogh (0846 677216).

PORTADOWN. **Portadown Golf Club** Carrickblacker, 192 Gilford Road, Portadown BT63 5LF (Portadown (0762) 355356). *Location:* two miles from Portadown on main Banbridge Road. Parkland. 18 holes, 5621 metres. S.S.S. 70 off white tees; 68 off green tees. *Green Fees:* weekdays £7.00, weekends and Bank Holidays £10.00. Eating facilities: bar and restuamt. *Visitors:* welcome all days excpet Tuesdays and Saturdays. *Society Meetings:* catered for. Professional: Paul Stevenson (0762 334655). Secretary: Mrs M.E. Holloway (0762 355356).

PORTRUSH. **Rathmore Golf Club,** Bushmills Road, Portrush BT56 8JE (0265 822285). *Location:* north east coast – six miles from Colraine, beside roundabout on road to Bushmills. Flat seaside links. 18 holes, 6273 yards. S.S.S. 71. *Green Fees:* £12.00 weekdays, £16.00 weekends. *Eating facilities:* bar but no eating facilities. *Visitors:* Saturday and Sunday 1.30 to 2.30pm, Monday to Friday no restrictions except Tuesday after 11.00am September to March. *Society Meetings:* must register at Royal Portrush Golf Club and green fees paid before commencement of play. Professional: Dai Stevenson (R.P.G.C.) (0265 823335). Secretary: Derek Ross Williamson (0265 822996).

PORTRUSH. **Royal Portrush Golf Club,** Bushmills Road, Portrush BT56 8JQ (Portrush (0265) 822314). *Location:* one mile from Portrush on the Bushmills Road. Seaside links, three courses: Dunluce Course 18 holes, 6772 yards. S.S.S 72. Valley Course 18 holes, 6273 yards. S.S.S. 71. Skerries course 9 holes, 1187 yards. Two practice grounds. *Green Fees:* Dunluce £20.00 weekdays, £25.00 weekends; Valley £12.00 weekdays, £16.00 weekends, parties over 16 £7.50 weekdays; Skerries £1.00 weekdays and weekends. *Eating facilities:* restaurant, snacks, meals, à la carte menu available. *Visitors:* welcome with prior reservation except Wednesdays, Friday afternoons and Saturdays. *Society Meetings:* catered for except Saturday. Professional: Dai Stevenson (0265 823335). Secretary: Miss W. Erskine (0265 822311).

Armagh

ARMAGH. **County Armagh Golf Club,** The Demesne, Newry Road, Armagh (Armagh (0861) 522501). 18 holes, 6150 yards. S.S.S. 69. *Green Fees:* £7.00 weekdays, £10.00 weekends. *Eating facilities:* bar and restaurant, no catering Mondays. *Visitors:* welcome. *Society Meetings:* welcome except Saturdays or Thursdays. Professional: Alan Rankin (0861 525864). Secretary: Kay McBride (0861 525861).

LURGAN. **Lurgan Golf Club,** The Demesne, Lurgan BT67 9BN (Lurgan (0762) 322087). *Location:* one mile from motorway, half a mile from Town Centre. Parkland. 18 holes, 5561 metres. S.S.S. 70. Small practice

area. *Green Fees:* weekdays £10.00, weekends £12.00, reductions if playing with a member. *Eating facilities:* restaurant and lounge bar. *Visitors:* welcome except Saturdays. *Society Meetings:* welcome except Saturdays. Professional: D. Paul. Secretary: Mrs G. Turkington.

TANDRAGEE. **Tandragee Golf Club,** Markethill Road, Tandragee, Craigavon BT62 2ER (0762 840727). *Location:* 10 miles from Armagh, five miles from Portadown. Parkland/wooded. 18 holes, 5519 metres. S.S.S. 69. Practice area and net. *Green Fees:* £8.00 weekdays, £11.00 weekends. Societies £7.00 and £10.00. *Eating facilities:* full catering and bars. *Visitors:* welcome all days except Saturdays. *Society Meetings:* welcome by arrangement. Professional: John Black (0762 841761). Secretary: A. Best (0762 841272).

Down

ARDGLASS. **Ardglass Golf Club,** 4 Castle Place, Ardglass (Ardglass (0396) 841219). *Location:* nearest town – Downpatrick situated on the coast 30 miles due south of Belfast. Seaside links. 18 holes, 5462 metres . S.S.S. 69. *Green Fees:* weekdays £8.50, weekends £12.00. *Eating facilities:* bar and diningroom. *Visitors:* welcome.*Society Meetings:* catered for. Advance booking necessary. Professional: Kevin Dorrian (0396 841022). Secretary: Patricia Rooney (0396 841219).

BALLYARDLE. **Kilkeel Golf Club,** Moume Park, Ballyardle, Newry (Kilkeel (069-37) 62296). *Location:* 16 miles from Newcastle and three miles from Kilkeel on main road to Newry. Parkland, wooded, undulating. 9 holes, 5657 metres. S.S.S. 69. Practice area available. *Green Fees:* weekdays £7.50 for 18 holes, weekends £10.00 for 18 holes. *Eating facilities:* full catering services on application, bar facilities. *Visitors:* welcome all days of the week except Tuesdays and Saturdays. *Society Meetings:* catered for. Secretary: S. W. Rutherford (069-37 73660).

BALLYNAHINCH. **Spa Golf Club,** 20 Grove Road, Ballynahinch BT24 8PN (Ballynahinch (0232) 562365). *Location:* Ballynahinch, Co. Down half mile, Belfast 11 miles. Parkland, wooded. 18 holes, 5938 yards. S.S.S. 72. Practice area. *Green Fees:* weekdays £5.00, playing with member £4.00, weekends £10.00, playing with member £5.00. *Eating facilities:* bar snacks. *Visitors:* welcome Mondays, Tuesdays and Thursdays, Sundays with member and Wednesdays not after 3.00pm. *Society Meetings:* welcome Monday, Tuesday, Thursday; Sunday 10.00 to 11.45am. Secretary: John M. Glass (Belfast (0232) 812340).

BANBRIDGE. **Banbridge Golf Club,** Huntly Road, Banbridge (Banbridge (08206) 22342). *Location:* half-a-mile out of Banbridge on Huntly road. Parkland. 12 holes, 5724 yards. S.S.S. 68. Practice ground. *Green Fees:* weekdays £6.00, weekends £10.00. Reduction if playing with a member. *Eating facilities:* bar facilities. Meals for Societies by arrangement. *Visitors:* welcome. Restrictions on Ladies' Day (Tuesday) and Men's Competition (Saturday). *Society Meetings:* catered for. Arrange with Secretary/Manager. Secretary/Manager: Thomas F. Fee (08206 23831).

BANGOR. **Bangor Golf Club,** Bangor BT20 4RH (Bangor (0247) 270922). *Location:* one mile from Bangor Rail Station. Parkland. 18 holes, 6372 yards. S.S.S. 70. Practice facilities. *Green Fees:* weekdays £12.00, weekends £17.50. *Eating facilities:* dining-room (booking essential), lunches and evening meals, bar snacks. *Visitors:* welcome Monday, Wednesday, Friday, weekends after 6.00pm. *Society Meetings:* advance booking necessary. Professional: Norman Drew (0247 462164). Secretary: David Wilson (0247 270922).

BANGOR. **Carnalea Golf Club,** Station Road, Bangor (Bangor (0247) 465004). *Location:* one minute walk from Carnalea Railway Station. Seaside parkland. 18 holes, 5564 yards. S.S.S. 67. *Green Fees:* weekdays £7.00, weekends £10.00. *Eating facilities:* full restaurant and two bars. *Visitors:* welcome without reservation. *Society Meetings:* catered for. Parties over 20 persons – £5.20 each. Professional: M. McGee (0247 270122). Secretary: J.H. Crozier (0247 270368).

BANGOR. **Helen's Bay Golf Club,** Golf Road, Helen's Bay, Bangor BT19 1TL (Helen's Bay (0247) 852601). *Location:* A2 from Belfast – 9 miles. 9 holes, 5154 yards. S.S.S. 67. *Green Fees:* information not provided. *Eating facilities:* available. *Visitors:* welcome. *Society Meetings:* catered for. Professional: Thomas Loughran. Secretary: John H. Ward.

BELFAST. **Balmoral Golf Club Ltd,** 518 Lisburn Road, Belfast BT9 6GX (Belfast (0232) 68540). *Location:* two miles south of Belfast City Centre, Lisburn Road, next to King's Hall. Flat course. 18 holes, 6177 yards, 5702 metres. S.S.S. 70. *Green Fees:* weekdays £12.00, weekends £15.00. *Eating facilities:* full restaurant facilities and bars. *Visitors:* Ladies' Day Tuesdays and Fridays; Gentlemen Wednesdays and Saturdays; members priority 1.00pm to 2.00pm daily; visitors welcome at all other times. *Society Meetings:* Mondays and Thursdays – £10.00. Professional: John Fisher (0232 667747). General Manager: B. Jenkins OBE, MBIM (0232 381514).

BELFAST. **Belvoir Park Golf Club,** 73 Church Road, Newtownbreda, Belfast BT8 4AN (Belfast (0232) 641159 or 692817). *Location:* three miles from city centre on road to Newcastle. Parkland – well wooded. 18 holes, 6476 yards, 5922 metres. S.S.S. 71. Practice area. *Green Fees:* weekdays (excluding Wednesday) £12.00, weekends and Wednesdays £15.00. *Eating facilities:* dining and snack meals – bar. *Visitors:* welcome except Saturday. *Society Meetings:* by prior booking only. Professional: M. Kelly (0232 646714). Secretary: W.I. Davidson (0232 491693 and 646113).

BELFAST. **Knock Golf Club,** Summerfield, Dundonald, Belfast BT16 0QX (Dundonald (02318) 3251/ 2249). *Location:* four miles east of Belfast. 18 holes, 5845 metres. S.S.S. 71. *Green Fees:* weekdays £12.00, weekends and Bank Holidays £16.00. *Eating facilities:* catering and bar facilities available. *Visitors:* welcome. *Society Meetings:* catered for Mondays and Thursdays. Professional: G. Fairweather. Secretary/Manager: S.G. Managh.

BELFAST. **Knockbracken Golf and Country Club,** 24 Ballymaconaghy Road, Knockbracken, Belfast BT8 4SB (0232 792100). *Location:* south from the centre of Belfast on the Ormeau Road to "Four Winds" public house and restaurant, half a mile out on Ballymaconaghy Road, on left by ski slopes. Parkland on undulating ground. 18 holes, 5312 yards. S.S.S. 68. *Green Fees:* £6.00 weekdays, £5.00 with member; £8.00 weekends and Public Holidays, £6.00 with member. *Eating facilities:* full meals and snacks served from 11.00am to 10.00pm seven days a week. *Visitors:* welcome, no restrictions except from 8.30am to 11.30am on Saturdays. *Society Meetings:* acceptable on any day of the week by arrangement. Professional: Don Patterson (0232 401811). Secretary: M. Grose (0232 401811).

BELFAST. **Mahee Island Golf Club,** Comber, Newtownards, Belfast (Killinchy (0238) 541234). *Location:* take Comber to Killyleagh road and turn left a mile from Comber signposted "Ardmillan" bear left for six miles and arrive on the island (no through road). Parkland/ seaside. 9 holes, 5588 yards, 5108 metres. S.S.S. 67. Par 68 over 18 holes. Practice net, green and chipping area. *Green Fees:* weekdays £6.00, weekends £10.00. Half fees playing with member. *Eating facilities:* by arrangement (no bar). *Visitors:* welcome, restricted Wednesdays after 4.00pm and Saturdays until 4.00pm. *Society Meetings:* welcome, booking by letter. 50p reduction when 16 or more. Professional: F. Marshall. Hon. Secretary: T. Reid.

BELFAST. **Ormeau Golf Club,** Ravenhill Road, Belfast BT6 (Belfast (0232) 641069). *Location:* Belfast south/east. Parkland course. 9 holes, 2653 yards, 2425 metres. S.S.S. 65. *Green Fees:* £5.00 weekdays, £7.00 weekends. *Eating facilities:* bar facilities only. *Visitors:* welcome everyday except Saturdays. *Society Meetings:* on application. Secretary: J.L. Cooke.

BELFAST. **Shandon Park Golf Club,** 73 Shandon Park, Belfast BT5 6NY (Belfast (0232) 401856). 18 holes, 5714 metres. S.S.S. 70. *Green Fees:* information not provided. *Visitors:* welcome. Professional: Barry Wilson. General Manager: H. Wallace.

CRAIGAVON. **Craigavon Golf and Ski Club,** Turemoyra Lane, Lurgan, Craigavon (Lurgan (0762) 326606). 18 hole course, 9 hole course, S.S.S. 71. Driving range. *Green Fees:* weekdays £5.00, weekends £7.00. *Eating facilities:* full restaurant facilities. *Visitors:* open to everyone. Modern clubhouse, showers and lockers. Manager: Mr V. McCorry.

DONAGHADEE. **Donaghadee Golf Club,** Warren Road, Donaghadee BT21 0PQ (Donaghadee (0247) 888697). *Location:* six miles outside Bangor on coast road. 15 miles from Belfast via Newtownards. Seaside links and parkland. 18 holes, 5576 metres. S.S.S. 69. *Green Fees:* weekdays £8.00, weekends £10.00. On Saturdays and Public Holidays visitors must be accompanied by a member. *Eating facilities:* catering every day except Monday, two lounge bars and TV room. *Visitors:* welcome any day except on Saturdays and Public Holidays when they must play with a member. *Society Meetings:* welcome Monday, Wednesday, Thursday but must book in advance. Professional: Gordon Drew (0247 882392). Secretary: C.D. McCutcheon (0247 883624).

DOWNPATRICK. **Bright Castle Golf Club,** 14 Coniamstown Road, Bright, Downpatrick BT30 8LU (0396 841319). *Location:* off the main Downpatrick/ Killough road approximately two and a half miles, and five miles from Downpatrick. Parkland – excellent fairways and greens, plenty of trees, 16th hole 735 yards. 18 holes, 7029 yards. S.S.S. 72. Putting green. *Green Fees:* £4.00 weekdays, £6.00 weekends. Summer evenings weekdays only £2.50 after 6.00pm. *Eating facilities:* snacks available. *Visitors:* very welcome, no restrictions. *Society Meetings:* very welcome, tee can be reserved. Secretary: Raymond Reid.

DOWNPATRICK. **Downpatrick Golf Club,** Saul Road, Downpatrick (Downpatrick (0396) 612152). 18 holes, 5304 metres. S.S.S. 68. *Green Fees:* information not provided. *Eating facilities:* available except Mondays. *Visitors:* welcome weekdays without reservation. Hon. Secretary: A. Cannon.

HOLYWOOD. **Holywood Golf Club,** Demesne Road, Holywood (Holywood (023 17) 2138). 18 holes, 5885 yards. *Green Fees:* information not provided. *Eating facilities:* bars and restaurant. *Visitors:* welcome. Secretary/Manager: Gerald R. Magennis. Professional: Michael Bannon.

HOLYWOOD. **Royal Belfast Golf Club,** Station Road, Craigavad, Holywood BT18 0BP (Holywood (02317 2368). *Location:* east of Belfast on A2. Parkland. 18 holes, 5963 yards. S.S.S. 69. *Green Fees:* weekdays £16.00, Saturdays after 4.30pm, Sundays and Public Holidays £20.00. *Eating facilities:* full facilities available. *Visitors:* welcome, introduced by members or with a letter of introduction from own club Secretary, by prior arrangement. *Society Meetings:* catered for by arrangement. Professional: D.H. Carson (02317 2910). Secretary: I.M. Piggot (0232 428165).

NEWCASTLE. **Royal County Down Golf Club,** Newcastle BT33 0AN (Newcastle (03967) 23314). *Location:* adjacent to north side of Newcastle, approach from town centre. Championship Course: 18 holes, 6968 yards. S.S.S. 73. No. 2 Course: 18 holes, 4100 yards. S.S.S. 63. *Green Fees:* information not provided. *Eating facilities:* by arrangement. *Visitors:* welcome with prior reservation. *Society Meetings:* catered for. Professional: E.T. Jones (03967 22419). Secretary: P.E. Rolph (03967 23314).

NEWTOWNARDS. **Clandeboye Golf Club,** Tower Road, Conlig, Newtownards BT23 3PN (0247 271767). *Location:* Conlig village off A21 between Bangor and Newtownards. Wooded, undulating parkland/heathland. 18 holes, 5915 metres, S.S.S. 72. 18

holes, 5172 metres, S.S.S. 67. Practice ground. *Green Fees:* weekdays £12.00 and £10.00, weekends £15.00 and £12.00. *Eating facilities:* full catering and bar. *Visitors:* welcome weekdays; Saturdays and certain times on Sundays must be accompanied by member. (Thursday ladies' day). *Society Meetings:* welcome weekdays except Thursdays (in winter Mondays and Wednesdays only). Reduced rates for parties over 20. Professional: Peter Gregory (0247 271750). Secretary/ Manager: Ian Marks (0247 271767).

NEWTOWNARDS. **Kirkistown Golf Club,** Cloughey, Newtownards (Portavogie (02477) 71223). *Location:* A20 west of Belfast then B173. 18 holes, 6176 yards. S.S.S. 70. *Green Fees:* information not provided. *Visitors:* welcome. *Society Meetings:* catered for. Professional: Jonathan Peden.

NEWTOWNARDS. **Scrabo Golf Club,** Scrabo Road, Newtownards (Newtownards (0247) 812355). *Location:* approximately 10 miles from Belfast off main Belfast to Newtownards road. 18 holes, 5506 metres. S.S.S. 71. *Green Fees:* £8.00 weekdays; £11.00 weekends. *Eating facilities:* catering available except Mondays. *Visitors:* welcome weekdays without reservation. *Society Meetings:* catered for weekdays. Secretary/Manager: (0247 812355).

WARRENPOINT. **Warrenpoint Golf Club,** Lower Dromore Road, Warrenpoint (Warrenpoint (06937) 72219). *Location:* five miles south of Newry on coast road. Parkland. 18 holes, 5640 metres. S.S.S. 70. *Green Fees:* weekdays £10.00, weekends £14.00. *Eating facilities:* full catering and bar facilities. *Visitors:* welcome Sunday, Monday, Thursday, Friday. Squash, snooker facilities available. *Society Meetings:* catered for by prior arrangement. Professional: Nigel Shaw (06937 72371). Secretary: John McMahon (06937 73695).

Fermanagh

ENNISKILLEN. **Enniskillen Golf Club,** Castlecoole, Enniskillen BT74 6HZ (0365 25250). *Location:* one mile north east of Enniskillen (off Tempo Road) on Castlecoole Estate. Parkland. 18 holes, 5990 yards, 5574 metres. S.S.S. 70. *Green Fees:* weekdays and weekends £7.50, £6.00 for Societies or visitors playing with member. *Eating facilities:* bar snacks daily – full catering by arrangement. *Visitors:* welcome without restriction. *Society Meetings:* welcome. Secretary: Brendan O'Neill (0365 26580).

Londonderry

Tyrone

CASTLEROCK. **Castlerock Golf Club,** 65 Circular Road, Castlerock BT51 4TJ (Coleraine (0265) 848214). *Location:* A2, six miles west of Coleraine, one mile Coleraine side of Mussenden Temple. Seaside links, testing course. 18 holes, 6121 metres. S.S.S. 72. 9 holes, 2457 metres. S.S.S. 34. Large practice area. *Green Fees:* weekdays £10.00, weekends £20.00. *Eating facilities:* full restaurant facilities, two bars. *Visitors:* Monday/Friday no restrictions. *Society Meetings:* welcome Monday to Friday. Professional: R. Kelly (0265 848314). Secretary: R.G. McBride (0265 848314).

MAGHERAFELT. **Moyola Park Golf Club,** Shanemullagh, Castledawson, Magherafelt BT45 8DG (0648 68468). *Location:* on main Belfast to Londonderry road, half a mile through Castledawson. Wooded parkland course. *Green Fees:* £9.00 weekdays, with member £6.00; £11.00 weekends, with member £8.00. *Eating facilities:* full bar and catering facilities. *Visitors:* always welcome by prior arrangement. Snooker. *Society Meetings:* catered for mid-week and Sundays, not Saturdays. Professional: V. Teague (0648 68830). Hon. Secretary: Michael A. Steele (0648 68392).

PORTSTEWART. **Portstewart Golf Club,** Strand Head, Portstewart (Portstewart (026583) 2015). Coastal links. Strand (No. 1) course 18 holes. Town (No. 2) course 18 holes. Strand 6784 yards, S.S.S. 72; Town 4733 yards, S.S.S. 63. *Green Fees:* £12.00 weekdays; £17.00 weekends. *Eating facilities:* meals available – advance orders. *Visitors:* welcome Mondays to Fridays with reservation. *Society Meetings:* catered for. Professional: A. Hunter (026583 2601). Secretary: Michael Moss.

PREHEN. **City of Derry Golf Club,** 49 Victoria Road, Prehen BT47 2PU (0504 311610). *Location:* three miles from city centre on the road to Strabane – follow the River Foyle. Parkland, wooded. 18 holes, 6362 yards. S.S.S. 71. Also 9 hole course, 4708 yards. S.S.S. 63. Practice area. *Green Fees:* £8.00 weekdays, £11.00 weekends. *Eating facilities:* catering and bar facilities available. *Visitors:* welcome on weekdays up to 4.30pm, weekends please contact Professional. Convenient for hotel and guest houses. *Society Meetings:* welcome please contact Secretary. Professional: M. Doherty (0504 46496). Secretary: P.J. Doherty (0504 46369).

COOKSTOWN. **Killymoon Golf Club,** Killymoon Road, Cookstown (Cookstown (06487) 62254). *Location:* private road off A29. Signposted at Dungannon end of town opposite Drum Road. Parkland course, scenic beauty. 18 holes, 5878 yards, 5513 metres. S.S.S. 69. *Green Fees:* weekdays £9.00, weekends and Bank Holidays £12.00, not Saturday afternoons. *Eating facilities:* full catering at club, à la carte and table d'hôte. Order in advance. *Visitors:* welcome especially mid-week, Thursdays ladies' priority, Saturday afternoons members only. *Society Meetings:* catered for mid-week. Professional: Paul Leonard (06487 63460). Secretary: Dr J. McBride (06487 63762).

DUNGANNON. **Dungannon Golf Club,** Springfield Lane, Dungannon (Dungannon (086-87) 22098). *Location:* one mile west of Dungannon. 18 holes, 5904 yards. S.S.S. 68. *Green Fees:* £7.00 weekdays, £10.00 weekends and Bank Holidays. *Visitors:* welcome. Hon. Secretary: J. McCausland. Secretary/Manager: B. Doyle (086-87 27338).

FINTONA. **Fintona Golf Club,** Kiln Street, Ecclesville, Demesne, Fintona (0662 841480). *Location:* eight miles south of Omagh, county town of Tyrone. Parkland with a river running through the course. 9 holes, 5716 metres. S.S.S. 70. *Green Fees:* information not provided. *Eating facilities:* bar food. *Visitors:* welcome daily but check by telephoning at weekends. Snooker tables. *Society Meetings:* catered for by advance booking. Secretary: G. McNulty (0662 841514).

NEWTOWNSTEWART. **Newtownstewart Golf Club,** 38 Golf Course Road, Newtownstewart, Omagh BT78 4HH (Newtownstewart (06626) 61466). *Location:* signposted from Strabane Road (A57) at Newtownstewart, two miles west of Newtownstewart on B84. Parkland. 18 holes, 5982 yards, 5468 metres. S.S.S. 69. Practice ground adjacent to clubhouse. *Green Fees:* weekdays £6.00, weekends £8.00, weekly £20.00, monthly £40.00. *Eating facilities:* available. *Visitors:* welcome at all times except during club competitions. *Society Meetings:* catered for. Secretary/Manageress: Miss D. Magee.

OMAGH. **Omagh Golf Club,** 83a Dublin Road, Omagh BT78 1HQ (Omagh (0662 3160). *Location:* one mile from Omagh on Belfast/Dublin road. Parkland. 18 holes, 4870 metres. S.S.S. 66. *Green Fees:* weekdays £5.00, with member £3.00; weekends and Bank Holidays £7.00, with member £5.00. *Eating facilities:* snacks and bar facilities. *Visitors:* welcome any day except Tuesday and Saturday. *Society Meetings:* welcome. Hon. Secretary: Joseph A. McElholm (0662 41442 or 3160).

Republic of Ireland

COUNTY CLARE

LAHINCH. **Lahinch Golf Club,** Lahinch (065 81003) FAX (065 81592). *Location:* 30 miles north-west of Shannon Airport, 200 yards from Lahinch village on Lisconner Road. Links course. Old Course, 18 holes, 6699 yards. S.S.S. 73. Castle Course, 18 holes, 5265 yards. S.S.S. 67. *Green Fees:* on application. *Visitors:* weekdays only, by arrangement. *Society Meetings:* catered for by arrangement. Professional: R. McCavery (065 81408). Secretary: M. Murphy.

COUNTY CORK

LITTLE ISLAND. **Cork Golf Club,** Little Island (021 353263). *Location:* five miles east of Cork, half-mile off Cork/Cobh road. Parkland, very scenic championship course. 18 holes, 6065 metres. S.S.S. 72. Practice ground. *Green Fees:* weekdays £17.00, weekends £20.00. Special rates for groups of 20 or more £13.00. *Eating facilities:* full catering facilities, bar. *Visitors:* welcome Mondays, Tuesdays, Wednesdays and Fridays except 12.30 to 2.00pm; weekends ring in advance. *Society Meetings:* catered for, arrange with Secretary/Manager. Professional: David Higgins (021 353037). Secretary: Matt Sands (021 353451).

TIVOLI. **Silver Springs Golf Club,** Tivoli (021 507533). *Location:* five minutes from Cork city centre. 9 holes, 4680 yards. S.S.S. 62 for 18 holes, Par 34 (68). *Green Fees:* information not provided. Special rates for group of 20 or more. *Eating facilities:* full catering facilities, bar. *Visitors:* welcome, ring beforehand. Hotel on site, accommodation available. Full sports centre, indoor pool, squash, indoor tennis, sauna & steam bath, gym. Manager: Ian Foulger.

COUNTY DONEGAL

BUNDORAN. **Bundoran Golf Club,** Great Northern Hotel, Bundoran (072 41302). *Location:* 25 miles west of Enniskillen, 25 miles north of Sligo (on coast). Undulating seaside and parkland (no trees). 18 holes, 6328 yards, 5785 metres. S.S.S. 71. *Green Fees:* weekdays £9.00, weekends £10.00. Special rates for Societies, 16 or more £7.00. *Eating facilities:* snacks and bar. Hotel on course. *Visitors:* generally welcome. Weekends busy, advance booking necessary. Most weekend competitions from Easter to end October are open. *Society Meetings:* very welcome if can be accommodated. Professionals: Leslie and David Robinson (072 41302). Secretary: Liam M. Devitt (072 51161).

COUNTY DUBLIN

DUBLIN. **Elm Park Golf and Sports Club,** Nutley House, Donnybrook, Dublin 4 (0001 693438). *Location:* between R.T.E. and St. Vincent's Hospital. Flat parkland course. 18 holes, 5929 yards, 5422 metres. S.S.S. 68. *Green Fees:* £17.00 weekdays, £22.00 weekends. *Eating facilities:* full bar and dining facilities. *Visitors:* welcome but must telephone to arrange times with Professional. *Society Meetings:* by special arrangement. Professional: S. Green (0001 692650). Secretary: H. Montag.

DUBLIN. **Royal Dublin Golf Club,** Bull Island, Dollymount, Dublin 3 (0001 337153). *Location:* City centre three and a quarter miles, on coast road to Howth. Seaside links. 18 holes, 6568 yards. S.S.S. 73. *Green Fees:* on application. *Visitors:* unrestricted, except Saturdays. Professional: L. Owens (0001 336477). Secretary : J.A. Lambe (0001 336346).

FOXROCK. **Leopardstown Golf Course,** Foxrock (01 895341). *Location:* five miles south of Dublin city centre, situated in Leopardstown race course. 9 holes, 5516 yards. Par 34 (68). Also 18-hole Par 3 course, 2795 yards. *Green Fees:* information not provided. Special rates for societies and groups. *Eating facilities:* restaurant. *Visitors:* welcome. Manager: Michael Hoey.

HOWTH. **Deer Park Golf Club,** Howth (01 322624). *Location:* eight miles NE of Dublin. 18 holes, 6647 yards. S.S.S. 73. Par 72. Par 3 and Pitch and Putt courses available. *Green Fees:* on application. *Visitors:* unrestricted. Secretary: Jim Brady.

PORTMARNOCK. **Portmarnock Golf Club,** Portmarnock (0001 323082). *Location:* eight miles NE of Dublin along north coast, four miles from Airport. Seaside links – winds. Three courses: 'A' – 27 holes, 7097 yards. S.S.S. 75. 'B' – 7047 yards. S.S.S. 75. 'C' – 6596 yards. S.S.S. 74. Practice area. *Green Fees:* £IR35.00 weekdays, £IR45.00 weekends. *Eating facilities:* available. *Visitors:* by arrangement, restriction weekends and Bank Holidays. *Society Meetings:* on application. Professional: P. Townsend (0001 325157). Secretary: W. Bornemann (0001 323082).

COUNTY GALWAY

CLIFDEN. **Connemara Golf Club,** Aillebrack, Ballyconnelly, Near Clifden (095 23502). *Location:* nine miles south of Clifden. Seaside links. Championship course, 18 holes, 6124 metres. S.S.S. 73. Medal course, 18 holes, 6186 metres. S.S.S. 73. Practice fairway. *Green Fees:* £14.00. *Eating facilities:* à la carte restaurant and bar. *Visitors:* unrestricted, but handicap required. *Society Meetings:* groups of 20 or more £7.00 per person. Secretary: Norbert Fallon.

COUNTY KERRY

BALLYBUNION. **Ballybunion Golf Club,** Ballybunion (068 27146). *Location:* nearest town Ballybunion. Seaside links. Old Course – 18 holes, 6542 yards. S.S.S. 72. New Course – 18 holes, 6278 yards. S.S.S. 73. *Green Fees:* Old Course £30.00 per round, New course £20.00 per round. One round on each in one day £40.00. *Eating facilities:* full bar and catering facilities. *Visitors:* there are no restrictions on visitors but weekends are extremely busy – to be avoided when possible. *Society Meetings:* catered for from 1st October to 1st April, no Societies on Old Course at weekends. Professional: E. Higgins (068 27209). Secretary: S. Walsh (068 27611).

KILLARNEY. **Killarney Golf Club,** Mahoney's Point, Killarney (064 31034). *Location:* three miles west of town. Undulating lakeside courses. Mahoney's Point 18 holes, 6677 yards. S.S.S. 70. Killeen 18 holes, 6798 yards. S.S.S. 72. *Green Fees:* on application. *Visitors:* unrestricted. Professional: T. Coveney (064 31615). Secretary: T. Prendergast.

TRALEE. **Tralee Golf Club,** West Barrow, Ardfert, Tralee (066 36355). *Location:* eight miles west of Tralee. Seaside links. 18 holes, 6252 metres. S.S.S. 72. *Green Fees:* £18.00 weekdays, £25.00 weekends. *Eating facilities:* bar and restaurant. *Visitors:* unrestricted except Wednesdays and weekends. *Society Meet-* ings: catered for with advance bookings. Secretary: Peter Colleran (066 36379).

WATERVILLE. **Waterville Golf Links,** Waterville Lake Hotel, Ring of Kerry, Waterville (0667 4237). *Location:* quarter of a mile from main road, half-way around Ring of Kerry. Seaside links. 18 holes, 7184 yards. S.S.S. 74. Practice ground, putting green. *Green Fees:* weekdays £25.00 per round, weekends £30.00 per round, per person. Group/outing rates on request. *Eating facilities:* lounge bar, full catering available. *Visitors:* unrestricted except on special event days. Electric golf carts available. *Society Meetings:* welcome. Professional: Liam Higgins (0667 4102). Caddiemaster: Noel Cronin.

COUNTY KILDARE

CURRAGH. **Curragh Golf Club,** Curragh (045 41238). *Location:* three miles south of Newbridge. Parkland. 18 holes, 6003 metres. S.S.S. 71. Practice grounds. *Green fees:* weekdays £10.00, weekends and Bank Holidays £12.00. *Eating facilities:* full catering. *Visitors:* restricted, please check in advance for course availability. *Society Meetings:* by appointment. Professional: Phil Lawlor (045 41896). Secretary: Ann Culleton (045 41714).

COUNTY LOUTH

COUNTY SLIGO

DROGHEDA. **County Louth Golf Club,** Baltray, Drogheda (041 22327). *Location:* Drogheda, five miles north east. Championship links course. 18 holes, 6757 yards. S.S.S. 72. *Green Fees:* weekdays £18.00, weekends £25.00. *Eating facilities:* restaurant, coffee shop and bar. *Visitors:* welcome weekdays except Tuesdays on application, weekends restricted. Accommodation available for 20 persons. *Society Meetings:* on application. Professional: Paddy McGuirk (041 22444). Secretary: Michael Delany (041 22329).

ENNISCRONE. **Enniscrone Golf Club,** Enniscrone, (096 36297). *Location:* on Ballina road south of Enniscrone. Seaside links. 18 holes, 6487 yards. S.S.S. 72. Practice ground and putting green. *Green Fees:* weekdays and weekends £10.00. Society Green Fee £8.00 per day. *Eating facilities:* lounge bar and restaurant (order prior to play). *Visitors:* welcome without reservation mid-week. Play available at weekends – please telephone beforehand. *Society Meetings:* through Club Society Organiser: Mr S. Marren (096 36335 after 5pm). Secretary: John Fleming (home 096 36243, office 096 21472).

Isle of Man

DOUGLAS. **Douglas Golf Club (playing over Municipal Course),** Pulrose Golf Course, Pulrose Road, Douglas (0624 75952). *Location:* one mile from Douglas Pier, near to large Cooling Tower landmark. Buses every 15 minutes. Parkland – testing course, often venue for Manx Championship. 18 holes, 5922 yards. S.S.S. 68. *Green Fees:* information not provided. *Eating facilities:* light meals available in licensed clubhouse. *Visitors:* welcome without reservation. *Society Meetings:* catered for after prior notification. Professional:K. Parry. Hon. Secretary: J.D. Tooms.

DOUGLAS. **Pulrose Golf Course,** Douglas. *Location:* one mile from town centre, next to power station. Undulating parkland with memorable 17th hole. 18 holes, 5922 yards. S.S.S. 68. Putting and practice area. *Green Fees:* information not provided. *Eating facilities:* bar; meals available at all times. *Visitors:* welcome, no restrictions. *Society Meetings:* by arrangement with Professional. Professional: K. Parry (0624 75952). Secretary: J. Tooms.

FORT ISLAND. **Castletown Golf Club,** Castletown Golf Links Hotel, Fort Island, Derbyhaven (Castletown (0624) 822201). *Location:* 12 miles from Douglas. Three miles from Ronaldsway airport. Seaside links course. 18 holes, 6731 yards. S.S.S. 73. *Green Fees:* residents £12.50, visitors Mondays to Thursdays £18.00, Fridays, weekends and Bank Holidays £22.00. *Eating facilities:* a la carte restaurant, main restaurant, snack bar and three bars. *Visitors:* welcome without reservation. Accommodation available, plus sauna, sunbeds, swimming pool, changing rooms. *Society Meetings:* catered for. Professional: Murray S. Crowe (0624 822211). General Manager: J. Fowlds (0624 822201).

ONCHAN. **Howstrake Golf Club,** King Edward Bay Course, Onchan (Douglas (0624) 20430). *Location:* three miles from Douglas centre, (entrance at Groudle Road). Seaside/moorland course. 18 holes, 5367 yards, 4908 metres. S.S.S. 66. *Green fees:* £6.00 per day. *Eating facilities:* full catering available. *Visitors:* welcome without reservation. *Society Meetings:* catered for. Secretary: J.C. Davies (0624 76794). Golf Shop available.

PEEL. **Peel Golf Club,** Rheast Lane, Peel (0624 842227). *Location:* 10 miles west of Douglas. Park-land/seaside links. 18 holes, 5914 yards. S.S.S. 69. Practice ground. *Green Fees:* weekdays £10.00, weekends £12.00. *Eating facilities:* bar snacks, meals to order. *Visitors:* welcome, but for parties advise prior check at weekends. *Society Meetings:* catered for. Secretary: D.R. Forth (0624 843456).

PORT ERIN. **Rowany Golf Club,** Port Erin (0624 834108). *Location:* off the Promenade. Hilly setting by the seaside. 18 holes, 5840 yards. S.S.S. 68. Driving range. *Green Fees:* £8.00 weekdays, £12.00 weekends. 25 per cent discount for parties of eight and over. *Eating facilities:* restaurant and bar. *Visitors:* welcome all year round. Accommodation can be arranged. *Society Meetings:* welcome by arrangement. General Manager: R.G. Jackson (0624 73284).

PORT ST. MARY. **Port St. Mary Golf Club,** Kallow Point Road, Port St. Mary (0624 834932). *Location:* clearly signposted after entering Port St. Mary. Seaside links with beautiful panoramic views. 9 holes, 2754 yards. S.S.S. 66. *Green Fees:* £3.00 per day. Parties of 10 or more 10 per cent discount. *Eating facilities:* restaurant and bar open all day. *Visitors:* welcome at all times. Secretary: (0624 832274).

RAMSEY. **Ramsey Golf Club,** Brookfield (0624 812224). *Location:* west boundary of Ramsey. 18 holes, 6019 yards. S.S.S. 69. *Green fees:* weekdays £10.00, weekends £12.00. One week £50.00, two weeks £70.00, four weeks £100.00. *Eating facilities:* lunches served, order in advance. *Visitors:* welcome without reservation. *Society Meetings:* catered for. Professional: Peter Lowey. Secretary: S.A. Lockwood (0624 812397).

Channel Islands

ALDERNEY. **Alderney Golf Club,** Route des Carrieres, Alderney (Alderney (048182 2835). *Location:* one mile east of St. Anne. Seaside links with sea views from every hole. 9 holes, 2498 yards. S.S.S. 65. Putting and practice area. *Green Fees:* weekdays £10.00, weekends £14.00 (half these rates if playing with member). *Eating facilities:* bar and meals. *Visitors:* welcome all year. Parties over 4 must contact Club for availability. *Society Meetings:* welcome by arrangement. Secretary: Bill Barthram (office 048182 2293 or home 048182 3504).

GUERNSEY. **Royal Guernsey Golf Club,** L'Ancresse, Vale, Guernsey (0481 47022). *Location:* three miles from St. Peter Port. 18 holes, 6141 yards. S.S.S. 70. *Green Fees:* £15.00 per round, £10.00 playing with a member; Juniors £5.00 per day. *Eating facilities:* restaurant and two bars. *Visitors:* welcome except Thursday and Saturday afternoons and Sunday until 5.00 p.m. Must be a member of a recognised club and have Handicap Certificate. *Society Meetings:* October to March only, with prior notice. Professional: Norman Wood (0481 45070). Secretary: G.J. Nicolle (0481 46523).

Please mention this guide when you write or phone to enquire about accommodation.

GUERNSEY. **St. Pierre Park Golf Club,** Ronais, St. Peter Port, Guernsey (0481 27039). *Location:* 10 minutes from St. Peter Port. Wooded parkland with numerous lakes. 9 holes, 2511 yards. S.S.S. 27. Driving range. *Green Fees:* weekdays £7.00 (£3.50 if resident at hotel), weekends £8.00 (£4.50 if resident at hotel). Weekly rate for residents of Hotel £25.00. *Eating facilities:* two restaurants and two bars in hotel. Hotel accommodation 135 rooms. Professional: Barry Melville (0481 27039). Secretary: David Hinshaw (0481 28282).

JERSEY. **Jersey Recreation Grounds,** Greve D'Azette, St. Clement, Jersey (0534 21938). *Location:* inner coast road near St. Helier. Flat course with some water hazards. 9 holes, 2244 yards. S.S.S. 30. Practice range and putting green. *Green Fees:* information not provided. *Eating facilities:* licensed buffet. *Visitors:* welcome at all times. *Society Meetings:* welcome. Managing Director: P.A.O. Graham.

JERSEY. **La Moye Golf Club,** St. Brelade, Jersey (0534 42701). *Location:* on road to Corbiere Lighthouse at La Moye, St. Brelade. Turn right at airport crossroads, right again at crossroads traffic lights. Seaside links championship course. 18 holes, 6512 yards. S.S.S. 72. Practice ground. *Green Fees:* on application. *Eating facilities:* full restaurant/snack facilities, three bars. *Visitors:* weekdays 9.30 – 11am and 2 – 3.30pm, weekends 2.30pm onwards. Must have handicap certificate. *Society Meetings:* by prior appointment only. Professional: Mr David Melville (0534 43130). Secretary: Pat Clash (0534 43401).

JERSEY. **Royal Jersey Golf Club,** Grouville, Jersey (0534 51042). *Location:* four miles east of St. Helier (follow coast road). Links course. 18 holes, 6023 yards. S.S.S. 69. *Green Fees:* weekdays £22.00 per round, £30.00 per day; weekends and Bank Holidays £25.00 per day (after 2.30pm). *Eating facilities:* restaurant and two bars. *Visitors:* welcome if member of recognised club. Handicap Certificate required. *Society Meetings:* welcome by prior arrangement. Professional: Tommy A. Horton (0534 52234). Secretary: R.C. Leader (0534 54416).

Golf in Portugal
WHERE TO PLAY • WHERE TO STAY

by BRIAN NUTTALL, FRICS, author of 'The Algarve Travel and Property Guide', published by Robertson McCarta, London

Golf in Portugal goes back to 1890, when the first course was built at Espino, twenty miles from Oporto by English port wine merchants. There are three distinct golf regions in mainland Portugal, at Oporto in the north, around Lisbon and the most popular region, the Algarve.

THE ALGARVE

There are presently six golf locations, four having multiple courses. Five more are under construction and should be open in 1991. The latter are at Quarteira (Vila Sol), Olhos da Agua (Pine Cliffs, 9 holes), Carvoeiro Club de Golf, Jorge de Lagos Country Club, Carvoeiro (9 holes), and the Alvor Club, Alvor.

CENTRAL ALGARVE
VALE DO LOBO. A well known and established 27-hole complex with the Dona Filipa Hotel (Trust House Forte) and self-catering villas. Another nine holes are planned.
QUINTA DO LAGO. This highly rated 27 holes has hosted the Portuguese Open Championship for several years. A new 18-hole course is under construction, to be known as Pinieros Altos and nearby Sao Lourenco has opened with 18 holes.
VILAMOURA. Two separate 18-hole courses, each different in character. Vilamoura 1 is the oldest and a fine test of golf. Hotels and self-catering are in abundance at Vilamoura.

WESTERN ALGARVE
PENINA. 18 holes plus two short 9's adjoining the excellent Penina Hotel. A

long, flat testing course designed by Henry Cotton interspersed with lakes and ditches.
PALMARES. An 18-hole course, part links with fine views over Lagos Bay. Nearest accommodation is in Lagos (Hotel de Lagos), an attractive town with many restaurants.
PARQUE DA FLORESTA. A new undulating 18 holes, still maturing, on a large development of villas and apartments.

OPORTO AND THE NORTH

This area has three 18-hole courses on the coast and at Vidago, a 9-hole course, set inland at a spa resort with the Victorian-style Vidago Palace Hotel. The Oporto and Miramar links courses are close together, both served by the 4-star Hotel Praia Golf. The Estela Golf Club is thirty kilometres north of Oporto, again a links course where the 4-star hotels Ofir and Vermar and Estalagem Santo Andre provide good facilities.

LISBON, ESTORIL COAST AND TROIA

This central region offers seven courses and all the facilities of the capital, Estoril and Cascais. The courses are Troia Golf Club, Lisbon Sports Club, Portugal Country Club, Estoril Palacio Golf Club, Guia Estoril Sol (9 holes), Guia Quinta da Marina, Vimiero Golf Club (9 holes). Troia, Estoril Palacio, and Quinta da Marina all have quality accommodation, most notably the Estoril Palacio Hotel.

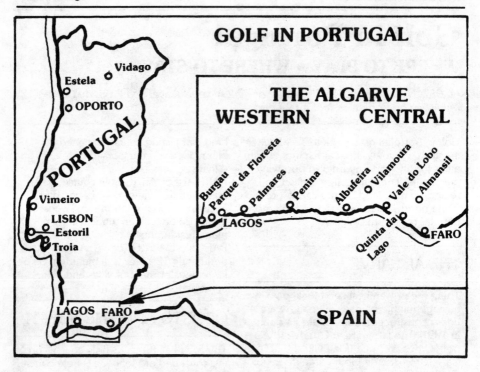

ALGARVE

ALMANSIL. **Quinta do Lago Golf Club,** Almansil, Loule 8100 (089 94529. Fax: 089 94683. Telex: 56000). *Location:* close to the sea on the luxury Quinta do Lago estate, 15 km west of Faro. Fine picturesque course with pine trees and lakes, generally in excellent condition. 27 holes, average 18-hole length 7000 yards. S.S.S. 72. *Facilities:* excellent leisure facilities of all sorts nearby, including the 5 star Hotel Quinta do Lago.

ALMANSIL. **Sao Lourenco Golf Club,** Quinta do Lago, Almansil, Loule 8100 (089 94141). *Location:* around the Ria Formosa estuary, close to Quinta do Lago. New, testing course, water a feature. 18 holes. *Facilities:* Sao Lourenco Hotel, Dona Filipa Hotel.

ALMANSIL. **Val do Lobo Golf Club,** Vale do Lobo, Almansil, Loule 8100 (089 94444. Telex: 56842). *Location:* on the cliff edge, overlooking the sea, 15 minutes' drive west from Faro. 27 holes, three loops of 9; average 18-hole length 6600 yards. S.S.S. 72. *Facilities:* clubhouse with restaurant, bar and shop. Nearby the 5 star Dona Filipa Hotel and luxury villa estate with leisure complexes.

BUDENS/SALEMA. **Parque da Floresta Golf Club,** Vale do Poco, Budens, Vila do Bispo 8650 (082 6533. Telex: 57173). *Location:* above the fishing village of Salema, 16 km west of Lagos. Hilly, new course. 18 holes, 6440 yards. S.S.S. 72. *Facilities:* clubhouse with bar, restaurant and shop.

Vilar do Golf

Quinta do Lago, 8135, Almancil
Algarve, Portugal

Telephone: 089-396647/685/615
Telex: 58864 VILARG P   Fax: 089-396659/695

Trafalgar House offers the supreme golf destination in the Algarve. Vilar do Golf, with 180 villas and apartments in the heart of Quinta do Lago. Available for rental or freehold purchase. Vilar do Golf have 50% of the starting times on the A, B, C and D courses at Quinta do Lago, reserved for their guests at a 50% discount from the public rate. Facilities also include, a David Lloyd Tennis Centre, three swimming pools, squash, saunas, the Belvedere Restaurant, on-site mini-market and medical clinic. Horseriding, watersports, beach and a shopping plaza are within Quinta do Lago and less than three minutes from Vilar do Golf. *Come and visit the site of the 1990 Portuguese Open!*

TRAFALGAR HOUSE EUROPE

LAGOS. **Palmares Golf Club**, Meia Praia, Lagos 8600 (082 62961. Telex: 57434). *Location:* attractively placed astride the Portimao/Lagos main road, east of Lagos. Part hilly, part alongside beach. 18 holes, 5919 yards. S.S.S. 72. *Facilities:* clubhouse with restaurant, bar and shop. Plenty of hotels, apartments and villas nearby, including th 4 star Hotel do Lagos and 5 star Hotel Penina, with the Alvor Casino.

PORTIMAO/PENINA. **Penina Golf Club**, Penina Golf Hotel, Penina, Portimao 8500 (082 22051. Telex: 57307). *Location:* five km west of Portimao, 12 km east of Lagos. Long, flat course with lakes, trees and bunkers. 18 holes plus two 9 holes, 6620 yards. S.S.S. 73. *Facilities:* clubhouse with bar and snack-bar. Restaurant and leisure facilities at Hotel Penina (5 star).

VILAMOURA. **Vilamoura One (The Old Course)**, Vilamoura, Quarteira 8125 (089 33652. Telex: 56914). *Location:* 25 km west of Faro, near the coast; narrow fairways with trees – a well-established course opened in 1969. 18 holes, 6924 yards. S.S.S. 72. *Facilities:* clubhouse with restaurant, bar and shop. Hotels close by such as Dom Pedro, Golf, Marinotel etc.

VILAMOURA. **Vilamoura Two (The New Course)**, as Vilamoura One. 18 holes, 6770 yards. S.S.S 71.

LISBON

ESTORIL. **Estoril Palacio Golf Club**, Estoril (2680176). *Location:* an undulating links course with views of the Atlantic, north west of Lisbon. Pine trees and natural hazards. 27 holes including 18-hole championship course, 5700 yards. S.S.S. 69. *Facilities:* clubhouse with restaurant, bar and swimming pool. The 5 star Estoril Palacio Hotel one mile away with superb amenities.

ESTORIL. **Estoril Sol Golf Club**, Linho, Sintra 2710 (923 2461. Telex: 12624). *Location:* 35 km from Lisbon, close to the Estoril coast resorts. 9 holes with 18 tees; trees and water. 4620 yards. S.S.S. 66. *Facilities:* clubhouse with bar and snack-bar. Hotels, shopping, night-life and casino nearby.

ESTORIL. **Quinta da Marinha Golf Club**, Guia, Quinta da Marinha, Cascais 2750 (289881). *Location:* 30 km north west of Lisbon, close to Estoril and Cascais. Open rocky course with trees. 18 holes, 6684 yards. S.S.S. 71. *Facilities:* clubhouse with bar and restaurant.

LISBON. **Lisbon Sports Club**, Casal da Carregueira, Bela, Queluz 2745 (960077). *Location:* 25 km from Lisbon. Quiet, hilly course. 18 holes, 5720 yards. S.S.S. 67. *Facilities:* clubhouse with restaurant, bar and swimming pool.

TROIA. **Troia Golf Club**, Troia, Setubal 2900 (065 44151. Telex: 18138). *Location:* on the Troia Peninsula, 50 km south of Lisbon. Attractive course in this popular coastal resort. 18 holes, 6930 yards. S.S.S. 74. *Facilities:* clubhouse with bar, shop and restaurant. All resort facilities, including hotels, in Troia.

VIMEIRO. **Vimeiro Golf Club**, Praia do Porto Novo, Vimeiro, Torres Vedras 25600 (98157. Telex: 43353). *Location:* approximately 70 km north of Lisbon, overlooking the sea. A level course, divided by a river and sheltered by rocky cliffs. 9 holes with 18 tees, 5228 yards. S.S.S. 67. *Facilities:* the neighbouring Hotel Golf Mar offers all facilities.

OPORTO

ESPINHO. **Oporto Golf Club**, Lugar do Sisto, Paranos, Espinho 4500 (722008. Telex: 20254). *Location:* 18 km south of Oporto. An old links course with trees, opened in 1890. 18 holes, 6500 yards. S.S.S. 70. *Facilities:* clubhouse with bar and restaurant. Beach, hotels, casino nearby.

ESTELA. **Sopete Golf Club**, Estela, Povoa de Varzim 4490 (052 68567. Fax: 052 684277. Telex: 29538). *Location:* 30 km north of Oporto, alongside the beach. Dunes and green fairways with natural and artificial lakes. 18 holes, 6878 yards. S.S.S. 72. *Facilities:* clubhouse with restaurant, bar, shop and private beach. Hotels nearby.

PRAIA DE MIRAMAR. **Miramar Golf Club**, Av. Sacadura Cabral, Miramar, Valadares 4405 (7622067. Fax: 7627859). *Location:* approximately 13 km south of Oporto. Flat coastal course amongst dunes alongside the beach. 9 holes with 18 tees, 5540 yards. S.S.S. 66. *Facilities:* clubhouse with restaurant, bar and swimming pool. Hotels, restaurants and casino nearby.

VIDAGO. **Vidago Golf Club**, Vidago 5425 (97106. Telex: 238888). *Location:* mountain valley course, in spa/resort area well inland, only 25 km from Spanish border. Short 9-hole course, 1000ft high, 2678 yards. S.S.S. 63 (18 holes). *Facilities:* Vidago Palace Hotel.

Please mention this guide when you write or phone to enquire about accommodation.

Golf in Majorca
WHERE TO PLAY • WHERE TO STAY

The climate of Majorca, like its Balearic neighbours Minorca and Ibiza, is ideal for golf. Play is possible every day in the year. Little wonder that Majorca attracts short- and long-stay visitors for its golfing opportunities as well as the island's attractions as a year-round resort.

Majorca is no more than 3-4 hours' flying time from virtually all major European cities and less from most. From Palma airport you needn't travel far to reach any one of the high-quality golf clubs and courses established within the last 30 years. New courses are still being built and in planning.

Excellent hotels, self-catering and timeshare facilities exist for holiday accommodation and there is a steady growth in longer-term residential opportunities in apartments, villas and exclusive club communities.

Club Abudillas, alongside the 11th, 12th and 13th fairways of the testing Santa Ponsa course, is a recent and impressive example of a luxurious international development aimed very much at the golf enthusiast. On a 17-acre estate, with priority golfing rights, the residents can enjoy the privacy of their own sun terrace and pool or socialise at the private Club Abudillas swimming-pool and bar.

However, one of the delights of Majorca is its widespread appeal. It is

Your villa at Club Abubillas overlooks the Santa Ponsa Championship course.

possible to have the fullest golfing pleasure as a short-break tourist escaping the Northern European winter for a few days just as much as an 'expatriate' resident in exclusive luxury. The golf course is a great leveller!

CALA D'OR. **Vall D'Or Golf Club,** Apartado 23, 07660 Cala D'Or (57.60.99). *Location:* approximately 60km east of Palma on the road from Porto Colom to Cala D'Or. Flat, winding course, with trees. 9 holes, average 18-hole length 5973 yards. S.S.S. 70. *Facilities:* clubhouse, bar and restaurant; driving range. Nearby hotels include Cala D'Or, Rocador, Rocador Playa.

MAGALLUF. **Poniente Golf Club,** Ctra. Cala Figuera, Calvia (68.01.48). *Location:* 18km west of Palma, 1km from Magalluf on the Andratx Road. A long course with trees and water, near the sea. 18 holes, 6175 yards. S.S.S. 74. *Facilities:* clubhouse, restaurant and bar; driving range. Nearby hotels include Son Callu, Club Galatzo.

PALMA. **Real Golf Bendinat,** C. Formentera, 07184 Calvia (40.52.00). *Location:* 5km west of Palma on the Andratx road. In a valley surrounded by pines and low hills. 9 holes, average 18-hole length 4840 yards. S.S.S. 64. *Facilities:* club, restaurant, bar and shop; driving range. Nearby hotels include Maricel, Mar Sol, Bonanza Playa, Bon Sol.

PALMA. **Son Vida Golf Club,** Urb. Son Vida, 07013 Palma (23.76.20). *Location:* 5km north-west of Palma. Majorca's oldest course (1964) winding through trees and estate villas with lakes and gentle slopes. 18 holes, 5920 yards. S.S.S. 68/69. *Facilities:* clubhouse, bar and restaurant; driving range. Nearby hotels include Victoria Sol, Son Vida Sheraton, Racquet Club.

POLLENSA. **Pollensa Golf Club,** Ctra. Palma Pollensa, 07460 Pollensa (53.32.16/55). *Location:* 49km from Palma on Majorca's north coast, 3km from Pollensa town. In a gently sloping valley with scenic views. 18 holes, 5931 yards. S.S.S. 72. *Facilities:* clubhouse, restaurant, bar and swimming pool; driving range. Nearby hotels include Daina, Illa D'Or, Formentor.

SANTA PONSA. **Santa Ponsa Golf Club,** Santa Ponsa, 07184 Calvia (69.02.11). *Location:* 18km west of Palma, south of the main road to Santa Ponsa. Long gently sloping course with water and scenic views. The 645-yard 10th is one of the world's longest holes. Has hosted the Balearic Open and attracted players like Ballesteros, Woosman and Lyle. 18 holes, 7130 yards. S.S.S. 72/74. *Facilities:* impressive clubhouse, bar, restaurant, accommodation and swimming pool; driving range. Nearby hotels include Villamil, Golf Santa Ponsa, Club Galatzo.

SON SERVERA. **Son Servera Golf Club,** Costa de los Pinos, 07550 Son Servera (56.78.02). *Location:* on Majorca's east coast, north of the Caves of Drach and approximately 60km from Palma. Flattish and narrow course, set among pine trees. 9 holes, average 18-hole length 6212 yards. S.S.S. 70. *Facilities:* club, bar and restaurant; driving range. Nearby hotels include Eurotel Golf Punta Roja, Rotja, Flamenco, Royal Mediterranea, Gran Sol.

Driving Ranges

LONDON

LONDON. **Chingford Golf Range,** Waltham Way, London E4 8AQ (081-529 2409). *Location:* two miles south of Junction 26 M25. Covered, floodlit, two-tier range, 23 bays. PGA Professional. *Fees:* 100 balls £2.30, 60 balls £1.60, 40 balls £1.30. *Opening hours:* 9am to 10pm.

LONDON. **Ealing Golf Range,** Rowdell Road, Northolt UB5 6AG (081-841 6162). *Location:* A40 target roundabout, Northolt. Golf range with 36 covered bays and 4 open. *Fees:* £1.00 for 40 balls. *Eating facilities:* available, also bar. Professional: David Elliot (081-845 4967).

WOKINGHAM. **Downshire Driving Range,** Easthampstead Park, Wokingham RG11 3DH (0344 424066). *Location:* between Bracknell and Wokingham, off the Nine Mile Ride. 22 bays. 18 hole golf course and 9 hole pitch and putt. Professional tuition available. *Fees:* large basket £2.00, mini basket £1.00. *Opening hours:* 8.00am to dark. *Eating facilities:* club house with bar and cafe.

WOKINGHAM. **Sindlesham Driving Range,** Mole Road, Wokingham RG11 5DJ (0734 788494). *Location:* two minutes from M4 Junction 11. 25 covered, floodlit bays. Professional tuition available. *Fees:* £1.00 per bucket. *Opening hours:* 7am to 10pm. *Eating facilities:* restaurant and bar. Health club and squash club. Professional: Paul Watson (0734 788494).

BEDFORDSHIRE

DUNSTABLE. **Tilsworth Golf Centre,** Dunstable Road, Tilsworth, Near Leighton Buzzard LU7 9PU (0525 210721/2). *Location:* two miles north of Dunstable off A5 at Tilsworth turn off. 30 bay covered floodlit driving range. *Fees:* £1.25 for 50 balls, £2.00 for 100 balls. *Opening hours:* weekdays 8am – 10pm, weekends 7am. *Eating facilities:* restaurant and bar, function suite. Large Pro shop, tuition and 9 hole course open to public.

BERKSHIRE

COLNBROOK. **Galleymead Golf Driving Range,** Colnbrook S.C., Galleymead Road, Colnbrook SL3 0EN (0753 682670/625127). *Location:* four miles west of Heathrow Airport, one mile from Junction 5 of M4, one mile from Junction 14 of M25, east end of Colnbrook Village. 27 bays, 12 covered, floodlit, grassed. *Fees:* £1.00 for 36 balls, 50p for 18 balls (machine); £1.00 coin dispenser machine. *Opening hours:* 9am to 10.30pm. *Eating facilities:* fully licensed bar 11am to 11pm six days a week, catering anything from snacks to full à la carte – excellent resident chef. Professional: Graham Hepsworth; Assistant: Paul Laycock. Very well equipped golf shop. Full tuition, video assisted lessons given.

MAIDENHEAD. **Hawthorn Hill Golf Centre,** Drift Road, Hawthorn Hill, Near Maidenhead SL6 3ST (0344 75588/26035). *Location:* on A330 Ascot to Maidenhead road. 36 covered, floodlit bays. 18 hole 'pay and play' course. Professionals. Tuition. *Fees:* information not provided. *Opening hours:* 8am to 10pm daily. *Eating facilities:* "Racecourse Restaurant" and Golfers bar and terrace.

BUCKINGHAMSHIRE

MILTON KEYNES. **Windmill Hill Golf Complex,** Tattenhoe Lane, Bletchley, Milton Keynes MK3 7RB (0908 648149). *Location:* M1 Junction 14, take A421 to Buckingham (10 miles from M1). 23 bays (6 grassed). *Fees:* 45 balls, £1.25, 90 balls £2.25. 18 hole championship golf course. Lessons 7 days a week. *Opening hours:* Monday to Friday 9.30am to 9pm, weekends 9.30am to 8.00pm. *Eating facilities:* restaurant and bar open all day. Professional: Colin Clingan (0908 378623).

CAMBRIDGESHIRE

ST. NEOTS. **Abbotsley Golf and Squash Club,** Eynesbury, Hardwicke, St Neots PE19 4XN (0480 215153/74000). *Location:* two miles east of A1 (M1), near St Neots, 12 miles Exit 13 off M11. Covered, floodlit range, 20 bays. 18 hole golf course, lessons available. *Fees:* £1.80 per bucket (80 balls). *Opening hours:* 8am to 10pm. *Eating facilities:* bar and food available all day. Residential golf school, 15 bedroom hotel, 6 squash courts, 2 sun beds, sauna.

CHESHIRE

STOCKPORT. **Cranford Golf Driving Range,** Harwood Road, Heaton Mersey, Stockport SK4 3AW (061-432 8242). *Location:* five minutes from M63 and M56 motorways. 30 all-weather covered tees, fully floodlit, open seven days a week. *Fees:* £1.90 per bucket (50 balls). No booking or membership required. *Eating facilities:* bar available weekends and evenings. Professional: available.

ESSEX

BRAINTREE. **Towerlands Driving Range,** Panfield Road, Braintree CM7 5BJ (0376 26802). *Location:* on B1053 out of Braintree. 6 grassed bays. 9 hole golf course. *Fees:* £1.50 for 50 balls. *Opening hours:* 8.30am onwards. *Eating facilities:* full bar and restaurant. Indoor bowls, squash, full sports hall and equestrian facilities.

COLCHESTER. **Colchester Golf Range,** Old Ipswich Road, Ardleigh, Colchester (0206 230974). *Location:* next to the Crown Inn, Old Ipswich Road. Covered, floodlit range, 12 bays. Professional tuition available. Putting green. *Opening hours:* weekdays 10am to 9pm, weekends 10am to 5pm. *Eating facilities:* The Crown Inn, 50 yards from course.

ILFORD. **Fairlop Waters,** Forest Road, Barkingside, Ilford IG6 3JA (081 500 9911). *Location:* two miles north of Ilford, half a mile from A12, one and a half miles from southern end of M11. Covered, floodlit range, 36 bays. 18 hole golf course, 9 hole Par 3 course. Individual or group tuition available. *Fees:* information not provided. *Opening hours:* 9am to 10pm. *Eating facilities:* three bars and restaurant. Banqueting facilities and conferences. 38 acre sailing lake, 25 acre country park, children's play area. Professional: Tony Bowers (081 501 1881). Manager: John Topping.

GLOUCESTERSHIRE

GLOUCESTER. **Gloucester Hotel and Country Club.** Robinswood Hill, Matson Lane, Gloucester GL4 9EA (0452 25653). 12 bays. 18 hole and 9 hole par 3 course. *Fees:* £1.00 per basket, £15 per round weekdays, £19 per round weekends. *Opening hours:* Monday to Friday 10am to 10pm, Saturday 10am to 10pm, Sunday 10am to 9pm. *Eating facilities:* available. Dry ski slope, indoor swimming pool, sauna, solarium, gymnasium, 6 squash courts, two tennis courts, snooker, pool, skittles etc.

HAMPSHIRE

BORDON near. **Kingsley Golf Club,** Main Road, Kingsley, Near Bordon GU35 9NG (04203 88195). *Location:* B3004 off A325 Farnham to Petersfield road. *Fees:* information not provided. Indoor computerised driving bay, equipment superstore, golf school for tuition. Professional/Acting Secretary: Richard Adams.

HERTFORDSHIRE

ROYSTON. **Whaddon Golf Range,** Whaddon, Royston SG8 5RX (0223 207325). *Location:* four miles north of Royston, nine miles south of Cambridge off

A14. 9 open bays, 14 covered, floodlit and grassed. *Fees:* £1.00 for 50 balls. *Opening hours:* 9am to 9pm weekdays, 9am to dusk weekends. Professional coaching by appointment. Putting and Par 3 pitch and putt.

WELWYN GARDEN CITY. **Gosling Stadium,** Stanborough Road, Welwyn Garden City AL8 6XE (0707 331056). *Location:* aim Welwyn Garden City exit follow signs, one mile. 24 bays, covered, floodlit driving range. *Fees:* to be arranged. *Opening hours:* 9am to 11pm. *Eating facilities:* extensive. Resident Professional, tuition and shop. Extensive facilities with skiing, tennis, athletics, bowls, cycling, badminton. Health suite, etc.

KENT

CHATHAM. **Chatham Golf Centre,** Street End Road, Chatham ME5 0BG. *Location:* five minutes drive from Rochester Airport. Covered, floodlit range, 30 bays. Tuition available. *Fees:* information not provided. *Opening hours:* 10am to 10pm. *Eating facilities:* bar and food available. Fully stocked Pro Shop. Professional: Colin Brentley (0634 848925). Secretary: R. Burden (0634 848907).

EDENBRIDGE. **Tony Noble Professional Golf Management,** Edenbridge Golf Driving Range, Crouch House Road, Edenbridge TN8 6LQ (0732 865202). *Location:* one mile from B2026. 14 covered floodlit bays. *Fees:* £1.90 per basket. *Opening hours:* 8am to 10pm, last balls sold 9.30pm. *Eating facilities:* available at clubhouse. Three teaching professionals in attendance. Also an 18 hole course and 9 hole beginners course with another 18 hole course opening early 1991.

MAIDSTONE. **Langley Park Driving Range,** Sutton Road, Maidstone ME17 3NQ (0622 842776). *Location:* south of Maidstone on A274, first turning after Parkwood Industrial Estate. 26 covered, floodlit bays. 9 hole Par 3 course. *Fees:* £1.00 for 35 balls. *Eating facilities:* bar snacks available. *Opening hours:* 10am to 9pm. Professional tuition and Professional's Golf Shop.

ORPINGTON. **Ruxley Golf Centre Driving Range,** Sandy Lane, St. Pauls Cray, Orpington BR5 3HY (0689 71490). *Location:* off A20 at Ruxley roundabout. 26-bays, covered, floodlit. 18 hole golf course. Professional tuition. Well stocked shop. *Fees:* 100 balls £4.00, 50 balls £2.30. *Opening hours:* range open 8.30am to 10.30pm. *Eating facilities:* breakfast, lunch available, bar open. Membership available to Ruxley Park Golf Club.

LANCASHIRE

KEARSLEY. **Kearsley Golf Driving Range,** Moss Lane, Kearsley, Bolton BL4 8SF (Farnworth (0204) 75726). *Location:* Manchester to Bolton A666. Small 9 hole pitch and putt attached. *Fees:* £1.00 for multiples of 25 balls. *Opening hours:* weekdays 11am to 9.30pm; weekends 11am to 4.30pm. *Eating facilities:* bar and snack bar. *Visitors:* welcome. Professional: E. Raymond Warburton.

NORTHAMPTONSHIRE

NORTHAMPTON. **Delapre Golf Complex,** Eagle Drive, Nene Valley Way, Northampton NN4 0DU (0604 763957). *Location:* two and a half miles from M1 Junction 15 towards Wellingborough. 39 covered, floodlit bays. 18 hole golf course, one 9 hole Par 3 courses, one 9 hole pitch and putt and 18 hole putting greens. Tuition available. *Fees:* small basket £1.10, medium £1.80, large £2.60. *Opening hours:* 7am to 10.30pm. *Eating facilities:* cooked meals served daily from 9am until 9pm.

NOTTINGHAMSHIRE

NOTTINGHAM. **Carlton Forum Leisure Centre (South),** Foxhill Road, Carlton, Nottingham N64 1RL. Covered, floodlit range, 28 bays. Private lessons available. *Fees:* £1.40 per basket (approximately 70 balls), Monday to Friday until 4.00pm, £1.65 at all other times. *Opening hours;* Monday noon to 10.30pm, Tuesday-Sunday 9.30am to 10.30pm. *Eating facilities:* bar and restaurant. Function suite, dry ski slope and 32 acres of pitches.

SURREY

CHESSINGTON. **Chessington Golf Centre,** Garrison Lane, Chessington KT9 2LW (081-391 0948). *Location:* as Chessington Course entry. Covered, floodlit range, 18 bays. 9 hole course. Private and group tuition available. *Fees:* £1.00 per 40-45 balls. *Opening hours:* 9am to 10pm. *Eating facilities:* available.

COBHAM. **Silvermere Driving Range,** Redhill Road, Cobham KT11 1EF (0932 67275). *Location:* half a mile from Junction 10 on M25, take B366. Covered, floodlit range, 34 bays. 18 hole course. Teaching available. *Fees:* £2.00 and £1.00 buckets. *Opening hours:* 9am to 10pm. *Eating facilities:* full facilities.

CROYDON. **Croydon Driving Range,** 175 Long Lane, Addiscombe, Croydon CR0 7TE (081-654 7859). *Location:* on A222 about two miles east of Croydon. 24-bay driving range. *Fees:* information not provided. *Eating facilities:* licensed bar and snacks available. *Visitors:* very welcome at all times, open to the public. Professional: Nick Parfrement (081-656 1690).

ESHER. **Sandown Golf Centre,** More Lane, Esher KT10 8AN (0372 65921). *Location:* middle of Sandown race course. 31 covered, floodlit grassed bays. *Fees:* £2.00 per bucket. *Opening hours:* 10am to 10pm. *Eating facilities:* available. 9 hole main course – par 3 course – pitch and putt. Snooker club.

OLD WOKING. **Hoebridge Golf Centre,** Old Woking Road, Old Woking, GU22 8JH (Woking [048-62] 22611). Covered, floodlit range. 25 bays. Two 18 hole courses and 9 hole course. *Fees:* information not provided. *Opening hours:* dawn to dusk in summer, 8am to 11pm in winter. *Eating facilities:* available.

RICHMOND. **Richmond Golf Range,** The Athletic Ground, Kew Foot Road, Richmond TW9 2SS (081-940 5570). *Location:* next to Richmond swimming pool. Covered, floodlit driving range, 23 bays and grassed area. PGA Professional. Lessons available. *Fees:* 40 balls £1.40, 75 balls £2.00. *Opening hours:* weekdays 9.30am to 9pm, weekends 9am to 5.30pm. *Eating facilities:* some catering. Professional: Sean Simpson.

EAST SUSSEX

HORAM. **Horam Park Golf Course and Floodlit Driving Range,** Chiddingly Road, Horam TN21 0JJ (04353 3477), (Fax 04353 3677). *Location:* 13 miles north of Eastbourne, 7 miles east of Uckfield. Covered, floodlit range. 18 bays. 5 PGA golf Professionals, lessons and tuition available. Golf shop. *Fees:* £2.00 per bucket. *Opening hours:* weekdays 7.30am-10.30pm, weekends and Bank Holidays 5.00am-10.30pm. *Eating facilities:* licensed bar and restaurant.

WEST SUSSEX

CRAWLEY. **Gatwick Manor Golf Club,** Gatwick Manor Hotel, London Road, Lowfield Heath, Crawley RH10 2ST (0293 26301). *Location:* A23 Crawley to Gatwick airport on London Road on right. 9 grassed tees. *Fees:* £3.00, £2.00 Juniors and Senior Citizens. *Eating facilities:* hotel facilities at Gatwick Manor. *Opening hours:* 9am to 8.00pm seven days a week.

TYNE AND WEAR

NEWCASTLE-UPON-TYNE. **Gosforth Park Golfing Company Ltd,** High Gosforth Park, Newcastle-Upon-Tyne NE3 5HQ (091 2364480). *Location:* off A1 for Gosforth Park. Covered, floodlit range, 30 bays. 18 hole golf course and 9 hole pitch and putt. Professional tuition available. *Fees:* information not provided. *Opening hours:* 8am to 10.30pm. *Eating facilities:* bar and restaurant.

WASHINGTON. **Washington Moat House,** Stone Cellar Road, District 12, Washington NE37 2NG (091 4172626). *Location:* just off the A1 motorway, North Washington. Floodlit driving range, 21 bays. 18 hole golf course. *Fees:* information not available. *Opening hours:* 7am to 8.30pm. *Eating facilities:* 'Bunkers Bar' open 11am-11pm, serves snacks, buffets by arrangement. Snooker club, leisure club with swimming pool, squash courts, solarium, spa bath etc.

WARWICKSHIRE

COVENTRY. **John Reay Golf Centres,** Sandpits Lane, Coventry CV7 8NJ (0203 333920). *Location:* three miles from Coventry city centre along A51 Tamworth Road. Covered, floodlit range. 30 bays. Golf club repair facility. Teaching professionals using latest video techniques. *Fees:* 45 balls £1. *Opening hours:* weekdays 9am to 10pm. *Eating facilities:* Hogans Bar & Bistro open every day.

WARWICK. **Warwick Golf Centre,** Race Course, Warwick CV34 6HW (0926 494316). *Location:* Race Course, Warwick. Covered, floodlit range, 28 bays. Par 34 9 hole golf course. *Fees:* large basket £2.00, medium basket £1.70 and small basket £1.00. *Opening hours:* 10am to 9pm. *Eating facilities:* bar only.

WEST MIDLANDS

DUDLEY near. **Swindon Ridge Golf Driving Range,** Bridgnorth Road, Swindon, Near Dudley DY3 4PU (0902 896191). *Location:* B4176 Bridgnorth/Dudley Road, three miles from Himley A449. 27 floodlit bays (10 covered). *Fees:* £1.20 for small bucket, £1.90 for large bucket, £3.50 for extra large bucket. Tuition £6.00 per half hour. *Opening hours:* 9am to 9.30pm weekdays, 8.30am to 6pm weekends. *Eating facilities:* full bar and restaurant. *Visitors:* welcome. 18 hole golf course and 9 hole Par 3 course open seven days dawn till dusk. Day fishing tickets £3.00. *Society Meetings:* welcome weekdays. Two teaching Professionals, lessons available. Group or individual tuition. Golf shop.

WOLVERHAMPTON. **Three Hammers Golf Complex,** Old Stafford Road, Coven, Wolverhampton WV10 7PP (0902 790428). *Location:* Junction 2 M54 north on A449, one mile on right. 24 covered floodlit bays. *Fees:* information not provided. *Eating facilities:* brasserie and full à la carte restaurant. *Opening hours:* seven days a week 10am to 10pm. Professional tuition is available, and regular golf courses are available for beginners. 2000 sq ft golf shop, Henry Cotton-designed 18-hole short course. Bedroom accommodation is planned in the near future.

WILTSHIRE

SWINDON. **Broome Manor Golf Complex,** Pipers Way, Swindon SN3 1RG. *Location:* two miles from Junction 15 on M4 (follow signs for "Golf Complex").

Covered, floodlit range, 25 bays. 18 hole course, 9 hole course, short game practice area, pitch and putt, simulated clay pigeon shooting. *Fees:* information not provided. *Opening hours:* 8.00am to 9.00pm. *Eating facilities:* full service available. Professional: Barry Sandry (0793 532403). Manager: Tom Watt (0793 495761).

CHANNEL ISLANDS

ST. OUEN'S. **Les Mielles Golf Course,** The Mount, Val de la Mabe, St. Ouen's, Jersey (0534 82787). *Location:* centre of St. Ouen's Bay. 36 bay grassed driving range. *Fees:* 21 balls 50p, clubs 30p. 12 hole course £4.00, clubs £2.00. *Opening hours:* dawn till dusk. *Eating facilities:* kiosk. Professional golf teacher. Crazy golf, putting green, public golf facility. Manager: J.A. Le Brun.

EDINBURGH & LOTHIANS

EDINBURGH. **Port Royal Golf Range,** Eastfield Road, Ingliston, Edinburgh EH28 8NX (031-333 4377). *Location:* follow signs to Edinburgh Airport, on slip road approximately 100 yards from airport entrance. Five miles from centre of Edinburgh. 36 bays, 24 covered, floodlit and 12 grassed. Pro shop, Professional and tuition. *Fees:* £1.25 per basket of 50 balls. *Eating facilities:* bar and lounge area, bar meals all day. 1000 square yard putting green and 9 hole, par 3 golf course. Open all year.

GLASGOW & DISTRICT

UDDINGSTON. **Clydeway Golf Centre,** Blantyre Farm Road, Uddingston G71 7RR (041-641-8899). *Location:* B758 off Main Street, Uddingston, near Glasgow Zoo. 25 covered floodlit bays. *Fees:* £1.20 for 50 balls, £2.00 for 100 balls. Evening classes in Winter. Very modern large Golf Shop. Professional: Gary Mitchell.

RENFREWSHIRE

RENFREW. **Normandy Golf Range,** Inchinnan Road, Renfrew PA4 9EG (041-886 7477). *Location:* take M8; turn off Glasgow Airport turn off; take Renfrew Road one mile away. 25 bays covered, floodlit. *Fees:* £1.30 for 50 balls, £2.00 for 90 balls. *Opening hours:* 9.30am to 9pm weekdays, 9.30am to 6pm weekends. *Eating facilities:* full hotel facilities. Professional, assistants, tuition anytime. Adjacent to Renfrew Golf Club. Large comprehensive stock of all leading golf equipment.

WEST GLAMORGAN

SWANSEA. **Birchgrove Golf Driving Range,** Gwernllwynchwyth Road, Birchgrove, Swansea SA7 9PL. *Location:* M4 Junction 44 take A48 to Morriston turn right at first lights, approximately half a mile on right. 20 covered, floodlit bays. *Fees:* £1.50 per 80 balls, no time limit. *Opening hours:* 9am to 9pm weekdays, 9am to 7pm weekends. Professional: John Burns (0792 796164).

ANTRIM

NEWTOWNABBEY. **Ballyearl Golf and Leisure Centre,** 585 Doagh Road, Newtownabbey BT36 8RZ (0232 48287). *Location:* six miles north of Belfast on M2 then first right onto Doagh Road from Belfast to Larne Road. 32 bay covered, floodlit, grassed/artificial range. *Fees:* £1.50 small bucket (50 balls), £2.00 medium bucket (80 balls), £2.50 large bucket (160 balls). Golf Club hire 50p. *Opening hours:* 9am to 10pm. Professional services, pro shop, private lessons. Par 3 Golf Course. Hi-Tech Fitness Suite, 6 squash courts; also private bar and club.

ARMAGH

CRAIGAVON. **Craigavon Golf and Ski Centre,** Turmoyra, Silverwood, Lurgan, Craigavon BT66 6NF (0762 326606). *Location:* beside the Silverwood Hotel. Floodlit driving range, with 10 covered and 10 grassed bays. 18 hole golf course. 9 hole par 3 course. 12 hole pitch and putt. Putting green and professional tuition. *Fees:* information not provided. *Opening hours:* weekdays 9.00am to 9.30 pm, weekends 9.00am to 5.30pm. *Eating facilities:* light refreshments. Floodlit ski slope.

COUNTY DOWN

KNOCKBRACKEN. **Knockbracken Golf Centre,** 24 Ballymaconaghy Road, Knockbracken, Belfast BT8 4SB (0232 792108). *Location:* outskirts of Belfast, approximately three miles from centre along Ormeau Road near "Four Winds" Restaurant and Public House. 36 bays covered, floodlit and grassed. *Fees:* £2.50 for 140 balls, £1.50 for 80 balls, £1.00 for 50 balls. *Opening hours:* 9am to 11pm. *Eating facilities:* available at Golf Club seven days a week. Tuition (bookable) by leading PGA Irish coach Don Patterson and assistant. Video TV courses.

COUNTY DUBLIN

FOXROCK. **Leopardstown Driving Range,** Foxrock (01 895341). *Location:* five miles south of Dublin city centre situated in Leopardstown race course. 38 indoor, 38 outdoor floodlit bays. *Fees:* information not provided. *Opening hours:* 9am to 10pm. *Eating facilities:* restaurant. Professional tuition – practice green. 9 hole golf course and 18 hole par 3.

Index

Index to Advertisers

ORDER NOW! *See Overleaf*

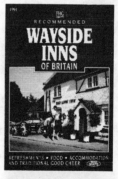

ONE FOR YOUR FRIEND 1991

FHG Publications have a large range of attractive holiday accommodation guides for all kinds of holiday opportunities throughout Britain. They also make useful gifts at any time of year. Our guides are available in most bookshops and larger newsagents but we will be happy to post you a copy direct if you have any difficulty. We will also post abroad but have to charge separately for post or freight.

The inclusive cost of posting and packing the guides to you or your friends in the UK is as follows:

Farm Holiday Guide
ENGLAND, WALES and IRELAND
Board, Self-catering, Caravans/Camping,
Activity Holidays. About 600 pages. **£3.60**

Farm Holiday Guide SCOTLAND
All kinds of holiday accommodation. **£2.60**

SELF-CATERING & FURNISHED HOLIDAYS
Over 1000 addresses throughout for
Self-catering and caravans in Britain. **£3.00**

BRITAIN'S BEST HOLIDAYS
A quick-reference general guide
for all kinds of holidays. **£2.50**

The FHG Guide to CARAVAN & CAMPING HOLIDAYS
Caravans for hire, sites and
holiday parks and centres. **£2.60**

BED AND BREAKFAST STOPS
Over 1000 friendly and comfortable
overnight stops. **£3.00**

CHILDREN WELCOME! FAMILY HOLIDAY GUIDE
Family holidays with details of
amenities for children and babies. **£2.50**

Recommended SHORT BREAK HOLIDAYS IN BRITAIN
'Approved' accommodation for quality bargain
breaks. Introduced by John Carter. **£3.50**

Recommended COUNTRY HOTELS OF BRITAIN
Including Country Houses, for
the discriminating. **£3.50**

Recommended WAYSIDE INNS OF BRITAIN
Pubs, Inns and small hotels. **£3.50**

PGA GOLF GUIDE
Where to play and where to stay
Over 2000 golf courses with convenient
accommodation. Endorsed by the PGA. **£6.50**

PETS WELCOME!
The unique guide for holidays for
pet owners and their pets. **£3.00**

BED AND BREAKFAST IN BRITAIN
Over 1000 choices for touring and
holidays throughout Britain. **£2.50**

LONDON'S BEST BED AND BREAKFAST HOTELS
Inspected and recommended with prices. Over 120
safe, clean and friendly small hotels. **£3.25**

THE FRENCH FARM AND VILLAGE HOLIDAY GUIDE
The official guide to self-catering
holidays in the 'Gîtes de France'. **£7.50**

Tick your choice and send your order and payment to FHG PUBLICATIONS, ABBEY MILL BUSINESS CENTRE, SEEDHILL, PAISLEY PA1 1JN (TEL: 041-887 0428. FAX: 041-889 7204). **Deduct** 10% for 2/3 titles or copies; 20% for 4 or more.

Send to: NAME ....

ADDRESS ....

....

.... POST CODE ....

I enclose Cheque/Postal Order for £ ....

SIGNATURE .... DATE ....

SHETLAND ISLANDS

A B C D E F

1

ORKNEY *MAINLAND*
Stromness   Kirkwall

HOY

YELL

2

MAINLAND

Lerwick

Durness   Thurso   John o'Groats
Bettyhill
Tongue   *A836*

3

Scourie   Wick

Lochinver   Lybster

LEWIS
WESTERN
ISLES

Sumburgh

Lairg   Helmsdale

Ullapool   Golspie
Gairloch   Poolewe   Bonar Bridge
Dornoch

4

Tain

Portree   Dingwall   Rosemarkie   Elgin   Cullen   Banff   Fraserburgh
SKYE   Beauly   Nairn   Forres   Fochabers
Keith   Peterhead

5

Kyle of Lochalsh   Inverness   Huntly
Broadford   Kyleakin   Dornie
Grantown-on-Spey   Inverurie
Carrbridge   Tomintoul   Aberdeen
Mallaig   Fort Augustus   Aviemore   *GRAMPIAN*

6

Kingussie   Banchory   Stonehaven
Braemar

INNER HEBRIDES

Fort William   Kinloch Rannoch   Pitlochry   Brechin
Kinlochleven   Montrose
Tobermory   Ballachulish   Aberfeldy   *TAYSIDE*   Forfar   Arbroath

7

MULL   Oban   Taynuilt   Dunkeld   Blairgowrie   Carnoustie
Dalmally   Killin   Dundee
Crianlarich   Lochearnhead   Perth   Cupar   St Andrews
Inveraray   Crieff
Arrochar   Tarbet   Callander   *FIFE*

8

Lochgilphead   Luss   Aberfoyle   Kinross
Ardrishaig   *CENTRAL*   Stirling   Kirkcaldy   North Berwick
Dunoon   Drymen   Dunfermline
Tarbert   Gourock   Balloch   EDINBURGH   Dunbar
JURA   Rothesay   Greenock   Dumbarton   Dalkeith   Haddington
Largs   Paisley   Glasgow   *LOTHIAN*   Eyemouth

9

ISLAY   Hamilton   Lauder   Chirnside
STRATHCLYDE   Peebles   Duns   Berwick upon Tweed
Ardrossan   Coldstream   Cornhill-on-Tweed
KINTYRE   Brodick   Kilmarnock   Lanark   Selkirk   Galashiels   Bamburgh
Lamlash   Irvine   Biggar   Kelso   Wooler   Seahouses
Campbeltown   Troon   Abington   Hawick   Jedburgh
Prestwick   New   *BORDERS*   Alnwick
ARRAN   Ayr   Cumnock   Maybole   Moffat

10

Girvan   Beattock   *NORTHUMBER-*
Langholm   *LAND*   Morpeth
DUMFRIES & GALLOWAY   Bellingham   Whitley Bay
New Galloway   Dumfries   Gretna   Longtown   Newcastle-upon-Tyne
Newton Stewart   Castle Douglas   Annan   Greenhead   Hexham   Corbridge
Stranraer   Gatehouse of Fleet   Silloth   Carlisle

11

Portpatrick   Wigtown   Kirkcudbright   *CUMBRIA*   Alston   Durham
Port William   Bassenthwaite   Penrith

A B C D 5 **E F** 6 **G**

© GEOprojects (U.K.) Ltd
Crown Copyright Reserved

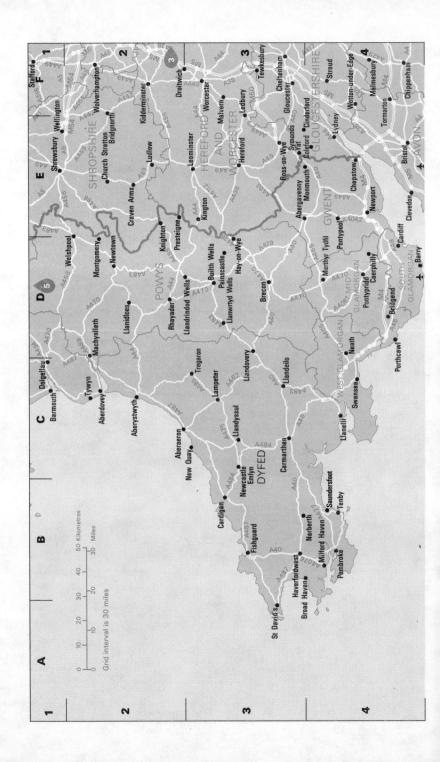

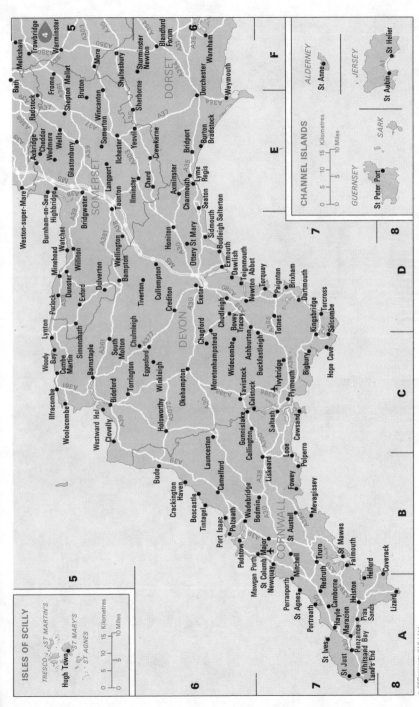

ISLES OF SCILLY

TRESCO • ST MARTIN'S
ST MARY'S
Hugh Town •
• ST AGNES

0 5 10 15 Kilometres
0   5   10 Miles

CORNWALL

St Ives
St Just
Penzance
Whitsand Bay
Land's End
Marazion
Praa Sands
Helston
Lizard
Coverack
Helford
Falmouth
St Mawes
Truro
Redruth
Camborne
Hayle
Portreath
St Agnes
Perranporth
Newquay
Mawgan Porth
St Columb Major
Mitchell
St Austell
Mevagissey
Bodmin
Wadebridge
Polzeath
Port Isaac
Tintagel
Boscastle
Crackington Haven
Bude
Camelford
Fowey
Liskeard
Looe
Polperro
Cawsand
Saltash
Callington
Gunnislake
Calstock
Launceston

DEVON

Holsworthy
Winkleigh
Eggesford
Okehampton
Moretonhampstead
Chagford
Tavistock
Widecombe
Bovey Tracey
Chudleigh
Ashburton
Buckfastleigh
Plymouth
Ivybridge
Bigbury
Hope Cove
Totnes
Kingsbridge
Salcombe
Torcross
Dartmouth
Brixham
Paignton
Torquay
Newton Abbot
Teignmouth
Dawlish
Exmouth
Exeter
Crediton
Tiverton
Cullompton
Honiton
Ottery St Mary
Sidmouth
Budleigh Salterton
Seaton
Lyme Regis
Charmouth
Axminster
Chard
Ilminster
Wellington
Bampton
South Molton
Dulverton
Exford
Simonsbath
Barnstaple
Torrington
Bideford
Clovelly
Westward Ho!
Woolacombe
Ilfracombe
Combe Martin
Woody Bay
Lynton
Porlock
Minehead
Watchet
Dunster
Williton

SOMERSET

Weston-super-Mare
Burnham-on-Sea
Highbridge
Bridgwater
Taunton
Langport
Ilchester
Yeovil
Crewkerne
Bridport
Burton Bradstock
Somerton
Glastonbury
Street
Wells
Cheddar
Wedmore
Axbridge
Radstock
Bath
Melksham
Trowbridge
Warminster
Frome
Shepton Mallet
Bruton
Wincanton
Sherborne
Mere
Shaftesbury
Sturminster Newton
Blandford Forum

DORSET

Dorchester
Wareham
Weymouth

CHANNEL ISLANDS

ALDERNEY
St Anne

GUERNSEY
St Peter Port

SARK

JERSEY
St Aubin
St Helier

0 5 10 15 Kilometres
0   5   10 Miles

1 2 3 4 5 6 7 8
A B C D E F

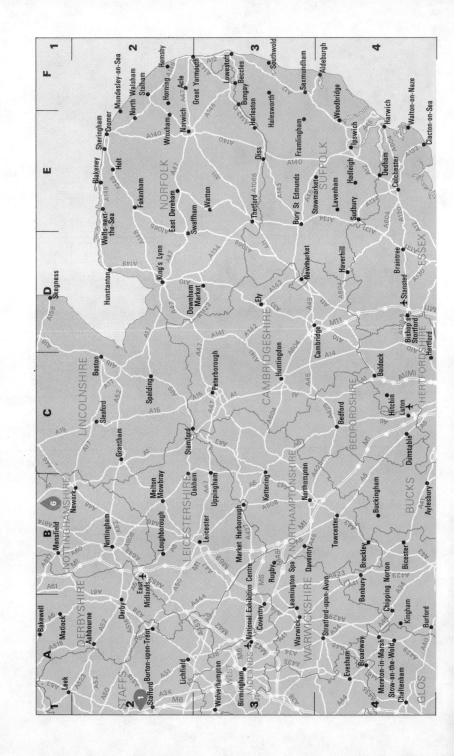

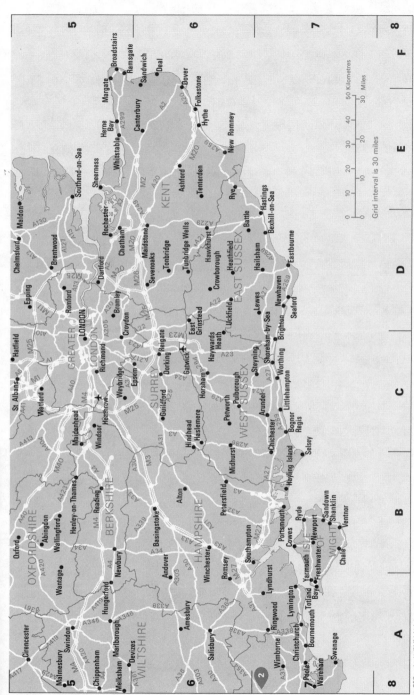